A-Level

Mathematics

for Edexcel Core 4

CGP
— books —
like no other!

CGP

The Complete Course for Edexcel C4

Contents

Chapter 6

Integration 2

Chapter 7

Vectors

Reference

About this book

In this book you'll find...

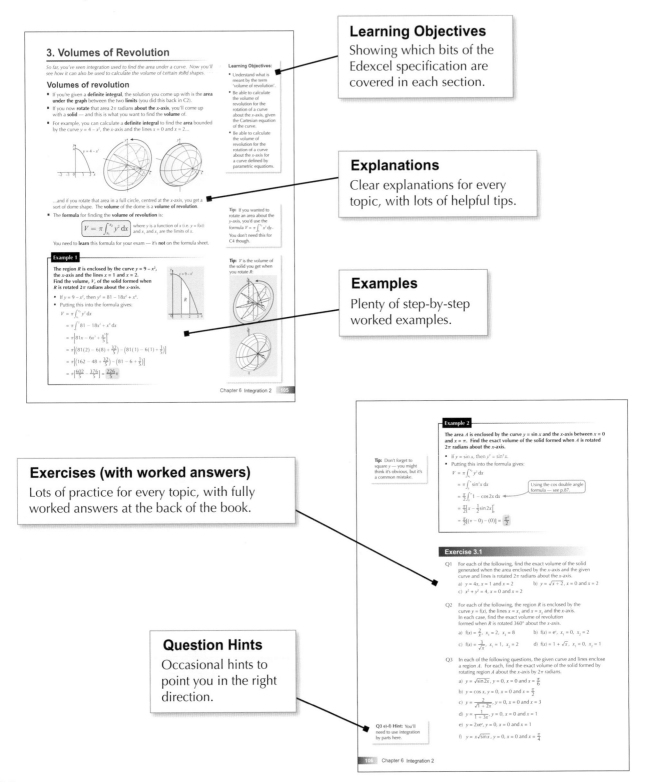

Learning Objectives
Showing which bits of the Edexcel specification are covered in each section.

Explanations
Clear explanations for every topic, with lots of helpful tips.

Examples
Plenty of step-by-step worked examples.

Exercises (with worked answers)
Lots of practice for every topic, with fully worked answers at the back of the book.

Question Hints
Occasional hints to point you in the right direction.

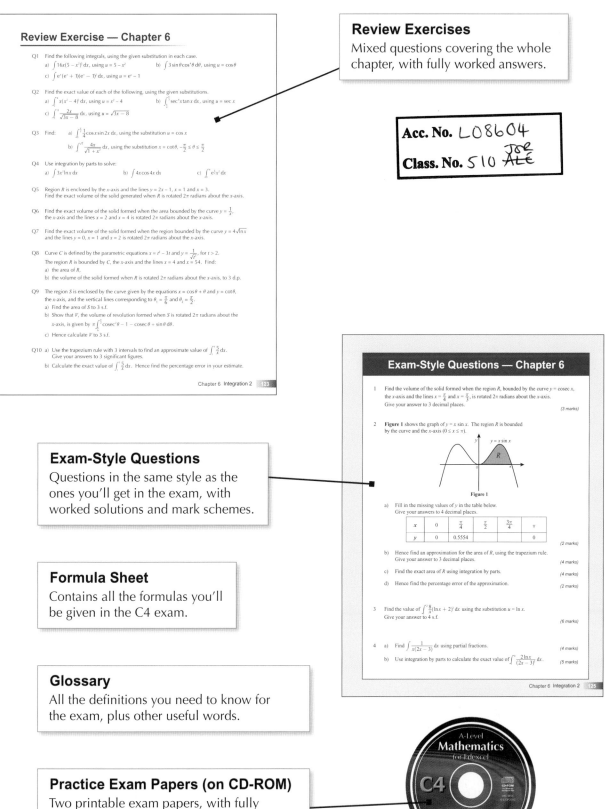

Review Exercise — Chapter 6

Q1 Find the following integrals, using the given substitution in each case.
   a) $\int 16x(5-x^2)\,dx$, using $u = 5 - x^2$
   b) $\int 3\sin\theta\cos^3\theta\,d\theta$, using $u = \cos\theta$
   c) $\int e^x(e^x+1)(e^x-1)^2\,dx$, using $u = e^x - 1$

Q2 Find the exact value of each of the following, using the given substitutions.
   a) $\int_2^4 x(x^2-4)^2\,dx$, using $u = x^2 - 4$
   b) $\int_{\frac{\pi}{3}}^{\frac{\pi}{2}} \sec^2 x\tan x\,dx$, using $u = \sec x$
   c) $\int_3^4 \frac{2x}{\sqrt{3x-8}}\,dx$, using $u = \sqrt{3x-8}$

Q3 Find:
   a) $\int_0^{\frac{\pi}{2}} \frac{1}{4}\cos x\sin 2x\,dx$, using the substitution $u = \cos x$
   b) $\int \frac{4x}{\sqrt{1+x^2}}\,dx$, using the substitution $x = \cot\theta$, $-\frac{\pi}{2} \le \theta \le \frac{\pi}{2}$

Q4 Use integration by parts to solve:
   a) $\int 3x^2\ln x\,dx$
   b) $\int 4x\cos 4x\,dx$
   c) $\int e^{\frac{1}{2}x}x^2\,dx$

Q5 Region R is enclosed by the x-axis and the lines $y = 2x - 1$, $x = 1$ and $x = 3$.
   Find the exact volume of the solid generated when R is rotated 2π radians about the x-axis.

Q6 Find the exact volume of the solid formed when the area bounded by the curve $y = \frac{1}{x}$,
   the x-axis and the lines $x = 2$ and $x = 4$ is rotated 2π radians about the x-axis.

Q7 Find the exact volume of the solid formed when the region bounded by the curve $y = 4\sqrt{\ln x}$
   and the lines $y = 0$, $x = 1$ and $x = 2$ is rotated 2π radians about the x-axis.

Q8 Curve C is defined by the parametric equations $x = t^3 - 3t$ and $y = \frac{1}{\sqrt{t}}$, for $t > 2$.
   The region R is bounded by C, the x-axis and the lines $x = 4$ and $x = 54$. Find:
   a) the area of R,
   b) the volume of the solid formed when R is rotated 2π radians about the x-axis, to 3 d.p.

Q9 The region S is enclosed by the curve given by the equations $x = \cos\theta + \theta$ and $y = \cot\theta$,
   the x-axis, and the vertical lines corresponding to $\theta_1 = \frac{\pi}{6}$ and $\theta_2 = \frac{\pi}{2}$.
   a) Find the area of S to 3 s.f.
   b) Show that V, the volume of revolution formed when S is rotated 2π radians about the
      x-axis, is given by $\pi\int_{\frac{\pi}{6}}^{\frac{\pi}{2}} \csc^2\theta - 1 - \csc\theta + \sin\theta\,d\theta$.
   c) Hence calculate V to 3 s.f.

Q10 a) Use the trapezium rule with 3 intervals to find an approximate value of $\int_1^4 \frac{5}{x}\,dx$.
       Give your answers to 3 significant figures.
    b) Calculate the exact value of $\int_1^4 \frac{5}{x}\,dx$. Hence find the percentage error in your estimate.

Review Exercises
Mixed questions covering the whole chapter, with fully worked answers.

Acc. No. L08604
Class. No. 510 ALE

Exam-Style Questions — Chapter 6

1 Find the volume of the solid formed when the region R, bounded by the curve $y = \csc x$,
   the x-axis and the lines $x = \frac{\pi}{4}$ and $x = \frac{\pi}{3}$, is rotated 2π radians about the x-axis.
   Give your answer to 3 decimal places.
   (3 marks)

2 **Figure 1** shows the graph of $y = x\sin x$. The region R is bounded
   by the curve and the x-axis $(0 \le x \le \pi)$.

   Figure 1

   a) Fill in the missing values of y in the table below.
      Give your answers to 4 decimal places.

x	0	$\frac{\pi}{4}$	$\frac{\pi}{2}$	$\frac{3\pi}{4}$	π
y	0	0.5554			0

   (2 marks)

   b) Hence find an approximation for the area of R, using the trapezium rule.
      Give your answer to 3 decimal places.
      (4 marks)
   c) Find the exact area of R using integration by parts.
      (4 marks)
   d) Hence find the percentage error of the approximation.
      (2 marks)

3 Find the value of $\int_2^3 \frac{8}{x}(\ln x + 2)^2\,dx$ using the substitution $u = \ln x$.
   Give your answer to 4 s.f.
   (6 marks)

4 a) Find $\int \frac{1}{x(2x-3)}\,dx$ using partial fractions.
      (4 marks)
   b) Use integration by parts to calculate the exact value of $\int_2^4 \frac{2\ln x}{(2x-3)^2}\,dx$.
      (5 marks)

Exam-Style Questions
Questions in the same style as the ones you'll get in the exam, with worked solutions and mark schemes.

Formula Sheet
Contains all the formulas you'll be given in the C4 exam.

Glossary
All the definitions you need to know for the exam, plus other useful words.

Practice Exam Papers (on CD-ROM)
Two printable exam papers, with fully worked answers and mark schemes.

A-Level
Mathematics
for Edexcel

C4

Exam Practice Papers
& Worked Answers
CGP

Published by CGP

Editors:
Paul Jordin, Sharon Keeley-Holden, Simon Little, Kirstie McHale, Caley Simpson, Charlotte Whiteley, Dawn Wright.

Contributors:
Claire Creasor, Anna Gainey, Dave Harding, Phil Harvey, Barbara Mascetti, Rosemary Rogers.

ISBN: 978 1 84762 814 5

With thanks to Alastair Duncombe for the proofreading.

Printed by Elanders Ltd, Newcastle upon Tyne.
Clipart from Corel®

1. Partial Fractions

Sometimes an algebraic fraction with a complicated denominator can be split into a sum of simpler fractions. In this chapter you'll see a couple of methods you can use to do this, depending on what type of denominator you've got.

Expressing in partial fractions

- You can split a fraction with **more than one linear factor** in the denominator into **partial fractions**.
- This means writing it as a **sum** of two or more **simpler fractions**.
- The **denominators** of these simpler fractions will be **factors** of the denominator of the original fraction.

Learning Objectives:

- Be able to write algebraic fractions as partial fractions, including fractions with denominators of the form $(ax + b)(cx + d)(ex + f)$ and $(ax + b)(cx + d)^2$.

Examples

- $\dfrac{7x - 7}{(2x + 1)(x - 3)}$ can be written as

  partial fractions of the form $\dfrac{A}{(2x + 1)} + \dfrac{B}{(x - 3)}$.

- $\dfrac{9x^2 + x + 16}{(x + 2)(2x - 1)(x - 3)}$ can be written as

  partial fractions of the form $\dfrac{A}{(x + 2)} + \dfrac{B}{(2x - 1)} + \dfrac{C}{(x - 3)}$.

- $\dfrac{21x - 2}{9x^2 - 4}$ can be written as partial fractions of the form $\dfrac{A}{(3x - 2)} + \dfrac{B}{(3x + 2)}$.

Tip: If you're asked to write an algebraic fraction as partial fractions, start by writing the partial fractions out with A, B and C as numerators as shown here. You might have to factorise the denominator first, like in the last example.

The tricky bit is **working out** what A, B and C are. Follow this method:

- **Write out** the expression as an identity, e.g.
  $$\dfrac{7x - 7}{(2x + 1)(x - 3)} \equiv \dfrac{A}{(2x + 1)} + \dfrac{B}{(x - 3)}$$
- **Add** the partial fractions together,
  i.e. write them over a **common denominator**.
- **Cancel** the denominators from both sides (they'll be the same).
- This will give you an **identity** for A and B, for example:
  $$7x - 7 \equiv A(x - 3) + B(2x + 1)$$
- Use the **Substitution** method or the Equating Coefficients method:

Substitution	Equating Coefficients
Substitute a number for x to leave you with just one constant on the right hand side.	Equate the constant terms, coefficients of x and coefficients of x^2, then solve the equations simultaneously.

Example 1

Express $\dfrac{9x^2 + x + 16}{(x + 2)(2x - 1)(x - 3)}$ **in partial fractions.**

- Write it out as an **identity**:
$$\frac{9x^2 + x + 16}{(x + 2)(2x - 1)(x - 3)} \equiv \frac{A}{(x + 2)} + \frac{B}{(2x - 1)} + \frac{C}{(x - 3)}$$

- **Add** the partial fractions —
  this means writing them over a **common denominator**:
$$\frac{A}{(x + 2)} + \frac{B}{(2x - 1)} + \frac{C}{(x - 3)} \equiv$$
$$\frac{A(2x - 1)(x - 3) + B(x + 2)(x - 3) + C(2x - 1)(x + 2)}{(x + 2)(2x - 1)(x - 3)}$$

- **Cancel** the denominators from both sides of the original identity,
  so the numerators are **equal**:
$$9x^2 + x + 16 \equiv A(2x - 1)(x - 3) + B(x + 2)(x - 3) + C(2x - 1)(x + 2)$$

Substitution Method

Substitute values of x which make one of the expressions in brackets
equal zero to get rid of all but one of A, B and C.

- Substituting $x = 3$ gets rid of A and B:
$$(9 \times 3^2) + 3 + 16 = 0 + 0 + C((2 \times 3) - 1)(3 + 2)$$
$$100 = 25C \qquad \Rightarrow \boldsymbol{C = 4}$$

- Substituting $x = -2$ gets rid of B and C:
$$(9 \times (-2)^2) + (-2) + 16 = A((2 \times -2) - 1)(-2 - 3) + 0 + 0$$
$$50 = 25A \qquad \Rightarrow \boldsymbol{A = 2}$$

- Substituting $x = 0.5$ gets rid of A and C:
$$(9 \times (0.5^2)) + 0.5 + 16 = 0 + B(0.5 + 2)(0.5 - 3) + 0$$
$$18.75 = -6.25B \qquad \Rightarrow \boldsymbol{B = -3}$$

Equating Coefficients Method

- Compare coefficients in the numerators:
$$9x^2 + x + 16 \equiv$$
$$A(2x - 1)(x - 3) + B(x + 2)(x - 3) + C(2x - 1)(x + 2)$$

Equating x^2 coefficients:	$9 = 2A + B + 2C$
Equating x coefficients:	$1 = -7A - B + 3C$
Equating constant terms:	$16 = 3A - 6B - 2C$

> You'll need to multiply out the brackets on the RHS for this, e.g.
> $A(2x - 1)(x - 3)$
> $= 2Ax^2 - 7Ax + 3A$

- Solving these equations simultaneously gives:
  $\boldsymbol{A = 2}$, $\boldsymbol{B = -3}$ and $\boldsymbol{C = 4}$ (the same as the substitution method).

- Finally, **replace** A, B and C in the original identity:

$$\frac{9x^2 + x + 16}{(x + 2)(2x - 1)(x - 3)} \equiv \frac{2}{(x + 2)} - \frac{3}{(2x - 1)} + \frac{4}{(x - 3)}$$

Tip: The adding step can be a bit fiddly, so you should always check that each term will cancel to produce the original fraction. Another method is to multiply both sides of the original identity by the left hand denominator to get the identity you want.

Tip: For some questions one method will be easier than the other — if one seems too tricky try the other. Sometimes you might want to use a combination of both methods.

Tip: Generally it's easier to use the substitution method first. In this example, it's actually quite tricky to solve the simultaneous equations that you get by equating coefficients, so you're better off using substitution.

Tip: Don't forget to write out your solution like this once you've done all the working.

Example 2

Express $\dfrac{3-x}{x^2+x}$ in partial fractions.

- First you need to **factorise** the denominator: $\dfrac{3-x}{x^2+x} \equiv \dfrac{3-x}{x(x+1)}$.

- Now write as an **identity** with partial fractions: $\dfrac{3-x}{x(x+1)} \equiv \dfrac{A}{x} + \dfrac{B}{x+1}$.

- **Add** the partial fractions and **cancel** the denominators from both sides:

  $$\dfrac{3-x}{x(x+1)} \equiv \dfrac{A(x+1)+Bx}{x(x+1)} \quad \Rightarrow \quad 3-x \equiv A(x+1)+Bx$$

- In this example it's easier to **equate** coefficients because A is the only letter that appears in the constant term on the right hand side.

- **Compare coefficients** in $3-x \equiv A(x+1)+Bx$:

  Equating constant terms: $3 = A$

  Equating x coefficients: $-1 = A + B \Rightarrow -1 = 3 + B \Rightarrow B = -4$

- **Replace** A and B in the identity: $\dfrac{3-x}{x^2+x} \equiv \dfrac{3}{x} - \dfrac{4}{(x+1)}$

Tip: In this example equating coefficients is a good bet because you get one of the constants without any work.

Exercise 1.1

Q1   Express $\dfrac{3x+3}{(x-1)(x-4)}$ in the form $\dfrac{A}{x-1} + \dfrac{B}{x-4}$.

Q2   Express $\dfrac{5x-1}{x(2x+1)}$ in the form $\dfrac{A}{x} + \dfrac{B}{2x+1}$.

Q1 & 2 Hint: Use the substitution method for Q1, and equate coefficients for Q2.

Q3   Find the values of the constants A and B in the identity $\dfrac{3x-2}{x^2+x-12} \equiv \dfrac{A}{x+4} + \dfrac{B}{x-3}$.

Q4   Write $\dfrac{2}{x^2-16}$ in partial fractions.

Q4 Hint: Look out for the difference of two squares.

Q5   Factorise $x^2 - x - 6$ and hence express $\dfrac{5}{x^2-x-6}$ in partial fractions.

Q6   Write $\dfrac{11x}{2x^2+5x-12}$ in partial fractions.

Q7   a)   Factorise $x^3 - 9x$ fully.

      b)   Hence write $\dfrac{x^2-3x+2}{x^3-9x}$ in partial fractions.

Q8   Write $\dfrac{4x^2-14}{x^3-36x}$ in the form $\dfrac{A}{x} + \dfrac{B}{x+6} + \dfrac{C}{x-6}$.

Q9   a)   Use the factor theorem to fully factorise $x^3 - 7x - 6$.

      b)   Hence write $\dfrac{5x^2-7x-4}{x^3-7x-6}$ in partial fractions.

Q9 a) Hint: Have a look back at your C2 notes for a reminder of the factor theorem.

Q10   Express $\dfrac{6x^2-x+5}{(x+4)(x-1)(x+1)}$ in partial fractions.

Q11   Express $\dfrac{3x^2-6x+3}{x^3-6x^2+3x+10}$ in partial fractions.

Repeated factors

If the denominator of an algebraic fraction has **repeated linear factors** the partial fractions will take a slightly **different form**, as shown in the examples below.

> The **power** of the repeated factor tells you **how many** times that factor should appear in the partial fractions.
>
> - $\dfrac{3x^2 - 7x + 5}{(x+1)^2(x-4)}$ is written as $\dfrac{A}{(x+1)} + \dfrac{B}{(x+1)^2} + \dfrac{C}{(x-4)}$.
>   A factor that's **squared** in the original denominator will appear in the denominator of **two** of your partial fractions — once squared and once just as it is.
>
> - $\dfrac{7x^2 + 31x - 14}{x^2(2x+7)}$ is written as $\dfrac{A}{x} + \dfrac{B}{x^2} + \dfrac{C}{(2x+7)}$.
>
> - $\dfrac{x^2 + 4x + 6}{(x+3)^3}$ is written as $\dfrac{A}{(x+3)} + \dfrac{B}{(x+3)^2} + \dfrac{C}{(x+3)^3}$.
>   A factor that's **cubed** will appear **three** times — once cubed, once squared and once just as it is.

Tip: Make sure you don't miss repeated factors like x^2 and x^3.

Example 1

Express $\dfrac{2x^2 + 9x - 9}{x^2(x-3)}$ in partial fractions.

x is a **repeated factor** so the answer will be of the form $\dfrac{A}{x} + \dfrac{B}{x^2} + \dfrac{C}{(x-3)}$.

- Write it out as an **identity**: $\dfrac{2x^2 + 9x - 9}{x^2(x-3)} \equiv \dfrac{A}{x} + \dfrac{B}{x^2} + \dfrac{C}{(x-3)}$.

- **Add** the partial fractions:
$$\frac{2x^2 + 9x - 9}{x^2(x-3)} \equiv \frac{Ax(x-3) + B(x-3) + Cx^2}{x^2(x-3)}$$

- **Cancel** the denominators from both sides, so the numerators are **equal**:
$$2x^2 + 9x - 9 \equiv Ax(x-3) + B(x-3) + Cx^2.$$

- **Substituting** $x = 3$ gets rid of A and B:
$$(2 \times 3^2) + (9 \times 3) - 9 = 0 + 0 + C(3^2)$$
$$36 = 9C \qquad\qquad \Rightarrow C = 4$$

- **Substituting** $x = 0$ gets rid of A and C:
$$(2 \times 0^2) + (9 \times 0) - 9 = 0 + B(0 - 3) + 0$$
$$-9 = -3B \qquad\qquad \Rightarrow B = 3$$

- There's no value of x you can substitute to get rid of B and C and just leave A, so **equate coefficients** of x^2:

  Coefficients of x^2 are: $\quad 2 = A + C$
  You know $C = 4$, so: $\quad 2 = A + 4 \qquad \Rightarrow A = -2$

- **Replace** A, B and C in the identity: $\dfrac{2x^2 + 9x - 9}{x^2(x-3)} \equiv -\dfrac{2}{x} + \dfrac{3}{x^2} + \dfrac{4}{(x-3)}$

Tip: You don't need to multiply through by every denominator to add these fractions together. Have a look back at your C3 notes on adding fractions if you're not sure about this.

Tip: You could equate coefficients of x here instead, but you can't equate constant terms because A only appears as a coefficient of x or x^2 in the identity.

Example 2

Express $\dfrac{x^2 + 17x + 16}{(x + 2)^2(3x - 1)}$ in **partial fractions.**

- Write the **identity**: $\dfrac{x^2 + 17x + 16}{(x + 2)^2(3x - 1)} \equiv \dfrac{A}{(x + 2)} + \dfrac{B}{(x + 2)^2} + \dfrac{C}{(3x - 1)}$

- **Add** the partial fractions:
$$\dfrac{A}{(x + 2)} + \dfrac{B}{(x + 2)^2} + \dfrac{C}{(3x - 1)} \equiv$$
$$\dfrac{A(x + 2)(3x - 1) + B(3x - 1) + C(x + 2)^2}{(x + 2)^2(3x - 1)}$$

- **Cancel** the denominators from both sides:
$$x^2 + 17x + 16 \equiv A(x + 2)(3x - 1) + B(3x - 1) + C(x + 2)^2.$$

- **Substituting** $x = -2$ gets rid of A and C:
$$(-2)^2 + (17 \times -2) + 16 = 0 + B((3 \times -2) - 1) + 0$$
$$-14 = -7B \qquad\qquad \Rightarrow B = 2$$

- **Substituting** $x = \frac{1}{3}$ gets rid of A and B:
$$\left(\tfrac{1}{3}\right)^2 + \left(17 \times \tfrac{1}{3}\right) + 16 = 0 + 0 + C\left(\tfrac{1}{3} + 2\right)^2$$
$$\frac{196}{9} = \frac{49}{9}C \qquad\qquad \Rightarrow C = 4$$

- There's no value of x you can substitute to get rid of B and C to just leave A, so try **equating coefficients** instead:

  Equate coefficients of x^2: $\qquad 1 = 3A + C$
  You know $C = 4$, so: $\qquad\qquad -3 = 3A \qquad \Rightarrow A = -1$

- **Replace** A, B and C in the original identity:
$$\dfrac{x^2 + 17x + 16}{(x + 2)^2(3x - 1)} \equiv -\dfrac{1}{(x + 2)} + \dfrac{2}{(x + 2)^2} + \dfrac{4}{(3x - 1)}$$

> **Tip:** Remember, you won't need to multiply through by all of the denominators.
> E.g. for the second fraction you just need to multiply the top and bottom by $(3x - 1)$.

> **Tip:** Another method you can use when there's no value of x which will get rid of B and C is to substitute in any simple value of x, e.g. $x = 1$, and the values that you have calculated for B and C to work out A.

Exercise 1.2

Q1   Express $\dfrac{3x}{(x + 5)^2}$ in the form $\dfrac{A}{(x + 5)} + \dfrac{B}{(x + 5)^2}$.

Q2   Write $\dfrac{x^2 - 5x + 2}{x^2(x + 1)}$ in the form $\dfrac{A}{x} + \dfrac{B}{x^2} + \dfrac{C}{(x + 1)}$.

Q3   Express $\dfrac{x^2 + 5x - 1}{(x - 2)^3}$ in the form $\dfrac{A}{(x - 2)} + \dfrac{B}{(x - 2)^2} + \dfrac{C}{(x - 2)^3}$.

Q4   Write the following in partial fractions.

   a) $\dfrac{2x - 7}{(x - 3)^2}$ b) $\dfrac{x + 4}{(x + 2)^2}$ c) $\dfrac{2x^2 - 9x + 5}{(x - 4)^2(x + 2)}$ d) $\dfrac{3x^2 - 7x - 25}{x(x - 5)^2}$

Q5   Express $\dfrac{5x^2 - 10x - 5}{x^3 - 10x^2 + 25x}$ in partial fractions.

> **Q5 Hint:** Factorising the denominator should leave you with a repeated factor.

Improper fractions as partial fractions

- The **numerator** of an **improper** algebraic fraction has a degree **equal to or greater than** the degree of the **denominator**.

- The **degree** of a polynomial is the highest power of x.

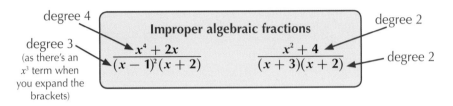

degree 4

degree 3
(as there's an x^3 term when you expand the brackets)

degree 2

degree 2

Improper algebraic fractions

$$\frac{x^4 + 2x}{(x-1)^2(x+2)} \qquad \frac{x^2 + 4}{(x+3)(x+2)}$$

- Before you can express an **improper fraction** as partial fractions, you first need to **divide** the numerator by the denominator to give $q(x) + \dfrac{r(x)}{d(x)}$ (where $\dfrac{r(x)}{d(x)}$ is a **proper fraction**).

Tip: You've seen methods of algebraic division in C3 — have a look back at your C3 notes to remind yourself of them if you need to. Remember $q(x)$ = quotient, $d(x)$ = divisor and $r(x)$ = remainder.

Tip: You can use whichever algebraic division method you like — it doesn't have to be long division.

Tip: You could check your answer by multiplying both sides by $(x-3)(x-2)$, and then multiplying out the brackets on the RHS.

Example

a) **Use division to get the improper fraction** $\dfrac{x^4 - 3x^3 - 3x^2 + 10x + 5}{(x-3)(x-2)}$ **in the form q(x) + $\dfrac{r(x)}{d(x)}$.**

- You're working out $(x^4 - 3x^3 - 3x^2 + 10x + 5) \div (x-3)(x-2)$:

- To use **long division** you'll need to multiply out $(x-3)(x-2)$:
$$(x-3)(x-2) = (x^2 - 5x + 6)$$

- Now **divide** $(x^4 - 3x^3 - 3x^2 + 10x + 5)$ by $(x^2 - 5x + 6)$:

$$
\begin{array}{r}
x^2 + 2x + 1 \\
(x^2 - 5x + 6)\overline{)x^4 - 3x^3 - 3x^2 + 10x + 5} \\
\underline{-(x^4 - 5x^3 + 6x^2)} \\
2x^3 - 9x^2 + 10x + 5 \\
\underline{-(2x^3 - 10x^2 + 12x)} \\
x^2 - 2x + 5 \\
\underline{-(x^2 - 5x + 6)} \\
3x - 1
\end{array}
$$

- So: $\dfrac{x^4 - 3x^3 - 3x^2 + 10x + 5}{(x-3)(x-2)} \equiv (x^2 + 2x + 1) + \dfrac{3x - 1}{(x-3)(x-2)}$

b) **Hence express** $\dfrac{x^4 - 3x^3 - 3x^2 + 10x + 5}{(x-3)(x-2)}$ **as partial fractions.**

Express the **proper fraction** as **partial fractions** by the usual method:

- Write out the **identity**: $\dfrac{3x - 1}{(x-3)(x-2)} \equiv \dfrac{A}{(x-3)} + \dfrac{B}{(x-2)}$.

- **Add** the partial fractions and **cancel** the denominators from both sides:

$$\frac{3x-1}{(x-3)(x-2)} \equiv \frac{A(x-2) + B(x-3)}{(x-3)(x-2)} \quad \Rightarrow \quad 3x - 1 \equiv A(x-2) + B(x-3)$$

- **Substituting** $x = 2$ gets rid of A:

$$(3 \times 2) - 1 = 0 + B(2 - 3)$$
$$5 = -B \qquad\qquad \Rightarrow \mathbf{B = -5}$$

- **Substituting** $x = 3$ gets rid of B:

$$(3 \times 3) - 1 = A(3 - 2) + 0$$
$$8 = A \qquad\qquad \Rightarrow \mathbf{A = 8}$$

- **Replacing** A and B in the partial fractions identity gives that:

$$\frac{3x - 1}{(x - 3)(x - 2)} \equiv \frac{8}{(x - 3)} - \frac{5}{(x - 2)}$$

- **Go back** to the expression you worked out for $(x^4 - 3x^3 - 3x^2 + 10x + 5) \div (x - 3)(x - 2)$:

$$\frac{x^4 - 3x^3 - 3x^2 + 10x + 5}{(x - 3)(x - 2)} \equiv x^2 + 2x + 1 + \frac{3x - 1}{(x - 3)(x - 2)}$$

Tip: Don't forget to put the partial fractions you've worked out back into your expression for the improper fraction.

- **Replace** the **proper fraction** with the **partial fractions**:

$$\frac{x^4 - 3x^3 - 3x^2 + 10x + 5}{(x - 3)(x - 2)} \equiv x^2 + 2x + 1 + \frac{8}{(x - 3)} - \frac{5}{(x - 2)}$$

Exercise 1.3

Q1 a) Use algebraic division to express $\dfrac{2x^2 - 4x + 6}{(x - 3)(x + 1)}$ in the form $q(x) + \dfrac{r(x)}{d(x)}$.

b) Hence express $\dfrac{2x^2 - 4x + 6}{(x - 3)(x + 1)}$ using partial fractions.

Q1 b) Hint: It's $\dfrac{r(x)}{d(x)}$ that you want to express in partial fractions.

Q2 Express the improper fraction $\dfrac{3x^3 + 4x^2 + 2x - 5}{(x + 2)(x + 3)}$ in partial fractions.

Q3 Show that the fraction $\dfrac{2x^2 + 4x + 7}{(x - 1)(x + 2)}$ can be expressed in the form $A + \dfrac{B}{(x - 1)} + \dfrac{C}{(x + 2)}$, and find the constants A, B and C.

Q4 Use algebraic division to show that:

$$\frac{3x^2 - 5x + 2}{(x - 3)^2} \equiv A + \frac{B}{(x - 3)} + \frac{C}{(x - 3)^2}.$$

and find the values of A, B and C.

Q5 Show that the improper fraction $\dfrac{x^3 - 3x^2 - 3x + 9}{x^2 + 3x - 4}$ can be expressed in

the form $Ax + B + \dfrac{C}{(x + 4)} + \dfrac{D}{(x - 1)}$.

Find the values of the constants A, B, C and D.

Q6 Express $\dfrac{x^3 + 4x^2 - 3x + 8}{x^2(x - 2)}$ in partial fractions.

Q6 Hint: Remember x^2 is a repeated factor.

Review Exercise — Chapter 1

Q1   Write $\dfrac{2x}{(x-5)(x+5)}$ as partial fractions in the form $\dfrac{A}{(x-5)}+\dfrac{B}{(x+5)}$.

Q2   Find the values of the constants A and B in the identity $\dfrac{2-x}{(3x+2)(x+1)} \equiv \dfrac{A}{(3x+2)}+\dfrac{B}{(x+1)}$.

Q3   Find the values of the constants A, B and C in the identity $\dfrac{x^2-3x-8}{x^3+3x^2+2x} \equiv \dfrac{A}{x}+\dfrac{B}{(x+1)}+\dfrac{C}{(x+2)}$.

Q4   Express the following as partial fractions:

a) $\dfrac{2}{(x+1)(x-1)}$
b) $\dfrac{4}{x^2+x}$

c) $\dfrac{4x+5}{(x+4)(2x-3)}$
d) $\dfrac{-7x-7}{(3x+1)(x-2)}$

e) $\dfrac{x-18}{(x+4)(3x-4)}$
f) $\dfrac{5x}{x^2+x-6}$

g) $\dfrac{6+4y}{9-y^2}$
h) $\dfrac{10x^2+32x+16}{(x+3)(2x+4)(x-2)}$

i) $\dfrac{-11x^2+6x+11}{(2x+1)(3-x)(x+2)}$
j) $\dfrac{4x^2+12x+6}{x^3+3x^2+2x}$

Q5   Find constants A, B and C such that $\dfrac{2x^2-3x+1}{(x-3)^2(x-8)} \equiv \dfrac{A}{(x-3)}+\dfrac{B}{(x-3)^2}+\dfrac{C}{(x-8)}$.

Q6   Show, by finding the values of A, B and C,

that $\dfrac{2x^2+2x-5}{x(x-5)^2}$ can be written in the form $\dfrac{A}{x}+\dfrac{B}{(x-5)}+\dfrac{C}{(x-5)^2}$.

Q7   Express the following as partial fractions.

a) $\dfrac{2x+2}{(x+3)^2}$
b) $\dfrac{6x^2+17x+5}{x(x+2)^2}$

c) $\dfrac{-18x+14}{(2x-1)^2(x+2)}$
d) $\dfrac{8x^2-x-5}{x^3-x^2}$

Q8   Show that $\dfrac{5x^2-10x+42}{(5x-1)(x+2)} \equiv A+\dfrac{B}{(5x-1)}+\dfrac{C}{(x+2)}$,

and find the values of the constants A, B and C.

Q9   Express the improper fraction $\dfrac{4x^3+12x^2-x-5}{(x+1)(2x-1)}$ in partial fractions.

Q10   Express the following improper fractions as partial fractions:

a) $\dfrac{2x^2+18x+26}{(x+2)(x+4)}$
b) $\dfrac{3x^2+9x+2}{x(x+1)}$

c) $\dfrac{3x^3-2x^2-2x-3}{(x+1)(x-2)}$
d) $\dfrac{24x^2-70x+53}{(2x-3)^2}$

1   Given that $\dfrac{5 + 9x}{(1 + 3x)^2} \equiv \dfrac{A}{(1 + 3x)^2} + \dfrac{B}{(1 + 3x)}$,

where A and B are integers, find the values of A and B.

(3 marks)

2   Show that $\dfrac{18x^2 - 15x - 62}{(3x + 4)(x - 2)} \equiv A + \dfrac{B}{(3x + 4)} + \dfrac{C}{(x - 2)}$,

and find the values of the integers A, B and C.

(4 marks)

3   $f(x) = \dfrac{5x^2 + 3x + 6}{(3 - x)(2x - 1)^2}$

Given that $f(x)$ can be expressed in the form $f(x) = \dfrac{A}{(3 - x)} + \dfrac{B}{(2x - 1)^2} + \dfrac{C}{(2x - 1)}$,

find the values of A, B and C.

(4 marks)

4   Show that the algebraic fraction $\dfrac{-80x^2 + 49x - 9}{(5x - 1)(2 - 4x)}$ can be written as $4 + \dfrac{A}{(5x - 1)} + \dfrac{B}{(2 - 4x)}$,

where A and B are constants.

Find the values of A and B.

(4 marks)

5   a)   Express the algebraic fraction $\dfrac{3x^2 + 12x - 11}{(x + 3)(x - 1)}$ in the form $A + \dfrac{B + Cx}{(x + 3)(x - 1)}$,

where A, B and C are constants.

(1 mark)

b)   Hence express $\dfrac{3x^2 + 12x - 11}{(x + 3)(x - 1)}$ as partial fractions.

(4 marks)

6   $f(x) = \dfrac{x^2 - 2x - 9}{x(x + 1)(x - 5)} \equiv \dfrac{A}{x} + \dfrac{B}{x + 1} + \dfrac{C}{x - 5}$

Find the values of the constants A, B and C.

(4 marks)

7   Express $\dfrac{6x-1}{x^2+4x+4}$ in partial fractions.

(4 marks)

8   Given that $\dfrac{-2x^3-4x^2+18x+6}{x^2+2x-3}$ can be expressed in the form:

$$Ax + B + \frac{C}{(x+3)} + \frac{D}{(x-1)}$$

find the values of A, C and D, and show that $B = 0$.

(5 marks)

9   a)   Fully factorise $2x^3 - 19x^2 + 32x + 21$.

(2 marks)

      b)   Hence express $\dfrac{x^2-9x-21}{2x^3-19x^2+32x+21}$ in partial fractions.

(4 marks)

10

$$\mathrm{f}(x) = \frac{7x^2-34x+10}{(2x-4)^2(x+3)}$$

Given that $\mathrm{f}(x)$ can be expressed in the form

$$\mathrm{f}(x) = \frac{A}{(2x-4)} + \frac{B}{(2x-4)^2} + \frac{C}{(x+3)},$$

find the values of B and C and show that $A = 0$.

(4 marks)

11   Express $\dfrac{4x^3-3x^2+12x-16}{x^2-9}$ in partial fractions.

(4 marks)

12    $\dfrac{18x^3-57x^2+38}{(x-3)(3x+2)} \equiv Ax + B + \dfrac{C}{(x-3)} + \dfrac{D}{(3x+2)}$

Find the values of the constants A, B, C and D.

(5 marks)

1. Parametric Equations of Curves

Parametric equations are ones where you have x and y in separate equations, both defined in terms of another variable. It sounds complicated, but it can often make things a lot easier, as you'll see in this chapter.

Finding coordinates from parametric equations

- Normally, graphs in the (x, y) plane are described using a **Cartesian equation** — a single equation linking x and y. Sometimes, particularly for more complicated graphs, it's easier to have two linked equations, called **parametric equations**.

- In parametric equations, x and y are each defined separately in terms of a **third variable**, called a **parameter**. The parameter is usually either t or θ.

- Parametric equations are often used to model the path of a moving particle, where its **position** (given by x and y) depends on time, t.

Learning Objectives:

- Be able to calculate Cartesian coordinates for a curve given in parametric form.

- Be able to find the coordinates of intersection points between a parametric curve and other lines.

Example 1

Sketch the graph given by the parametric equations $y = t^3 - 1$ and $x = t + 1$.

- Start by making a **table of coordinates**.
  Choose some values for t and calculate x and y at these values:

t	-2	-1	0	1	2
x	-1	0	1	2	3
y	-9	-2	-1	0	7

$x = -2 + 1 = -1$,
and $y = (-2)^3 - 1 = -9$.

$x = 1 + 1 = 2$,
and $y = 1^3 - 1 = 0$.

Tip: The exam specification says you won't be expected to sketch a curve from its parametric equations — but you do need to know how to find the Cartesian coordinates.

- Now plot the **Cartesian (x, y) coordinates** on a set of axes as usual:

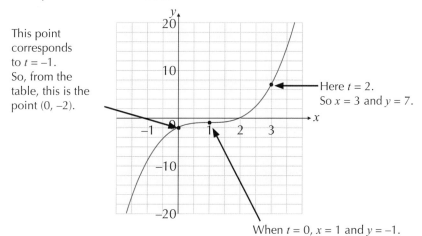

This point corresponds to $t = -1$. So, from the table, this is the point $(0, -2)$.

Here $t = 2$. So $x = 3$ and $y = 7$.

When $t = 0$, $x = 1$ and $y = -1$.

Example 2

Sketch the graph given by
$x = \cos\theta$ **and** $y = \sin\theta + 1$.

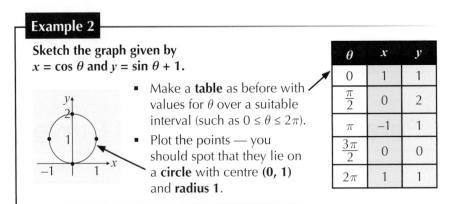

- Make a **table** as before with values for θ over a suitable interval (such as $0 \le \theta \le 2\pi$).
- Plot the points — you should spot that they lie on a **circle** with centre **(0, 1)** and **radius 1**.

θ	x	y
0	1	1
$\frac{\pi}{2}$	0	2
π	−1	1
$\frac{3\pi}{2}$	0	0
2π	1	1

Tip: $x = a + r\cos\theta$, $y = b + r\sin\theta$ are the general parametric equations for a circle with centre (a, b). If r takes different values in the x and y equations, the curve is an ellipse.

You can use the parametric equations to find **coordinates** of points on a graph, and to find the value of the **parameter** for given x- or y-coordinates.

Examples

A curve is defined by the parametric equations $y = \dfrac{1}{3t}$ and $x = 2t - 3$, $t \neq 0$.

a) Find the x- and y- values of the point the curve passes through when $t = 4$.

Just **substitute** the value for t into the equations for x and y:

When $t = 4$: $\quad x = 2(4) - 3 = \boxed{5}\quad$ and $\quad y = \dfrac{1}{3(4)} = \boxed{\dfrac{1}{12}}$

b) What value of t corresponds to the point where $y = 9$?

When $y = 9$: $\quad 9 = \dfrac{1}{3t} \Rightarrow 3t = \dfrac{1}{9} \Rightarrow t = \dfrac{1}{3 \times 9} = \boxed{\dfrac{1}{27}}$

c) What is the value of y when $x = -15$?

Use the equation for x to find t first... $\quad -15 = 2t - 3 \Rightarrow t = -6$

...then use it in the other equation to find y: $\quad y = \dfrac{1}{3(-6)} = \boxed{-\dfrac{1}{18}}$

Exercise 1.1

Q1 A curve is defined by the parametric equations $x = 3t$, $y = t^2$.
   a) Find the coordinates of the point where $t = 5$.
   b) Find the value of t at the point where $x = 18$.
   c) Find the possible values of x at the point where $y = 36$.

Q2 A curve is defined by the parametric equations $x = 2t - 1$, $y = 4 - t^2$.
   a) Find the coordinates of the point where $t = 7$.
   b) Find the value of t at the point where $x = 15$.
   c) Find the possible values of x at the point where $y = -5$.

Q3 b) & c) Hint: There is only one acute value of θ possible in b) $(0 < \theta < \frac{\pi}{2})$, and only one obtuse value of θ possible in c) $(\frac{\pi}{2} < \theta < \pi)$.

Q3 A curve has parametric equations $x = 2 + \sin\theta$, $y = -3 + \cos\theta$.
   a) Find the coordinates of the point where $\theta = \frac{\pi}{4}$.
   b) Find the acute value of θ at the point where $x = \dfrac{4 + \sqrt{3}}{2}$.
   c) Find the obtuse value of θ at the point where $y = -\dfrac{7}{2}$.

Q4 A curve is defined by the parametric equations $x = 5 \cos 2t$, $y = 3 \sin t$.

    a) Find the acute value(s) of t at the point where $x = \dfrac{5\sqrt{3}}{2}$.

    b) Find two possible values of t at the point where $y = -\dfrac{3\sqrt{3}}{2}$.

Q5 Complete the table below, and hence sketch the curve represented by the parametric equations $x = 5t$, $y = \dfrac{2}{t}$.

t	-5	-4	-3	-2	-1	0	1	2	3	4	5
x											
y											

Q6 Complete the table below and hence sketch the curve represented by the parametric equations $x = t^2$, $y = t + 1$.

t	-5	-4	-3	-2	-1	0	1	2	3	4	5
x											
y											

Q7 Sketch the curve represented by the parametric equations $x = 1 + \sin \theta$, $y = 2 + \cos \theta$ for the values $0 \le \theta \le 2\pi$.
Use the table below to help you, and give your answers to 2 d.p.

> **Q7 Hint:** Make sure your calculator's set to radians.

θ	0	$\dfrac{\pi}{4}$	$\dfrac{\pi}{3}$	$\dfrac{\pi}{2}$	$\dfrac{2\pi}{3}$	$\dfrac{3\pi}{4}$	π	$\dfrac{4\pi}{3}$	$\dfrac{3\pi}{2}$	$\dfrac{5\pi}{3}$	2π
x											
y											

Q8 Sketch the curve represented by the parametric equations $x = 3 \sin t$, $y = 5 \cos t$ for the values $0 \le t \le 2\pi$.
Use the table below to help you, giving your answers to 2 d.p.

t	0	$\dfrac{\pi}{4}$	$\dfrac{\pi}{2}$	$\dfrac{3\pi}{4}$	π	$\dfrac{5\pi}{4}$	$\dfrac{3\pi}{2}$	$\dfrac{7\pi}{4}$	2π
x									
y									

Q9 Sketch the curve $x = t - 1$, $y = 16 - t^2$ for the values $-5 \le t \le 5$.
Use a table of values if you need to.

Finding intersections

A lot of parametric equations questions involve identifying points on the curve defined by the equations. You'll often be given the parametric equations of a curve, and asked to find the coordinates of the **points of intersection** of this curve with another line (which could be the x- or y-axis).

Use the information in the question to **solve for t** at the intersection point(s). Then **substitute the value(s) of t** into the parametric equations to work out the x **and y values** (i.e. the **coordinates**) at the intersection point(s).

The example on the next page shows how to tackle a question like this.

The curve shown has the
parametric equations
$y = t^3 - t$ and $x = 4t^2 - 1$.

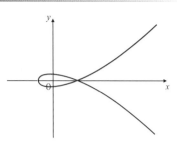

Find the coordinates of the points
where the graph crosses:
a) the *x*-axis,   b) the *y*-axis,
and c) the line $8y = 3x + 3$.

a) On the *x*-axis, $y = 0$.

- Use the parametric equation for *y* to find the values of *t* where the graph
  crosses the *x*-axis. This involves factorising and solving the cubic:

$$0 = t^3 - t \implies t(t^2 - 1) = 0 \implies t(t + 1)(t - 1) = 0$$
$$\implies t = 0, \, t = -1, \, t = 1$$

- Now use those values of *t* to find the *x*-coordinates:

> When $t = 0$: $x = 4(0)^2 - 1 = -1$
> When $t = -1$: $x = 4(-1)^2 - 1 = 3$
> When $t = 1$: $x = 4(1)^2 - 1 = 3$

Tip: $t = -1$ and $t = 1$
give the same coordinates
— that's where the curve
crosses over itself.

- So the graph crosses the *x*-axis at the points $(-1, 0)$ and $(3, 0)$.

b) On the *y*-axis, $x = 0$.

> So: $0 = 4t^2 - 1 \implies t^2 = \frac{1}{4} \implies t = \pm\frac{1}{2}$
>
> When $t = \frac{1}{2}$: $y = \left(\frac{1}{2}\right)^3 - \frac{1}{2} = -\frac{3}{8}$
>
> When $t = -\frac{1}{2}$ $y = \left(-\frac{1}{2}\right)^3 - \left(-\frac{1}{2}\right) = \frac{3}{8}$

So the graph crosses the *y*-axis at the points $\left(0, -\frac{3}{8}\right)$ and $\left(0, \frac{3}{8}\right)$.

Tip: The sketch shows
there are two points
where the graph crosses
each axis.

c) Part c) is just a little trickier.

- First, **substitute** the **parametric equations** into $8y = 3x + 3$:

> $8y = 3x + 3 \implies 8(t^3 - t) = 3(4t^2 - 1) + 3$

- **Rearrange** and **factorise** to find the values of *t* you need:

> $8t^3 - 8t = 12t^2 \implies 8t^3 - 12t^2 - 8t = 0 \implies t(2t + 1)(t - 2) = 0$
> $\implies t = 0, \, t = -\frac{1}{2}, \, t = 2$

- Go back to the parametric equations to find the *x*- and *y*-coordinates:

> When $t = 0$: $x = -1, \, y = 0$
>
> When $t = -\frac{1}{2}$: $x = 4\left(\frac{1}{4}\right) - 1 = 0, \, y = \left(-\frac{1}{2}\right)^3 + \frac{1}{2} = \frac{3}{8}$
>
> When $t = 2$: $x = 4(4) - 1 = 15, \, y = 2^3 - 2 = 6$

Tip: You can check
the answers by sticking
these values back into
$8y = 3x + 3$.

- So the graph crosses the line $8y = 3x + 3$ at the following points:

$$(-1, 0), \, \left(0, \frac{3}{8}\right), \, (15, 6)$$

Q1 The curve with parametric equations $x = 3 + t$, $y = -2 + t$ meets the x-axis at the point A and the y-axis at the point B. Find the coordinates of A and B.

Q1 Hint: A lies on the x-axis and B lies on the y-axis, so in each case you know one of the coordinates.

Q2 The curve C has parametric equations $x = 2t^2 - 50$, $y = 3t^3 - 24$.
a) Find the value of t where the curve meets the x-axis.
b) Find the values of t where the curve meets the y-axis.

Q3 The curve with parametric equations $x = 64 - t^3$, $y = \frac{1}{t}$ meets the y-axis at the point P. Find the coordinates of the point P.

Q4 Find the coordinates of the point of intersection, P, of the line $y = x - 3$ and the curve with parametric equations $x = 2t + 1$, $y = 4t$.

Q4 Hint: Replace the x and y in the Cartesian equation with the parametric equations.

Q5 Find the coordinates of the point(s) of intersection of the curve $y = x^2 + 32$ and the curve with parametric equations $x = 2t$, $y = 6t^2$.

Q6 Find the points of intersection of the circle $x^2 + y^2 = 32$ and the curve with parametric equations $x = t^2$, $y = 2t$.

Q7 The curve with parametric equations $x = a(t - 2)$, $y = 2at^2 + 3$ (where $a \neq 0$), meets the y-axis at the point $(0, 4)$.
a) Find the value of the constant a.
b) Hence determine whether the curve meets the x-axis.

Q8 A curve has parametric equations $x = \frac{2}{t}$, $y = t^2 - 9$.
a) Find the point(s) at which the curve crosses the x-axis.
b) Does the curve meet the y-axis? Explain your answer.
c) Find the coordinates of the point(s) at which this curve meets the curve $y = \frac{10}{x} - 3$.

Q9 A curve has parametric equations $x = 3 \sin t$, $y = 5 \cos t$ and is defined for the domain $-2\pi \leq t \leq 2\pi$.
a) Determine the coordinates at which this curve meets the x- and y-axes.
b) Find the points where the curve meets the line $y = \left(\frac{5\sqrt{3}}{9}\right)x$.

2. Parametric and Cartesian Equations

Learning Objective:

- Be able to convert between the parametric and Cartesian forms of an equation.

As well as finding Cartesian coordinates for a curve given in parametric form, you might have to work out its Cartesian equation too.

Converting parametric equations to Cartesian equations

Some parametric equations can be **converted** into **Cartesian equations**. There are two main ways to do this:

> - **Rearrange** one of the equations to make the **parameter** the subject, then **substitute** the result into the **other** equation.

> - If your equations involve **trig functions**, use **trig identities** to **eliminate** the parameter.

Tip: You'll have come across loads of trig identities in both C2 and C3. Look back at your notes for these modules if you need to refresh your memory.

You can use the first method to combine the parametric equations used in the examples on pages 11-12, as shown below.

Examples

Give the Cartesian equations, in the form $y = f(x)$, of the curves represented by the following pairs of parametric equations:

a) $y = t^3 - 1$ and $x = t + 1$,

b) $y = \dfrac{1}{3t}$ and $x = 2t - 3$, $t \neq 0$.

a) You want the answer in the form $y = f(x)$, so leave y alone for now, and **rearrange** the equation for x to **make t the subject**:

$$x = t + 1 \implies t = x - 1$$

Now you can **eliminate** t from the equation for y:

Tip: Just replace every 't' in the equation for y with '$x - 1$'.

$$y = t^3 - 1$$
$$\implies y = (x - 1)^3 - 1 = (x - 1)(x^2 - 2x + 1) - 1$$
$$\implies y = x^3 - 2x^2 + x - x^2 + 2x - 1 - 1$$
$$\implies y = x^3 - 3x^2 + 3x - 2$$

So the Cartesian equation is $y = x^3 - 3x^2 + 3x - 2$.

Tip: You could use the binomial theorem or Pascal's triangle to find the coefficients in the expansion of $(x - 1)^3$.

b) Use the same method as above:

$$x = 2t - 3 \implies t = \frac{x + 3}{2}$$

$$\text{So } y = \frac{1}{3t} \implies y = \frac{1}{3\left(\frac{x + 3}{2}\right)}$$

$$\implies y = \frac{1}{\left(\frac{3(x + 3)}{2}\right)} \implies y = \frac{2}{3x + 9}$$

Trigonometric functions

Things get a little trickier when the likes of sin and cos decide to put in an appearance. For trig functions you need to use **trig identities**.

Example 1

A curve has parametric equations $x = 1 + \sin\theta$, $y = 1 - \cos 2\theta$.
Give the Cartesian equation of the curve in the form $y = f(x)$.

- If you try to make θ the subject of these equations, things will just get messy. The trick is to find a way to get both x and y in terms of the **same trig function**. You can get $\sin\theta$ into the equation for y using the identity $\cos 2\theta \equiv 1 - 2\sin^2\theta$:

$$y = 1 - \cos 2\theta = 1 - (1 - 2\sin^2\theta) = 2\sin^2\theta$$

- **Rearranging** the equation for x gives: $\sin\theta = x - 1$

- **Replace** '$\sin\theta$' in the equation for y with '$x - 1$' to get y in terms of x:

$$y = 2\sin^2\theta \implies y = 2(x-1)^2 = 2x^2 - 4x + 2$$

- So the **Cartesian equation** is $\boxed{y = 2x^2 - 4x + 2.}$

> **Tip:** If one of the parametric equations includes $\cos 2\theta$ or $\sin 2\theta$, that's probably the one you need to substitute — so make sure you know the **double angle formulas** from C3.

Example 2

A curve is defined parametrically by $x = 4\sec\theta$, $y = 4\tan\theta$.
Give the equation of the curve in the form $y^2 = f(x)$, and hence determine whether the curve intersects the line $y + 3x = 4$.

- Start by **rearranging** each equation to make the **trig function** the subject:

$$x = 4\sec\theta \implies \sec\theta = \frac{x}{4} \quad \text{and} \quad y = 4\tan\theta \implies \tan\theta = \frac{y}{4}$$

- Find an **identity** that contains both **$\sec\theta$** and **$\tan\theta$**:

$$\sec^2\theta \equiv 1 + \tan^2\theta$$

- **Substitute** the trig functions with the x and y terms:

$$\left(\frac{x}{4}\right)^2 = 1 + \left(\frac{y}{4}\right)^2$$

- **Rearrange** to get an equation in the right form:

$$x^2 = 16 + y^2 \implies \boxed{y^2 = x^2 - 16}$$

- To see whether the curve intersects $y + 3x = 4$, **rearrange** to $y = 4 - 3x$ and **replace** in the equation of the curve:

$$(4 - 3x)^2 = x^2 - 16$$
$$\implies 16 - 24x + 9x^2 = x^2 - 16$$
$$\implies 8x^2 - 24x + 32 = 0$$
$$\implies x^2 - 3x + 4 = 0$$

- There are **no real roots** to this equation ($b^2 - 4ac < 0$), so the line and the curve **do not intersect**.

> **Tip:** Note that you're asked for the equation in the form $y^2 = f(x)$ not $y = f(x)$.

> **Tip:** The last bit comes from the **quadratic formula**. For a quadratic $ax^2 + bx + c = 0$, there are only real solutions when $b^2 - 4ac \geq 0$, because of the $\sqrt{b^2 - 4ac}$ bit in the formula.

Q1 For each of the following parametrically-defined curves, find the Cartesian equation of the curve in an appropriate form.

a) $x = t + 3$, $y = t^2$

b) $x = 3t$, $y = \dfrac{6}{t}$

c) $x = 2t^3$, $y = t^2$

d) $x = t + 7$, $y = 12 - 2t$

e) $x = t + 4$, $y = t^2 - 9$

f) $x = \sin \theta$, $y = \cos \theta$

g) $x = 1 + \sin \theta$, $y = 2 + \cos \theta$

h) $x = \sin \theta$, $y = \cos 2\theta$

i) $x = \cos \theta$, $y = \cos 2\theta$

j) $x = \cos \theta - 5$, $y = \cos 2\theta$

Q2 By eliminating the parameter θ, express the curve defined by the parametric equations $x = \tan \theta$, $y = \sec \theta$ in the form $y^2 = f(x)$.

Q3 Write the curve $x = 2 \cot \theta$, $y = 3 \csc \theta$ in the form $y^2 = f(x)$.

Q4 A circle is defined by the parametric equations $x = 5 + \sin \theta$, $y = -3 + \cos \theta$.

a) Find the coordinates of the centre of the circle, and the radius of the circle.

b) Write the equation of the curve in Cartesian form.

Q5 A curve has parametric equations $x = \dfrac{1 + 2t}{t}$, $y = \dfrac{3 + t}{t^2}$.

a) Express t in terms of x.

b) Hence show that the Cartesian equation of the curve is: $y = (3x - 5)(x - 2)$.

c) Sketch the curve.

Q6 Express $x = \dfrac{2 - 3t}{1 + t}$, $y = \dfrac{5 - t}{4t + 1}$ in Cartesian form.

Q7 Find the Cartesian equation of the curve defined by the parametric equations $x = 5 \sin^2 \theta$, $y = \cos \theta$. Express your answer in the form $y^2 = f(x)$.

Q8 b) Hint: Find the x- and y-intercepts first — it will give you an idea of the graph's shape.

Q8

a) Express $x = a \sin \theta$, $y = b \cos \theta$ in Cartesian form.

b) Use your answer to a) to sketch the curve.

c) What type of curve has the form $x = a \sin \theta$, $y = b \cos \theta$?

Q9 A curve has parametric equations $x = 3t^2$, $y = 2t - 1$.

a) Show that the Cartesian equation of the curve is $x = \dfrac{3}{4}(y + 1)^2$.

b) Hence find the point(s) of intersection of this curve with the line $y = 4x - 3$.

Q10 Hint: You might need to look back at your notes on transformations of curves in C1 and C3 — it's much easier to sketch if you can transform a standard curve shape.

Q10 Find the Cartesian equation of the curve $x = 7t + 2$, $y = \dfrac{5}{t}$ in the form $y = f(x)$ and hence sketch the curve, labelling any asymptotes and points of intersection with the axes clearly.

3. Parametric Integration

You should be really familiar with integration by now from the previous Core modules. Integrating parametric equations takes this one step further.

Learning Objective:

- Be able to use integration to find the area under a curve given its parametric equations.

The area under a curve

- Normally, to find the **area** under a graph, you can do a **simple integration**. But if you've got **parametric equations**, things are more difficult — you can't find $\int y \, dx$ if y isn't written in terms of x.
- There's a sneaky way to get around this. Suppose your parameter's t, then:

$$\int y \, dx = \int y \frac{dx}{dt} \, dt$$

- Both y and $\frac{dx}{dt}$ are written **in terms of** t, so you can **multiply** them together to get an expression you can **integrate with respect to** t.

Tip: This comes from the chain rule for differentiation (see C3). If you think of dx as $\frac{dx}{1}$, then $\frac{dx}{1} = \frac{dx}{dt} \times \frac{dt}{1}$.

Example

A curve is defined by the parametric equations
$y = t^2 + 2t + 3$ and $x = t^3 + 3$.
Show that $\int y \, dx = \int 3t^4 + 6t^3 + 9t^2 \, dt$.

- $\frac{dx}{dt} = 3t^2$, so using the formula above:

$$\int y \, dx = \int y \frac{dx}{dt} \, dt = \int (t^2 + 2t + 3)(3t^2) \, dt = \int 3t^4 + 6t^3 + 9t^2 \, dt$$

Tip: If you did the integration, you'd get the solution $\frac{3}{5}t^5 + \frac{3}{2}t^4 + 3t^3 + C$.

Definite integrals

With a **definite integral** (i.e. the area under a curve between two given limits), you need to **alter the limits** as well. So if you have x-values as limits, work out the corresponding values of t before you integrate.

Tip: There's more about altering the limits of definite integrals on pages 97-98.

Example

The shaded region marked A on the sketch below is bounded by the x-axis, the line $x = 2$, and by the curve with parametric equations $x = t^2 - 2$ and $y = t^2 - 9t + 20$, $t \geq 0$, which crosses the x-axis at $x = 14$.
Find the area of A.

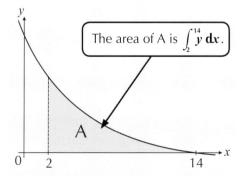

The area of A is $\int_2^{14} y \, dx$.

- We're going to use $\int y\,dx = \int y\frac{dx}{dt}\,dt$ to integrate, so first find...

$$\frac{dx}{dt} = \frac{d}{dt}(t^2 - 2) = 2t$$

- Now sort out the **limits**. 14 and 2 are the limits for integrating **with respect to x**. We need to find the **corresponding values of t**:

$$x = 2 \Rightarrow t^2 - 2 = 2 \Rightarrow t^2 = 4 \Rightarrow t = 2$$
$$x = 14 \Rightarrow t^2 - 2 = 14 \Rightarrow t^2 = 16 \Rightarrow t = 4$$

Tip: $t \geq 0$ so ignore the negative square roots.

- Now **integrate** to find the area of A:

$$A = \int_2^{14} y\,dx = \int_2^4 y\frac{dx}{dt}\,dt$$
$$= \int_2^4 (t^2 - 9t + 20)(2t)\,dt = \int_2^4 2t^3 - 18t^2 + 40t\,dt$$
$$= \left[\frac{1}{2}t^4 - 6t^3 + 20t^2\right]_2^4$$
$$= \left(\frac{1}{2}(4)^4 - 6(4)^3 + 20(4)^2\right) - \left(\frac{1}{2}(2)^4 - 6(2)^3 + 20(2)^2\right)$$
$$= 64 - 40 = \boxed{24}$$

Exercise 3.1

Q1 Hint: You don't need to integrate these, but you will need to differentiate to get dx/dt, so you might want to brush up on your differentiation from the previous core modules.

Q1 For each of the following curves, find an expression in parametric form that is equivalent to the indefinite integral $\int y\,dx$.
  a) $x = \frac{3}{t}$, $y = 4t^2$
  b) $x = \sqrt{t}$, $y = 3t^2 - 4$
  c) $x = \sin^2\theta$, $y = \cos\theta$
  d) $x = \tan 5\theta$, $y = \sec^2 5\theta$

Q2 For each of the following curves, find an expression equivalent to $\int y\,dx$ and integrate it.
  a) $x = t - 2$, $y = 4t + 3$
  b) $x = 3t^2$, $y = 5t - 1$
  c) $x = (4t - 5)^2$, $y = t^2 - 3t$
  d) $x = t^2 + 3$, $y = 4t - 1$

Q3 Hint: You'll need to use a trig identity.

Q3 A curve has parametric equations $x = \cos 3\theta + 4$, $y = 2\cos 3\theta$. Show that $\int y\,dx$ is equivalent to $\int -3\sin 6\theta\,d\theta$.

Q4 A curve has parametric equations $x = 3t + 6$, $y = 2t - 8$. Find an expression for $y\frac{dx}{dt}$, and hence evaluate $\int_{-2}^2 y\frac{dx}{dt}\,dt$.

Q5 Hint: Don't forget to change the limits — they're given as values for x but you need the corresponding values of t.

Q5 A curve has parametric equations $x = 3t^2$, $y = \frac{5}{t}$, where $t > 0$. Find an expression for $y\frac{dx}{dt}$, and hence evaluate $\int_3^{75} y\,dx$.

Q6 The curve shown here has parametric equations $x = 4t(t + 1)$, $y = 3t^3$.
  a) Find the values t_1 and t_2 that correspond to $x = 8$ and $x = 120$, given that $t > 0$.
  b) Hence find a parametric integral corresponding to $\int_8^{120} y\,dx$, and evaluate this to find the area A.

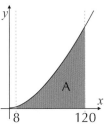

Review Exercise — Chapter 2

Q1 A curve is defined by the parametric equations $x = \frac{1}{t}$, $y = \frac{2}{t^2}$ $(t \neq 0)$.

a) Find the value of t when $x = \frac{1}{4}$ and hence find the corresponding y-coordinate.

b) Find the possible values of t when $y = \frac{1}{50}$.

Q2 A curve is defined by the parametric equations $y = 2t^2 + t + 4$ and $x = \frac{6 - t}{2}$.

a) Find the values of x and y when $t = 0$, 1, 2 and 3.

b) What are the values of t when: (i) $x = -7$ (ii) $y = 19$?

c) Find the Cartesian equation of the curve, in the form $y = f(x)$.

Q3 The parametric equations of a curve are $x = 2 \sin \theta$ and $y = \cos^2 \theta + 4$, $-\frac{\pi}{2} \leq \theta \leq \frac{\pi}{2}$.

a) What are the coordinates of the points where: (i) $\theta = \frac{\pi}{4}$ (ii) $\theta = \frac{\pi}{6}$?

b) What is the Cartesian equation of the curve?

c) What restrictions are there on the values of x for this curve?

Q4 The curve C is defined by the parametric equations $x = \frac{\sin \theta}{3}$ and $y = 3 + 2 \cos 2\theta$.
Find the Cartesian equation of C.

Q5 A curve has parametric equations $y = 4 + \frac{3}{t}$ and $x = t^2 - 1$ $(t \neq 0)$.

a) What are the coordinates of the points where this curve crosses
    (i) the y-axis   (ii) the line $x + 2y = 14$?

b) Write the integral $\int y \, dx$ in the form $\int f(t) \, dt$. (You don't need to do the integration.)

Q6 The curve on the right has the
parametric equations $x = t^2 + 3$, $y = 4t - 1$.

a) Given that $t > 0$, find the values of t
   when $x = 4$ and $x = 12$.

b) Hence find the shaded area.

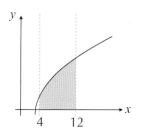

Q7 The curve below has parametric equations $x = 2t^3$, $y = \frac{2}{t}$ $(t \neq 0)$.

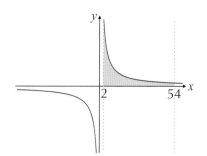

Show that the shaded area between the curve, the lines $x = 2$ and $x = 54$ and the x-axis is 48.

1   The curve C is defined by the parametric equations

$$x = 1 - \tan \theta, \quad y = \tfrac{1}{2} \sin 2\theta, \quad -\tfrac{\pi}{2} < \theta < \tfrac{\pi}{2}.$$

(a) P is the point on curve C where $\theta = \tfrac{\pi}{3}$. Find the exact coordinates of P.

(2 marks)

(b)   Point Q on curve C has coordinates $(2, -\tfrac{1}{2})$. Find the value of θ at Q.

(2 marks)

(c)   Using the identity $\sin 2\theta \equiv \dfrac{2 \tan \theta}{1 + \tan^2 \theta}$,

show that the Cartesian equation of C is $y = \dfrac{1 - x}{x^2 - 2x + 2}$.

(3 marks)

2

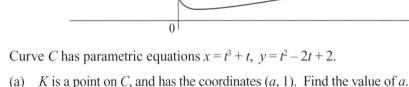

Curve C has parametric equations $x = t^3 + t, \ y = t^2 - 2t + 2$.

(a) K is a point on C, and has the coordinates $(a, 1)$. Find the value of a.

(2 marks)

(b)   The line $8y = x + 6$ passes through C at points K, L and M.
Find the coordinates of L and M, given that the x-coordinate of M is
greater than the x-coordinate of L.

(6 marks)

3   The curve below has parametric equations $x = 3 \sin \theta, \ y = 4 \cos \theta$.

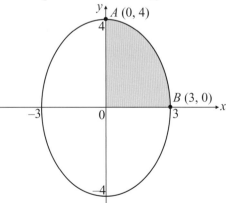

(a)   For $0 \le \theta \le \tfrac{\pi}{2}$, find the values of θ that correspond to the points A and B.

(2 marks)

(b)   Hence show that the shaded area is equal to the integral $6 \displaystyle\int_0^{\frac{\pi}{2}} (\cos 2\theta + 1) \, d\theta.$ *(3 marks)*

4

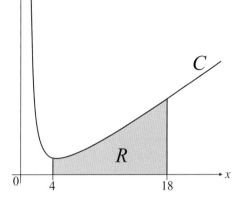

The curve C has parametric equations
$$x = t^2 + 3t, \quad y = t^2 + \frac{1}{t^3}, \quad t > 0.$$

The shaded region marked R is enclosed by C, the x-axis and the lines $x = 4$ and $x = 18$.

(a) Show that the area of R is given by $\int_1^3 \frac{(t^5 + 1)(2t + 3)}{t^3} \, dt$.

(4 marks)

(b) Find the area of R.

(4 marks)

5

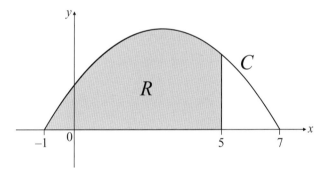

The parametric equations of curve C are
$$x = 3 + 4\sin\theta, \quad y = \frac{1 + \cos 2\theta}{3}, \quad -\frac{\pi}{2} \le \theta \le \frac{\pi}{2}.$$

Point H on C has coordinates $(5, \frac{1}{2})$.

(a) Find the value of θ at point H.

(2 marks)

The region R is enclosed by C, the line $x = 5$, and the x-axis, as shown.

(b) Show that the area of R is given by the integral $\frac{8}{3}\int_{-\frac{\pi}{2}}^{\frac{\pi}{6}} \cos^3\theta \, d\theta$.

(5 marks)

(c) Show that the Cartesian equation of C can be written $y = \frac{-x^2 + 6x + 7}{24}$.

(4 marks)

(d) State the domain of values of x for the curve C.

(1 mark)

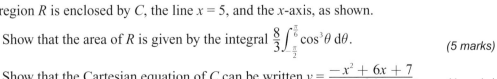

1. The Binomial Expansion

Learning Objectives:

- Be able to expand $(p + qx)^n$ for any rational n using the general formula for binomial expansions.

- Be able to state the validity of the expansion — i.e. the values of x for which the expansion is valid.

You might well recognise binomial expansions from C2. This chapter should refresh your memory on the formula and take it a step further — including what to do if you have to raise an expression to a fractional or negative power.

Expansions where n is a positive integer

The **binomial expansion** is a way to raise a given expression to any power. For simpler cases it's basically a fancy way of multiplying out brackets. You can also use it to approximate more complicated expressions.

This is the **general formula** for binomial expansions:

$$(1 + x)^n = 1 + nx + \frac{n(n - 1)}{1 \times 2}x^2 + \dots + \frac{n(n - 1)\dots(n - r + 1)}{1 \times 2 \times \dots \times r}x^r + \dots$$

From the general formula, it looks like the expansion always goes on forever. But if n **is a positive integer**, the binomial expansion is **finite**.

Example 1

Give the binomial expansion of $(1 + x)^5$.

Use the **general formula** and plug in $n = 5$:

$$\overset{n = 5}{(1 + x)^5} = 1 + 5x + \frac{5(5 - 1)}{1 \times 2}x^2 + \frac{5(5 - 1)(5 - 2)}{1 \times 2 \times 3}x^3$$

$$+ \frac{5(5 - 1)(5 - 2)(5 - 3)}{1 \times 2 \times 3 \times 4}x^4 + \frac{5(5 - 1)(5 - 2)(5 - 3)(5 - 4)}{1 \times 2 \times 3 \times 4 \times 5}x^5$$

$$+ \frac{5(5 - 1)(5 - 2)(5 - 3)(5 - 4)(5 - 5)}{1 \times 2 \times 3 \times 4 \times 5 \times 6}x^6 + \dots$$

Tip: It may seem a bit dull to write all the steps out in this way for simple expansions, but it's important for more complex ones to make sure you don't miss anything out.

$$= 1 + 5x + \frac{5 \times 4}{1 \times 2}x^2 + \frac{5 \times 4 \times 3}{1 \times 2 \times 3}x^3 + \frac{5 \times 4 \times 3 \times 2}{1 \times 2 \times 3 \times 4}x^4$$

$$+ \frac{5 \times 4 \times 3 \times 2 \times 1}{1 \times 2 \times 3 \times 4 \times 5}x^5 + \frac{5 \times 4 \times 3 \times 2 \times 1 \times 0}{1 \times 2 \times 3 \times 4 \times 5 \times 6}x^6 + \dots$$

You can stop here — all the terms after this one are **zero**.

Tip: The expansion is finite because at some point you introduce an $(n - n)$ (i.e. zero) term in the numerator which then appears in every coefficient from that point on, making them all zero.

$$= 1 + 5x + \frac{20}{2}x^2 + \frac{60}{6}x^3 + \frac{120}{24}x^4 + \frac{120}{120}x^5 + \frac{0}{720}x^6 + \dots$$

$$= 1 + 5x + 10x^2 + 10x^3 + 5x^4 + x^5$$

The formula still works if the coefficient of x **isn't 1**, i.e. $(1 + ax)^n$ — just **replace** each 'x' in the formula with (ax). The 'a' should be raised to the **same power** as the 'x' in each term, and included in the coefficient when you simplify at the end. This next example shows you how it's done.

Example 2

Give the binomial expansion of $(1 - 3x)^4$.

Use the **formula** with $n = 4$, but replace every x with $-3x$. Think of this as $(1 + (-3x))^4$ — put the **minus** into the formula as well as the $3x$.

$n = 4 \quad n(n-1)$

$(1 - 3x)^4 = 1 + 4(-3x) + \dfrac{4 \times 3}{1 \times 2}(-3x)^2 + \dfrac{4 \times 3 \times 2}{1 \times 2 \times 3}(-3x)^3$

$\qquad + \dfrac{4 \times 3 \times 2 \times 1}{1 \times 2 \times 3 \times 4}(-3x)^4 + \dfrac{4 \times 3 \times 2 \times 1 \times 0}{1 \times 2 \times 3 \times 4 \times 5}(-3x)^5 + \ldots$

Don't forget to square the -3 as well.

Stop here.

$= 1 + 4(-3x) + \dfrac{12}{2}(9x^2) + \dfrac{4}{1}(-27x^3) + (81x^4) + \dfrac{0}{5}(-243x^5) + \ldots$

$= 1 - 12x + 54x^2 - 108x^3 + 81x^4$

Tip: Make life easier for yourself by cancelling down the fractions before you multiply.

Validity

Some binomial expansions are **only valid for certain values of** x. When you find a binomial expansion, you usually have to state which values of x the expansion is valid for.

> If n is a **positive integer**, the binomial expansion of $(p + qx)^n$ is valid for **all values of** x.

There's more on the validity of other expansions on page 27.

Tip: So far you've only dealt with expansions of $(p + qx)^n$ where p is 1, but there are more complicated examples to come on page 30.

Exercise 1.1

Use the binomial expansion formula to expand each of the following functions in ascending powers of x.

Q1 Expand fully: $(1 + x)^3$

Q2 Expand $(1 + x)^7$ up to and including the term in x^3.

Q3 Expand fully: $(1 - x)^4$

Q4 Give the first 3 terms of $(1 + 3x)^6$.

Q5 Give the first 4 terms of $(1 + 2x)^8$.

Q6 Expand $(1 - 5x)^5$ up to and including the term in x^2.

Q7 Expand fully: $(1 - 4x)^3$

Q8 Expand $(1 + 6x)^6$ up to and including the term in x^3.

Q3 Hint: Watch out for that minus sign — replace 'x' in the formula with ($-x$).

Expansions where n is negative or a fraction

n is negative

If n is **negative**, the expansion gets more complicated. You can still use the **formula** in the same way, but it will produce an **infinite** number of terms (see the example below). You can just write down the **first few terms** in the series, but this will only be an **approximation** to the whole expansion.

Tip: The question will usually tell you how many terms to give.

This type of expansion can be 'hidden' as a fraction — remember:

$$\frac{1}{(1+x)^n} = (1+x)^{-n}$$

Example

Find the binomial expansion of $\dfrac{1}{(1+x)^2}$ up to and including the term in x^3.

- First, **rewrite** the expression: $\dfrac{1}{(1+x)^2} = (1+x)^{-2}$.

- Now you can use the **general formula**. This time $n = -2$:

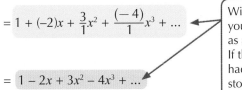

$$(1+x)^{-2} = 1 + (-2)x + \frac{(-2) \times (-2-1)}{1 \times 2}x^2$$
$$+ \frac{(-2) \times (-2-1) \times (-2-2)}{1 \times 2 \times 3}x^3 + \ldots$$

$$= 1 + (-2)x + \frac{(-2) \times (-3)}{1 \times 2}x^2 + \frac{(-2) \times (-3) \times (-4)}{1 \times 2 \times 3}x^3 + \ldots$$

$$= 1 + (-2)x + \frac{3}{1}x^2 + \frac{(-4)}{1}x^3 + \ldots$$

$$= 1 - 2x + 3x^2 - 4x^3 + \ldots$$

With a negative n, you'll never get zero as a coefficient. If the question hadn't told you to stop, the expansion could go on forever.

Tip: Again, you can cancel down before you multiply — but be careful with those minus signs.

- We've left out all the terms after $-4x^3$, so the cubic expression you've ended up with is an **approximation** to the original expression.

- You could also write the answer like this:

$$\frac{1}{(1+x)^2} \approx 1 - 2x + 3x^2 - 4x^3$$

---

n is a fraction

The binomial expansion formula doesn't just work for integer values of n. If n is a **fraction**, you'll have to take care multiplying out the fractions in the coefficients, but otherwise the formula is **exactly the same**.

Remember that **roots** are fractional powers:

$$\sqrt[n]{1+x} = (1+x)^{\frac{1}{n}}$$

Example

Find the binomial expansion of $\sqrt[3]{1 + 2x}$, up to and including the term in x^3.

- First rewrite the expression as a fractional power: $\sqrt[3]{1 + 2x} = (1 + 2x)^{\frac{1}{3}}$

- This time $n = \frac{1}{3}$, and you also need to replace x with $2x$:

$$\begin{aligned}
(1 + 2x)^{\frac{1}{3}} &= 1 + \frac{1}{3}(2x) + \frac{\frac{1}{3} \times \left(\frac{1}{3} - 1\right)}{1 \times 2}(2x)^2 \\
&\quad + \frac{\frac{1}{3} \times \left(\frac{1}{3} - 1\right) \times \left(\frac{1}{3} - 2\right)}{1 \times 2 \times 3}(2x)^3 + \ldots
\end{aligned}$$

where $n = \frac{1}{3}$ and $n(n-1)$.

$$= 1 + \frac{2}{3}x + \frac{\frac{1}{3} \times \left(-\frac{2}{3}\right)}{1 \times 2}(4x^2) + \frac{\frac{1}{3} \times \left(-\frac{2}{3}\right) \times \left(-\frac{5}{3}\right)}{1 \times 2 \times 3}(8x^3) + \ldots$$

$$= 1 + \frac{2}{3}x + \frac{\left(-\frac{2}{9}\right)}{2}(4x^2) + \frac{\left(\frac{10}{27}\right)}{6}(8x^3) + \ldots$$

$$= 1 + \frac{2}{3}x + \left(-\frac{1}{9}\right)(4x^2) + \left(\frac{5}{81}\right)(8x^3) + \ldots$$

$$= 1 + \frac{2}{3}x - \frac{4}{9}x^2 + \frac{40}{81}x^3 - \ldots$$

Tip: Cancelling down is much trickier with this type of expansion — it's often safer to multiply everything out fully.

Tip: Exam questions often ask for the coefficients as simplified fractions.

Validity when n is negative or a fraction

Binomial expansions where n is negative or a fraction are **not valid** for **all** values of x. The **rule** to work out the validity of an expansion is as follows:

> If n is a negative integer or a fraction,
> the binomial expansion of $(p + qx)^n$ is **valid** when $\left|\frac{qx}{p}\right| < 1$,
> i.e. when $|x| < \left|\frac{p}{q}\right|$.

This just means that the **absolute value** (or **modulus**) of x (i.e. ignoring any negative signs) must be **smaller** than the absolute value of $\frac{p}{q}$ for the expansion to be valid.

Tip: You might already know the rules
$|ab| = |a||b|$
and $\left|\frac{a}{b}\right| = \frac{|a|}{|b|}$.

If you don't, then get to know them — they're handy for rearranging these limits.

Examples

State the validity of the expansions given in the previous two examples.

a) For the expansion $(1 + x)^{-2} = 1 - 2x + 3x^2 - 4x^3 + \ldots$, $p = 1$ and $q = 1$.

So the expansion is valid if $\left|\frac{1x}{1}\right| < 1$, i.e. if $|x| < 1$.

b) For $(1 + 2x)^{\frac{1}{3}} = 1 + \frac{2}{3}x - \frac{4}{9}x^2 + \frac{40}{81}x^3 - \ldots$, $p = 1$ and $q = 2$.

So the expansion is valid if $|2x| < 1 \Rightarrow 2|x| < 1 \Rightarrow |x| < \frac{1}{2}$.

Combinations of expansions

- You can use the binomial expansion formula for more complicated combinations of expansions — e.g. where different brackets raised to different powers are **multiplied together**.

- Start by dealing with the different expansions **separately**, then **multiply** the expressions together at the end.

- For situations where one bracket is being **divided** by another, change the **sign** of the **power** and **multiply** instead (e.g. $\dfrac{(1 + x)}{(1 + 2x)^3} = (1 + x)(1 + 2x)^{-3}$).

- For the **combined** expansion to be **valid**, x must be in the valid range for **both** expansions, i.e. where they overlap. In practice this just means sticking to the **narrowest** of the valid ranges for each separate expansion.

Example

Write down the first three terms in the expansion of $\dfrac{(1 + 2x)^3}{(1 - x)^2}$.

State the range of x for which the expansion is valid.

- First re-write the expression as a product of two expansions:

$$\frac{(1 + 2x)^3}{(1 - x)^2} = (1 + 2x)^3(1 - x)^{-2}$$

- Expand each of these separately using the formula:

$$(1 + 2x)^3 = 1 + 3(2x) + \frac{3 \times 2}{1 \times 2}(2x)^2 + \frac{3 \times 2 \times 1}{1 \times 2 \times 3}(2x)^3$$
$$= 1 + 6x + 3(4x^2) + 8x^3 = 1 + 6x + 12x^2 + 8x^3$$

$$(1 - x)^{-2} = 1 + (-2)(-x) + \frac{(-2) \times (-3)}{1 \times 2}(-x)^2 + \frac{(-2) \times (-3) \times (-4)}{1 \times 2 \times 3}(-x)^3 + \ldots$$
$$= 1 + 2x + 3x^2 + 4x^3 + \ldots$$

- **Multiply** the two expansions together. Since you're only asked for the **first three terms**, ignore any terms with **higher powers** of x than x^2.

$$(1 + 2x)^3(1 - x)^{-2} = (1 + 6x + 12x^2 + 8x^3)(1 + 2x + 3x^2 + 4x^3 + \ldots)$$
$$= 1(1 + 2x + 3x^2) + 6x(1 + 2x) + 12x^2(1) + \ldots$$
$$= 1 + 2x + 3x^2 + 6x + 12x^2 + 12x^2 + \ldots$$
$$= \boxed{1 + 8x + 27x^2 + \ldots}$$

- Now find the **validity** of each expansion:

$(1 + 2x)^3$ is valid for all values of x, since n is a positive integer.

$(1 - x)^{-2}$ is valid if $|-x| < 1 \Rightarrow |x| < 1$.

So the combined expression $\dfrac{(1 + 2x)^3}{(1 - x)^2}$ is only valid if $\boxed{|x| < 1,}$

since this is the narrower range of the two separate expansions.

Q1 Use the binomial formula to find the first four terms in the expansion of $(1 + x)^{-4}$.

Q2 a) Find the binomial expansion of $(1 - 6x)^{-3}$, up to and including the term in x^3.
   b) For what values of x is this expansion valid?

Q3 Use the binomial formula to find the first three terms in the expansion of:
   a) $(1 + 4x)^{\frac{1}{3}}$
   b) $(1 + 4x)^{-\frac{1}{2}}$
   c) For each of the expansions above, state the range of x for which the expansion is valid.

Q4 Find the binomial expansion of the following functions, up to and including the term in x^3.

   a) $\dfrac{1}{(1 - 4x)^2}$ for $|x| < \dfrac{1}{4}$

   b) $\sqrt{1 + 6x}$ for $|x| < \dfrac{1}{6}$

   c) $\dfrac{1}{\sqrt{1 - 3x}}$ for $|x| < \dfrac{1}{3}$

   d) $\sqrt[3]{1 + \frac{x}{2}}$ for $|x| < 2$

Q5 a) Find the coefficient of the x^3 term in the expansion of $\dfrac{1}{(1 + 7x)^4}$.
   b) For what range of x is this expansion valid?

> **Q5-6 Hint:** You don't need to bother doing the full expansion — just work out the coefficient of the term you need.

Q6 a) What is the coefficient of x^5 in the expansion of $\sqrt[4]{1 - 4x}$?
   b) For what values of x is the binomial expansion of $\sqrt[4]{1 - 4x}$ valid?

Q7 a) Write down the first three terms of the expansion of $(1 - 5x)^{\frac{1}{6}}$.
   b) Hence find the binomial expansion of $(1 + 4x)^4 (1 - 5x)^{\frac{1}{6}}$, up to and including the term in x^2.
   c) State the validity of the expansion in b).

Q8 a) Find the first three terms of the binomial expansion of $\dfrac{(1 + 3x)^4}{(1 + x)^3}$.
   b) State the range of x for which the expansion is valid.

Expanding $(p + qx)^n$

- You've seen over the last few pages that the general binomial expansion of $(1 + x)^n$ works for **any n**, and that you can replace the x with other x-terms.

- However, the 1 at the start **has to be a 1** before you can expand.

- If it's **not a 1**, you'll need to **factorise first** before you can use the formula.

- This means you have to rewrite the expression as follows:

$$(p + qx)^n = p^n\left(1 + \frac{qx}{p}\right)^n$$

Tip: This rearrangement uses the power law $(ab)^k = a^k b^k$ — note that the p outside the brackets is still raised to the power n.

Example 1

Give the binomial expansion of $(3 - x)^4$ and state its validity.

- To use the general formula, you need the constant term in the brackets to be 1. You can take the 3 outside the brackets by factorising:

$$3 - x = 3\left(1 - \frac{1}{3}x\right)$$

$$\Rightarrow (3 - x)^4 = \left[3\left(1 - \frac{1}{3}x\right)\right]^4$$

> The aim here is to get an expression in the form $c(1 + dx)^n$, where c and d are constants.

$$= 3^4\left(1 - \frac{1}{3}x\right)^4$$

$$= 81\left(1 - \frac{1}{3}x\right)^4$$

Tip: Don't forget to raise the 3 to the power 4.

- Now use the general formula, with $n = 4$, and $-\frac{1}{3}x$ instead of x:

$$\left(1 - \frac{1}{3}x\right)^4 = 1 + 4\left(-\frac{1}{3}x\right) + \frac{4 \times 3}{1 \times 2}\left(-\frac{1}{3}x\right)^2 + \frac{4 \times 3 \times 2}{1 \times 2 \times 3}\left(-\frac{1}{3}x\right)^3$$
$$+ \frac{4 \times 3 \times 2 \times 1}{1 \times 2 \times 3 \times 4}\left(-\frac{1}{3}x\right)^4$$

$$= 1 - \frac{4}{3}x + 6\left(\frac{1}{9}x^2\right) + 4\left(-\frac{1}{27}x^3\right) + \frac{1}{81}x^4$$

$$= 1 - \frac{4x}{3} + \frac{2x^2}{3} - \frac{4x^3}{27} + \frac{x^4}{81}$$

Tip: For this example, you could just pop $a = 3$ and $b = -x$ into the formula for $(a + b)^n$, which will be given to you in the exam. This formula only works when n is a positive integer though, so you'll need to use the method shown here if the power is negative or a fraction.

- Finally, put this back into the original expression:

$$(3 - x)^4 = 81\left(1 - \frac{1}{3}x\right)^4$$

$$= 81\left(1 - \frac{4x}{3} + \frac{2x^2}{3} - \frac{4x^3}{27} + \frac{x^4}{81}\right)$$

$$= 81 - 108x + 54x^2 - 12x^3 + x^4$$

- The expansion is valid for **all values of x**.

  This is because n is a positive integer — so the expansion is finite.

Example 2

Give the first 3 terms in the binomial expansion of $(3x + 4)^{\frac{3}{2}}$.

- Again, you need to **factorise** before using the formula, taking care to choose the **right factor**...

$$3x + 4 = 4 + 3x = 4\left(1 + \frac{3}{4}x\right)$$

> Make sure you've got the bracket written in the form $(p + qx)^n$ before you factorise.

Tip: It's tempting to take the 3 outside the brackets because of the order the numbers are written in, but don't be fooled.

$$\Rightarrow (3x + 4)^{\frac{3}{2}} = \left[4\left(1 + \frac{3}{4}x\right)\right]^{\frac{3}{2}}$$

$$= 4^{\frac{3}{2}}\left(1 + \frac{3}{4}x\right)^{\frac{3}{2}}$$

$$= 8\left(1 + \frac{3}{4}x\right)^{\frac{3}{2}}$$

- Use the **general formula** with $n = \frac{3}{2}$, and $\frac{3}{4}x$ instead of x:

$$\left(1 + \frac{3}{4}x\right)^{\frac{3}{2}} = 1 + \frac{3}{2}\left(\frac{3}{4}x\right) + \frac{\frac{3}{2} \times \left(\frac{3}{2} - 1\right)}{1 \times 2}\left(\frac{3}{4}x\right)^2 + \dots$$

$$= 1 + \frac{9}{8}x + \frac{\frac{3}{2} \times \frac{1}{2}}{2}\left(\frac{9}{16}x^2\right) + \dots$$

$$= 1 + \frac{9x}{8} + \frac{27x^2}{128} + \dots$$

- Put this back into the **original expression**:

$$(3x + 4)^{\frac{3}{2}} = 8\left(1 + \frac{3}{4}x\right)^{\frac{3}{2}} = 8\left(1 + \frac{9x}{8} + \frac{27x^2}{128} + \dots\right)$$

$$= 8 + 9x + \frac{27x^2}{16} + \dots$$

Tip: This expansion is only valid for $\left|\frac{qx}{p}\right| < 1$, i.e. $\left|\frac{3x}{4}\right| < 1 \Rightarrow |x| < \frac{4}{3}$.

Example 3

Expand $\dfrac{1 + 2x}{(2 - x)^2}$ up to the term in x^3.

State the range of x for which the expansion is valid.

- First you need to **rearrange** and **separate** the different expansions:

$$\frac{1 + 2x}{(2 - x)^2} = (1 + 2x)(2 - x)^{-2}$$

$$p = 2 \qquad q = -1$$

- The first bracket doesn't need expanding, so deal with the second bracket as usual, **factorising** first...

$$2 - x = 2\left(1 - \frac{1}{2}x\right) \quad \Rightarrow \quad (2 - x)^{-2} = 2^{-2}\left(1 - \frac{1}{2}x\right)^{-2} = \frac{1}{4}\left(1 - \frac{1}{2}x\right)^{-2}$$

Tip: For expressions where both brackets need expanding, just take your time and set everything out in steps, only combining the expansions at the end.

- ... then using the **formula** with $n = -2$, and $-\frac{1}{2}x$ instead of x:

$$\left(1 - \frac{1}{2}x\right)^{-2} = 1 + (-2)\left(-\frac{1}{2}x\right) + \frac{-2 \times -3}{1 \times 2}\left(-\frac{1}{2}x\right)^2$$

$$+ \frac{-2 \times -3 \times -4}{1 \times 2 \times 3}\left(-\frac{1}{2}x\right)^3 + \dots$$

$$= 1 + x + \frac{3x^2}{4} + \frac{x^3}{2} + \dots$$

- So this means that:

$$(2 - x)^{-2} = \tfrac{1}{4}\left(1 - \tfrac{1}{2}x\right)^{-2} = \tfrac{1}{4}\left(1 + x + \tfrac{3x^2}{4} + \tfrac{x^3}{2} + \ldots\right)$$

$$= \tfrac{1}{4} + \tfrac{x}{4} + \tfrac{3x^2}{16} + \tfrac{x^3}{8} + \ldots$$

- Putting all this into the **original expression** gives:

$$\frac{1 + 2x}{(2 - x)^2} = (1 + 2x)(2 - x)^{-2} = (1 + 2x)\left(\tfrac{1}{4} + \tfrac{x}{4} + \tfrac{3x^2}{16} + \tfrac{x^3}{8} + \ldots\right)$$

$$= \tfrac{1}{4} + \tfrac{x}{4} + \tfrac{3x^2}{16} + \tfrac{x^3}{8} + 2x\left(\tfrac{1}{4} + \tfrac{x}{4} + \tfrac{3x^2}{16}\right) + \ldots$$

$$= \tfrac{1}{4} + \tfrac{x}{4} + \tfrac{3x^2}{16} + \tfrac{x^3}{8} + \tfrac{x}{2} + \tfrac{x^2}{2} + \tfrac{3x^3}{8} + \ldots$$

$$= \boxed{\tfrac{1}{4} + \tfrac{3x}{4} + \tfrac{11x^2}{16} + \tfrac{x^3}{2} + \ldots}$$

- The **validity** of the whole expansion will depend on the validity of the expansion of $(2 - x)^{-2}$.

  This is valid only if $\left|\tfrac{-x}{2}\right| < 1 \Rightarrow |x| < 2$

Tip: Remember — if both expansions have a limited validity, choose the one with the narrower valid range of x for the combined expansion.

Exercise 1.3

Q1 Find the binomial expansion of the following functions, up to and including the term in x^3:

a) $(2 + 4x)^3$
b) $(3 + 4x)^5$
c) $(4 + x)^{\frac{1}{2}}$
d) $(8 + 2x)^{-\frac{1}{3}}$

Q2 Hint: Work out the x^2 term of the expansion in terms of a.

Q2 If the x^2 coefficient of the binomial expansion of $(a + 5x)^5$ is 2000, what is the value of a?

Q3 a) Find the binomial expansion of $(2 - 5x)^7$ up to and including the term in x^2.

   b) Hence, or otherwise, find the binomial expansion of $(1 + 6x)^3(2 - 5x)^7$, up to and including the term in x^2.

Q4 a) Find the binomial expansion of $\left(1 + \tfrac{6}{5}x\right)^{-\frac{1}{2}}$, up to and including the term in x^3, stating the range of x for which it is valid.

Q4 b) Hint: Rewrite the expression in the form $z\left(1 + \tfrac{6}{5}x\right)^{-\frac{1}{2}}$, where z is a number or another expression.

   b) Hence, or otherwise, express $\sqrt{\dfrac{20}{5 + 6x}}$ in the form $a + bx + cx^2 + dx^3 + \ldots$

Q5 $f(x) = \dfrac{1}{\sqrt{5 - 2x}}$

   a) Find the binomial expansion of $f(x)$ in ascending powers of x, up to and including the term in x^2.

   b) Hence show that $\dfrac{3 + x}{\sqrt{5 - 2x}} \approx \dfrac{3}{\sqrt{5}} + \dfrac{8x}{5\sqrt{5}} + \dfrac{19x^2}{50\sqrt{5}}$.

Q6 a) Find the binomial expansion of $(9 + 4x)^{-\frac{1}{2}}$, up to and including the term in x^2.

   b) Hence, or otherwise, find the binomial expansion of $\dfrac{(1 + 6x)^4}{\sqrt{9 + 4x}}$, up to and including the term in x^2.

2. Using the Binomial Expansion as an Approximation

One of the reasons that binomial expansions are so useful is that they can be used to estimate nasty-looking roots, powers and fractions. All you need to work out is the right value of x to use.

Learning Objective:

- Be able to substitute values into a binomial expansion in order to find approximations.

Approximating with binomial expansions

- When you've done an expansion, you can use it to work out the **value** of the original expression for **given values of x**, by **substituting** those values into the **expansion**.

- For most expansions this will only be an **approximate** answer, because you'll have had to limit the expansion to the first few terms.

- Often you'll have to do some **rearranging** of the expression so that you know what value of x to substitute.

- For example, $\sqrt[3]{1.3}$ can be written as $(1 + 0.3)^{\frac{1}{3}}$, which can be approximated by expanding $(1 + x)^{\frac{1}{3}}$ and substituting $x = 0.3$ into the expansion.

Tip: You also need to check the validity of the expansion — the approximation will only work for values of x in the valid range.

Example 1

The binomial expansion of $(1 + 3x)^{-1}$ up to the term in x^3 is:

$(1 + 3x)^{-1} \approx 1 - 3x + 9x^2 - 27x^3$. **The expansion is valid for $|x| < \frac{1}{3}$.**

Use this expansion to approximate $\frac{100}{103}$. Give your answer to 4 d.p.

- For this type of question, you need to find the **right value of x** to make the expression you're expanding equal to the thing you're looking for.

- This means a bit of clever **rearranging**:

$$\frac{100}{103} = \frac{1}{1.03} = \frac{1}{1 + 0.03} = (1 + 0.03)^{-1}$$

- This is the same as an expansion of $(1 + 3x)^{-1}$ with $3x = 0.03 \Rightarrow x = \mathbf{0.01}$.

- Check that this value is in the **valid range**:

$0.01 < \frac{1}{3}$, so the expansion is valid for this value of x.

- **Substituting** this value for x into the expansion gives:

$(1 + 3(0.01))^{-1} \approx 1 - 3(0.01) + 9(0.01^2) - 27(0.01^3)$

$= 1 - 0.03 + 0.0009 - 0.000027$

$= 1.0009 - 0.030027$

$= 0.970873$

$(1 + 3(0.01))^{-1} \approx \boxed{0.9709 \text{ to 4 d.p.}}$

> This is the expansion given in the question, with $x = 0.01$.

> $\frac{100}{103} = 0.97087...$ so this is a pretty good approximation.

Tip: You need to use a "$\approx$" when you give the answer — it's an approximation because you're only using the first few terms of the expansion.

In some cases you might have to **rearrange the expansion** first to get it into a form that fits with the given expression.

Example 2

The binomial expansion of $(1 - 5x)^{\frac{1}{2}}$ up to the term in x^2 is $(1 - 5x)^{\frac{1}{2}} \approx 1 - \frac{5x}{2} - \frac{25x^2}{8}$. The expansion is valid for $|x| < \frac{1}{5}$.

a) Use $x = \frac{1}{50}$ in this expansion to find an approximate value for $\sqrt{10}$.

- First, substitute $x = \frac{1}{50}$ into **both sides** of the given expansion:

$$\sqrt{\left(1 - 5\left(\tfrac{1}{50}\right)\right)} \approx 1 - \frac{5}{2}\left(\tfrac{1}{50}\right) - \frac{25}{8}\left(\tfrac{1}{50}\right)^2$$

$$\sqrt{\left(1 - \tfrac{1}{10}\right)} \approx 1 - \frac{1}{20} - \frac{1}{800}$$

$$\boxed{\sqrt{\frac{9}{10}} \approx \frac{759}{800}}$$

- Now **simplify the square root**...

$$\sqrt{\frac{9}{10}} = \frac{\sqrt{9}}{\sqrt{10}} = \frac{3}{\sqrt{10}} \approx \frac{759}{800}$$

- ...and **rearrange** to find an estimate for $\sqrt{10}$:

$$\frac{3}{\sqrt{10}} \approx \frac{759}{800}$$

$$3 \times 800 \approx 759\sqrt{10}$$

$$\sqrt{10} \approx \frac{3 \times 800}{759}$$

$$\boxed{\sqrt{10} \approx \frac{800}{253}}$$

b) **Find the percentage error in your approximation, to 2 s.f.**

Work out the percentage error by finding the difference between your estimate and a calculated 'real' value, and give this as a percentage of the real value:

$$\left|\frac{\text{real value} - \text{estimate}}{\text{real value}}\right| \times 100$$

$$= \left|\frac{\sqrt{10} - \frac{800}{253}}{\sqrt{10}}\right| \times 100$$

$$= 0.0070\% \text{ (to 2 s.f.)}$$

Tip: If you're not quite sure how the expansion's going to fit, the best thing to do is put the numbers in and see what comes out. It's much clearer at this stage in the example where your $\sqrt{10}$ is coming from, but you'd be forgiven for not making the link at the start of the question.

Tip: The modulus sign means you always get a positive answer, whether the estimate is bigger or smaller than the real value. You're only interested in the difference between them.

The % error is really small, which means the approximation is very close to the real answer.

Exercise 2.1

Q1 a) Find the binomial expansion of $(1 + 6x)^{-1}$,
up to and including the term in x^2.

b) What is the validity of the expansion in part a)?

c) Use an appropriate substitution to find an approximation for $\frac{100}{106}$.

d) What is the percentage error of this approximation?
Give your answer correct to 1 significant figure.

Q1 c) Hint: Always check that the value you've decided to use for x is within the valid range for the expansion.

Q2 a) Use the binomial theorem to expand $(1 + 3x)^{\frac{1}{4}}$ in ascending powers of x, up to and including the term in x^3.

b) For what values of x is this expansion valid?

c) Use this expansion to find an approximate value of $\sqrt[4]{1.9}$ correct to 4 decimal places.

d) Find the percentage error of this approximation, correct to 3 significant figures.

Q3 a) Find the first four terms in the binomial expansion of $(1 - 2x)^{-\frac{1}{2}}$.

b) For what range of x is this expansion valid?

c) Use $x = \frac{1}{10}$ in this expansion to find an approximate value of $\sqrt{5}$.

d) Find the percentage error of this approximation, correct to 2 significant figures.

Q3 c) Hint: Put the value for x into both sides of the expansion, and rearrange the left-hand side until you get $\sqrt{5}$.

Q4 a) Expand $(2 - 5x)^6$ up to and including the x^2 term.

b) By substituting an appropriate value of x into the expansion in a), find an approximate value for 1.95^6.

c) What is the percentage error of this approximation?
Give your answer to 2 significant figures.

Q5 a) Find the first three terms in the binomial expansion of $\sqrt{3 - 4x}$.

b) For what values of x is this expansion valid?

c) Use $x = \frac{3}{40}$ in this expansion to estimate the value of $\frac{3}{\sqrt{10}}$.
Leave your answer as a fraction.

d) Find the percentage error of this approximation, correct to 1 significant figure.

3. Binomial Expansion and Partial Fractions

Learning Objective:

- Be able to split rational functions into partial fractions, then find the binomial expansion of the function.

You'll need to deal with some tricky expressions in C4 — but you can use partial fractions to make things simpler. You met these back in Chapter 1.

Finding binomial expansions using partial fractions

You can find the binomial expansion of more complicated functions by:

- splitting them into **partial fractions** first,
- expanding **each fraction** using the formula (usually with $n = -1$),
- then **adding** the expansions together.

Example

The function $f(x) = \dfrac{x - 1}{(3 + x)(1 - 5x)}$ can be expressed

as partial fractions in the form: $\dfrac{A}{(3 + x)} + \dfrac{B}{(1 - 5x)}$.

a) Find the values of A and B, and hence express $f(x)$ as partial fractions.

- Start by writing out the problem as an **identity**:

$$\frac{x - 1}{(3 + x)(1 - 5x)} \equiv \frac{A}{(3 + x)} + \frac{B}{(1 - 5x)}$$

> Add the fractions together and cancel the denominators on either side of the identity.

$$\Rightarrow \frac{x - 1}{(3 + x)(1 - 5x)} \equiv \frac{A(1 - 5x) + B(3 + x)}{(3 + x)(1 - 5x)}$$

$$\Rightarrow \qquad x - 1 \equiv A(1 - 5x) + B(3 + x)$$

- You can then work out the values of A and B by putting in values of x that make each bracket in turn equal to zero.
  (This is known as the '**substitution**' method.)

Let $x = -3$, then: $\qquad -3 - 1 = A(1 - (-15))$

$$\Rightarrow -4 = 16A$$

$$\Rightarrow \boxed{A = -\frac{1}{4}}$$

Let $x = \frac{1}{5}$, then: $\qquad \frac{1}{5} - 1 = B\left(3 + \frac{1}{5}\right)$

$$\Rightarrow -\frac{4}{5} = \frac{16}{5}B$$

$$\Rightarrow \boxed{B = -\frac{1}{4}}$$

- So $f(x)$ can also be written as: $\quad \boxed{-\dfrac{1}{4(3 + x)} - \dfrac{1}{4(1 - 5x)}}$

Tip: Look back at pages 1-2 for a recap on this method.

Tip: You could also **equate the coefficients** of x and the constant terms to find A and B.

Tip: Remember to put A and B back into the expression to give $f(x)$ as partial fractions.

b) Use your answer to part a) to find the binomial expansion of f(x), up to and including the term in x^2.

- Start by **rewriting** the **partial fractions** from a) in $(p + qx)^n$ form:

$$f(x) = -\frac{1}{4}(3 + x)^{-1} - \frac{1}{4}(1 - 5x)^{-1}$$

- Now do the two binomial expansions **separately**:

$$(3 + x)^{-1} = \left(3\left(1 + \frac{1}{3}x\right)\right)^{-1}$$

$$= \frac{1}{3}\left(1 + \frac{1}{3}x\right)^{-1}$$

$$= \frac{1}{3}\left(1 + (-1)\left(\frac{1}{3}x\right) + \frac{(-1)(-2)}{2}\left(\frac{1}{3}x\right)^2 + \ldots\right)$$

$$= \frac{1}{3}\left(1 - \frac{1}{3}x + \frac{1}{9}x^2 - \ldots\right)$$

$$= \frac{1}{3} - \frac{1}{9}x + \frac{1}{27}x^2 - \ldots$$

$$(1 - 5x)^{-1} = 1 + (-1)(-5x) + \frac{(-1)(-2)}{2}(-5x)^2 + \ldots$$

$$= 1 + 5x + 25x^2 + \ldots$$

> **Tip:** There are a lot of different stages to this type of question — which means a lot of places that you could make a mistake, especially with all these negatives and fractions flying around. Set your working out clearly and don't skip stages.

- Finally, put everything together by adding the expansions in the rearranged form of f(x):

$$f(x) = -\frac{1}{4}(3 + x)^{-1} - \frac{1}{4}(1 - 5x)^{-1}$$

$$\approx -\frac{1}{4}\left(\frac{1}{3} - \frac{1}{9}x + \frac{1}{27}x^2\right) - \frac{1}{4}(1 + 5x + 25x^2)$$

$$= -\frac{1}{12} + \frac{x}{36} - \frac{x^2}{108} - \frac{1}{4} - \frac{5x}{4} - \frac{25x^2}{4}$$

$$= -\frac{1}{3} - \frac{11x}{9} - \frac{169x^2}{27}$$

c) Find the range of values of x for which your answer to part b) is valid.

- The two expansions from b) are valid for **different values of x**.

- The **combined** expansion of f(x) is valid where these **two ranges overlap**, i.e. over the **narrower** of the two ranges.

  (This is the same as when you combine expansions by multiplying them together, as shown on page 28.)

  The expansion of $(3 + x)^{-1}$ is valid when $\left|\frac{x}{3}\right| < 1 \Rightarrow |x| < 3$.

  The expansion of $(1 - 5x)^{-1}$ is valid when $|-5x| < 1 \Rightarrow |x| < \frac{1}{5}$.

- The expansion of f(x) is valid for values of x in both ranges, so the expansion of f(x) is valid for $|x| < \frac{1}{5}$.

> **Tip:** Remember, the expansion of $(p + qx)^n$ is valid when $\left|\frac{qx}{p}\right| < 1$.

Q1 a) $\dfrac{5 - 12x}{(1 + 6x)(4 + 3x)} \equiv \dfrac{A}{(1 + 6x)} + \dfrac{B}{(4 + 3x)}$. Find A and B.

b) (i) Find the binomial expansion of $(1 + 6x)^{-1}$, up to and including the term in x^2.

(ii) Find the binomial expansion of $(4 + 3x)^{-1}$, up to and including the term in x^2.

c) Hence find the binomial expansion of $\dfrac{5 - 12x}{(1 + 6x)(4 + 3x)}$, up to and including the term in x^2.

d) For what values of x is this expansion valid?

Q2 $f(x) = \dfrac{60x^2 + 5x + 7}{(4 - 3x)(1 + 4x)^2}$

a) Show that $f(x)$ can be expressed as:
$$\dfrac{3}{(4 - 3x)} - \dfrac{1}{(1 + 4x)} + \dfrac{2}{(1 + 4x)^2}.$$

b) Give the binomial expansion of $f(x)$ in ascending powers of x, up to and including the term in x^2.

c) Find the percentage error when you use this expansion to estimate $f(0.01)$, giving your answer to 2 significant figures.

Q3 a) Factorise fully $6x^3 + 11x^2 + 4x$.

b) Hence express $\dfrac{22x^2 + 40x + 12}{6x^3 + 11x^2 + 4x}$ as partial fractions.

c) Find the binomial expansion of $\dfrac{22x^2 + 40x + 12}{6x^3 + 11x^2 + 4x}$, up to and including the term in x^2.

d) For what values of x is this expansion valid?

> **Q3 c) Hint:** You'll end up with a term in x^{-1}, which you wouldn't usually get with a binomial expansion — this comes from the partial fractions and you can just leave it as it is.

Q4 $f(x) = \dfrac{12x^2 - 27x - 33}{(3x + 1)(2x - 5)}$

a) Express $f(x)$ in the form $A + \dfrac{B}{(3x + 1)} + \dfrac{C}{(2x - 5)}$, where A, B and C are all integers to be found.

b) Hence, or otherwise, use the binomial theorem to expand $f(x)$ in ascending powers of x, up to and including the term in x^2.

> **Q4 Hint:** This is a top heavy fraction, so you can multiply out the denominator and divide top by bottom to find the constants. This should give you 'A', then split the **remainder** into partial fractions. See page 6 for more on this.

Review Exercise — Chapter 3

Q1 Give the binomial expansion of:
   a) $(1 + 2x)^3$
   b) $(1 - x)^5$
   c) $(1 - 4x)^4$

Q2 For what values of n does the binomial expansion of $(1 + x)^n$ result in a finite expression?

Q3 a) If the x^2 coefficient of the binomial expansion of $(1 + ax)^7$ is 189, and a is a positive integer, what is the value of a?
   b) If the x^4 coefficient of the binomial expansion of $(1 - ax)^6$ is 240, and a is positive, what is the value of a?

Q4 If the full binomial expansion of $(c + dx)^n$ is an infinite series, what values of x is the expansion valid for?

Q5 Find the binomial expansion of each of the following, up to and including the term in x^3:
   a) $\dfrac{1}{(1 + x)^5}$
   b) $\dfrac{1}{(1 - 3x)^3}$
   c) $\sqrt{1 - 5x}$

Q6 For which values of x are the expansions from question 5 valid?

Q7 a) Give the binomial expansions of the following, up to and including the term in x^2. State which values of x each expansion is valid for.
   (i) $\dfrac{1}{(3 + 2x)^2}$
   (ii) $\sqrt[3]{8 - x}$
   b) Use your answers to a) to give the binomial expansion of $\dfrac{\sqrt[3]{8 - x}}{(3 + 2x)^2}$, up to and including the term in x^2. State the range of x that this expansion is valid for.
   c) (i) Use the expansion in a)(ii) to find an approximate value of $\sqrt[3]{7}$, leaving your answer as a fraction.
   (ii) Find the percentage error of this approximation, correct to 2 significant figures.

Q8 a) Show that $\dfrac{5 - 10x}{(1 + 2x)(2 - x)}$ can be expressed as: $\dfrac{4}{(1 + 2x)} - \dfrac{3}{(2 - x)}$.
   b) Give the binomial expansion of the expression in a), up to and including the term in x^2.
   c) Find the percentage error when you use $x = 0.1$ in this expansion to estimate $\dfrac{4}{1.2 \times 1.9}$, giving your answer to 2 significant figures.

1
$$f(x) = \frac{1}{\sqrt{(9 - 4x)}}, \text{ for } |x| < \frac{9}{4}.$$

   a)   Find the binomial expansion of f(x), up to and including the term in x^3.

      (5 marks)

   b)   Hence find the first three terms in the expansion of:

$$\frac{2 - x}{\sqrt{(9 - 4x)}}$$

      (4 marks)

2
$$f(x) = \frac{36x^2 + 3x - 10}{(4 + 3x)(1 - 3x)^2}$$

   a)   Given that f(x) can be expressed in the form

$$f(x) = \frac{A}{(4 + 3x)} + \frac{B}{(1 - 3x)} + \frac{C}{(1 - 3x)^2}$$

      find the values of A, B and C.

      (4 marks)

   b)   Find the binomial expansion of f(x), up to and including the term in x^2.

      (6 marks)

   c)   Find the range of values of x for which the binomial expansion of f(x) is valid.

      (2 marks)

3   a)   Find the binomial expansion of:

$$(16 + 3x)^{\frac{1}{4}}, \text{ for } |x| < \frac{16}{3},$$

      up to and including the term in x^2.

      (5 marks)

   b)   (i)   Estimate $\sqrt[4]{12.4}$ by substituting a suitable value of x into your expansion from part (a). Give your answer to 6 decimal places.

      (2 marks)

      (ii)   What is the percentage error in this estimate? Give your answer to 3 s.f.

      (2 marks)

4 a) Find the binomial expansion of $\left(1 - \frac{4}{3}x\right)^{-\frac{1}{2}}$,

   up to and including the term in x^3.

   (4 marks)

   b) Hence find the values of integer constants a, b and c, such that

   $$\sqrt{\frac{27}{(3 - 4x)}} \approx a + bx + cx^2,$$

   and state the range of values of x for which this approximation is valid.

   (3 marks)

5 a) (i) Show that:

   $$\sqrt{\frac{1 + 2x}{1 - 3x}} \approx 1 + \frac{5}{2}x + \frac{35}{8}x^2$$

   (5 marks)

   (ii) For what values of x is your expansion valid?

   (2 marks)

   b) Using the above expansion with $x = \frac{2}{15}$,

   show that $\sqrt{19} \approx \frac{127}{30}$.

   (2 marks)

6 a) Find the values of A and B such that

   $$\frac{13x - 17}{(5 - 3x)(2x - 1)} \equiv \frac{A}{(5 - 3x)} + \frac{B}{(2x - 1)}.$$

   (3 marks)

   b) (i) Find the binomial expansion of $(2x - 1)^{-1}$,
        up to and including the term in x^2.

   (2 marks)

   (ii) Show that:

   $$\frac{1}{(5 - 3x)} \approx \frac{1}{5} + \frac{3}{25}x + \frac{9}{125}x^2,$$

   for $|x| < \frac{5}{3}$.

   (5 marks)

   c) Using your answers to parts (a) and (b), find the first three terms

   of the binomial expansion of $\frac{13x - 17}{(5 - 3x)(2x - 1)}$.

   (2 marks)

1. Differentiation with Parametric Equations

You met parametric equations in Chapter 2 — they're equations where x and y are defined separately in terms of a third variable. Differentiating them is simpler than you might expect — but you need to remember how to differentiate things like trig functions, exponentials and logs.

Differentiating parametric equations

- A curve can be defined by **two parametric equations**, often with the parameter t: $y = f(t)$ and $x = g(t)$.

- To find the gradient, $\dfrac{dy}{dx}$, you could convert the equations into **Cartesian** form (see pages 16-17), but this isn't always possible or convenient.

- The **chain rule** you met in C3 can be used to differentiate parametric equations without needing to convert to Cartesian form. It looks like this:

$$\frac{dy}{dx} = \frac{dy}{dt} \div \frac{dx}{dt}$$

- So to find $\dfrac{dy}{dx}$ from parametric equations, **differentiate** each equation with respect to the parameter t, then put them into the formula.

Tip: In C3 you'll have seen it given as '$\times \dfrac{dt}{dx}$' instead of '$\div \dfrac{dx}{dt}$', but it means the same thing.

Example

The curve C is defined by the parametric equations
$y = t^3 - 3t + 4$ and $x = t^2 - 1$.

a) Find $\dfrac{dy}{dx}$ in terms of t.

- Start by **differentiating** the two parametric equations **with respect to t**:

$$y = t^3 - 3t + 4 \quad \Rightarrow \quad \frac{dy}{dt} = 3t^2 - 3 = 3(t^2 - 1)$$

$$x = t^2 - 1 \quad \Rightarrow \quad \frac{dx}{dt} = 2t$$

- Now use the **chain rule** to combine them:

$$\frac{dy}{dx} = \frac{dy}{dt} \div \frac{dx}{dt} = \frac{3(t^2 - 1)}{2t}$$

b) Find the gradient of C when $t = -2$.

- Use the answer to a) to find the gradient for a specific value of t. So, when $t = -2$:

$$\frac{dy}{dx} = \frac{3((-2)^2 - 1)}{2(-2)} = \frac{3(3)}{-4} = -\frac{9}{4}$$

c) Find the coordinates of the turning points.

Tip: Make sure you're familiar with turning points — you covered these in C2.

- The turning points occur when $\frac{dy}{dx} = 0$, so solve to find the values of t at the turning points:

$$\frac{dy}{dx} = \frac{3(t^2 - 1)}{2t} = 0$$

$$\Rightarrow 3(t^2 - 1) = 0 \Rightarrow t^2 = 1 \Rightarrow t = \pm 1$$

- Now put these values for t into the original parametric equations to find the Cartesian coordinates of the turning points:

Tip: Remember — Cartesian coordinates are just the (x, y) coordinates.

When $t = 1$ $x = (1)^2 - 1 = 0$

$y = (1)^3 - 3(1) + 4 = 2$

So there's a turning point at $(0, 2)$ ...

When $t = -1$ $x = (-1)^2 - 1 = 0$

$y = (-1)^3 - 3(-1) + 4 = 6$

...and there's another one at $(0, 6)$.

Exercise 1.1

Q1 For each curve C, defined by the parametric equations given below, find $\frac{dy}{dx}$ in terms of t.

   a) $x = t^2,\ y = t^3 - t$.

   b) $x = t^3 + t,\ y = 2t^2 + 1$

   c) $x = t^4,\ y = t^3 - t^2$

   d) $x = \cos t,\ y = 4t - t^2$

Q2 The curve C is defined by the parametric equations $x = t^2,\ y = e^{2t}$.

   a) Find $\frac{dy}{dx}$ in terms of t.

   b) Find the gradient of C when $t = 1$.

Q2-6 Hint: You need to remember how to differentiate trig functions, e^x and $\ln x$ — you did them in C3.

Q3 The curve C is defined by the parametric equations $x = e^{3t},\ y = 4t^3 - 2t^2$.

   a) Find $\frac{dy}{dx}$ in terms of t.

   b) Find the gradient of C when $t = 0$.

Q4 The curve C is defined by the parametric equations $x = t^3,\ y = t^2 \cos t$.

   a) Find $\frac{dy}{dx}$ in terms of t.

   b) Find the gradient of C when $t = \pi$.

Q4-5 Hint: You'll need to use the product rule to find dy/dt and dx/dt. Look back at your C3 notes if you need to.

Q5 The curve C is defined by the parametric equations $x = t^2 \sin t,\ y = t^3 \sin t + \cos t$.

   a) Find $\frac{dy}{dx}$ in terms of t.

   b) Find the gradient of C when $t = \pi$.

Q6 The curve C is defined by the parametric equations $x = \ln t,\ y = 3t^2 - t^3$.

   a) Find $\frac{dy}{dx}$ in terms of t.

   b) Evaluate $\frac{dy}{dx}$ when $t = -1$.

   c) Find the exact coordinates of the turning point of the curve C.

Finding tangents and normals

Once you've found the gradient of a parametric curve at a particular point, you can use this to find the **equation** of the **tangent** or **normal** to the curve at that point. You'll have seen this before, but here's a recap of the method:

- The gradient of the **tangent** is the **same** as the gradient of the curve at that point.
- The gradient of the **normal** at that point is $\dfrac{-1}{\text{gradient of tangent}}$.
- Put the values for the gradient, m, and the (x, y) coordinates of the point into **y = mx + c** to find the equation of the line.

Tip: You could also use $y - y_1 = m(x - x_1)$ to get the equation.

Example

The curve C is defined by the following parametric equations:
$x = \sin t, y = 2t \cos t.$

a) Find the gradient of the curve, and the (x, y) coordinates, when $t = \pi$.

$$\frac{dx}{dt} = \cos t$$

$$\frac{dy}{dt} = 2\cos t - 2t \sin t$$

$\longrightarrow$ $\dfrac{dy}{dx} = \dfrac{2\cos t - 2t\sin t}{\cos t} = \boxed{2 - 2t \tan t}$

When $t = \pi$, $\dfrac{dy}{dx} = 2 - 2\pi(0) = 2$

When $t = \pi$, $x = 0$, and $y = -2\pi$, so the coordinates are $(0, -2\pi)$.

b) Hence find the equation of the tangent to C when $t = \pi$.

- The gradient of the tangent at $t = \pi$ is the same as $\dfrac{dy}{dx}$ at that point, i.e. 2.
- So substitute m = 2, $x = 0$ and $y = -2\pi$ into $y = mx + c$, to find c:

$$y = mx + c$$
$$-2\pi = 2(0) + c \implies c = -2\pi$$

- Putting c back into the equation gives:

$$\boxed{y = 2x - 2\pi \ \text{ or } \ y = 2(x - \pi)}$$

c) Find the equation of the normal to C when $t = \pi$.

- The gradient of the normal at $t = \pi$ is $-\dfrac{1}{2}$.
- So substitute m = $-\dfrac{1}{2}$, $x = 0$ and $y = -2\pi$ into $y = mx + c$, to find c:

$$y = mx + c$$
$$-2\pi = -\frac{1}{2}(0) + c \implies c = -2\pi$$

- Putting c back into the equation gives:

$$\boxed{y = -\frac{1}{2}x - 2\pi \ \text{ or } \ x + 2y + 4\pi = 0}$$

Exercise 1.2

Q1 A curve is defined by the parametric equations $x = t^2$, $y = t^3 - 6t$. Find the equation of the tangent to the curve at $t = 3$, giving your answer in the form $ax + by + c = 0$.

Q2 A curve C is defined parametrically by $x = t^3 - 2t^2$, $y = t^3 - t^2 + 5t$. Find the equation of the tangent at the point $t = -1$.

Q3 A curve C is defined by the parametric equations
$x = \sin 2t$, $y = t \cos t + 2 \sin t$.
Find the equation of the normal to the curve at $t = \pi$.

Q4 The parametric representation of a curve is given by
$x = t \ln t$, $y = t^3 - t^2 + 3$.
Find the equation of the tangent to the curve at $t = 1$.

Q4 Hint: Use the product rule to differentiate $t \ln t$.

Q5 The path of a particle is given parametrically by
$x = \theta \sin 2\theta$, $y = \theta^2 + \theta \cos \theta$.
Find the equation of the normal to the particle's path at $\theta = \dfrac{\pi}{2}$.

Q6 The motion of a particle is described by the parametric equations
$x = t^2 - t$, $y = 3t - t^3$.
a) Find the equation of the tangent to the path of the particle when $t = 2$, giving your answer in a suitable form.
b) Find the Cartesian coordinates of the point at which the normal to the path at $t = 2$ cuts the x-axis.

Q7 A particle moves along a path given by the parametric equations
$x = \sin 2\theta + 2 \cos \theta$, $y = \theta \sin \theta$.
a) Find the gradient $\dfrac{dy}{dx}$ of the particle's path in terms of θ.
b) Evaluate $\dfrac{dy}{dx}$ at $\theta = \dfrac{\pi}{2}$ and hence obtain equations of the tangent and normal to the path at this point.

Q8 A particle moves along a path given parametrically by
$x = s^3 \ln s$, $y = s^3 - s^2 \ln s$.
a) Give the value(s) of s at which the path cuts the y-axis.
b) Hence show that the equation of a tangent to the curve when $x = 0$ is $y = 2x + 1$.

Q9 A curve is given parametrically by $x = \theta^2 \sin \theta$, $y = \dfrac{\cos \theta}{\theta^3}$.

a) Show that the gradient of the curve when $\theta = \pi$ is $-\dfrac{3}{\pi^6}$.
b) Hence find the equation of the normal to the curve at this point.

Q9 Hint: Use the quotient rule to find $\dfrac{dy}{d\theta}$.

2. Implicit Differentiation

Learning Objectives:

- Be able to differentiate functions defined implicitly.
- Be able to find the equations of tangents and normals to curves given implicitly.

For equations that you can't write in the form $y = f(x)$, you need to use implicit differentiation. It works for equations that contain a mixture of x and y terms, such as xy^2.

Implicit differentiation

An '**implicit relation**' is the mathematical name for any equation in x and y that's written in the form $\mathbf{f(x, y) = g(x, y)}$ instead of $y = f(x)$. For example, $y^2 = xy + x + 2$ is implicit.

Some implicit relations are either awkward or impossible to rewrite in the form $y = f(x)$. This can happen, for example, if the equation contains a number of different powers of y, or terms where x is multiplied by y.

This can make implicit relations tricky to differentiate — the solution is **implicit differentiation**:

Tip: $f(x, y)$ and $g(x, y)$ don't actually both have to include x and y — one of them could even be a constant.

To find $\dfrac{dy}{dx}$ for an implicit relation between x and y:

- **Step 1:** Differentiate terms in x **only** (and **constant** terms) with respect to x, as normal.

- **Step 2:** Use the **chain rule** to differentiate terms in y **only**:
$$\frac{d}{dx}f(y) = \frac{d}{dy}f(y)\frac{dy}{dx}$$ In practice, this means 'differentiate with respect to y, and stick a $\dfrac{dy}{dx}$ on the end'.

- **Step 3:** Use the **product rule** to differentiate terms in **both x and y**:
$$\frac{d}{dx}u(x)v(y) = u(x)\frac{d}{dx}v(y) + v(y)\frac{d}{dx}u(x)$$

- **Step 4:** **Rearrange** the resulting equation in x, y and $\dfrac{dy}{dx}$ to make $\dfrac{dy}{dx}$ the subject.

Tip: $\dfrac{d}{dx}f(y)$ just means 'the derivative of $f(y)$ with respect to x'.

Tip: This version of the product rule is slightly different from the one you'll have seen in C3 — it's got $v(y)$ instead of $v(x)$.

Example 1

a) Use implicit differentiation to find $\dfrac{dy}{dx}$ for $y^3 + y^2 = e^x + x^3$.

We need to differentiate each term of the equation with respect to x. Start by sticking '$\dfrac{d}{dx}$' in front of each term:

Step 1: Differentiate the terms in x only.

$$\frac{d}{dx}y^3 + \frac{d}{dx}y^2 = \boxed{\frac{d}{dx}e^x} + \boxed{\frac{d}{dx}x^3}$$

$$\frac{d}{dx}y^3 + \frac{d}{dx}y^2 = e^x + 3x^2$$

Step 2: Use the **chain rule** for the terms in y only.

$$\boxed{\frac{d}{dx}y^3} + \boxed{\frac{d}{dx}y^2} = e^x + 3x^2$$

$$3y^2\frac{dy}{dx} + 2y\frac{dy}{dx} = e^x + 3x^2$$

Tip: Just differentiate with respect to y, but don't forget to put a $\frac{dy}{dx}$ after each term.

Step 3: There are no terms in both x and y to deal with, so...

Step 4: Rearrange to make $\frac{dy}{dx}$ the subject: $(3y^2 + 2y)\frac{dy}{dx} = e^x + 3x^2$

$$\Rightarrow \frac{dy}{dx} = \frac{e^x + 3x^2}{3y^2 + 2y}$$

Example 2

a) Use implicit differentiation to find $\dfrac{dy}{dx}$ for $2x^2y + y^3 = 6x^2 - 15$.

- Again, start by sticking '$\frac{d}{dx}$' in front of each term:

$$\frac{d}{dx}2x^2y + \frac{d}{dx}y^3 = \frac{d}{dx}6x^2 - \frac{d}{dx}15$$

- First, deal with the **terms in x** and **constant** terms
  — in this case that's the two terms on the right-hand side:

$$\frac{d}{dx}2x^2y + \frac{d}{dx}y^3 = 12x + 0$$

- Now use the **chain rule** on the term in y.

$$\frac{d}{dx}2x^2y + 3y^2\frac{dy}{dx} = 12x + 0$$

- Use the **product rule** on the term in x and y, where $u(x) = 2x^2$ and $v(y) = y$:

$$2x^2\frac{d}{dx}(y) + y\frac{d}{dx}(2x^2) + 3y^2\frac{dy}{dx} = 12x + 0$$

$$\Rightarrow 2x^2\frac{dy}{dx} + y4x + 3y^2\frac{dy}{dx} = 12x + 0$$

This $\frac{dy}{dx}$ term comes from using the chain rule:
$$\frac{d}{dx}(y) = \frac{d}{dy}(y)\frac{dy}{dx} = 1\frac{dy}{dx} = \frac{dy}{dx}$$

Tip: Once you're happy with this method you might not need to write all the steps out separately, but you can do if you find it easier.

Tip: Take your time using the product rule as it's easy to forget terms if you're not careful. Always start by identifying $u(x)$ and $v(y)$, and do it in steps if you need to.

- Finally, **rearrange** to make $\frac{dy}{dx}$ the subject:

$$\frac{dy}{dx}(2x^2 + 3y^2) = 12x - 4xy \Rightarrow \frac{dy}{dx} = \frac{12x - 4xy}{2x^2 + 3y^2}$$

b) Find the gradient of the curve $2x^2y + y^3 = 6x^2 - 15$ at the point $(2, 1)$.

Just substitute the values for x and y into $\frac{dy}{dx}$:

$$\frac{dy}{dx} = \frac{12(2) - 4(2)(1)}{2(2)^2 + 3(1)^2} = \frac{16}{11}$$

Q1 Use implicit differentiation to find $\frac{dy}{dx}$ for each of these curves:

a) $y + y^3 = x^2 + 4$

b) $x^2 + y^2 = 2x + 2y$

c) $3x^3 - 4y = y^2 + x$

d) $5x - y^2 = x^5 - 6y$

e) $\cos x + \sin y = x^2 + y^3$

f) $x^3 y^2 + \cos x = 4xy$

g) $e^x + e^y = x^3 - y$

h) $3xy^2 + 2x^2 y = x^3 + 4x$

Q2 Find the gradient, $\frac{dy}{dx}$, for each of these curves given below:

a) $x^3 + 2xy = y^4$

b) $x^2 y + y^2 = x^3$

c) $y^3 x + y = \sin x$

d) $y \cos x + x \sin y = xy$

e) $e^x + e^y = xy$

f) $\ln x + x^2 = y^3 + y$

g) $e^{2x} + e^{3y} = 3x^2 y^2$

h) $x \ln x + y \ln x = x^5 + y^3$

Q3 a) Hint: Evaluate the left-hand and right-hand sides of the equation separately to show they're the same.

Q3

a) Show that the curve C, defined implicitly by $e^x + 2 \ln y = y^3$, passes through (0, 1).

b) Find the gradient of the curve at this point.

Q4 A curve is defined implicitly by $x^3 + y^2 - 2xy = 0$

a) Find $\frac{dy}{dx}$ for this curve.

b) Show that $y = -2 \pm 2\sqrt{3}$ when $x = -2$.

c) Evaluate the gradient at $(-2, -2 + 2\sqrt{3})$, leaving your answer in surd form.

Q5 The curve $x^3 - xy = 2y^2$ passes through the points (1, -1) and (1, a).

a) Find the value of a.

b) Evaluate the gradient of the curve at each of these points.

Q6 A curve is defined implicitly by $x^2 y + y^2 x = xy + 4$.

a) At which two values of y does the line $x = 1$ cut the curve?

b) By finding $\frac{dy}{dx}$, evaluate the gradient at each of these points.

Applications of implicit differentiation

Most implicit differentiation questions aren't really that different from any other differentiation question. Once you've got an expression for the gradient, you'll have to use it to do the sort of things you'd normally expect, like finding stationary points of curves and equations of tangents and normals.

Example 1

Curve A has the equation $x^2 + 2xy - y^2 = 10x + 4y - 21$.

a) Show that when $\dfrac{dy}{dx} = 0$, $y = 5 - x$.

For starters, we're going to need to find $\dfrac{dy}{dx}$ by implicit differentiation:

$$\frac{d}{dx}x^2 + \frac{d}{dx}2xy - \frac{d}{dx}y^2 = \frac{d}{dx}10x + \frac{d}{dx}4y - \frac{d}{dx}21$$

$\Rightarrow \quad 2x + \dfrac{d}{dx}2xy - \dfrac{d}{dx}y^2 = 10 + \dfrac{d}{dx}4y - 0$ ← Differentiate x^2, $10x$ and 21 with respect to x.

$\Rightarrow \quad 2x + \dfrac{d}{dx}2xy - 2y\dfrac{dy}{dx} = 10 + 4\dfrac{dy}{dx}$ ← Use the chain rule to differentiate y^2 and $4y$.

$\Rightarrow \quad 2x + 2x\dfrac{dy}{dx} + y\dfrac{d}{dx}2x - 2y\dfrac{dy}{dx} = 10 + 4\dfrac{dy}{dx}$

$\Rightarrow \quad 2x + 2x\dfrac{dy}{dx} + 2y - 2y\dfrac{dy}{dx} = 10 + 4\dfrac{dy}{dx}$ ← Use the product rule to differentiate $2xy$.

$\Rightarrow \quad 2x\dfrac{dy}{dx} - 2y\dfrac{dy}{dx} - 4\dfrac{dy}{dx} = 10 - 2x - 2y$

$\Rightarrow \quad (2x - 2y - 4)\dfrac{dy}{dx} = 10 - 2x - 2y$

$\Rightarrow \quad \dfrac{dy}{dx} = \dfrac{10 - 2x - 2y}{2x - 2y - 4} = \dfrac{5 - x - y}{x - y - 2}$

So when $\dfrac{dy}{dx} = 0$:

$$\frac{5 - x - y}{x - y - 2} = 0 \Rightarrow 5 - x - y = 0 \Rightarrow \boxed{y = 5 - x}$$

b) Find the coordinates of the stationary points of A.

Use the answer to part a) to find the points where $\dfrac{dy}{dx} = 0$.

When $\dfrac{dy}{dx} = 0$, $y = 5 - x$. So at the stationary points:

$x^2 + 2xy - y^2 = 10x + 4y - 21$

$\Rightarrow \quad x^2 + 2x(5 - x) - (5 - x)^2 = 10x + 4(5 - x) - 21$

$\Rightarrow \quad x^2 + 10x - 2x^2 - 25 + 10x - x^2 = 10x + 20 - 4x - 21$

$\Rightarrow \quad -2x^2 + 14x - 24 = 0$

$\Rightarrow \quad x^2 - 7x + 12 = 0$ Put each value of x into $y = 5 - x$ to find the corresponding y-coordinate.

$\Rightarrow \quad (x - 3)(x - 4) = 0$

$\Rightarrow \quad x = 3$ or $x = 4$

$x = 3 \Rightarrow y = 5 - 3 = 2 \qquad x = 4 \Rightarrow y = 5 - 4 = 1$

So the stationary points of A are $\boxed{(3, 2) \text{ and } (4, 1)}$.

Tip: Here you're just putting $y = 5 - x$ into the original equation to find the values of x at the stationary points.

Example 2

A curve defined implicitly by $\sin x - y \cos x = y^2$ passes through two points (π, a) and (π, b), where $a < b$.

a) Find the values of a and b.

- Put $x = \pi$ into the equation and solve for y:

$$\sin \pi - y \cos \pi = y^2$$
$$\Rightarrow 0 + y = y^2$$
$$\Rightarrow y^2 - y = 0$$
$$\Rightarrow y(y - 1) = 0$$
$$\Rightarrow y = 0 \text{ and } y = 1$$

- So $a = 0$ and $b = 1$.

b) Find the equations of the tangents to the curve at each of these points.

- First find $\dfrac{dy}{dx}$ using implicit differentiation as usual:

$$\cos x + y \sin x - \cos x \, \frac{dy}{dx} = 2y \, \frac{dy}{dx}$$

$$\Rightarrow \frac{dy}{dx} = \frac{\cos x + y \sin x}{2y + \cos x}$$

- Now put in $x = \pi$ and $y = 0$ to find the gradient at $(\pi, 0)$.

$$\frac{dy}{dx} = \frac{\cos \pi + 0 \sin \pi}{2(0) + \cos \pi} = 1$$

Tip: It's good to know some standard trig results off by heart. $\cos \pi = -1$ and $\sin \pi = 0$.

- So the gradient of the tangent at $(\pi, 0)$ is 1. Putting these values into $y = mx + c$ gives:

$$0 = \pi + c \Rightarrow c = -\pi$$

So the equation of the tangent at $(\pi, 0)$ is $y = x - \pi$.

- Do the same to find the equation of the tangent at $(\pi, 1)$.

$$\frac{dy}{dx} = \frac{\cos \pi + \sin \pi}{2(1) + \cos \pi} = -1$$

$$1 = -\pi + c \Rightarrow c = 1 + \pi$$

So the equation of the tangent at $(\pi, 1)$ is $y = 1 + \pi - x$.

c) Show that the tangents intersect at the point $\left(\dfrac{1 + 2\pi}{2}, \dfrac{1}{2}\right)$.

- The two tangents intersect when:

$$x - \pi = 1 + \pi - x$$
$$\Rightarrow 2x = 1 + 2\pi$$
$$\Rightarrow x = \frac{1 + 2\pi}{2}$$

- Putting this value of x into one of the equations gives:

$$y = \left(\frac{1 + 2\pi}{2}\right) - \pi = \frac{1}{2} + \pi - \pi = \frac{1}{2}$$

- So they intersect at $\left(\dfrac{1 + 2\pi}{2}, \dfrac{1}{2}\right)$.

Exercise 2.2

Q1 A curve is defined implicitly by $x^2 + 2x + 3y - y^2 = 0$.

   a) Find the coordinates of the stationary points (to 2 decimal places).

   b) Show that the curve intersects the y-axis when $y = 0$ and $y = 3$.
   Hence find the equation of the tangent at each of these points.

Q2 A curve is defined implicitly by $x^3 + x^2 + y = y^2$.

   a) Find the coordinates of the stationary points (to 2 decimal places).

   b) Show that the curve intersects the line $x = 2$ when $y = 4$ and $y = -3$.
   Hence find the equation of the tangent at each of these points.

Q2 Hint: You should find 4 stationary points.

Q3 A curve is defined implicitly by $x^2y + y^3 = x + 7$.

   a) Calculate the x-coordinates of the points on the curve where $y = 1$
   and hence find the equations of the normals at these points.

   b) Find the coordinates of the point where the normals intersect.

Q4 $e^x + y^2 - xy = 5 - 3y$ is a curve passing through two points $(0, a)$
   and $(0, b)$, where a < b.

   a) Find the values of a and b and show that one of these points
   is a stationary point of the curve.

   b) Find the equations of the tangent and normal to the curve at the
   other point.

Q5 The curve C is defined by $\ln x + y^2 = x^2y + 6$.

   a) Show that C passes through $(1, 3)$ and $(1, -2)$.

   b) Find the equations of the normals to the curve at each of these
   points and explain why these normals cannot intersect.

Q6 A curve is defined implicitly by $e^y + x^2 = y^3 + 4x$.
   Find the equations of the tangents that touch the curve at $(a, 0)$ and
   $(b, 0)$. Leave your answer in surd form.

Q6 Hint: Work out the values of a and b first.

Q7 Show that any point on the curve $y \ln x + x^2 = y^2 - y + 1$ which
   satisfies $y + 2x^2 = 0$ is a stationary point.

Q8 A curve is defined by $e^{2y} + e^x - e^4 = 2xy + 1$.

   a) Find the equation of the tangent to the curve when $y = 0$.

   b) Find the equation of the normal to the curve when $y = 0$.

   c) Show that these two lines intersect when $x = \dfrac{4e^8 - 144}{e^8 + 36}$.

Q8 Hint: Remember — $\dfrac{1}{e^x}$ is the same as e^{-x}.

Q9 $y^2x + 2xy - 3x^3 = x^2 + 2$ passes through two points where $x = 2$.
   Find the equations of the tangents to the curve at these points,
   and hence show that they intersect at $\left(-\dfrac{14}{25}, -1\right)$.

Q10 The curve C is defined implicitly by $\cos y \cos x + \cos y \sin x = \dfrac{1}{2}$.

   a) Find y when $x = \dfrac{\pi}{2}$ and when $x = \pi$, $0 \le y \le \pi$.

   b) Find the equations of the tangents at these points.

Q10 Hint: You won't need your calculator for the trig here but you will need to remember your common angles.

3. Differentiation of a^x

Learning Objective:

- Be able to differentiate functions of the form $y = a^x$ and $y = a^{f(x)}$.

In the 'real world', when you're dealing with exponential growth and decay you often use functions of the form $y = a^x$, where a is a constant. So you need to know how to differentiate functions like this.

Differentiating a^x

For any constant a:

Tip: The rule $\frac{d}{dx}(e^x) = e^x$ is actually just a special case of this rule —
$\frac{d}{dx}(e^x) = e^x \ln e = e^x \times 1 = e^x.$

$$\frac{d}{dx}(a^x) = a^x \ln a$$

With a bit of implicit differentiation, you can **prove the rule**:

- Take **ln** of both sides of the equation:

$$y = a^x \Rightarrow \ln y = \ln a^x$$

- Use the **log laws** to rearrange the right-hand side:

$$\ln y = x \ln a$$

- Now use **implicit differentiation** on this equation:

$$\frac{d}{dx}(\ln y) = \frac{d}{dx}(x \ln a)$$

Since a is a **constant**, **ln** a is also a constant.

Use the **chain rule** to deal with $\frac{d}{dx}(\ln y)$

$$\frac{1}{y}\frac{dy}{dx} = \ln a$$

Tip: Remember — $\frac{d}{dy}\ln y = \frac{1}{y}.$

$$\frac{dy}{dx} = y \ln a$$

- Use the original equation to get rid of y:

$$\frac{dy}{dx} = a^x \ln a$$

Examples

Differentiate the following:

a) $y = 2^x$

$$\frac{dy}{dx} = 2^x \ln 2$$

b) $y = \left(\frac{1}{2}\right)^x$

Use the **log laws** to tidy this up...

$$\frac{dy}{dx} = \left(\frac{1}{2}\right)^x \ln\left(\frac{1}{2}\right) = -2^{-x} \ln 2$$

$$\left(\frac{1}{2}\right)^x = 2^{-x} \qquad \ln\left(\frac{1}{2}\right) = -\ln 2$$

Differentiating $a^{f(x)}$

Use the **chain rule** to differentiate functions of the form $a^{f(x)}$, by differentiating $y = a^u$ and $u = f(x)$ separately, then using the **formula**:

$$\frac{dy}{dx} = \frac{dy}{du} \times \frac{du}{dx}$$

Example

Find the equation of the tangent to the curve $y = 3^{-2x}$ at the point $\left(\frac{1}{2}, \frac{1}{3}\right)$.

- Use the **chain rule** to find $\frac{dy}{dx}$:

  Let $u = -2x$ and $y = 3^u$. Differentiating separately gives:

  $\frac{du}{dx} = -2$ and $\frac{dy}{du} = 3^u \ln 3$

  So $\frac{dy}{dx} = \frac{dy}{du} \times \frac{du}{dx} = 3^u \ln 3 \times -2 = -2(3^{-2x} \ln 3)$

- Now we can find the **gradient** of the tangent:

  At $\left(\frac{1}{2}, \frac{1}{3}\right)$, $\frac{dy}{dx} = -2(3^{-1} \ln 3) = -\frac{2}{3} \ln 3$

  So if the equation of the tangent at $\left(\frac{1}{2}, \frac{1}{3}\right)$ has the form $y = mx + c$, then

  $\frac{1}{3} = (-\frac{2}{3} \ln 3)\frac{1}{2} + c \implies c = \frac{1}{3} + \frac{1}{3} \ln 3$

- So the equation of the tangent to $y = 3^{-2x}$ at $\left(\frac{1}{2}, \frac{1}{3}\right)$ is:

  $y = -\frac{2x}{3} \ln 3 + \frac{1}{3} + \frac{1}{3} \ln 3$ or $3y = (1 - 2x)\ln 3 + 1$

Tip: As with all the other types of differentiation in this chapter, you'll probably be asked to find and use a value of the gradient at a certain point — e.g. to find equations of tangents and normals. After the differentiation bit, the method's exactly the same.

Exercise 3.1

Q1 Differentiate the following:
  a) $y = 3^x$　　　　　　b) $y = 5^x$
  c) $y = 10^x$　　　　　　d) $y = p^x$

Q2 Differentiate the following:
  a) $y = 3^{2x}$　　　　　　b) $y = 6^{3x}$
  c) $y = 10^{-x}$　　　　　　d) $y = p^{qx}$

Q3 A curve has the equation $y = 2^{4x}$.

  a) Show that the gradient of the curve is $\frac{dy}{dx} = 4(2^{4x} \ln 2)$.

  b) Find the equation of the tangent to the curve when $x = 2$.

Q3 b) Hint: You can leave your answer in terms of ln if you're not asked for a specific degree of accuracy. That way you're giving the exact answer.

Q4 The curve C has the equation $y = 3^{3x}$.
  a) Find the gradient of C.
  b) Find the equation of the normal to the curve when $x = -1$.

Q5 A curve has the equation $y = 5^{2x}$.

    a) Show that the curve passes through (2, 625).

    b) By finding the gradient $\dfrac{dy}{dx}$ of the curve at (2, 625), find the equation of the tangent at this point.

Q6 A curve $y = 2^{px}$ passes through the point (1, 32).

    a) Find p.

    b) Hence find the gradient of the curve at this point.

Q7 The curve C has the equation $y = 7^{x^2}$.

    a) Show that the gradient of the curve is $\dfrac{dy}{dx} = 2x(7^{x^2} \ln 7)$.

    b) Find the gradient of the curve when $x = 3$, giving your answer in standard index form to 3 s.f.

Q8 Hint: Leave the ln's in your working and final answer.

Q8 A curve has the equation $y = p^{x^3}$.

    a) Show that the gradient of the curve is $\dfrac{dy}{dx} = 3x^2(p^{x^3} \ln p)$.

    b) If the curve passes through the point (2, 6561), find p.

    c) Hence find the equation of the tangent to the curve when $x = 1$.

Q9 The curve $y = 4^{\sqrt{x}}$ passes through the point (25, a).

    a) Find a.

    b) Find the gradient of the curve.

    c) Hence show that the equation of the tangent to the curve at (25, a) is $y = 142x - 2520$ (to 3 s.f.).

Q10 A curve C has the equation $y = 2^{-3x}$. It passes through the point (2, b).

    a) Find the gradient $\dfrac{dy}{dx}$ of the curve.

    b) Find b and the gradient of the curve at (2, b).

    c) Hence show that the equation of the tangent to the curve at (2, b) is $64y = 1 + 6 \ln 2 - (3 \ln 2)x$.

Q11 A curve has the equation $y = x^2 a^x$, where $a > 0$. It passes through the point P with coordinates (2, 1).

    a) Find the value of a.

Q11 b) Hint: You'll have to use the product rule to differentiate, as well as the log laws to simplify.

    b) Show that the gradient of the curve is $\dfrac{dy}{dx} = \dfrac{2x - x^2 \ln 2}{2^x}$.

    c) Find the equation of the tangent to the curve at P. Leave your answer in terms of $\ln 2$.

4. Connected Rates of Change

A derivative like $\dfrac{dy}{dx}$ is also called a 'rate of change' — it's the rate of change in y with respect to x. You can apply different rates of change to a given situation, and if they have variables in common you say they're 'connected'.

Learning Objective:

- Be able to form differential equations from situations involving connected rates of change.

Connected rates of change

- Some situations have a number of **linked variables**, like length, surface area and volume; or distance, speed and acceleration.

- If you know the **rate of change** of one of these linked variables, and the equations that connect the variables, you can use the **chain rule** to help you find the rate of change of the other variables.

- An equation connecting variables with their rates of change (i.e. with a derivative term) is called a **differential equation**.

- When something changes over **time**, the derivative is $\dfrac{d}{dt}$ of that variable.

Tip: There's more on solving differential equations in Chapter 6 (see pages 114-122).

Examples

a) If $y = 3e^{5x}$ and $\dfrac{dx}{dt} = 2$, work out $\dfrac{dy}{dt}$ when $x = -1$.

- Start off by **differentiating** the expression for y, with respect to x:

$$y = 3e^{5x} \Rightarrow \frac{dy}{dx} = 15e^{5x}$$

- Write out the **chain rule** for $\dfrac{dy}{dt}$, using the information available:

$$\frac{dy}{dt} = \frac{dx}{dt} \times \frac{dy}{dx}$$

> Multiplying by $\dfrac{dy}{dx}$ effectively cancels out the 'dx' and gives you the 'dy' you need on top.

Tip: Sometimes it helps to write out the chain rule first so you know which rate of change is missing and needs to be worked out.

- Put in all the things you know to work out $\dfrac{dy}{dt}$.

$$\frac{dy}{dt} = 2 \times 15e^{5x} = 30e^{5x}$$

- Now find the value of $\dfrac{dy}{dt}$ at $x = -1$: $\quad \dfrac{dy}{dt} = \boxed{30e^{-5}}$

b) **y is the surface area of a sphere, and x is its radius.**
   The rate of change of the radius, $\dfrac{dx}{dt} = -2$. Find $\dfrac{dy}{dt}$ when $x = 2.5$.

- This is trickier because you're not given the expression for y. But you should know (or be able to look up) that for the surface area of a sphere:

$$y = 4\pi x^2$$

- Now **differentiate** as before: $\quad \dfrac{dy}{dx} = 8\pi x$

Tip: This formula is on the C1 formula sheet — it'll probably be given as $4\pi r^2$.

- Write out the **chain rule** for $\dfrac{dy}{dt}$:

$$\frac{dy}{dt} = \frac{dx}{dt} \times \frac{dy}{dx} = -2 \times 8\pi x = -16\pi x$$

- Now find $\dfrac{dy}{dt}$ when $x = 2.5$:

$$\frac{dy}{dt} = -16\pi \times 2.5 = \boxed{-40\pi}$$

Often you'll see much 'wordier' questions involving related rates of change, like the one in the example below, where you have to do a bit more work to figure out where to start.

Example

A scientist is testing how a new material expands when it is gradually heated. The diagram below shows the sample being tested, which is shaped like a triangular prism.

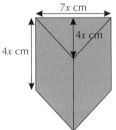

After t minutes, the triangle that forms the base of the prism has base length $7x$ cm and height $4x$ cm, and the length of the prism is also $4x$ cm.

If the sample expands at a constant rate, given by $\frac{dx}{dt} = 0.05$ cm min⁻¹, find an expression in terms of x for $\frac{dV}{dt}$, where V is the volume of the prism.

- The best way to start this kind of question is to write down what you know. We've got enough information to write an expression for the **volume of the prism**:

Area of cross-section   Length of prism

$$V = \left(\frac{1}{2} \times 7x \times 4x\right) \times 4x$$

$$\Rightarrow V = 56x^3 \text{ cm}^3$$

- **Differentiate** this expression for the volume with respect to x:

$$\frac{dV}{dx} = 168x^2$$

- We know that $\frac{dx}{dt} = 0.05$ cm min⁻¹.

  So we can use the **chain rule** to find $\frac{dV}{dt}$:

$$\frac{dV}{dt} = \frac{dV}{dx} \times \frac{dx}{dt}$$

$$\Rightarrow \frac{dV}{dt} = 168x^2 \times 0.05 = \boxed{8.4x^2 \text{ cm}^3 \text{ min}^{-1}}$$

Tip: If you've forgotten the formulas for areas and volumes of 3D solids, you should brush up on them now. They crop up quite a bit in these questions.

There are a couple of tricks in this type of question that could catch you out if you're not prepared for them. In the example coming up on the next page, you have to spot that there's a hidden derivative described in words.

You also need to remember the rule $\frac{dy}{dx} = \frac{1}{\left(\frac{dx}{dy}\right)}$.

A giant metal cube from space is cooling after entering the Earth's atmosphere. As it cools, the surface area of the cube decreases at a constant rate of 0.027 m² s⁻¹.

If the side length of the cube after t seconds is x m,
find $\dfrac{dx}{dt}$ at the point when $x = 15$ m.

Tip: There's a 'hidden' derivative here — the rate of decrease in area. You can see from the units (m² s⁻¹) that it's a change in area (m²) with respect to time (s).

- Start with what you know:

> The cube has side length x **m**.
>
> So the surface area of the cube is: $A = 6x^2 \Rightarrow \dfrac{dA}{dx} = 12x$.
>
> A **decreases** at a constant rate of 0.027 m² s⁻¹.
> We can write this as $\dfrac{dA}{dt} = -0.027$.
>
> This value is negative because A is decreasing.
>
> Use $\dfrac{d}{dt}$ because it's a rate of time.

- Now use the **chain rule** to find $\dfrac{dx}{dt}$:

$$\frac{dx}{dt} = \frac{dx}{dA} \times \frac{dA}{dt} = \frac{1}{\left(\dfrac{dA}{dx}\right)} \times \frac{dA}{dt} = \frac{1}{12x} \times -0.027 = -\frac{0.00225}{x}$$

Tip: $\dfrac{dx}{dt}$ is a change in length over time. Throughout the question the units used for length are metres, and the units for time are seconds, so $\dfrac{dx}{dt}$ must be in units of m s⁻¹.

- So when $x = 15$, $\dfrac{dx}{dt} = -\dfrac{0.00225}{x} = -\dfrac{0.00225}{15} = \boxed{-0.00015 \text{ m s}^{-1}}$

Exercise 4.1

Q1 A cube with sides x cm is cooling and shrinking by 0.1 cm min⁻¹. Find an expression for $\dfrac{dV}{dt}$, the rate of change of volume with respect to time.

Q2 A cuboid block of sides $2x$ cm by $3x$ cm by $5x$ cm expands when heated such that x increases at a rate of 0.15 cm °C⁻¹. If the volume of the cuboid at temperature θ °C is V cm³, find $\dfrac{dV}{d\theta}$ when $x = 3$.

Q3 A snowball of radius r cm is melting. Its radius decreases by 1.6 cm h⁻¹. If the surface area of the snowball at time t hours is A cm², find $\dfrac{dA}{dt}$ when $r = 5.5$ cm. Give your answer to 2 d.p.

Q3 Hint: Model the snowball as a sphere (Surface area $A = 4\pi r^2$).

Q4 A spherical satellite, radius r m, expands as it enters the atmosphere. It grows by 2×10^{-2} mm for every 1 °C rise in temperature. Find an expression $\dfrac{dV}{d\theta}$ for the rate of change of volume with respect to temperature.

Q4 Hint: Take extra care with the units here.

Q5 Heat, H, is lost from a closed cylindrical tank of radius r cm and height $3r$ cm at a rate of 2 J cm⁻² of surface area, A. Find $\dfrac{dH}{dr}$ when $r = 12.3$. Give your answer to 2 d.p.

Q6 A cylindrical polishing block of radius r cm and length H cm is worn down at one circular end at a rate of 0.5 mm h^{-1}. Find an expression for the rate of change of the volume of the block with respect to time.

Q7 A crystal of a salt is shaped like a prism. Its cross section is an equilateral triangle with sides x mm and the height of the crystal is 20 mm. New material is deposited only on the rectangular faces of the prism (i.e. the height does not change), at a rate of 0.6 mm per day.

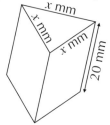

a) Find an expression for the area of the end of the prism in terms of x.

b) Find an expression for the rate of change of the volume of the crystal with respect to time.

c) Find the rate of change of the volume of the crystal with respect to time when $x = 0.5$.

Q8 The growth of a population of bacteria in a sample dish is modelled by the equation:

$$D = 1 + 2^{\lambda t}$$

where D is the diameter of the colony in mm, t is time in days, and λ is a constant. The number of bacteria in the colony, n, is proportional to the diameter, and can be written as $n = kD$. A biologist counts the number of bacteria in a small area of the colony and estimates that $k = 104$.

a) Find an expression for the rate of change of n with respect to time.

b) Find the rate of increase in number of bacteria after 1 day if $\lambda = 5$.

Q9 Water is dripping from a hole in the base of a cylinder of radius r cm, where the water height is h cm, at a rate of 0.3 cm^3 s^{-1}.

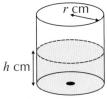

a) Find an expression for $\frac{dh}{dt}$, the rate at which the water level falls in the cylinder.

b) Hence find the rate of change in the water level, per minute, in a cylinder of radius 6 cm when the height of water is 4 cm.

Q10 The volume, V, of a hemisphere of radius r cm, changes with temperature at a rate of k cm^3 °C^{-1}, where k is a constant depending on the material of which the hemisphere is made.

a) Find an expression for the rate of change of radius with respect to temperature.

b) Hence find $\frac{dr}{d\theta}$ for a material with $k = 1.5$, when $V = 4$ cm^3.

Review Exercise — Chapter 4

Q1 A curve is defined by the parametric equations $x = t^2$, $y = 3t^3 - 4t$.

    a) Find $\dfrac{dy}{dx}$ for this curve.

    b) Find the coordinates of the stationary points of the curve.

Q2 The curve C is defined by the parametric equations $x = t \ln t$, $y = 2t^3 - t^2$.

    a) Find $\dfrac{dy}{dx}$ in terms of t.

    b) Find the gradient of C when $t = 1$.

    c) Explain why you cannot evaluate $\dfrac{dy}{dx}$ when $t = 0$.

Q3 The path of a particle is described parametrically by $x = t^2 - 6t$, $y = 2t^3 - 6t^2 - 18t$.

    a) Find $\dfrac{dy}{dx}$ in terms of t.

    b) Hence find any stationary points on the path of the particle.

Q4 A curve C defined by $x = t^3 - t^2$, $y = t^3 + 3t^2 - 9t$ has turning points at (a, b) and (c, d).

    a) Find the coordinates (a, b) and (c, d).

    b) Find the values of t at the points where C cuts the x-axis and hence show that C passes through the origin. Leave your answers in surd form if necessary.

    c) Find the equation of the tangent to C when $t = 2$.

Q5 A curve is given parametrically by $x = 3se^s$, $y = e^{2s} + se^{2s}$

    a) Find the equations of the tangents to the curve at $s = 0$ and $s = 2$.

    b) Hence find the coordinates of the point of intersection of these tangents, leaving your answer in terms of e.

Q6 Curve C is given by $x = \dfrac{\sin \theta}{\theta^2}$, $y = \theta \cos 2\theta$.

    a) Find the gradient of C when $\theta = \dfrac{\pi}{2}$.

    b) Hence find the equation of the tangent to the curve at this point.

    c) Find the values of θ where the curve cuts the x-axis ($\theta \geq 0$), and hence find the coordinates of the point with $0 \leq \theta \leq \dfrac{\pi}{2}$ where the curve cuts the x-axis.

Q7 The trajectory of a particle is given by the parametric equations $x = t^3 + t^2$, $y = \dfrac{1}{2}t^2 - 6t$.

    a) Find the gradient $\dfrac{dy}{dx}$ of the trajectory in terms of t.

    b) Hence find the turning point of the trajectory.

    c) Find the equations of the tangents to the trajectory when $y = 0$.

Q8 Use implicit differentiation to find $\dfrac{dy}{dx}$ for each of the following equations:

    a) $4x^2 - 2y^2 = 7x^2y$ b) $3x^4 - 2xy^2 = y$ c) $\cos x \sin y = xy$

Q9 Using your answers to Q8 above, find:

    a) the gradient of the tangent to the graph of $4x^2 - 2y^2 = 7x^2y$ at $(1, -4)$,

    b) the gradient of the normal to the graph of $3x^4 - 2xy^2 = y$ at $(1, 1)$.

Q10 The curve $x^2y + y^2 = x^2 + 1$ passes through the points $(1, -2)$ and $(1, a)$.

    a) Find a.

    b) Find the gradient of the curve at $(1, -2)$.

    c) Show that $(1, a)$ is a turning point of the curve.

Q11 A curve is defined implicitly by $y \cos x - y^2 = x \sin x$.

    a) Show that $x = 0$, $y = 1$ is a solution to the equation.

    b) Show that $(0, 1)$ is a turning point of the curve.

Q12 A curve is defined implicitly by $x \cos x + y \sin x = y^3$.

    a) Find the gradient $\dfrac{dy}{dx}$ of the curve.

    b) Show that at the stationary points of the curve, $y = x \tan x - 1$.

    c) Show that there are three points on the curve with coordinates $\left(\dfrac{\pi}{2}, a\right)$.

    d) Find the equations of the tangents at each of these points and hence show that two of these tangents will never intersect.

Q13 The curve $4y + x^2y^2 = 4x$ passes through the two points $(2, a)$ and $(2, b)$, where $a > b$.

By finding a and b and the gradient $\dfrac{dy}{dx}$ of the curve, show that the tangents to the curve at $(2, a)$ and $(2, b)$ intersect at $(5, 1)$.

Q14 The curve $x \ln x + x^2y = y^2x - 6x$ passes through two points $(1, a)$ and $(1, b)$, where $a > b$.

    a) Find a and b.

    b) Use implicit differentiation to find the gradient of the curve at each of these points and hence the equations of the normals passing through the points.

    c) Find the coordinates of the point where the normals intersect.

Q15 Write down the proof that $\dfrac{d}{dx}a^x = a^x \ln a$, where a is a constant.

Q16 A cuboid has length x cm, width $2x$ cm and height $3x$ cm.
The cuboid is expanding, for some unexplained reason.
If A is the surface area of the cuboid and V is its volume, find $\dfrac{dA}{dx}$ and $\dfrac{dV}{dx}$, and use them to show that if $\dfrac{dV}{dt} = 3$, then $\dfrac{dA}{dt} = \dfrac{22}{3x}$.

Q17 At the end of its life in the main sequence, a small star like our Sun first expands to a Red Giant and then shrinks to a White Dwarf.

    a) When the star becomes a Red Giant, it expands and cools. The rate of change of radius with respect to temperature is approximately -2500 km K^{-1}.

    Find an expression for the rate of change of volume (V) with temperature (θ). Model the star as a sphere.

    b) When the star collapses to a White Dwarf, density (ρ) and temperature both increase as the diameter decreases. The rate of change of diameter with respect to temperature, $\dfrac{dD}{d\theta}$, is approximately -215 km K^{-1}.

    Using the expression $V = kD^3$ for the volume of the star, find an expression for the rate of change of density $\dfrac{d\rho}{d\theta}$, if the mass of the star is m kg $(m = \rho V)$.

1   The curve C is defined by the parametric equations

$$x = 3\theta - \cos 3\theta, \quad y = 2 \sin \theta, \quad -\pi \le \theta \le \pi.$$

   a)   Find an expression for $\dfrac{dy}{dx}$.   *(3 marks)*

   b)   (i)   Show that the gradient of C at the point $(\pi + 1, \sqrt{3})$ is $\dfrac{1}{3}$.   *(3 marks)*

        (ii)   Find the equation of the normal to C when $\theta = \dfrac{\pi}{6}$.   *(4 marks)*

2   The equation of curve C is $6x^2y - 7 = 5x - 4y^2 - x^2$.

   a)   The line T has the equation $y = c$ and passes through a point on C where $x = 2$.
       Find c, given that $c > 0$.   *(2 marks)*

   b) T also crosses C at point Q.
       (i)   Find the coordinates of Q.   *(2 marks)*

       (ii)   Find the gradient of C at Q. Give your answer to 3 significant figures.   *(6 marks)*

3   a)   Curve A has the equation $y = 4^x$.
       What are the coordinates of the point on A where $\dfrac{dy}{dx} = \ln 4$?   *(2 marks)*

   b)   Curve B has the equation $y = 4^{(x-4)^3}$.
       Find the gradient of B at the point $(3, \frac{1}{4})$.   *(4 marks)*

4   A curve C is given by $x^2y + y^2x - 2y^2 - xy^3 = 0$.

   a)   Use implicit differentiation to find the gradient $\dfrac{dy}{dx}$ of the curve.   *(3 marks)*

   b)   Hence show that at the stationary points of the curve $x = \dfrac{y^2 - y}{2}$.   *(2 marks)*

   c)   Show that when $x = 2$, $y = 0$ or $y = \pm\sqrt{2}$.   *(2 marks)*

   d)   Find the equation of the tangent to the curve at $(2, \sqrt{2})$.   *(4 marks)*

5   The curve C has the equation $3e^x + 6y = 2x^2y$.

     a)   (i)   Use implicit differentiation to find an expression for $\frac{dy}{dx}$.

                              (3 marks)

         (ii)   Show that at the stationary points of C, $y = \frac{3e^x}{4x}$.

                              (2 marks)

     b)   Hence find the exact coordinates of the two stationary points of C.

                              (4 marks)

6   A curve, C, has parametric equations:

$$x = t^2 + 2t - 3, \quad y = 2 - t^3.$$

     a)   The line L is the tangent to C at $y = -6$.

         Show that the equation of L is $y = -2x + 4$.

                              (4 marks)

     b) L also meets C at point P.

         (i)   Find the coordinates of P.

                              (4 marks)

         (ii)   Find the equation of the normal to the curve at P.

                              (3 marks)

7

The triangular prism shown in the diagram is expanding.

The dimensions of the prism after t seconds are given in terms of x.

The prism is $4x$ m long, and its cross-section is an isosceles triangle with base $\frac{3}{2}x$ m and height x m.

     a)   Show that, if the surface area of the prism after t seconds is A m^2,

         then $A = \frac{35}{2}x^2$.

                              (3 marks)

The surface area of the prism is increasing at a constant rate of 0.07 m^2 s^{-1}.

     b)   Find $\frac{dx}{dt}$ when $x = 0.5$.

                              (3 marks)

     c)   If the volume of the prism is V m^3, find the rate of change of V when $x = 1.2$.

                              (4 marks)

1. Integration of $(ax + b)^n$

You've already seen how to integrate functions of the form x^n in C1. In this section you'll see how to integrate functions which are linear transformations of x^n — functions of the form $(ax + b)^n$.

Integrating $(ax + b)^n$, $n \neq -1$

In C1, you learnt to think of **integration** as the **opposite of differentiation**. This means that if you differentiate a function, then **integrating** the result will get you back to the function you started with. Here are a few examples to show how you can use this technique to integrate functions of the form $(ax + b)^n$.

Learning Objectives:

- Be able to integrate functions of the form $(ax + b)^n$, $n \neq -1$, where a, b and n are constants.

- Be able to solve integration problems with functions of the form $(ax + b)^n$.

Example 1

a) **Differentiate $(3x + 4)^5$ with respect to x.**

Using the **chain rule**, $\frac{d}{dx}(3x + 4)^5 = 5(3x + 4)^4 \times 3 = \boxed{15(3x + 4)^4}$.

b) **Use your answer to a) to find $\int (3x + 4)^4\, dx$.**

- From part a) you know that:

$$(3x + 4)^5 \xrightarrow{\text{Differentiation}} 15(3x + 4)^4$$

- Integration is the **opposite of differentiation** so:

$$(3x + 4)^5 + C \xleftarrow[\text{Integration}]{} 15(3x + 4)^4$$

This means:
$$\int 15(3x + 4)^4\, dx = (3x + 4)^5 + c$$

$$\Rightarrow 15 \int (3x + 4)^4\, dx = (3x + 4)^5 + c$$

$$\Rightarrow \int (3x + 4)^4\, dx = \frac{1}{15}(3x + 4)^5 + \frac{C}{15}$$

$$= \frac{1}{15}(3x + 4)^5 + C$$

$\frac{C}{15}$ is just another constant term — you can call it C.

Divide by the constant term to get the integral you're after.

Tip: The **chain rule** is used to differentiate a function of a function $f(g(x))$: If $y = f(u)$ and $u = g(x)$ then:
$$\frac{dy}{dx} = \frac{dy}{du} \times \frac{du}{dx}$$

Tip: Don't forget that for indefinite integrals (integrals without limits) you need to add a constant of integration, C.

Tip: You can take constant factors outside of integrations and put them at the front to make things easier (see C1).

Example 2

Given that $\frac{d}{dx}((2x - 3)^{-3}) = -6(2x - 3)^{-4}$, find $\int (2x - 3)^{-4}\, dx$.

Use the same method as above:

- $(2x - 3)^{-3}$ differentiates to give $-6(2x - 3)^{-4}$.
- So $\int -6(2x - 3)^{-4}\, dx = (2x - 3)^{-3} + c$

$$-6 \int (2x - 3)^{-4}\, dx = (2x - 3)^{-3} + c$$

$$\int (2x - 3)^{-4}\, dx = -\frac{1}{6}(2x - 3)^{-3} + C$$

Taking the constant out.

Dividing by –6.

This method gives us a **general result** for integrating all functions of the form $(ax + b)^n$.

> **Tip:** This doesn't work for $n = -1$ because you'd end up having to divide by $n + 1 = 0$. See page 68 for a method of integrating x^{-1} and $(ax + b)^{-1}$.

Differentiating $(ax + b)^{n+1}$ using the chain rule gives $a(n + 1)(ax + b)^n$.

So
$$\int a(n + 1)(ax + b)^n \, dx = (ax + b)^{n+1} + c$$
$$a(n + 1) \int (ax + b)^n \, dx = (ax + b)^{n+1} + c$$

Dividing by $a(n + 1)$ gives the general expression:

$$\int (ax + b)^n \, dx = \frac{1}{a(n + 1)}(ax + b)^{n+1} + C$$

Examples

Find the following integrals using the general expression for $\int (ax + b)^n \, dx$:

a) $\int (3 - 4x)^2 \, dx$

Write down the values of a, b and n and then substitute them into the formula. Here $a = -4$, $b = 3$ and $n = 2$.

$$\int (3 - 4x)^2 \, dx = \frac{1}{-4 \times 3}(3 - 4x)^3 + C = -\frac{1}{12}(3 - 4x)^3 + C$$

$a = -4$ $n + 1 = 3$

> **Tip:** You can always differentiate your answer to check it — you should get back to what you started with.

b) $\int (3x - 2)^{-2} \, dx$

Here $a = 3$, $b = -2$ and $n = -2$, so substitute these values into the formula.

$$\int (3x - 2)^{-2} \, dx = \frac{1}{3 \times -1}(3x - 2)^{-1} + C = -\frac{1}{3}(3x - 2)^{-1} + C$$

$a = 3$ $n + 1 = -1$

$$= -\frac{1}{3(3x - 2)} + C$$

c) $\int_4^{12} (2x + 1)^{\frac{1}{2}} \, dx$

This is a **definite integral** — it has limits, so your answer will be a **number** and you don't need to bother with the **constant of integration**.

Here $a = 2$, $b = 1$ and $n = \frac{1}{2}$, so substitute these values into the formula.

$$\int_4^{12} (2x + 1)^{\frac{1}{2}} \, dx = \left[\frac{1}{2 \times \frac{3}{2}}(2x + 1)^{\frac{3}{2}} \right]_4^{12} = \left[\frac{1}{3}(2x + 1)^{\frac{3}{2}} \right]_4^{12} = \frac{1}{3}\left[(2x + 1)^{\frac{3}{2}} \right]_4^{12}$$

$a = 2$ $n + 1 = \frac{3}{2}$

> Be careful adding 1 to fractional powers.

> **Tip:** Remember from C2 that when you integrate a definite integral, you put the function in square brackets and write the limits on the right.

Now evaluate the integral at the limits:

$$\int_4^{12} (2x + 1)^{\frac{1}{2}} \, dx = \frac{1}{3}\left[(2x + 1)^{\frac{3}{2}} \right]_4^{12} = \frac{1}{3}\left[((2 \times 12) + 1)^{\frac{3}{2}} \right] - \frac{1}{3}\left[((2 \times 4) + 1)^{\frac{3}{2}} \right]$$

$$= \frac{1}{3}\left[(25^{\frac{3}{2}}) \right] - \frac{1}{3}\left[(9^{\frac{3}{2}}) \right] = \frac{125}{3} - \frac{27}{3} = \frac{98}{3}$$

In C2, you learnt that definite integrals work out the **area** between a curve and the x-axis. To find the area between a curve $y = f(x)$ and the x-axis over an interval, just integrate $f(x)$ with respect to x over that interval.

Example

Work out the area enclosed by the curve $y = (x - 2)^3$, the x-axis and the lines $x = 2$ and $x = 3$.

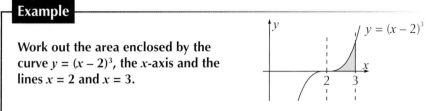

- You just need to integrate the curve $y = (x - 2)^3$ between $x = 2$ and $x = 3$,

  i.e. evaluate $\int_2^3 (x - 2)^3 \, dx$

- Use the formula with $a = 1$, $b = -2$ and $n = 3$ to work out the integral.

  $$\int_2^3 (x - 2)^3 \, dx = \tfrac{1}{4}[(x - 2)^4]_2^3$$

- Substitute in the limits of integration to find the area.

  $$\overset{x = 3}{} \qquad \overset{x = 2}{}$$

  $$\int_2^3 (x - 2)^3 \, dx = \tfrac{1}{4}[(3 - 2)^4] - \tfrac{1}{4}[(2 - 2)^4] = \tfrac{1}{4}[1^4] - \tfrac{1}{4}[0^4]$$

  $$= \tfrac{1}{4} - 0 = \boxed{\tfrac{1}{4}}$$

Exercise 1.1

Q1 Integrate with respect to x:
   a) $(2x + 9)^4$ b) $(x + 10)^{10}$ c) $(4x + 3)^5$ d) $(5x)^7$
   e) $(7x - 2)^{-8}$ f) $(3 - 5x)^{-2}$ g) $(10x - 3)^{\frac{11}{8}}$ h) $(3x - 4)^{-\frac{4}{3}}$

Q2 a) Show that $\int 8(2x - 4)^4 \, dx = \dfrac{4(2x - 4)^5}{5} + C$.

   b) Evaluate the definite integral $\int_{\frac{3}{2}}^{\frac{5}{2}} 8(2x - 4)^4 \, dx$.

Q3 Evaluate $\int_0^1 (6x + 1)^{-3} \, dx$.

Q4 The curve $y = f(x)$ goes through the point $\left(1, \dfrac{3}{35}\right)$ and $f'(x) = (8 - 7x)^4$. Find $f(x)$.

Q5 Find the area between the curve $y = (-x - 1)^{12}$ and the x-axis for $-1 \le x \le 0$.

Q6 Hint: You'll only need one constant of integration (each term produces a constant but you can just combine them into one term).

Q6 Integrate the function $(9 - y)^{\frac{1}{6}} + (9 - y)^{-6}$ with respect to y.

Q7 Show that $\int \dfrac{-6}{(12x + 5)^2} \, dx = \dfrac{1}{24x + 10} + C$.

2. Integration of e^x and $\dfrac{1}{x}$

Learning Objectives:

- Be able to integrate functions containing e^x and $\frac{1}{x}$ terms.

- Be able to integrate linear transformations of e^x and $\frac{1}{x}$, i.e. functions of the form e^{ax+b} and $\dfrac{1}{ax+b}$.

The functions e^x and $1/x$ are pretty easy to integrate — it's just the opposite of differentiating e^x and ln x. Simple.

Integrating e^x and e^{ax+b}

e^x differentiates to give e^x, so it makes sense that e^x **integrates** to give $\mathbf{e^x + C}$.

$$\int e^x \, dx = e^x + C$$

Example

Integrate the function $6x^2 - 4x + 3e^x$ with respect to x.

- When integrating a function like this, you integrate each term separately so:

$$\int 6x^2 - 4x + 3e^x \, dx = \int 6x^2 \, dx - \int 4x \, dx + \int 3e^x \, dx$$

- The first two terms are of the form x^n so they integrate to $2x^3$ and $2x^2$ respectively.

- Using the rule above, the third term is:

$$\int 3e^x \, dx = 3 \int e^x \, dx = 3e^x + c$$

- Putting this all together gives:

$$\int 6x^2 - 4x + 3e^x \, dx = \boxed{2x^3 - 2x^2 + 3e^x + C}$$

On p.63-64 you saw how to integrate **linear transformations** of x^n by differentiating with the **chain rule** and working backwards. You can do the same with functions of the form $\mathbf{e^{ax+b}}$ where a and b are constants. Start by considering what you get when you **differentiate** functions of the form e^{ax+b} using the chain rule and work backwards.

Tip: This method of differentiating $f(ax + b)$ using the chain rule and working backwards to find an integral can be used with any of the functions that you know the derivative of — you'll see it used a lot in the next few sections.

Example

a) Differentiate the function e^{4x-1} with respect to x.

Using the chain rule, $\dfrac{d}{dx}(e^{4x-1}) = \boxed{4e^{4x-1}}$

b) Using your answer to a), find the integral $\displaystyle\int e^{4x-1} \, dx$.

Reversing the process of differentiation to get integration we have:

$$\frac{d}{dx}(e^{4x-1}) = 4e^{4x-1} \Rightarrow \int 4e^{4x-1} \, dx = e^{4x-1} + c$$

$$\Rightarrow 4 \int e^{4x-1} \, dx = e^{4x-1} + c$$

Take out the factor of 4 and divide by it.

$$\Rightarrow \int e^{4x-1} \, dx = \boxed{\tfrac{1}{4}e^{4x-1} + C}$$

This method gives you a **general rule** for integrating functions of the form e^{ax+b}:

$$\int e^{ax+b}\,dx = \frac{1}{a}e^{ax+b} + C$$

This means you just need to **divide** by the **coefficient of** x and add a constant of integration — the e^{ax+b} bit **doesn't change**.

Examples

Integrate the following:

a) e^{7x}

If you differentiated e^{7x} you'd get $7e^{7x}$, so you need to divide by 7 (the coefficient of x) when integrating.

$$\int e^{7x}\,dx = \boxed{\frac{1}{7}e^{7x} + C}$$

b) $2e^{4-3x}$

Multiplying by 2 doesn't change the integration — the coefficient of x is -3, so divide by -3 and you're done.

$$\int 2e^{4-3x}\,dx = \boxed{-\frac{2}{3}e^{4-3x} + C}$$

> **Tip:** Notice that if you differentiated $2e^{4-3x}$, you'd get $-6e^{4-3x}$, so you need to divide by -3 when you integrate — it's simple really.

c) $e^{\frac{x}{2}}$

If you differentiated this one using the **chain rule**, you'd get $\frac{1}{2}e^{\frac{x}{2}}$, so you need to multiply by 2 (divide by $\frac{1}{2}$) to integrate.

$$\int e^{\frac{x}{2}}\,dx = \int e^{\frac{1}{2}x}\,dx = \boxed{2e^{\frac{x}{2}} + C}$$

Exercise 2.1

Q1 Evaluate the following, giving exact answers:

a) $\displaystyle\int 2e^x\,dx$

b) $\displaystyle\int 4x + 7e^x\,dx$

c) $\displaystyle\int e^{10x}\,dx$

d) $\displaystyle\int e^{-3x} + x\,dx$

e) $\displaystyle\int e^{\frac{7}{2}x}\,dx$

f) $\displaystyle\int e^{4x-2}\,dx$

g) $\displaystyle\int \frac{1}{2}e^{2-\frac{3}{2}x}\,dx$

h) $\displaystyle\int e^{4\left(\frac{x}{3}+1\right)}\,dx$

Q2 Find the equation of the curve that has the derivative $\dfrac{dy}{dx} = 10e^{-5x-1}$ and passes through the origin.

Q3 Integrate the function e^{8y+5} with respect to y.

Q4 Evaluate the following definite integrals, giving exact answers:

a) $\displaystyle\int_2^3 e^{2x}\,dx$

b) $\displaystyle\int_{-1}^0 12e^{12x+12}\,dx$

c) $\displaystyle\int_{-\frac{\pi}{2}}^{\frac{\pi}{2}} e^{\pi-2x}\,dx$

d) $\displaystyle\int_3^6 \sqrt[6]{e^x} + \frac{1}{\sqrt[3]{e^x}}\,dx$

> **Q4 d) Hint:** Remember:
> $$\sqrt[n]{e^x} = e^{\frac{x}{n}}$$
> $$\frac{1}{\sqrt[n]{e^x}} = e^{-\frac{x}{n}}$$

Integrating $\frac{1}{x}$ and $\frac{1}{ax+b}$

The method for integrating x^n and $(ax + b)^n$ on p. 63 doesn't work for $n = -1$. For these functions you need to consider the fact that $\frac{d}{dx}(\ln x) = \frac{1}{x}$, which you should remember from C3.

Example

Let $f(x) = \frac{1}{x}$, $x > 0$.

Integrate $f(x)$ with respect to x, given that $\frac{d}{dx}(\ln x) = \frac{1}{x}$.

Given the derivative of ln x, integration is the opposite of differentiation, so:

$$\ln x \xrightarrow{\quad\text{Differentiation}\quad} \frac{1}{x}$$

$$\ln x + C \xleftarrow{\quad\text{Integration}\quad} \frac{1}{x}$$

So $\int \frac{1}{x}\, dx = \boxed{\ln x + C.}$

Tip: You'll be working with logs all the time when integrating functions of the form $\frac{1}{x}$ — it'll help to remember the log laws:

$\log(ab) = \log a + \log b$

$\log\left(\frac{a}{b}\right) = \log a - \log b$

$\log(a^b) = b \log a$

So now we have a general result for integrating $\frac{1}{x}$:

$$\boxed{\int \frac{1}{x}\, dx = \ln|x| + C}$$

Notice that this result uses $|x|$ instead of just x. This is because the function ln x is **not defined** for **negative values** of x. Using the modulus means you'll never end up taking ln of a negative value.

Examples

Find the following integrals:

a) $\int \frac{5}{x}\, dx$

> 5 is a **constant coefficient** — you can take it outside the integral so that you're just integrating $\frac{1}{x}$.

$$\int \frac{5}{x}\, dx = 5\int \frac{1}{x}\, dx = \boxed{5\ln|x| + C}$$

b) $\int_3^9 \frac{1}{3x}\, dx$

- Here $\frac{1}{3}$ is the **coefficient**, so it goes outside the integral.

$$\int_3^9 \frac{1}{3x}\, dx = \frac{1}{3}\int_3^9 \frac{1}{x}\, dx = \frac{1}{3}[\ln|x|]_3^9$$

- Now put in the limits and use log laws to simplify:

$$= \frac{1}{3}(\ln|9| - \ln|3|) = \frac{1}{3}\left(\ln\left(\frac{9}{3}\right)\right) \longleftarrow \ln a - \ln b = \ln\frac{a}{b}$$

$$= \frac{1}{3}\ln 3$$

You can integrate **linear transformations** of $\frac{1}{x}$ (i.e. functions of the form $\frac{1}{ax+b}$) by considering the result of differentiating $\ln|ax+b|$.

Example

Given that $\frac{d}{dx}(\ln|4x+2|) = \frac{4}{4x+2}$, **evaluate** $\int \frac{1}{4x+2}\,dx$.

$$\frac{d}{dx}(\ln|4x+2|) = \frac{4}{4x+2} \Rightarrow \int \frac{4}{4x+2}\,dx = \ln|4x+2| + c$$

$$\Rightarrow 4\int \frac{1}{4x+2}\,dx = \ln|4x+2| + c$$

$$\Rightarrow \int \frac{1}{4x+2}\,dx = \boxed{\tfrac{1}{4}\ln|4x+2| + C}$$

The **general result** for integrating functions of the form $\frac{1}{ax+b}$ is:

$$\boxed{\int \frac{1}{ax+b}\,dx = \frac{1}{a}\ln|ax+b| + C}$$

Example

Evaluate $\int \frac{1}{2x+5}\,dx$.

Using the general rule, $a = 2$ and $b = 5$ so the integral is:

$$\int \frac{1}{2x+5}\,dx = \boxed{\tfrac{1}{2}\ln|2x+5| + C}$$

Tip: Evaluating $\int \frac{1}{3x}\,dx$ (from the example on page 68) in this way would give a 'different' answer, $\frac{1}{3}\ln|3x| + C$. But this expands to $\frac{1}{3}\ln|x| + \frac{1}{3}\ln 3 + C$ and the $\frac{1}{3}\ln 3$ becomes part of the constant of integration, so both answers are equivalent.

Exercise 2.2

Q1 Evaluate the following:

a) $\int \frac{19}{x}\,dx$ b) $\int \frac{1}{7x}\,dx$ c) $\int \frac{1}{7x+2}\,dx$ d) $\int \frac{4}{1-3x}\,dx$

Q2 Integrate $y = \frac{1}{8x} - \frac{20}{x}$ with respect to x.

Q3 a) Show that $\int \frac{6}{x} - \frac{3}{x}\,dx = \ln|x^3| + C$.

b) Evaluate $\int_4^5 \frac{6}{x} - \frac{3}{x}\,dx$, giving an exact answer.

Q4 Show that $\int_b^a 15(5+3x)^{-1}\,dx = \ln\left|\frac{5+3a}{5+3b}\right|^5$.

Q4 Hint: Use the log laws on p.68 to simplify your answer.

Q5 The graph of the curve $y = f(x)$ passes through the point (1, 2). The derivative of $f(x)$ is given by $f'(x) = \frac{4}{10-9x}$. Find $f(x)$.

Q6 a) Express the area bounded by the curve $y = \frac{-7}{16-2x}$, the x-axis, the y-axis, and the line $x = -3$ as an integral with respect to x.

b) Show that the area is equal to $\ln\left[\left(\frac{8}{11}\right)^{\frac{7}{2}}\right]$.

Q7 Given that $\int_1^A \frac{4}{6x-5}\,dx = 10$, find A, in terms of e.

3. Integration Using Partial Fractions

Learning Objective:

- Be able to integrate rational expressions in which the denominator can be written as a product of linear factors, by splitting them into partial fractions.

By rewriting algebraic expressions as partial fractions, you can turn difficult-looking integrations into ones you're more familiar with.

Use of partial fractions

You can integrate algebraic fractions where the denominator can be written as a product of **linear factors** by splitting them up into **partial fractions**. Each fraction can then be **integrated separately** using the methods on pages 68-69.

Example 1

Find $\int \dfrac{12x + 6}{4x^2 - 9}\, dx$ where $x > 2$.

- The first step is to write the function as **partial fractions** as follows:

  - **Factorise** the denominator:
    $$\frac{12x + 6}{4x^2 - 9} \equiv \frac{12x + 6}{(2x + 3)(2x - 3)}$$

  - Write as an **identity** with partial fractions:
    $$\frac{12x + 6}{4x^2 - 9} \equiv \frac{12x + 6}{(2x + 3)(2x - 3)} \equiv \frac{A}{2x + 3} + \frac{B}{2x - 3}$$

  - **Add** the partial fractions and **cancel** the denominators:
    $$\frac{12x + 6}{(2x + 3)(2x - 3)} \equiv \frac{A(2x - 3) + B(2x + 3)}{(2x + 3)(2x - 3)}$$
    $$12x + 6 \equiv A(2x - 3) + B(2x + 3)$$

  - Use the **substitution method** to find A and B:
    Substituting $x = \frac{3}{2}$ into the identity gives
    $$18 + 6 = 0A + 6B \Rightarrow 24 = 6B \Rightarrow B = 4$$
    Substituting $x = -\frac{3}{2}$ into the identity gives
    $$-18 + 6 = -6A + 0B \Rightarrow -12 = -6A \Rightarrow A = 2$$

  - Replace A and B in the **original identity**:
    $$\frac{12x + 6}{4x^2 - 9} \equiv \frac{2}{2x + 3} + \frac{4}{2x - 3}$$

- So $\int \dfrac{12x + 6}{4x^2 - 9}\, dx = \int \dfrac{2}{2x + 3} + \dfrac{4}{2x - 3}\, dx.$

- Integrate each term **separately** using methods from pages 68-69.
  $$= 2 \times \tfrac{1}{2}\ln|2x + 3| + 4 \times \tfrac{1}{2}\ln|2x - 3| + C$$
  $$= \ln|2x + 3| + 2\ln|2x - 3| + C$$

- $x > 2$ so $2x + 3 > 7$ and $2x - 3 > 1$ so remove the modulus signs:
  $$= \ln(2x + 3) + 2\ln(2x - 3) + C$$
  $$= \ln(2x + 3)(2x - 3)^2 + C$$

Tip: Writing expressions as partial fractions is covered in Chapter 1 — but it's recapped here to remind you what they're all about.

Tip: You could also use the 'equating coefficients' method to find A and B.

Tip: It's a good idea to tidy up your answers using the log laws.

Example 2

Find the exact value of $\int_3^4 \dfrac{2}{x(x-2)}\,dx$, writing it as a single logarithm.

- Start by writing $\dfrac{2}{x(x-2)}$ as **partial fractions**.

  - Write as an **identity** with partial fractions:
  $$\frac{2}{x(x-2)} \equiv \frac{A}{x} + \frac{B}{x-2}$$

  - **Add** the partial fractions and **cancel** the denominators:
  $$\frac{2}{x(x-2)} \equiv \frac{A(x-2) + Bx}{x(x-2)}$$
  $$\Rightarrow 2 \equiv A(x-2) + Bx$$

  - Use the **equating coefficients method** to find A and B:
  Equating constant terms: $2 = -2A \Rightarrow A = -1$
  Equating x coefficients: $0 = A + B \Rightarrow 0 = -1 + B \Rightarrow B = 1$

  - Replace A and B in the **original identity**:
  $$\frac{2}{x(x-2)} \equiv \frac{-1}{x} + \frac{1}{x-2} \equiv \frac{1}{x-2} - \frac{1}{x}$$

> **Tip:** When the constant term only contains one of the unknowns, it'll often be easier to compare coefficients than to substitute.

- So $\int_3^4 \dfrac{2}{x(x-2)}\,dx = \int_3^4 \dfrac{1}{(x-2)} - \dfrac{1}{x}\,dx$

- Integrate each term separately using methods from p.68-69.

$$= \left[\ln|x-2| - \ln|x|\right]_3^4$$

$\boxed{\log a - \log b = \log\left(\frac{a}{b}\right)}$

$$= \left[\ln\left|\frac{x-2}{x}\right|\right]_3^4 = \left[\ln\left|\frac{4-2}{4}\right|\right] - \left[\ln\left|\frac{3-2}{3}\right|\right]$$

$$= \ln\left(\frac{1}{2}\right) - \ln\left(\frac{1}{3}\right) = \ln\left(\frac{3}{2}\right)$$

> **Tip:** The question asks for the answer as a single logarithm so make sure you fully simplify your answer.

Example 3

Find $\int \dfrac{x^2 + 17x + 16}{(x+2)^2(3x-1)}\,dx$.

- First, write it as partial fractions.

  - It has a repeated factor so the $(x+2)$ needs to feature in two of the denominators, squared and on its own:

  $$\frac{x^2 + 17x + 16}{(x+2)^2(3x-1)} \equiv \frac{A}{(x+2)^2} + \frac{B}{(x+2)} + \frac{C}{(3x-1)}$$

  $$x^2 + 17x + 16 \equiv A(3x-1) + B(x+2)(3x-1) + C(x+2)^2$$

  - Use the substitution method (and equate coefficients to get B):

  Substituting $x = \frac{1}{3}$ gives: $\quad \dfrac{196}{9} = 0A + 0B + \dfrac{49}{9}C \Rightarrow C = 4$

  Substituting $x = -2$ gives: $\quad -14 = -7A + 0B + 0C \Rightarrow A = 2$

  Equate coefficients of x^2 to get B: $1 = 3B + C = 3B + 4$ so $B = -1$

- So you have:

$$\int \frac{x^2 + 17x + 16}{(x + 2)^2(3x - 1)}\, dx = \int \frac{2}{(x + 2)^2} - \frac{1}{(x + 2)} + \frac{4}{(3x - 1)}\, dx$$

(with arrow pointing to: $\int 2(x + 2)^{-2}\, dx$)

$$= -\frac{2}{x + 2} - \ln|x + 2| + \tfrac{4}{3}\ln|3x - 1| + C$$

- Use the log laws $\log a^b = b \log a$ and $\log a - \log b = \log\left(\frac{a}{b}\right)$ to simplify:

$$= \ln\left|\frac{(3x - 1)^{\frac{4}{3}}}{x + 2}\right| - \frac{2}{x + 2} + C$$

Exercise 3.1

Q1 Integrate the following functions by writing them as partial fractions:

a) $\int \frac{24(x - 1)}{9 - 4x^2}\, dx$

b) $\int \frac{-4x^2 - 21x + 82}{(5x + 2)(x - 3)(x - 4)}\, dx$

c) $\int \frac{7x + 4}{(x + 2)^2(x - 3)}\, dx$

Q2 Find $\int_0^1 \frac{x}{(x - 2)(x - 3)}\, dx$ by expressing as partial fractions.
Give your answer as a single logarithm.

Q3 a) Express $\frac{6}{2x^2 - 5x + 2}$ in partial fractions.

b) Hence find $\int \frac{6}{2x^2 - 5x + 2}\, dx$ where $x > 2$.

c) Evaluate $\int_3^5 \frac{6}{2x^2 - 5x + 2}\, dx$, expressing your answer as a single logarithm.

Q4 Express $\frac{3y + 5}{y(y + 10)}$ as the sum of partial fractions
and hence evaluate $\int_1^2 \frac{3y + 5}{y(y + 10)}\, dy$.

Q5 Given that f(x) = $3x^2 + 17x - 32$ and g(x) = $(x - 4)(x - 1)(x + 3)$,
find $\int_b^a \frac{f(x)}{g(x)}\, dx$, where $x > 4$, by expressing $\frac{f(x)}{g(x)}$ as partial fractions.

Q6 Show that $\int_0^{\frac{2}{3}} \frac{-(t + 3)}{(3t + 2)(t + 1)}\, dt = 2\ln\tfrac{5}{3} - \tfrac{7}{3}\ln 2$.

Q7 $\frac{18x^2 + 3x - 8}{(2x + 1)(3x - 1)} \equiv A + \frac{B}{(2x + 1)} + \frac{C}{(3x - 1)}$

a) Find the values of the constants A, B and C.

b) Hence show that the exact value of

$$\int_2^5 \frac{18x^2 + 3x - 8}{(2x + 1)(3x - 1)}\, dx = p + \ln q,$$

giving the values of the constants p and q.

Q7 Hint: This is an improper fraction (the degree of the numerator is the same as the degree of the denominator) — this is why it has a whole number, A, as well as the fractions. Have a look at p.6-7 if you need a reminder of how to deal with these.

Chapter 5 Integration 1

4. Integration of Trigonometric Functions

There are a few trig functions which are really easy to integrate — once you've learnt them, you'll be able to integrate loads of complicated-looking trig functions quickly.

Learning Objectives:

- Be able to integrate functions of sin x, cos x and sec^2 x.

- Be able to integrate other trig functions by considering the derivatives of cosec x, sec x and cot x.

Integration of sin x and cos x

You learnt how to differentiate sin x and cos x in C3 — you should remember that sin x differentiates to cos x, and cos x differentiates to –sin x.

Working backwards from this, we get:

$$\int \sin x \, dx = -\cos x + C$$
$$\int \cos x \, dx = \sin x + C$$

Examples

Find the following integrals:

a) $\int 4 \cos x \, dx$

$\int \cos x \, dx = \sin x + C$

$$\int 4 \cos x \, dx = 4 \int \cos x \, dx = \boxed{4 \sin x + C}$$

b) $\int_0^\pi \frac{\sin x}{2} + \frac{1}{\pi} \, dx$

- Integrate each term separately:

  Don't forget the minus sign.

  $$\int_0^\pi \frac{\sin x}{2} + \frac{1}{\pi} \, dx = \int_0^\pi \frac{1}{2}\sin x + \frac{1}{\pi} \, dx = \left[\frac{1}{2}(-\cos x) + \frac{1}{\pi}x \right]_0^\pi$$

  $$= \left[-\frac{1}{2}\cos x + \frac{1}{\pi}x \right]_0^\pi$$

- Put in the limits:

  $$\left[-\frac{1}{2}\cos x + \frac{1}{\pi}x \right]_0^\pi = \left[-\frac{1}{2}\cos \pi + \left(\frac{1}{\pi} \times \pi \right) \right] - \left[-\frac{1}{2}\cos 0 + \left(\frac{1}{\pi} \times 0 \right) \right]$$

  $$= \left[-\frac{1}{2}(-1) + 1 \right] - \left[-\frac{1}{2}(1) + 0 \right]$$

  $$= \left[\frac{1}{2} + 1 \right] - \left[-\frac{1}{2} + 0 \right] = \boxed{2}$$

c) $\int \frac{1}{2}(\cos x + 2\sin x) \, dx$

Multiply out and integrate each term separately:

$$\int \frac{1}{2}(\cos x + 2\sin x) \, dx = \int \frac{1}{2}\cos x + \sin x \, dx$$

$$= \frac{1}{2}\sin x + (-\cos x) + C$$

$$= \boxed{\frac{1}{2}\sin x - \cos x + C}$$

You can integrate **linear transformations** of sin x and cos x of the form sin$(ax + b)$ and cos $(ax + b)$.

- Differentiating sin$(ax + b)$ using the **chain rule** gives:

$$a\cos(ax + b)$$

- So when **integrating** cos$(ax + b)$, you need to divide by a, giving:

$$\frac{1}{a}\sin(ax + b).$$

The same can be done when integrating sin $(ax + b)$, so we get:

$$\int \sin(ax + b)\,dx = -\frac{1}{a}\cos(ax + b) + C$$
$$\int \cos(ax + b)\,dx = \frac{1}{a}\sin(ax + b) + C$$

Example

Find $\int \sin(1 - 6x)\,dx.$

Using the general formula with $a = -6$ and $b = 1$ gives:

$$\int \sin(1 - 6x)\,dx = \frac{1}{-6} \times -\cos(1 - 6x) + C$$
$$= \frac{1}{6}\cos(1 - 6x) + C$$

Tip: You could also do this by noticing that differentiating cos $(1 - 6x)$ with the chain rule gives $6\sin(1 - 6x)$, so

$$\int \sin(1 - 6x)\,dx$$
$$= \frac{1}{6}\cos(1 - 6x) + C$$

Exercise 4.1

Q1 Integrate the following functions with respect to x.

 a) $\frac{1}{7}\cos x$ b) $-3\sin x$ c) $-3\cos x - 3\sin x$

 d) $\sin 5x$ e) $\cos\left(\frac{x}{7}\right)$ f) $2\sin(-3x)$

 g) $5\cos\left(3x + \frac{\pi}{5}\right)$ h) $-4\sin\left(4x - \frac{\pi}{3}\right)$ i) $\cos(4x + 3) + \sin(3 - 4x)$

Q2 Integrate $\frac{1}{2}\cos 3\theta - \sin\theta$ with respect to θ.

Q3 Evaluate the following definite integrals:

 a) $\int_{0}^{\frac{\pi}{2}} \sin x\,dx$ b) $\int_{\frac{\pi}{6}}^{\frac{\pi}{3}} \sin 3x\,dx$ c) $\int_{-1}^{2} 3\sin(\pi x + \pi)\,dx$

Q4 Find an expression for the area between the curve $y = 2\pi\cos\left(\frac{\pi x}{2}\right)$ and the x-axis for $1 \le x \le 2$. State whether or not this area lies above the x-axis, justifying your answer.

Q5 Show that $\int_{\frac{\pi}{3}}^{\frac{\pi}{2}} \sin(-x) + \cos(-x)\,dx = \frac{1 - \sqrt{3}}{2}$.

Q6 Show that the area of the region bounded by the x-axis and the curve with equation $y = 5\cos\frac{x}{6}$, where $-2\pi \le x \le \pi$, is $15(1 + \sqrt{3})$.

Integration of sec² x

Another trigonometric function which is easy to integrate is the derivative of $\tan x$, **sec² x**. Since $\tan x$ differentiates to $\sec^2 x$, you get:

$$\int \sec^2 x \, dx = \tan x + C$$

Tip: This integral is given in the formula book — it's given as

$$\int \sec^2 kx \, dx = \frac{1}{k} \tan kx + C.$$

Example 1

Find $\int 2 \sec^2 x + 4x \, dx$.

Integrate each term separately.

$$\int 2 \sec^2 x + 4x \, dx = 2 \int \sec^2 x \, dx + \int 4x \, dx = \boxed{2 \tan x + 2x^2 + C}$$

Unsurprisingly, you can use the chain rule in reverse again to integrate functions of the form $\sec^2(ax + b)$:

$$\int \sec^2(ax + b) \, dx = \frac{1}{a} \tan(ax + b) + C$$

Example 2

Find $\int \cos 4x - 2\sin 2x + \sec^2\left(\frac{1}{2}x\right) dx$.

Integrate each term separately using the results from above and p. 73-74:

$$\int \sec^2\left(\tfrac{1}{2}x\right) dx = \frac{1}{\left(\frac{1}{2}\right)} \tan\left(\tfrac{1}{2}x\right) = 2\tan\left(\tfrac{1}{2}x\right)$$

$$\int \cos 4x \, dx = \frac{1}{4}\sin 4x$$

$$\int \cos 4x - 2\sin 2x + \sec^2\left(\tfrac{1}{2}x\right) dx = \boxed{\frac{1}{4}\sin 4x + \cos 2x + 2\tan\left(\tfrac{1}{2}x\right) + C}$$

$$\int -2\sin 2x \, dx = -2\left(-\tfrac{1}{2}\cos 2x\right) = \cos 2x$$

Exercise 4.2

Q1 Find the following integrals:

a) $\int 2\sec^2 x + 1 \, dx$ b) $\int \sec^2 9x \, dx$ c) $\int 20\sec^2 3y \, dy$

d) $\int \sec^2 \frac{x}{7} \, dx$ e) $\int_0^{\frac{\pi}{3}} -\frac{1}{\cos^2\theta} \, d\theta$ f) $\int_0^{\frac{\pi}{4}} 3\sec^2(-3x) \, dx$

Q2 Find the area of the region bounded by the x-axis, the curve with equation $y = \sec^2 x$, and the lines $x = \frac{2}{3}\pi$ and $x = \pi$.

Q3 Integrate $\sec^2(x + \alpha) + \sec^2(3x + \beta)$ with respect to x, where α and β are constants.

Q4 Let A be a constant. Integrate $5A\sec^2\left(\frac{\pi}{3} - 2\theta\right)$ with respect to θ between the limits of $\theta = \frac{\pi}{12}$ and $\theta = \frac{\pi}{6}$.

Integration of other trigonometric functions

There are some other more complicated trig functions which are really easy to integrate. They are the **derivatives** of the functions **cosec x**, **sec x** and **cot x**.

You may remember these derivatives from C3, but here's a recap:

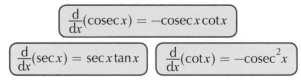

$$\frac{d}{dx}(\operatorname{cosec} x) = -\operatorname{cosec} x \cot x$$

$$\frac{d}{dx}(\sec x) = \sec x \tan x \qquad \frac{d}{dx}(\cot x) = -\operatorname{cosec}^2 x$$

Reversing the differentiation gives the following three integrals. They'll be really useful when integrating complicated trig functions.

$$\int \operatorname{cosec} x \cot x \, dx = -\operatorname{cosec} x + C$$

$$\int \sec x \tan x \, dx = \sec x + C$$

$$\int \operatorname{cosec}^2 x \, dx = -\cot x + C$$

As always, you can integrate **linear transformations** of these functions (functions of the form **cosec$(ax + b)$cot$(ax + b)$, sec$(ax + b)$tan$(ax + b)$** and **cosec²$(ax + b)$**) by **dividing** by the coefficient of x.

Tip: The $ax + b$ bit has to be the same in each trig function — e.g. you couldn't integrate sec x tan $3x$ using these formulas.

$$\int \operatorname{cosec}(ax + b)\cot(ax + b) \, dx = -\frac{1}{a}\operatorname{cosec}(ax + b) + C$$

$$\int \sec(ax + b)\tan(ax + b) \, dx = \frac{1}{a}\sec(ax + b) + C$$

$$\int \operatorname{cosec}^2(ax + b) \, dx = -\frac{1}{a}\cot(ax + b) + C$$

Examples

Find the following:

a) $\int 2 \sec x \tan x \, dx$

Take the constant outside the integral.

$$\int 2 \sec x \tan x \, dx = 2 \int \sec x \tan x \, dx = 2(\sec x + c) = \boxed{2 \sec x + C}$$

b) $\int_0^\pi \operatorname{cosec}^2\left(\frac{x}{2} - \frac{\pi}{4}\right) dx$

This is a definite integral, so you need to evaluate between the limits.

$$\int_0^\pi \operatorname{cosec}^2\left(\frac{x}{2} - \frac{\pi}{4}\right) dx = \left[-\frac{1}{\left(\frac{1}{2}\right)}\cot\left(\frac{x}{2} - \frac{\pi}{4}\right)\right]_0^\pi$$

Divide by the coefficient of x.

$\cot x = \dfrac{1}{\tan x}$

$$= -2\left[\cot\left(\frac{x}{2} - \frac{\pi}{4}\right)\right]_0^\pi = -2\left[\frac{1}{\tan\left(\frac{x}{2} - \frac{\pi}{4}\right)}\right]_0^\pi$$

Put in the limits.

$$= -2\left(\frac{1}{\tan\left(\frac{\pi}{2} - \frac{\pi}{4}\right)} - \frac{1}{\tan\left(0 - \frac{\pi}{4}\right)}\right)$$

$$= -2\left(\frac{1}{\tan\left(\frac{\pi}{4}\right)} - \frac{1}{\tan\left(-\frac{\pi}{4}\right)}\right) = -2\left(\frac{1}{1} - \frac{1}{(-1)}\right) = \boxed{-4}$$

c) $\int 8\cosec(2x+1)\cot(2x+1)\,dx$ Take the constant
outside the integral.

$$\int 8\cosec(2x+1)\cot(2x+1)\,dx = 8\int \cosec(2x+1)\cot(2x+1)\,dx$$

$$= 8\left(-\tfrac{1}{2}\cosec(2x+1)+c\right)$$

Don't forget to **divide** by the x coefficient.

$$= -4\cosec(2x+1)+C$$

Example

Find $\int 10\sec 5x\tan 5x + \tfrac{1}{2}\cosec 3x\cot 3x - \cosec^2(6x+1)\,dx$.

- Integrate each bit in turn:

$$\int 10\sec 5x\tan 5x\,dx = 10\left(\tfrac{1}{5}\sec 5x\right)$$
$$= 2\sec 5x$$

Tip: These three integrals should really all have a constant of integration on the end, but we'll just add a combined constant of integration when we do the final integration.

$$\int \tfrac{1}{2}\cosec 3x\cot 3x\,dx = \tfrac{1}{2}\left(-\tfrac{1}{3}\cosec 3x\right)$$
$$= -\tfrac{1}{6}\cosec 3x$$

Don't forget the minus that comes from the integration.

$$\int -\cosec^2(6x+1)\,dx = -\left(-\tfrac{1}{6}\cot(6x+1)\right)$$
$$= \tfrac{1}{6}\cot(6x+1)$$

- Putting these terms together and adding the constant gives:

$$\int 10\sec 5x\tan 5x + \tfrac{1}{2}\cosec 3x\cot 3x - \cosec^2(6x+1)\,dx$$

$$= 2\sec 5x - \tfrac{1}{6}\cosec 3x + \tfrac{1}{6}\cot(6x+1)+C$$

Exercise 4.3

Q1 Find the following integrals:

a) $\int \cosec^2 11x\,dx$ b) $\int 5\sec 10\theta\tan 10\theta\,d\theta$

c) $\int -\cosec(x+17)\cot(x+17)\,dx$ d) $\int -3\cosec 3x\cot 3x\,dx$

e) $\int 13\sec\left(\tfrac{\pi}{4}-x\right)\tan\left(\tfrac{\pi}{4}-x\right)\,dx$

Q2 Find $\int 10\cosec^2\left(\alpha-\tfrac{x}{2}\right) - 60\sec(\alpha-6x)\tan(\alpha-6x)\,dx$

Q3 Integrate the function $6\sec 2x\tan 2x + 6\cosec 2x\cot 2x$ with respect to x between the limits of $x = \tfrac{\pi}{12}$ and $x = \tfrac{\pi}{8}$.

Q4 Find the area of the region bounded by $y = \cosec^2(3x)$, the x-axis and the lines $x = \tfrac{\pi}{12}$ and $x = \tfrac{\pi}{6}$.

5. Integration of $\dfrac{f'(x)}{f(x)}$

Learning Objectives:

- Be able to integrate functions of the form $\dfrac{f'(x)}{f(x)}$, including multiples of these functions.

- Be able to integrate functions of cosec, sec and cot.

Fractions in which the numerator is the derivative of the denominator are pretty easy to integrate too — there is a general formula which comes from the chain rule.

Integrating $\dfrac{f'(x)}{f(x)}$

- If you have a fraction that has a function of x as the numerator and a different function of x as the denominator, e.g. $\dfrac{x-2}{x^3+1}$, you'll probably struggle to integrate it.

- However, if you have a fraction where the **numerator** is the **derivative** of the **denominator**, e.g. $\dfrac{3x^2}{x^3+1}$, it integrates to give ln of the denominator.

- In general terms, this is written as:

$$\int \frac{f'(x)}{f(x)}\, dx = \ln|f(x)| + C$$

- This rule won't surprise you if you remember differentiating $\ln|f(x)|$ using the chain rule in C3 — the derivative with respect to x of $\ln|f(x)|$ is $\dfrac{f'(x)}{f(x)}$.

The hardest bit about integrations like this is recognising that the denominator differentiates to give the numerator — once you've spotted that you can just use the formula.

Examples

Integrate the following functions with respect to x.

a) $\dfrac{2x}{x^2+1}$

- Differentiate the denominator to see what it gives:

$$\frac{d}{dx}(x^2+1) = 2x \quad \longleftarrow \text{This is the **numerator**.}$$

- The numerator is the derivative of the denominator so use the formula:

$$\int \frac{2x}{x^2+1}\, dx = \ln|x^2+1| + C$$

b) $\dfrac{x(3x-4)}{x^3-2x^2-1}$

- Differentiate the denominator:

$$\frac{d}{dx}(x^3-2x^2-1) = 3x^2-4x = x(3x-4) \quad \longleftarrow \text{This is the **numerator**.}$$

- Use the formula:

$$\int \frac{x(3x-4)}{x^3-2x^2-1}\, dx = \ln|x^3-2x^2-1| + C$$

Tip: You should get used to spotting when the numerator is the derivative of the denominator — you won't have to differentiate the denominator every time. Sometimes you might need to expand out some brackets before you notice it.

They might make the numerator a **multiple** of the derivative of the denominator just to confuse things. When this happens, just put the multiple **in front** of the ln.

Examples

Find:

a) $\int \dfrac{8x^3 - 4}{x^4 - 2x}\,dx$

- Differentiating: $\dfrac{d}{dx}(x^4 - 2x) = 4x^3 - 2$

  and $8x^3 - 4 = 2(4x^3 - 2)$

- The numerator is $2 \times$ the derivative of the denominator, so

  $$\int \dfrac{8x^3 - 4}{x^4 - 2x}\,dx = 2\int \dfrac{4x^3 - 2}{x^4 - 2x}\,dx = \boxed{2\ln|x^4 - 2x| + C}$$

b) $\int \dfrac{3\sin 3x}{\cos 3x + 2}\,dx$

- Differentiating:

  $$\dfrac{d}{dx}(\cos 3x + 2) = -3\sin 3x$$

- The numerator is **minus** the derivative of the denominator, so

  $$\int \dfrac{3\sin 3x}{\cos 3x + 2}\,dx = -\int \dfrac{-3\sin 3x}{\cos 3x + 2}\,dx = -\ln|\cos 3x + 2| + C$$

- You can make the answer a lot neater by combining it all into **one logarithm** — a question might ask you to do this.

  $$= -\ln|\cos 3x + 2| - \ln k = \boxed{-\ln|k(\cos 3x + 2)|}$$

  The minus sign is just to avoid fractions in the logarithm.

  C is just a constant. We can express C as a logarithm — call it $-\ln k$, where k is a constant.

Tip: Any constant can be expressed as a logarithm because the range of the ln function is $f(x) \in \mathbb{R}$.

You can use this method to integrate **trig functions** by writing them as fractions:

- You might have noticed from part b) above that you can work out the integral of **tan x** using this method:

  $$\tan x = \dfrac{\sin x}{\cos x}, \text{ and } \dfrac{d}{dx}(\cos x) = -\sin x$$

- The numerator is **minus** the **derivative** of the **denominator**, so

  $$\int \tan x\,dx = \int \dfrac{\sin x}{\cos x}\,dx = -\ln|\cos x| + C$$

Tip: The integral of tan is given in the formula book as $\ln|\sec x|$. This is the same as $-\ln|\cos x|$ by the laws of logs.

There are some other **trig functions** that you can integrate in the same way. These integrals are given in the **formula booklet**, so you won't need to learn them — just how to use them.

Tip: As always, if you're integrating a linear transformation of any of these functions, of the form f(ax + b), then divide by a when you integrate.

$$\int \mathrm{cosec}\, x \, dx = -\ln|\mathrm{cosec}\, x + \cot x| + C$$
$$\int \sec x \, dx = \ln|\sec x + \tan x| + C$$
$$\int \cot x \, dx = \ln|\sin x| + C$$

You can check these results easily by using **differentiation** — differentiate the right-hand side of the results to get the left-hand sides. Remember that differentiating $\ln |f(x)|$ gives $\dfrac{f'(x)}{f(x)}$.

Examples

Find the following integrals:

a) $\int 2\sec x \, dx$

Use the result for sec x above.
There is a constant of 2 so put that at the front.

$$\int 2\sec x \, dx = \boxed{2\ln|\sec x + \tan x| + C}$$

b) $\int \dfrac{\cot x}{5} \, dx$

Use the result for cot x above.
$\dfrac{\cot x}{5} = \dfrac{1}{5}\cot x$ so there is a constant of $\dfrac{1}{5}$ — put that at the front.

$$\int \dfrac{\cot x}{5} \, dx = \boxed{\dfrac{1}{5}\ln|\sin x| + C}$$

c) $\int 2(\mathrm{cosec}\, x + \sec x) \, dx$

$$\int 2(\mathrm{cosec}\, x + \sec x) \, dx = \int 2\,\mathrm{cosec}\, x + 2\sec x \, dx$$
$$= -2\ln|\mathrm{cosec}\, x + \cot x| + 2\ln|\sec x + \tan x| + C$$
$$= \boxed{2\ln\left|\dfrac{\sec x + \tan x}{\mathrm{cosec}\, x + \cot x}\right| + C}$$

Use log laws to simplify.

d) $\int \frac{1}{2} \operatorname{cosec} 2x \, dx.$

You can just use the result on the previous page — so all you have to do is work out what happens to the coefficient of x. The coefficient of x is 2, so divide by 2 when you integrate:

$$\int \frac{1}{2} \operatorname{cosec} 2x \, dx = -\frac{1}{4} \ln |\operatorname{cosec} 2x + \cot 2x| + C$$

Divide $\frac{1}{2}$ by 2.

Tip: Check this by differentiating (using the chain rule with $u = \operatorname{cosec} 2x + \cot 2x$).

Exercise 5.1

Q1 Find the following integrals:

a) $\int \frac{4x^3}{x^4 - 1} \, dx$

b) $\int \frac{2x - 1}{x^2 - x} \, dx$

c) $\int \frac{x^4}{3x^5 + 6} \, dx$

d) $\int \frac{12x^3 + 18x^2 - 3}{x^4 + 2x^3 - x} \, dx$

e) $\int \frac{e^x}{e^x + 6} \, dx$

f) $\int \frac{2(e^{2x} + 3e^x)}{e^{2x} + 6e^x} \, dx$

g) $\int \frac{e^x}{3(e^x + 3)} \, dx$

h) $\int \frac{2 \cos 2x}{1 + \sin 2x} \, dx$

i) $\int \frac{\sin 3x}{\cos 3x - 1} \, dx$

j) $\int \frac{3 \operatorname{cosec} x \cot x + 6x}{\operatorname{cosec} x - x^2 + 4} \, dx$

k) $\int \frac{\sec^2 x}{\tan x} \, dx$

l) $\int \frac{\sec x \tan x}{\sec x + 5} \, dx$

Q2 Show that $\int \frac{4 \cos(2x + 7)}{\sin(2x + 7)} \, dx = 2 \ln |k \sin(2x + 7)|$

Q3 Prove that:

a) $\int \sec x \, dx = \ln |\sec x + \tan x| + C$

b) $\int \operatorname{cosec} x \, dx = -\ln |\operatorname{cosec} x + \cot x| + C$

Q3 Hint: Try multiplying the bit inside the integral by $\frac{\sec x + \tan x}{\sec x + \tan x}$ in part a) — there's a similar trick for part b) as well.

Q4 Find the following integrals:

a) $\int 2 \tan x \, dx$

b) $\int \tan 2x \, dx$

c) $\int 4 \operatorname{cosec} x \, dx$

d) $\int \cot 3x \, dx$

e) $\int \frac{1}{2} \sec 2x \, dx$

f) $\int 3 \operatorname{cosec} 6x \, dx$

Q5 Find $\int \frac{\sec^2 x}{2 \tan x} - 4 \sec 2x \tan 2x + \frac{\operatorname{cosec} 2x \cot 2x - 1}{\operatorname{cosec} 2x + 2x} \, dx$

6. Integrating $\dfrac{du}{dx}$ f′(u)

Learning Objectives:

- Be able to integrate products of the form $\dfrac{du}{dx}$ f′(u) using the chain rule in reverse.
- Know and be able to use a result for integrating products of the form f′(x)[f(x)]^n.

This section will show you how to integrate certain products of functions. You can use the chain rule in reverse to integrate special products of functions and their derivatives.

Integrating using the reverse of the chain rule

In C3, you saw the chain rule for differentiating a **function of a function**.

- Here it is in the form it was given in C3:

  > If $y =$ f(u) and $u =$ g(x)
  > then:
  > $$\frac{dy}{dx} = \frac{dy}{du} \times \frac{du}{dx}$$

- Since integration is the opposite of differentiation, you have:

  $$y \xrightarrow{\text{Differentiation}} \frac{dy}{du} \times \frac{du}{dx}$$

  $$y + C \xleftarrow{\text{Integration}} \frac{dy}{du} \times \frac{du}{dx}$$

- So $\displaystyle\int \frac{dy}{du} \times \frac{du}{dx}\, dx = y + C$.

- Writing f(u) instead of y and f′(u) instead of $\dfrac{dy}{du}$ gives:

  $$\int \frac{du}{dx} \text{f}′(u)\, dx = \text{f}(u) + C$$

Tip: To evaluate integrals like this you have to integrate with respect to u (because f′(u) is $\dfrac{dy}{du}$).

If you're integrating an expression which contains a **function of a function**, f(u), try differentiating the function u. If the **derivative** of u is also part of the expression, you might be able to use the formula above.

This result's a bit more difficult to grasp — but after a few examples it should make complete sense.

Example

a) **Differentiate $y = \text{e}^{2x^2}$ using the chain rule.**

Let $u = 2x^2$, then $y = \text{e}^u$. By the chain rule,

$$\frac{dy}{dx} = \frac{dy}{du} \times \frac{du}{dx} = \text{e}^u \times 4x = \text{e}^{2x^2} \times 4x = \boxed{4x\text{e}^{2x^2}}$$

b) Find $\int 4x e^{2x^2}\, dx$ using your answer to part a).

Look for the bit that would have been u in the chain rule — here it's $2x^2$.

$$\frac{du}{dx} \quad f'(u) \quad f(u)$$

$$\int 4x\, e^{2x^2}\, dx = e^{2x^2} + C$$

Examples

Find the following integrals:

a) $\int 6x^5 e^{x^6}\, dx$

- Here, $u = x^6$ — it appears once differentiated ($\mathbf{6x^5}$) and once within a function (e^{x^6}).

- Split the integral into $\frac{du}{dx}$ and $f'(u)$: $\int 6x^5 e^{x^6}\, dx$

$$\frac{du}{dx} \qquad f'(u)$$

- Now use the formula $\int \frac{du}{dx} f'(u)\, dx = f(u) + C$ to write down the result.

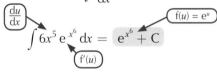

$$\int 6x^5 e^{x^6}\, dx = e^{x^6} + C$$

with labels: $\frac{du}{dx}$, $f(u) = e^u$, $f'(u)$

Tip: You might need to take a constant outside of the integral to get it in the form $\int \frac{du}{dx} f'(u)\, dx$. There's an example of this is part c).

b) $\int e^{\sin x} \cos x\, dx$

- Here, $u = \sin x$.

- Write $\frac{du}{dx}$ and $f'(u)$: $\qquad \frac{du}{dx} = \cos x \quad$ and $\quad f'(u) = e^{\sin x}$

- Use the formula to write down the result.

$$\int e^{\sin x} \cos x\, dx = e^{\sin x} + C$$

with labels: $\frac{du}{dx}$, $f'(u)$, $f(u) = e^u$

c) $\int x^4 \sin(x^5)\, dx$

- Here, $u = x^5$.
- You'll need to take out a constant to get the integral you want.

$$\int x^4 \sin(x^5)\, dx = \frac{1}{5} \int 5x^4 \sin(x^5)\, dx$$

- Now split up the integral: $\quad \frac{du}{dx} = 5x^4 \quad$ and $\quad f'(u) = \sin(x^5)$

- Use the formula.

$$\frac{1}{5} \int 5x^4 \sin(x^5)\, dx = \frac{1}{5}(-\cos(x^5) + c) = -\frac{1}{5}\cos(x^5) + C$$

with labels: $\frac{du}{dx}$, $f'(u)$, $f(u) = -\cos u$

Find the following integrals:

Q1 $\displaystyle\int 2x e^{x^2}\,dx$

Q2 $\displaystyle\int 6x^2 e^{2x^3}\,dx$

Q3 $\displaystyle\int \frac{1}{2\sqrt{x}} e^{\sqrt{x}}\,dx$

Q4 $\displaystyle\int x^3 e^{x^4}\,dx$

Q5 $\displaystyle\int (4x-1) e^{(x^2-\frac{1}{2}x)}\,dx$

Q6 $\displaystyle\int 2x \sin(x^2+1)\,dx$

Q7 $\displaystyle\int x^3 \cos(x^4)\,dx$

Q8 $\displaystyle\int x \sec^2(x^2)\,dx$

Q9 $\displaystyle\int e^{\cos x} \sin x\,dx$

Q10 $\displaystyle\int \cos 2x\, e^{\sin 2x}\,dx$

Q11 $\displaystyle\int \sec^2 x\, e^{\tan x}\,dx$

Q12 $\displaystyle\int \sec x \tan x\, e^{\sec x}\,dx$

Integrating f'(x) × [f(x)]ⁿ

Some products are made up of a **function** and its **derivative**:

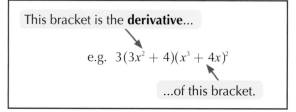

This bracket is the **derivative**...

e.g. $3(3x^2+4)(x^3+4x)^2$

...of this bracket.

If you spot that part of a product is the **derivative** of the other part of it (which is raised to a **power**), you can integrate it using this rule (which is just a special case of the 'reverse chain rule' on p.82):

Tip: To get this formula, rewrite the 'reverse chain rule' on p.82, replacing the function 'u' with 'f(x)' and the function 'f(u)' with '$[f(x)]^{n+1}$'.

Then $\dfrac{du}{dx}$ will be replaced with f'(x) and f'(u) will be replaced with $(n+1)[f(x)]^n$.

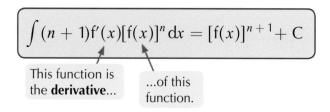

$$\int (n+1)f'(x)[f(x)]^n\,dx = [f(x)]^{n+1} + C$$

This function is the **derivative**...

...of this function.

Remember that this result needs you to have a multiple of $n+1$ (not n) — you can check this by **differentiating** the right-hand side using the **chain rule**.

Watch out for any other multiples too — you might have to **multiply** or **divide** by a **constant**.

This will probably make more sense if you have a look at some examples:

Evaluate the following integrals:

a) $\int 12x^3(2x^4 - 5)^2 \, dx$

- Here, $f(x) = 2x^4 - 5$, so $f'(x) = 8x^3$.
  $n = 2$, so $n + 1 = 3$.

  So $\int (n + 1)f'(x)[f(x)]^n \, dx = [f(x)]^{n+1} + C$
  $\Rightarrow \int 3(8x^3)(2x^4 - 5)^2 \, dx = \int 24x^3(2x^4 - 5)^2 \, dx = (2x^4 - 5)^3 + c$

- Divide everything by **2** to match the original integral:
  $$\int 12x^3(2x^4 - 5)^2 \, dx = \frac{1}{2}(2x^4 - 5)^3 + C$$

b) $\int 8\cosec^2x \cot^3x \, dx$

- For this one, $f(x) = \cot x$, so $f'(x) = -\cosec^2x$.
  $n = 3$, so $n + 1 = 4$.

  So $\int (n + 1)f'(x)[f(x)]^n \, dx = [f(x)]^{n+1} + c$
  $\Rightarrow \int -4\cosec^2x \cot^3x \, dx = \cot^4x + c$

- Multiply everything by **–2** to match the original integral:
  $$\int 8\cosec^2x \cot^3x \, dx = -2\cot^4x + C$$

Tip: This one looks pretty horrific, but it isn't too bad once you spot that $-\cosec^2x$ is the derivative of $\cot x$.

c) $\int (x - 2)\sqrt{x^2 - 4x + 5} \, dx$

- You can write the square root as a **fractional power**:
  $$\int (x - 2)\sqrt{x^2 - 4x + 5} \, dx = \int (x - 2)(x^2 - 4x + 5)^{\frac{1}{2}} \, dx$$

- Now, $f(x) = x^2 - 4x + 5$, so $f'(x) = 2x - 4$.
  $n = \frac{1}{2}$, so $n + 1 = \frac{3}{2}$.

  So $\int (n + 1)f'(x)[f(x)]^n \, dx = [f(x)]^{n+1} + c$
  $\Rightarrow \int \frac{3}{2}(2x - 4)(x^2 - 4x + 5)^{\frac{1}{2}} \, dx = (x^2 - 4x + 5)^{\frac{3}{2}} + c$

- $\frac{3}{2}(2x - 4) = 3(x - 2)$, so you need to divide everything by **3** to match the original integral:
  $$\int (x - 2)\sqrt{x^2 - 4x + 5} \, dx = \frac{1}{3}(x^2 - 4x + 5)^{\frac{3}{2}} + C$$

d) $\int \dfrac{\cos x}{\sin^4 x}\, dx$

- Write $\dfrac{1}{\sin^4 x}$ as a negative power.

$$\int \frac{\cos x}{\sin^4 x}\, dx = \int \frac{\cos x}{(\sin x)^4}\, dx = \int \cos x (\sin x)^{-4}\, dx$$

- Now, **f(x) = sin x**, so f′(x) = cos x.
  $n = -4$, so $n + 1 = -3$.

  So $\int (n + 1) f'(x)[f(x)]^n\, dx = [f(x)]^{n+1} + c$

  $\Rightarrow \int - 3\cos x(\sin x)^{-4}\, dx = (\sin x)^{-3} + c$

  $\Rightarrow \int \dfrac{-3\cos x}{\sin^4 x}\, dx = \dfrac{1}{\sin^3 x} + c$

- Divide everything by **−3** to match the original integral:

$$\int \frac{\cos x}{\sin^4 x}\, dx = \boxed{- \frac{1}{3\sin^3 x} + C}$$

Exercise 6.2

Q1 Find the following indefinite integrals:

a) $\int 6x(x^2 + 5)^2\, dx$

b) $\int (2x + 7)(x^2 + 7x)^4\, dx$

c) $\int (x^3 + 2x)(x^4 + 4x^2)^3\, dx$

d) $\int \dfrac{2x}{(x^2 - 1)^3}\, dx$

e) $\int \dfrac{6e^{3x}}{(e^{3x} - 5)^2}\, dx$

f) $\int \sin x \cos^5 x\, dx$

g) $\int 2\sec^2 x \tan^3 x\, dx$

h) $\int 3e^x (e^x + 4)^2\, dx$

i) $\int 32(2e^{4x} - 3x)(e^{4x} - 3x^2)^7\, dx$

j) $\int \dfrac{\cos x}{(2 + \sin x)^4}\, dx$

k) $\int 5\cosec x \cot x \cosec^4 x\, dx$

l) $\int 2\cosec^2 x \cot^3 x\, dx$

Q1-2 Hint: You'll need the derivatives of cosec, sec and cot:

$\dfrac{d}{dx}(\cosec x) = -\cosec x \cot x$

$\dfrac{d}{dx}(\sec x) = \sec x \tan x$

$\dfrac{d}{dx}(\cot x) = -\cosec^2 x$

Q2 Find the following integrals:

a) $\int 6\tan x \sec^6 x\, dx$

b) $\int \cot x \cosec^3 x\, dx$

Q3 Integrate the following functions with respect to x:

a) $4\cos x\, e^{\sin x}(e^{\sin x} - 5)^3$

b) $(\sin x\, e^{\cos x} - 4)(e^{\cos x} + 4x)^6$

Q4 Integrate:

a) $\int \dfrac{\sec^2 x}{\tan^4 x}\, dx$

b) $\int \cot x \cosec x \sqrt{\cosec x}\, dx$

7. Using Trigonometric Identities in Integration

You can sometimes use the trig identities that you learnt in C3 to manipulate difficult-looking trig integrations to give functions you know how to integrate.

Learning Objective:

- Be able to use the double angle formulas for sin, cos and tan alongside the methods learnt throughout this chapter to simplify difficult trig integrals.

Integrating using the double angle formulas

If you're given a tricky **trig function** to integrate, you might be able to simplify it using one of the **double angle formulas**. They're especially useful for things like $\cos^2 x$, $\sin^2 x$ and $\sin x \cos x$. Here are the double angle formulas from C3:

$$\sin 2x \equiv 2\sin x \cos x \qquad \cos 2x \equiv \cos^2 x - \sin^2 x$$

$$\tan 2x \equiv \frac{2\tan x}{1 - \tan^2 x}$$

In C3, you might have come across two other ways of writing the double angle formula for cos, which come from using the identity $\sin^2 x + \cos^2 x \equiv 1$:

$$\cos 2x \equiv 2\cos^2 x - 1 \qquad \cos 2x \equiv 1 - 2\sin^2 x$$

Once you've rearranged the original function using one of the **double angle formulas**, the function you're left with should be easier to integrate using the rules you've seen in this chapter.

Examples

Find the following:

a) $\int \sin^2 x \, dx$

- Rearranging the **cos** double angle formula: $\cos 2x \equiv 1 - 2\sin^2 x$
  gives $\sin^2 x \equiv \frac{1}{2}(1 - \cos 2x)$.

- So rewrite the integration:

$$\int \sin^2 x \, dx = \int \frac{1}{2}(1 - \cos 2x)dx = \frac{1}{2}\int (1 - \cos 2x)dx$$
$$= \frac{1}{2}\left(x - \frac{1}{2}\sin 2x\right) + C = \frac{1}{2}x - \frac{1}{4}\sin 2x + C$$

Tip: Use one of the cos double angle formulas when you've got a $\cos^2 x$ or a $\sin^2 x$ to integrate.

b) $\int \cos^2 5x \, dx$

- Rearranging the **cos** double angle formula: $\cos 2x \equiv 2\cos^2 x - 1$

  gives $\cos^2 x \equiv \frac{1}{2}(\cos 2x + 1)$.

Don't forget to double the x coefficient and to divide by 10 when you integrate.

- So rewrite the integration:

$$\int \cos^2 5x \, dx = \int \frac{1}{2}(\cos 10x + 1)dx = \frac{1}{2}\int (\cos 10x + 1)dx$$

$$= \frac{1}{2}\left(\frac{1}{10}\sin 10x + x\right) + C = \boxed{\frac{1}{20}\sin 10x + \frac{1}{2}x + C}$$

Tip: For a reminder on integrating $\sin x$ and $\cos x$ (and linear transformations of them) see pages 73-74.

Examples

Find the following integrals:

a) $\int \sin x \cos x \, dx$

Tip: If you need to integrate a function of the form $\sin x \cos x$, use the double angle formula for sin.

- Rearranging the **sin** double angle formula: $\sin 2x \equiv 2\sin x \cos x$

  gives $\sin x \cos x \equiv \frac{1}{2}\sin 2x$.

- So rewrite the integration:

$$\int \sin x \cos x \, dx = \int \frac{1}{2}\sin 2x \, dx = \frac{1}{2}\left(-\frac{1}{2}\cos 2x\right) + C = \boxed{-\frac{1}{4}\cos 2x + C}$$

b) $\int_0^{\frac{\pi}{4}} \sin 2x \cos 2x \, dx$

- Rearranging the **sin** double angle formula with x replaced with $2x$: $\sin 4x \equiv 2\sin 2x \cos 2x$

  gives $\sin 2x \cos 2x \equiv \frac{1}{2}\sin 4x$.

- So rewrite the integration:

Tip: Don't forget to 'double the angle' when using these formulas.

$$\int_0^{\frac{\pi}{4}} \sin 2x \cos 2x \, dx = \int_0^{\frac{\pi}{4}} \frac{1}{2}\sin 4x \, dx = \left[\frac{1}{2}\left(-\frac{1}{4}\cos 4x\right)\right]_0^{\frac{\pi}{4}} = -\frac{1}{8}[\cos 4x]_0^{\frac{\pi}{4}}$$

$$= -\frac{1}{8}\left(\left[\cos\frac{4\pi}{4}\right] - [\cos 0]\right) = \frac{1}{8}(\cos 0 - \cos \pi)$$

$$= \frac{1}{8}(1 - (-1)) = \frac{2}{8} = \boxed{\frac{1}{4}}$$

Example

Find $\int \dfrac{4\tan\frac{x}{2}}{1 - \tan^2\frac{x}{2}} \, dx$.

Tip: Remember the integral of $\tan x$ is $-\ln|\cos x| + C$ (which is the same as $\ln|\sec x| + C$ using the laws of logs). It comes from writing $\tan x = \frac{\sin x}{\cos x}$ (as shown on p.79).

- Rearrange, then use the double angle formula for **tan**:

$$\frac{4\tan\frac{x}{2}}{1 - \tan^2\frac{x}{2}} = 2\left(\frac{2\tan\frac{x}{2}}{1 - \tan^2\frac{x}{2}}\right) = 2\left(\tan\left(2 \times \frac{x}{2}\right)\right) = 2\tan x$$

- Rewrite the integration:

$$\int \frac{4\tan\frac{x}{2}}{1 - \tan^2\frac{x}{2}} \, dx = \int 2\tan x \, dx = \boxed{-2\ln|\cos x| + C}$$

Q1 Find the following indefinite integrals:

a) $\int \cos^2 x \, dx$

b) $\int 6 \sin x \cos x \, dx$

c) $\int \sin^2 6x \, dx$

d) $\int \dfrac{2 \tan 2x}{1 - \tan^2 2x} \, dx$

e) $\int 2 \sin 4x \cos 4x \, dx$

f) $\int 2 \cos^2 4x \, dx$

g) $\int \cos x \sin x \, dx$

h) $\int \sin 3x \cos 3x \, dx$

i) $\int \dfrac{6 \tan 3x}{1 - \tan^2 3x} \, dx$

j) $\int 5 \sin 2x \cos 2x \, dx$

k) $\int (\sin x + \cos x)^2 \, dx$

l) $\int 4 \sin x \cos x \cos 2x \, dx$

Q1 l) Hint: Use the sin double angle formula twice.

m) $\int (\cos x + \sin x)(\cos x - \sin x) \, dx$

n) $\int \sin^2 x \cot x \, dx$

Q2 Evaluate the following definite integrals:

a) $\int_0^{\frac{\pi}{4}} \sin^2 x \, dx$

b) $\int_0^{\pi} \cos^2 2x \, dx$

c) $\int_0^{\pi} \sin \frac{x}{2} \cos \frac{x}{2} \, dx$

d) $\int_{\frac{\pi}{4}}^{\frac{\pi}{2}} \sin^2 2x \, dx$

e) $\int_0^{\frac{\pi}{4}} \cos 2x \sin 2x \, dx$

f) $\int_{\frac{\pi}{4}}^{\frac{\pi}{2}} \sin^2 x - \cos^2 x \, dx$

Integrating using other trigonometric identities

- There are a couple of other **identities** you can use to simplify trig functions:

$$\sec^2 x \equiv 1 + \tan^2 x$$

$$\csc^2 x \equiv 1 + \cot^2 x$$

Tip: If you use one of these identities to get rid of a $\cot^2 x$ or a $\tan^2 x$, don't forget the stray 1s flying around — they'll just integrate to x.

- These identities are really useful if you have to integrate **tan²x** or **cot²x**, as you already know how to integrate $\sec^2 x$ and $\csc^2 x$ (see pages 75-76).

$$\int \sec^2 x \, dx = \tan x + C$$

$$\int \csc^2 x \, dx = -\cot x + C$$

Examples

Find the following integrals:

a) $\int \tan^2 x - 1 \, dx$

- Rewrite the function in terms of $\sec^2 x$: $\boxed{\sec^2 x \equiv 1 + \tan^2 x}$

$$\tan^2 x - 1 = (\sec^2 x - 1) - 1 = \sec^2 x - 2$$

- Now integrate:

$$\int \tan^2 x - 1 \, dx = \int \sec^2 x - 2 \, dx = \boxed{\tan x - 2x + C}$$

b) $\int \cot^2 3x \, dx$

- Get the function in terms of $\operatorname{cosec}^2 x$: $\boxed{\operatorname{cosec}^2 x \equiv 1 + \cot^2 x}$

$$\cot^2 3x = \operatorname{cosec}^2 3x - 1$$

- Remember to divide by 3, the coefficient of x, when you integrate:

$$\int \cot^2 3x \, dx = \int \operatorname{cosec}^2 3x - 1 \, dx = \boxed{-\frac{1}{3}\cot 3x - x + C}$$

c) $\int \cos^3 x \, dx$

- You don't know how to integrate $\cos^3 x$ but you can split it into $\cos^2 x$ and $\cos x$ and use identities.

$$\cos^3 x = \cos^2 x \cos x = (1 - \sin^2 x)\cos x$$
$$= \cos x - \cos x \sin^2 x$$
$$= \cos x - \cos x (\sin x)^2 \qquad \boxed{\sin^2 x + \cos^2 x \equiv 1}$$

- Now write out the integral:

$$\int \cos^3 x \, dx = \int \cos x - \cos x (\sin x)^2 \, dx$$
$$= \int \cos x \, dx - \int \cos x (\sin x)^2 \, dx$$

- The second integral is a product of a function (to a power) and its derivative so use the formula on p.84 with $f(x) = \sin x$, $f'(x) = \cos x$, $n = 2$ and $n + 1 = 3$:

$$\int 3\cos x \sin^2 x \, dx = \sin^3 x + c$$
$$\text{So } \int \cos x \sin^2 x \, dx = \frac{1}{3}\sin^3 x + c$$

- So the whole integral is:

$$\int \cos^3 x \, dx = \int \cos x \, dx - \int \cos x (\sin x)^2 \, dx$$
$$= \boxed{\sin x - \frac{1}{3}\sin^3 x + C}$$

Evaluate $\int_0^{\frac{\pi}{3}} 6\sin 3x \cos 3x + \tan^2 \frac{1}{2}x + 1 \, dx.$

- Using the **sin** double angle formula:
$$6\sin 3x \cos 3x \equiv 3\sin 6x$$

and using the identity for **tan² x**:
$$\tan^2 \frac{1}{2}x + 1 \equiv \sec^2 \frac{1}{2}x$$

- Now integrate:
$$\int_0^{\frac{\pi}{3}} 6\sin 3x \cos 3x + \tan^2 \frac{1}{2}x + 1 \, dx$$

$$= \int_0^{\frac{\pi}{3}} 3\sin 6x + \sec^2 \frac{1}{2}x \, dx = \left[-\frac{3}{6}\cos 6x + 2\tan \frac{1}{2}x \right]_0^{\frac{\pi}{3}}$$

$$= \left[-\frac{1}{2}\cos 6\left(\frac{\pi}{3}\right) + 2\tan \frac{1}{2}\left(\frac{\pi}{3}\right) \right] - \left[-\frac{1}{2}\cos 6(0) + 2\tan \frac{1}{2}(0) \right]$$

$$= \left[-\frac{1}{2}\cos(2\pi) + 2\tan \left(\frac{\pi}{6}\right) \right] - \left[-\frac{1}{2}\cos(0) + 2\tan(0) \right] \quad \text{Put in the limits.}$$

$$= \left[-\frac{1}{2}(1) + 2\left(\frac{1}{\sqrt{3}}\right) \right] - \left[-\frac{1}{2}(1) + 2(0) \right]$$

$$= -\frac{1}{2} + \frac{2}{\sqrt{3}} + \frac{1}{2}$$

$$= \frac{2}{\sqrt{3}} = \frac{2\sqrt{3}}{3} \quad \longleftarrow \quad \text{Rationalise the denominator.}$$

Exercise 7.2

Q1 Find the following integrals:
   a) $\int \cot^2 x - 4 \, dx$
   b) $\int \tan^2 x \, dx$
   c) $\int 3\cot^2 x \, dx$
   d) $\int \tan^2 4x \, dx$

Q2 Find the exact value of $\int_0^{\frac{\pi}{4}} \tan^2 x + \cos^2 x - \sin^2 x \, dx.$

Q3 Integrate the following functions with respect to x.
   a) $\tan^3 x + \tan^5 x$
   b) $\cot^5 x + \cot^3 x$
   c) $\sin^3 x$

> **Q3 Hint:** Factorise.

Find the integrals in Q4-7:

Q4 $\int (\sec x + \tan x)^2 \, dx$

Q5 $\int (\cot x + \csc x)^2 \, dx$

Q6 $\int 4 + \cot^2 3x \, dx$

Q7 $\int \cos^2 4x + \cot^2 4x \, dx$

Q8 a) Use the identity $\sin A + \sin B \equiv 2\sin\left(\frac{A+B}{2}\right)\cos\left(\frac{A-B}{2}\right)$
      to show that $2\sin 4x \cos x = \sin 5x + \sin 3x.$
   b) Hence find $\int 2\sin 4x \cos x \, dx$

> **Q8 Hint:** This is one of the 'factor formulas' which you learnt in C3. Like the double angle formulas, they are a consequence of the addition formulas.

Review Exercise — Chapter 5

Q1 a) Find $\int \dfrac{1}{\sqrt[3]{(2-11x)}}\,dx$

    b) Show that the area under the curve $y = \dfrac{1}{\sqrt[3]{(2-11x)}}$ between
$x = -\dfrac{62}{11}$ and $x = -\dfrac{123}{11}$ is $\dfrac{27}{22}$.

Q2 Find the equation of the curve that has the derivative $\dfrac{dy}{dx} = (1-7x)^{\frac{1}{2}}$
and goes through the point $(0,\,1)$.

Q3 Find the following integrals, giving your answers in terms of e or ln.

    a) $\displaystyle\int 4e^{2x}\,dx$ b) $\displaystyle\int e^{3x-5}\,dx$ c) $\displaystyle\int \dfrac{2}{3x}\,dx$ d) $\displaystyle\int \dfrac{2}{2x+1}\,dx$

Q4 If $\displaystyle\int \dfrac{8}{2-x} - \dfrac{8}{x}\,dx = \ln P + C$,

    where P is an expression in terms of x and C is a constant, find P.

Q5 Given that $\dfrac{3x+10}{(2x+3)(x-4)} \equiv \dfrac{A}{2x+3} + \dfrac{B}{x-4}$, find $\displaystyle\int \dfrac{3x+10}{(2x+3)(x-4)}\,dx$.

Q6 Given that $f(x) = \dfrac{-2x^2 + 12x + 31}{(x-3)^2(2x+1)} \equiv \dfrac{A}{(x-3)^2} + \dfrac{B}{(x-3)} + \dfrac{C}{(2x+1)}$, find $\displaystyle\int_4^9 f(x)\,dx$.

Q7 Find the following integrals (A and B are constants):

    a) $\displaystyle\int \cos(x+A)\,dx$ b) $\displaystyle\int \sin(A-x)\,dx$ c) $\displaystyle\int \cosec^2((A+B)t + A + B)\,dt$

Q8 Find the following integrals:

    a) $\displaystyle\int \cos 4x - \sec^2 7x\,dx$ b) $\displaystyle\int 6\sec 3x\tan 3x - \cosec^2\dfrac{x}{5}\,dx$.

Q9 Find the following integrals:

    a) $\displaystyle\int \dfrac{\cos x}{\sin x}\,dx$ b) $\displaystyle\int \dfrac{20x^4 + 12x^2 - 12}{x^5 + x^3 - 3x}\,dx$

Q10 Find the following integrals:

    a) $\displaystyle\int 3x^2 e^{x^3}\,dx$ b) $\displaystyle\int 2x\cos(x^2)e^{\sin(x^2)}\,dx$ c) $\displaystyle\int \sec 4x\tan 4x\,e^{\sec 4x}\,dx$

Q11 Use an appropriate trig identity to find $\displaystyle\int \dfrac{2\tan 3x}{1 - \tan^2 3x}\,dx$.

Exam-Style Questions — Chapter 5

1   Find

    a) $\int 3e^{(5-6x)}\,dx$.

    (2 marks)

    b) $\int \dfrac{\operatorname{cosec}^2 x - 2}{\cot x + 2x}\,dx$.

    (3 marks)

2   Use an appropriate identity to find $\int 2\cot^2 x\,dx$.

    (3 marks)

3   Use an appropriate identity to find $\int 2\tan^2 3x + 2\,dx$.

    (3 marks)

4    $f(x) = \dfrac{-8x^2 + x - 8}{(4x + 1)(1 - x)(x + 2)} \equiv \dfrac{A}{(4x + 1)} + \dfrac{B}{(1 - x)} + \dfrac{C}{(x + 2)}$

    a)   Find the values of the constants A, B and C.

    (4 marks)

    b)   (i)   Find $\int f(x)\,dx$.

    (4 marks)

        (ii)   Find the exact value of $\int_{-1}^{2} f(x)\,dx$ in the form $\ln \dfrac{p}{q}$ where p and q are integers.

    (3 marks)

5   The graph below shows part of a curve with equation $y = \dfrac{2}{3(\sqrt[3]{5x - 2})}$.

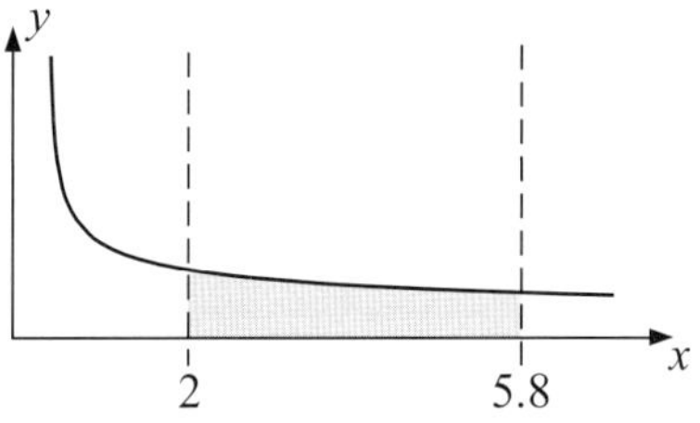

    Find, using integration, the area of the shaded region bounded by the curve, the x-axis, and the lines $x = 2$ and $x = 5.8$.

    (3 marks)

6    $f(x) = \dfrac{11x^2 + 42x + 36}{3x^3 + 16x^2 + 28x + 16}$

    a)   Express $f(x)$ in the form: $\dfrac{A}{(x + 2)^2} + \dfrac{B}{x + 2} + \dfrac{C}{3x + 4}$

    where A, B and C are all integers to be found.

    (4 marks)

    b)   Hence, or otherwise, find the integral of $f(x)$, with respect to x.

    (3 marks)

1. Integration by Substitution

Learning Objectives:

- Understand that integration by substitution is the reverse of differentiating using the chain rule.

- Use integration by substitution to integrate functions, including calculating definite integrals.

- Be able to integrate using substitutions that require trig identities.

There's a lot of integration in C4, and some of the integrals you'll come across look pretty nasty. So to start this chapter, there are a couple of really useful techniques you need to know which can make tricky-looking integrals easier to deal with. The first is integration by substitution.

Integration by substitution

You'll be familiar with using the **chain rule** to differentiate a **function of a function**. **Integration by substitution** is a way of **integrating** a function of a function by simplifying the integral. Like differentiating with the chain rule, to integrate by substitution you have to write part of the function in terms of u, where u is some **function** of x.

Here's the method:

- You'll be given an integral that's made up of **two functions of x**.
- **Substitute** u for one of the functions of x to give a function that's **easier to integrate**.
- Next, find $\dfrac{du}{dx}$, and **rewrite** it so that dx is on its own.
- **Rewrite** the original integral in terms of u and du.
- You should now be left with something that's **easier to integrate** — just **integrate** as normal, then at the last step **replace** u with the **original substitution**.

Tip: You might have to do a bit of rearranging to get u in terms of x.

Tip: You'll normally be told what substitution to use (unless it's a really easy one).

Tip: This integral is of the form $f'(x) \times [f(x)]^n$ (p.84-86). You could use the rule you learnt back there for this kind of integral, but you've been asked to do it by substitution.

Example 1

Use the substitution $u = x^2 - 2$ to find $\displaystyle\int 4x(x^2 - 2)^4 \, dx$.

- Start by differentiating u with respect to x:

$$u = x^2 - 2 \implies \frac{du}{dx} = 2x$$

- Now rearrange the equation for $\dfrac{du}{dx}$ to get dx on its own:

$$\frac{du}{dx} = 2x \implies du = 2x \, dx$$

$$\implies dx = \frac{1}{2x} du$$

$\dfrac{du}{dx}$ isn't really a fraction, but you can treat it like one for this bit.

- Substitute what you've got so far back into the original expression:

$$\int 4x(x^2 - 2)^4\, dx = \int 4xu^4 \frac{1}{2x} du = \int 2u^4 du$$

> The remaining x's cancel.

- Now you've got a much simpler expression to integrate with respect to u:

$$\int 2u^4 du = \frac{2}{5}u^5 + C$$

- And finally, substitute $u = x^2 - 2$ back in:

$$= \frac{2}{5}(x^2 - 2)^5 + C$$

That first example worked out nicely, because the x's **cancelled out** when you substituted in the expressions for **u** and **dx**. It isn't always quite so straightforward — sometimes you need to get rid of some x's by **rearranging** the equation for u.

Example 2

Find $\int x(3x + 2)^3\, dx$, using the substitution $u = 3x + 2$.

Tip: The expression in brackets is often the thing you substitute.

- Start by finding $\frac{du}{dx}$ and then rearrange to get dx on its own:

$$u = 3x + 2 \implies \frac{du}{dx} = 3 \implies dx = \frac{1}{3}du$$

Tip: Note that this integral cannot be done using methods from Chapter 5.

- If you substitute for u and dx, you end up with an x still in the integral:

$$\int x(3x + 2)^3\, dx = \int xu^3 \frac{1}{3}du$$

- To get rid of that x, you have to rearrange the equation for u:

$$u = 3x + 2 \implies x = \frac{u - 2}{3}$$

- So $\int x(3x + 2)^3\, dx$

$$\begin{aligned}
&= \int \left(\frac{u - 2}{3}\right)u^3 \frac{1}{3}du \\
&= \int \frac{u^4 - 2u^3}{9}\, du \\
&= \frac{1}{9}\left(\frac{u^5}{5} - \frac{u^4}{2}\right) + C \\
&= \frac{u^5}{45} - \frac{u^4}{18} + C \\
&= \frac{(3x + 2)^5}{45} - \frac{(3x + 2)^4}{18} + C
\end{aligned}$$

Tip: Don't forget to rewrite your answer in terms of x again at the end.

Some integrations look really tricky, but with a clever substitution they can be made a lot simpler.

Example 3

Find $\int 3x\sqrt{(2 - x^2)}\ dx$, using the substitution $u = \sqrt{2 - x^2}$.

- Start by differentiating both sides of the substitution with respect to x, then rearrange to get an expression for dx.

$$\text{So } u = \sqrt{2 - x^2} \implies \frac{du}{dx} = -\frac{x}{\sqrt{2 - x^2}} = -\frac{x}{u}$$

$$\implies u\frac{du}{dx} = -x$$

$$\implies -\frac{u}{x}du = dx$$

Tip: The chain rule is used here to differentiate.

- Now substitute what you've got into the original integral:

$$\int 3x\sqrt{(2 - x^2)}\ dx = \int 3x \times u \times -\frac{u}{x}du$$

$$= \int -3u^2\ du$$

$$= -u^3 + C$$

$$= -(\sqrt{2 - x^2})^3 + C$$

Exercise 1.1

Q1 Find the following integrals using the given substitutions:

a) $\int 12(x + 3)^5\ dx,\ u = x + 3$

b) $\int (11 - x)^4\ dx,\ u = 11 - x$

c) $\int 24x(x^2 + 4)^3\ dx,\ u = x^2 + 4$

d) $\int \sin^5 x\cos x\ dx,\ u = \sin x$

e) $\int x(x - 1)^5\ dx,\ u = x - 1$

f) $\int 6x\sqrt{(x + 1)}\ dx,\ u = \sqrt{x + 1}$

g) $\int \frac{x}{\sqrt{4 - x}}\ dx,\ u = \sqrt{4 - x}$

h) $\int \frac{15(\ln x)^4}{x}\ dx,\ u = \ln x$

Q2 Use an appropriate substitution to find:

a) $\int 21(x + 2)^6\ dx$

b) $\int (5x + 4)^3\ dx$

c) $\int x(2x + 3)^3\ dx$

d) $\int 24x(x^2 - 5)^7\ dx$

Q3 Use the substitution $u = \sqrt{2x - 1}$ to find $\int \frac{4x}{\sqrt{(2x - 1)}}\ dx$.

Q4 Use the substitution $u = 4 - \sqrt{x}$ to find $\int \frac{1}{4 - \sqrt{x}}\ dx$.

Q5 Use the substitution $u = 1 + e^x$ to find $\int \frac{e^{2x}}{1 + e^x}\ dx$.

Definite integrals

If you're given a **definite integral** to find using a substitution, it's important that you remember to **change the limits** to u. To do this, put the x-limits into the equation for u to find the corresponding values of u.

Doing it this way means you **don't** have to **put x back in** at the last step — just put the values of u into the integration for u.

Examples

a) **Use the substitution $u = \cos x$ to find $\int_{\frac{\pi}{2}}^{2\pi} -12 \sin x \cos^3 x \, dx$.**

Tip: You could also solve this one using the method on p.84.

- As with indefinite integrals, start by differentiating u, and rearranging to get dx on its own:

  $$u = \cos x \implies \frac{du}{dx} = -\sin x \implies dx = -\frac{1}{\sin x} du$$

- Now use the substitution to change the limits of the integral from x-values to u-values:

  $$x = \frac{\pi}{2} \implies u = \cos \frac{\pi}{2} = 0$$
  $$x = 2\pi \implies u = \cos 2\pi = 1$$

- Substitute all that back into the original integral, and solve:

  $$\int_{\frac{\pi}{2}}^{2\pi} -12 \sin x \cos^3 x \, dx = \int_0^1 -12 \sin x \, u^3 \frac{-1}{\sin x} du$$
  $$= \int_0^1 12 u^3 du$$
  $$= [3u^4]_0^1$$
  $$= [3(1)^4] - [3(0)^4] = 3 - 0 = \boxed{3}$$

b) **Find $\int_{2}^{\frac{7}{2}} x\sqrt{2x - 3} \, dx$, using the substitution $u = \sqrt{2x - 3}$.**

- Differentiate the substitution, and rearrange to get dx on its own:

  $$u = \sqrt{2x - 3} \implies \frac{du}{dx} = \frac{1}{\sqrt{2x - 3}} = \frac{1}{u} \implies dx = u \, du$$

- Rearrange the substitution to get an expression for x:

  $$u = \sqrt{2x - 3} \implies x = \frac{u^2 + 3}{2}$$

- Convert the limits from x-values to u-values:

  $$x = 2 \implies u = \sqrt{2(2) - 3} = \sqrt{1} = 1$$
  $$x = \frac{7}{2} \implies u = \sqrt{2\left(\frac{7}{2}\right) - 3} = \sqrt{4} = 2$$

- Substituting everything back into the original integral gives:

  $$\int_{2}^{\frac{7}{2}} x\sqrt{2x - 3} \, dx = \int_1^2 \frac{u^2 + 3}{2} \times u \times u \, du$$
  $$= \frac{1}{2}\int_1^2 u^4 + 3u^2 \, du$$
  $$= \frac{1}{2}\left[\frac{u^5}{5} + u^3\right]_1^2$$
  $$= \left[\frac{2^5}{10} + \frac{2^3}{2}\right] - \left[\frac{1^5}{10} + \frac{1^3}{2}\right] = \frac{36}{5} - \frac{3}{5} = \boxed{\frac{33}{5}}$$

Chapter 6 Integration 2   97

Tip: Swapping the limits and putting a minus in front of the integral might seem more complicated, but it often cancels with another minus, making the whole integration easier.

Sometimes when you convert the limits of a definite integral, the **upper limit** converts to a **lower number** than the **lower limit** does.

You can either keep the converted limits in the **same places** as the corresponding original limits and carry on as normal or **swap them** so the higher value is the upper limit and stick a **minus sign** in front of the whole integral (there's an example of this on p.108).

Exercise 1.2

Q1 Find the exact values of the following using the given substitutions:

a) $\int_{\frac{2}{3}}^{1} (3x - 2)^4 \, dx$, $u = 3x - 2$

b) $\int_{-2}^{1} 2x(x + 3)^4 \, dx$, $u = x + 3$

c) $\int_0^{\frac{\pi}{6}} 8 \sin^3 x \cos x \, dx$, $u = \sin x$

d) $\int_0^3 x\sqrt{x + 1} \, dx$, $u = \sqrt{x + 1}$

Q2 Use an appropriate substitution to find the exact value of each of the following:

a) $\int_2^{\sqrt{5}} x(x^2 - 3)^4 \, dx$

b) $\int_1^2 x(3x - 4)^3 \, dx$

c) $\int_2^{10} \frac{x}{\sqrt{x - 1}} \, dx$

Q3 Using the substitution $u = 3 - \sqrt{x}$, find the area bounded by the curve $y = \frac{1}{3 - \sqrt{x}}$, the x-axis and the lines $x = 1$ and $x = 4$.

Give your answer in the form $a + b\ln 2$, where a and b are integers.

Q4 Find $\int_0^1 2e^x(1 + e^x)^3 \, dx$, using the substitution $u = 1 + e^x$.

Give your answer to 1 decimal place.

Q5 Find the area bounded by the curve $y = \frac{x}{\sqrt{3x + 1}}$, the x-axis and the lines $x = 1$ and $x = 5$.

Use the substitution $u = \sqrt{3x + 1}$.

Q6 Hint: This one'll need some extra work, you won't be able to integrate using just a substitution. Look at the methods on p.70-72 if you're struggling.

Q6 Use the substitution $u = \sqrt{x}$ to find the exact value of $\int_9^{16} \frac{4}{\sqrt{x}(9x - 4)} \, dx$.

Trig identities

Tip: If you need a reminder of the trig identities, they're given in Chapter 5 Section 7 — see p.87 and p.89.

As you know by now, there's a vast range of **trig identities** and **formulas** to deal with in A-level maths. This can make for some pretty tricky **integration questions** involving trig functions. Here are a couple of examples:

Examples

a) **Use the substitution $u = \tan x$ to find $\int \frac{\sec^4 x}{\sqrt{\tan x}} \, dx$.**

- First, work out what all the substitutions will be. Start by finding dx:

$$u = \tan x \implies \frac{du}{dx} = \sec^2 x \implies dx = \frac{1}{\sec^2 x} du$$

- This substitution for dx will leave $\sec^2 x$ on the numerator — so now you need to find $\sec^2 x$ in terms of u:

From the identity $\sec^2 x \equiv 1 + \tan^2 x$

$$u = \tan x \implies \sec^2 x \equiv 1 + u^2$$

- Then substitute all these bits into the integral:

$$\int \frac{\sec^4 x}{\sqrt{\tan x}}\, dx = \int \frac{(1 + u^2) \times \sec^2 x}{\sqrt{u}} \times \frac{1}{\sec^2 x}\, du$$

$$= \int \frac{1}{\sqrt{u}} + \frac{u^2}{\sqrt{u}}\, du = \int u^{-\frac{1}{2}} + u^{\frac{3}{2}}\, du$$

$$= 2u^{\frac{1}{2}} + \frac{2}{5} u^{\frac{5}{2}} + C$$

$$= 2\sqrt{\tan x} + \frac{2}{5}\sqrt{\tan^5 x} + C$$

b) Calculate $\int_{\frac{1}{2}}^{\frac{\sqrt{3}}{2}} \frac{4}{\sqrt{1 - x^2}}\, dx$, **using the substitution** $x = \sin\theta$, **where** $-\frac{\pi}{2} \leq \theta \leq \frac{\pi}{2}$.

- Start by differentiating x with respect to θ, and use the result to find dx:

$$x = \sin\theta \quad \Rightarrow \quad \frac{dx}{d\theta} = \cos\theta \quad \Rightarrow \quad dx = \cos\theta\, d\theta$$

- Use the substitution to convert the limits from x to θ:

$$x = \sin\theta \quad \Rightarrow \quad \theta = \sin^{-1} x$$

So $x = \frac{\sqrt{3}}{2} \Rightarrow \theta = \frac{\pi}{3}$ and $x = \frac{1}{2} \Rightarrow \theta = \frac{\pi}{6}$

Tip: Notice that $\sin\theta$ has an inverse because θ is restricted to between $-\frac{\pi}{2}$ and $\frac{\pi}{2}$.

- Now solve the integral:

$$\int_{\frac{1}{2}}^{\frac{\sqrt{3}}{2}} \frac{4}{\sqrt{1 - x^2}}\, dx = \int_{\frac{\pi}{6}}^{\frac{\pi}{3}} \frac{4}{\sqrt{1 - \sin^2\theta}} \cos\theta\, d\theta$$

Use the identity $\sin^2\theta + \cos^2\theta \equiv 1$

$$= \int_{\frac{\pi}{6}}^{\frac{\pi}{3}} \frac{4\cos\theta}{\sqrt{\cos^2\theta}}\, d\theta$$

$$= \int_{\frac{\pi}{6}}^{\frac{\pi}{3}} 4\, d\theta$$

$$= [4\theta]_{\frac{\pi}{6}}^{\frac{\pi}{3}} = \frac{4\pi}{3} - \frac{2\pi}{3} = \frac{2\pi}{3}$$

Exercise 1.3

Q1 Find the exact value $\int_0^1 \frac{1}{1 + x^2}\, dx$ using the substitution $x = \tan\theta$ where $-\frac{\pi}{2} \leq \theta \leq \frac{\pi}{2}$.

Q1-4 Hint: Remember, the phrase 'exact value' is usually a clue that the answer will include a surd or π.

Q2 Find the exact value of $\int_0^{\frac{\pi}{6}} 3\sin x \sin 2x\, dx$ using the substitution $u = \sin x$.

Q3 Use the substitution $x = 2\sin\theta$, where $-\frac{\pi}{2} \leq \theta \leq \frac{\pi}{2}$, to find the exact value of $\int_1^{\sqrt{3}} \frac{1}{(4 - x^2)^{\frac{3}{2}}}\, dx$.

Q4 Find the exact value of $\int_{\frac{1}{2}}^1 \frac{1}{x^2\sqrt{1 - x^2}}\, dx$. Use the substitution $x = \cos\theta$ where $0 \leq \theta \leq \pi$.

Q5 Find $\int 2\tan^3 x\, dx$ using the substitution $u = \sec^2 x$.

2. Integration by Parts

Learning Objectives:

- Understand that integration by parts comes from the product rule.
- Be able to use integration by parts to integrate functions, including ln$x$.
- Be able to integrate functions where integration by parts has to be applied more than once.

Sadly, not every integration problem can be solved with a nifty substitution or a clever trick. Integration by parts is another way to deal with integrating a product of two functions — it involves both differentiation and integration.

Integration by parts

If you have a **product** to integrate but you can't use any of the methods you've learnt so far, you might be able to use **integration by parts**.

The **formula** for integrating by parts is:

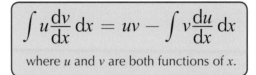

$$\int u\frac{dv}{dx}\,dx = uv - \int v\frac{du}{dx}\,dx$$

where u and v are both functions of x.

Here's the **proof** of this formula. You're **not** expected to know it for the exam, but you might find it useful.

Tip: You should be familiar with the product rule from C3.

Start with the **product rule**:

- If u and v are both functions of x, then

$$\frac{d}{dx}uv = u\frac{dv}{dx} + v\frac{du}{dx}$$

- Integrate both sides of the product rule with respect to x:

$$\int \frac{d}{dx}uv\,dx = \int u\frac{dv}{dx}\,dx + \int v\frac{du}{dx}\,dx$$

- On the left-hand side, uv is differentiated, then integrated — so you end up back at uv:

$$uv = \int u\frac{dv}{dx}\,dx + \int v\frac{du}{dx}\,dx$$

- Now just rearrange to get:

$$\int u\frac{dv}{dx}\,dx = uv - \int v\frac{du}{dx}\,dx$$

Tip: The integration by parts formula is sometimes written
$$\int uv'\,dx = uv - \int vu'\,dx$$
— you might find this version easier to use.

- The hardest thing about integration by parts is **deciding** which bit of your product should be u and which bit should be $\frac{dv}{dx}$.
- There's no set rule for this — you just have to look at both parts, see which one **differentiates** to give something **nice**, then set that one as u.
- For example, if you have a product that has a **single x** as one part of it, choose this to be u. It differentiates to **1**, which makes **integrating** $v\frac{du}{dx}$ very easy.

a) **Find $\int 2x e^x dx$.**

- Start by working out what should be u and what should be $\frac{dv}{dx}$
  — choose them so that $v\frac{du}{dx}$ is easier to integrate than $2x e^x$.

  The two factors are $2x$ and e^x, so try them both ways round:

  If $u = 2x$ and $\frac{dv}{dx} = e^x$, then $v\frac{du}{dx} = 2e^x$ ◄── Easier to integrate than $2x e^x$.

  If $u = e^x$ and $\frac{dv}{dx} = 2x$, then $v\frac{du}{dx} = x^2 e^x$

  So let $u = 2x$ and $\frac{dv}{dx} = e^x$.

- Put u, v, $\frac{du}{dx}$ and $\frac{dv}{dx}$ into the integration by parts formula:

  $u = 2x \Rightarrow \frac{du}{dx} = 2$, $\frac{dv}{dx} = e^x \Rightarrow v = e^x$

  $$\int 2x e^x dx = \int u\frac{dv}{dx} dx = uv - \int v\frac{du}{dx} dx$$

  $$= 2x e^x - \int 2 e^x dx$$

  $$= 2x e^x - 2e^x + C$$

  ◄── Don't forget the constant of integration.

Tip: You don't always need to work out both possible versions. Here, e^x won't change whether you integrate it or differentiate it, so you just need to think about whether the integration would be made easier by differentiating $2x$ or by integrating it.

b) **Find $\int x^3 \ln x \, dx$.**

- Choose u and $\frac{dv}{dx}$:

  Let $u = \ln x$ and $\frac{dv}{dx} = x^3$.

  $u = \ln x \Rightarrow \frac{du}{dx} = \frac{1}{x}$, $\frac{dv}{dx} = x^3 \Rightarrow v = \frac{x^4}{4}$

- Put u, v, $\frac{du}{dx}$ and $\frac{dv}{dx}$ into the integration by parts formula:

  $$\int x^3 \ln x \, dx = \frac{x^4 \ln x}{4} - \int \frac{x^4}{4} \times \frac{1}{x} dx$$

  $$= \frac{x^4 \ln x}{4} - \frac{1}{4}\int x^3 dx$$

  $$= \frac{x^4 \ln x}{4} - \frac{x^4}{16} + C$$

Tip: If you have a product that has $\ln x$ as one of its factors, let $u = \ln x$, as $\ln x$ is easy to differentiate but quite tricky to integrate (see page 102).

Until now, you haven't been able to integrate **ln x**, but **integration by parts** gives you a way to get around this. The trick is to write ln x as 1·ln x.

- You can write ln x as 1·ln x. So let $u = \ln x$ and let $\frac{dv}{dx} = 1$.

  $u = \ln x \Rightarrow \frac{du}{dx} = \frac{1}{x}$

  $\frac{dv}{dx} = 1 \Rightarrow v = x$

- Putting these into the formula gives:

  $\int \ln x \, dx = x \ln x - \int x \frac{1}{x} \, dx$

  $= x \ln x - \int 1 \, dx$

  $= x \ln x - x + C$

You can use **integration by parts** on definite integrals too. The only change from the method for indefinite integrals is that you have to **apply the limits** of the integral to the **uv** bit.

The integration by parts formula for definite integrals can be written like this:

$$\int_a^b u \frac{dv}{dx} \, dx = [uv]_a^b - \int_a^b v \frac{du}{dx} \, dx$$

Example

Find the exact value of $\int_0^{\frac{\pi}{2}} 4x \sin\left(\frac{x}{2}\right) dx$.

- Choose u and $\frac{dv}{dx}$.

  $\sin\left(\frac{x}{2}\right)$ will give a cos function whether you integrate or differentiate it, so the only way to get a simpler $\int v \frac{du}{dx} \, dx$ is to make $u = 4x$.

  Let $u = 4x$ and $\frac{dv}{dx} = \sin\left(\frac{x}{2}\right)$

  $u = 4x \Rightarrow \frac{du}{dx} = 4$

  $\frac{dv}{dx} = \sin\left(\frac{x}{2}\right) \Rightarrow v = -2\cos\left(\frac{x}{2}\right)$

- Substitute everything into the formula and complete the integration:

  $\int_0^{\frac{\pi}{2}} 4x \sin\left(\frac{x}{2}\right) dx = \left[-8x\cos\left(\frac{x}{2}\right)\right]_0^{\frac{\pi}{2}} - \int_0^{\frac{\pi}{2}} -8\cos\left(\frac{x}{2}\right) dx$

  $= -8\left[x\cos\left(\frac{x}{2}\right)\right]_0^{\frac{\pi}{2}} + 16\left[\sin\left(\frac{x}{2}\right)\right]_0^{\frac{\pi}{2}}$

  $= -8\left[\frac{\pi}{2}\cos\left(\frac{\pi}{4}\right) - 0\cos(0)\right] + 16\left[\sin\left(\frac{\pi}{4}\right) - \sin(0)\right]$

  $= -8\left[\frac{\pi}{2}\frac{1}{\sqrt{2}}\right] + 16\left[\frac{1}{\sqrt{2}}\right]$

  $= -\frac{4\pi}{\sqrt{2}} + \frac{16}{\sqrt{2}}$

  $= 8\sqrt{2} - 2\pi\sqrt{2}$

Tip: Go back to p.73 if you want a reminder about integrating trig functions.

Q1 Use integration by parts to find:

a) $\int xe^x \, dx$ b) $\int xe^{-x} \, dx$ c) $\int xe^{-\frac{x}{3}} \, dx$ d) $\int x(e^x + 1) \, dx$

Q2 Use integration by parts to find:

a) $\int_0^\pi x \sin x \, dx$ b) $\int 2x \cos x \, dx$

c) $\int 3x \cos\left(\frac{1}{2}x\right) dx$ d) $\int_{-\frac{\pi}{2}}^{\frac{\pi}{2}} 2x(1 - \sin x) \, dx$

Q3 Use integration by parts to find:

a) $\int 2 \ln x \, dx$ b) $\int x^4 \ln x \, dx$ c) $\int \ln 4x \, dx$ d) $\int \ln x^3 \, dx$

Q4 Use integration by parts to find:

a) $\int_{-1}^1 20x(x + 1)^3 \, dx$ b) $\int_0^{1.5} 30x\sqrt{(2x + 1)} \, dx$

Q5 Use integration by parts to find the exact values of the following:

a) $\int_0^1 12xe^{2x} \, dx$ b) $\int_0^{\frac{\pi}{3}} 18x \sin 3x \, dx$ c) $\int_1^2 \frac{1}{x^2} \ln x \, dx$

Q6 Find $\int \frac{x}{e^{2x}} \, dx$.

Q7 Find $\int (x + 1)\sqrt{(x + 2)} \, dx$.

Q8 Find $\int \ln(x + 1) \, dx$.

Repeated use of integration by parts

Sometimes **integration by parts** leaves you with a function for $v\frac{du}{dx}$ which is **simpler** than the function you started with, but still **tricky to integrate**. You might have to carry out integration by parts **again** to find $\int v\frac{du}{dx} \, dx$.

Example 1

Find $\int x^2 \sin x \, dx$.

- Let $u = x^2$ and let $\frac{dv}{dx} = \sin x$. Then $\frac{du}{dx} = 2x$ and $v = -\cos x$.

- Putting these into the formula gives:
$$\int x^2 \sin x \, dx = -x^2 \cos x - \int -2x \cos x \, dx = -x^2 \cos x + \int 2x \cos x \, dx$$

- $2x \cos x$ isn't very easy to integrate, but you can integrate by parts again:
Let $u_1 = 2x$ and let $\frac{dv_1}{dx} = \cos x$. Then $\frac{du_1}{dx} = 2$ and $v_1 = \sin x$.

- Putting these into the formula gives:
$$\int 2x \cos x \, dx = 2x \sin x - \int 2 \sin x \, dx = 2x \sin x + 2\cos x + C$$

- So $\int x^2 \sin x \, dx = -x^2 \cos x + \int 2x \cos x \, dx$
$$= -x^2 \cos x + 2x \sin x + 2\cos x + C$$

Tip: Calling the different parts u_1 and v_1 just means you don't get confused with the u and v used in the first integration.

Example 2

Use integration by parts to find $\int_2^3 x^2(x-1)^{-4}\,dx$.

Tip: The formula for integrating $(ax + b)^n$ is used a few times in this example — go back to p.63 if you've forgotten how it works.

- Let $u = x^2$ and let $\dfrac{dv}{dx} = (x-1)^{-4}$. Then $\dfrac{du}{dx} = 2x$ and $v = -\dfrac{1}{3}(x-1)^{-3}$.

- Putting these into the formula gives:

$$\int_2^3 x^2(x-1)^{-4}\,dx = \left[-\frac{x^2}{3}(x-1)^{-3}\right]_2^3 - \int_2^3 -\frac{2x}{3}(x-1)^{-3}\,dx$$

$$= \left[-\frac{x^2}{3}(x-1)^{-3}\right]_2^3 + \frac{2}{3}\int_2^3 x(x-1)^{-3}\,dx$$

- $\int_2^3 x(x-1)^{-3}\,dx$ is still tricky to integrate. Use integration by parts again:

  Let $u_1 = x$ and let $\dfrac{dv_1}{dx} = (x-1)^{-3}$. Then $\dfrac{du_1}{dx} = 1$ and $v_1 = -\dfrac{1}{2}(x-1)^{-2}$.

- Put these into the formula:

$$\int_2^3 x(x-1)^{-3}\,dx = \left[-\frac{x}{2}(x-1)^{-2}\right]_2^3 - \int_2^3 -\frac{1}{2}(x-1)^{-2}\,dx$$

$$= \left[-\frac{x}{2}(x-1)^{-2}\right]_2^3 - \frac{1}{2}\left[(x-1)^{-1}\right]_2^3$$

$$= \left[-\frac{3}{2}(2)^{-2} + \frac{2}{2}(1)^{-2}\right] - \frac{1}{2}\left[2^{-1} - 1^{-1}\right]$$

$$= \left[-\frac{3}{8} + 1\right] - \frac{1}{2}\left[\frac{1}{2} - 1\right]$$

$$= \frac{5}{8} + \frac{1}{4} = \boxed{\frac{7}{8}}$$

- Now you can evaluate the original integral:

$$\int_2^3 x^2(x-1)^{-4}\,dx = \left[-\frac{x^2}{3}(x-1)^{-3}\right]_2^3 + \frac{2}{3}\int_2^3 x(x-1)^{-3}\,dx$$

$$= \left[-\frac{x^2}{3}(x-1)^{-3}\right]_2^3 + \frac{2}{3}\left(\frac{7}{8}\right)$$

$$= \left[\left(-\frac{9}{3}(2)^{-3}\right) - \left(-\frac{4}{3}(1)^{-3}\right)\right] + \frac{7}{12}$$

$$= \left[-\frac{9}{24} + \frac{4}{3}\right] + \frac{7}{12}$$

$$= \frac{23}{24} + \frac{7}{12}$$

$$= \boxed{\frac{37}{24}}$$

Exercise 2.2

Q1   Use integration by parts twice to find:

    a) $\int x^3 e^x\,dx$ b) $\int x^2\cos x\,dx$

    c) $\int 4x^2\sin 2x\,dx$ d) $\int 40x^2(2x-1)^4\,dx$

Q2   Find $\int_{-1}^0 x^2(x+1)^4\,dx$ using integration by parts.

Q3   Use integration by parts to find the area enclosed by the curve $y = x^2 e^{-2x}$, the x-axis and the lines $x = 0$ and $x = 1$.

3. Volumes of Revolution

So far, you've seen integration used to find the area under a curve. Now you'll see how it can also be used to calculate the volume of certain solid shapes.

Volumes of revolution

- If you're given a **definite integral**, the solution you come up with is the **area under the graph** between the two **limits** (you did this back in C2).
- If you now **rotate** that area 2π radians **about the x-axis**, you'll come up with a **solid** — and this is what you want to find the **volume** of.
- For example, you can calculate a **definite integral** to find the **area** bounded by the curve $y = 4 - x^2$, the x-axis and the lines $x = 0$ and $x = 2$...

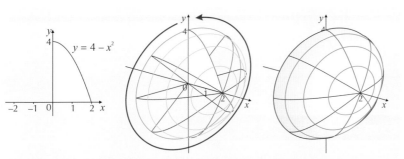

...and if you rotate that area in a full circle, centred at the x-axis, you get a sort of dome shape. The **volume** of the dome is a **volume of revolution**.

- The **formula** for finding the **volume of revolution** is:

$$V = \pi \int_{x_1}^{x_2} y^2 \, dx$$

where y is a function of x (i.e. $y = f(x)$) and x_1 and x_2 are the limits of x.

You need to **learn** this formula for your exam — it's **not** on the formula sheet.

Learning Objectives:

- Understand what is meant by the term 'volume of revolution'.
- Be able to calculate the volume of revolution for the rotation of a curve about the x-axis, given the Cartesian equation of the curve.
- Be able to calculate the volume of revolution for the rotation of a curve about the x-axis for a curve defined by parametric equations.

Tip: If you wanted to rotate an area about the y-axis, you'd use the formula $V = \pi \int_{y_1}^{y_2} x^2 \, dy$. You don't need this for C4 though.

Example 1

The region R is enclosed by the curve $y = 9 - x^2$, the x-axis and the lines $x = 1$ and $x = 2$. Find the volume, V, of the solid formed when R is rotated 2π radians about the x-axis.

- If $y = 9 - x^2$, then $y^2 = 81 - 18x^2 + x^4$.
- Putting this into the formula gives:

$$V = \pi \int_{x_1}^{x_2} y^2 \, dx$$

$$= \pi \int_1^2 81 - 18x^2 + x^4 \, dx$$

$$= \pi \left[81x - 6x^3 + \frac{x^5}{5} \right]_1^2$$

$$= \pi \left[\left(81(2) - 6(8) + \frac{32}{5} \right) - \left(81(1) - 6(1) + \frac{1}{5} \right) \right]$$

$$= \pi \left[\left(162 - 48 + \frac{32}{5} \right) - \left(81 - 6 + \frac{1}{5} \right) \right]$$

$$= \pi \left[\frac{602}{5} - \frac{376}{5} \right] = \frac{226}{5} \pi$$

Tip: V is the volume of the solid you get when you rotate R:

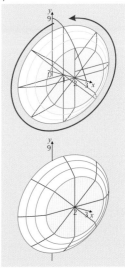

Example 2

The area A is enclosed by the curve $y = \sin x$ and the x-axis between $x = 0$ and $x = \pi$. Find the exact volume of the solid formed when A is rotated 2π radians about the x-axis.

Tip: Don't forget to square y — you might think it's obvious, but it's a common mistake.

- If $y = \sin x$, then $y^2 = \sin^2 x$.
- Putting this into the formula gives:

$$V = \pi \int_{x_1}^{x_2} y^2 \, dx$$

$$= \pi \int_0^\pi \sin^2 x \, dx$$

$$= \frac{\pi}{2} \int_0^\pi 1 - \cos 2x \, dx$$

Using the cos double angle formula — see p.87.

$$= \frac{\pi}{2}\left[x - \frac{1}{2}\sin 2x \right]_0^\pi$$

$$= \frac{\pi}{2}[(\pi - 0) - (0)] = \frac{\pi^2}{2}$$

Exercise 3.1

Q1 For each of the following, find the exact volume of the solid generated when the area enclosed by the x-axis and the given curve and lines is rotated 2π radians about the x-axis.

a) $y = 4x$, $x = 1$ and $x = 2$

b) $y = \sqrt{x + 2}$, $x = 0$ and $x = 2$

c) $x^2 + y^2 = 4$, $x = 0$ and $x = 2$

Q2 For each of the following, the region R is enclosed by the curve $y = f(x)$, the lines $x = x_1$ and $x = x_2$ and the x-axis. In each case, find the exact volume of revolution formed when R is rotated $360°$ about the x-axis.

a) $f(x) = \frac{2}{x}$, $x_1 = 2$, $x_2 = 8$

b) $f(x) = e^x$, $x_1 = 0$, $x_2 = 2$

c) $f(x) = \frac{3}{\sqrt{x}}$, $x_1 = 1$, $x_2 = 2$

d) $f(x) = 1 + \sqrt{x}$, $x_1 = 0$, $x_2 = 1$

Q3 In each of the following questions, the given curve and lines enclose a region A. For each, find the exact volume of the solid formed by rotating region A about the x-axis by 2π radians.

a) $y = \sqrt{\sin 2x}$, $y = 0$, $x = 0$ and $x = \frac{\pi}{6}$

b) $y = \cos x$, $y = 0$, $x = 0$ and $x = \frac{\pi}{2}$

c) $y = \frac{2}{\sqrt{1 + 2x}}$, $y = 0$, $x = 0$ and $x = 3$

d) $y = \frac{1}{1 + 3x}$, $y = 0$, $x = 0$ and $x = 1$

e) $y = 2xe^x$, $y = 0$, $x = 0$ and $x = 1$

Q3 e)-f) Hint: You'll need to use integration by parts here.

f) $y = x\sqrt{\sin x}$, $y = 0$, $x = 0$ and $x = \frac{\pi}{4}$

Finding volumes of revolution using parametric equations

In Chapter 2, you met curves with **parametric equations** — where x and y are functions of a **parameter** (usually t or θ).

You saw how to **integrate** them on p.19. Once you know how to do that, it's easy to find a **volume of revolution** that's defined using parametrics.

Here are the **formulas** you need for a curve with parametric equations $x = f(t)$ and $y = g(t)$ and limits t_1 and t_2.

The **area** under the curve is given by:

$$A = \int_{t_1}^{t_2} y\,\frac{dx}{dt}\,dt$$

The **volume of revolution** (for a rotation of 2π radians about the x-axis) is:

$$V = \pi \int_{t_1}^{t_2} y^2\,\frac{dx}{dt}\,dt$$

Tip: The limits in both formulas are values of t. If the question gives the limits as x-values, don't forget to convert them using the parametric equation for x.

Again, these **aren't** given on the formula sheet, so make sure you **learn them**.

Example 1

Curve C is given by the parametric equations $x = t^2 + 2t$, $y = \sqrt{\dfrac{3}{t}}$, for $t > 0$.

The region R is bounded by C, the x-axis and the lines $x = 3$ and $x = 24$.

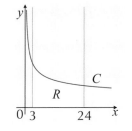

a) **Find the area of R to 2 decimal places.**

- First convert the limits from x to t:

$$x_1 = 3 \implies t^2 + 2t - 3 = 0$$
$$\implies (t + 3)(t - 1) = 0 \implies t_1 = 1 \ \ (\text{as } t > 0)$$
$$x_2 = 24 \implies t^2 + 2t - 24 = 0$$
$$\implies (t + 6)(t - 4) = 0 \implies t_2 = 4 \ \ (\text{as } t > 0)$$

Tip: Don't forget that the parameter can sometimes only take a certain range of values — you might need to consider that range when you're converting the limits of the integral.

- Differentiate x with respect to t:

$$\frac{dx}{dt} = 2t + 2$$

- So using the area formula:

$$A = \int_{t_1}^{t_2} y\,\frac{dx}{dt}\,dt = \int_1^4 \sqrt{3}\,t^{-\frac{1}{2}}(2t + 2)\,dt$$
$$= 2\sqrt{3}\int_1^4 t^{\frac{1}{2}} + t^{-\frac{1}{2}}\,dt$$
$$= 2\sqrt{3}\left[\frac{2}{3}t^{\frac{3}{2}} + 2t^{\frac{1}{2}}\right]_1^4$$
$$= 2\sqrt{3}\left[\left(\frac{16}{3} + 4\right) - \left(\frac{2}{3} + 2\right)\right]$$
$$= 2\sqrt{3}\left[\frac{20}{3}\right]$$
$$= \boxed{23.09 \text{ to 2 d.p.}}$$

b) Find the volume of the solid generated when R is rotated 2π radians about the x-axis, to 2 decimal places.

Use the same values of $\dfrac{dx}{dt}$ and t that you calculated in part a).

$$V = \pi \int_{t_1}^{t_2} y^2 \frac{dx}{dt} \, dt = \pi \int_{1}^{4} \frac{3}{t}(2t + 2) \, dt$$
$$= 6\pi \int_{1}^{4} 1 + \frac{1}{t} \, dt$$
$$= 6\pi[t + \ln t]_1^4$$
$$= 6\pi[(4 + \ln 4) - (1 + \ln 1)]$$
$$= 6\pi[3 + \ln 4]$$
$$= \boxed{82.68 \text{ to 2 d.p.}}$$

Example 2

Curve J is given by the parametric equations $x = 2 + \cos\theta$, $y = \sin 2\theta$, for $0 \le t \le \pi$.

The region K is bounded by J and the x-axis and between $x = 2$ and $x = 3$.

Calculate the area of region K, and the volume of the solid made by rotating K 2π radians about the x-axis.

Tip: Don't be put off if the parametric equations are written in terms of something other than t (trig equations will sometimes be given in terms of θ) — just change $\dfrac{dx}{dt}$ to $\dfrac{dx}{d\theta}$ and dt to $d\theta$ (or to whatever the variable is).

- First convert the limits from x to θ:

$$x_1 = 2 \Rightarrow 2 + \cos\theta_1 = 2 \Rightarrow \cos\theta_1 = 0 \Rightarrow \theta_1 = \frac{\pi}{2}$$

$$x_2 = 3 \Rightarrow 2 + \cos\theta_2 = 3 \Rightarrow \cos\theta_2 = 1 \Rightarrow \theta_2 = 0$$

- Differentiate x with respect to θ:

$$\frac{dx}{d\theta} = -\sin\theta$$

Tip: Here the limits have been swapped so the higher number is on top, and the whole integral has been made negative. You can just leave the limits where they are (like on the next page) if you prefer.

- So using the area formula:

$$A = \int_{\theta_1}^{\theta_2} y \frac{dx}{d\theta} \, d\theta = \int_{\frac{\pi}{2}}^{0} \sin 2\theta \times -\sin\theta \, d\theta = -\int_{0}^{\frac{\pi}{2}} \sin 2\theta \times -\sin\theta \, d\theta$$
$$= \int_{0}^{\frac{\pi}{2}} 2\sin\theta\cos\theta \times \sin\theta \, d\theta$$
$$= 2\int_{0}^{\frac{\pi}{2}} \sin^2\theta\cos\theta \, d\theta$$

Tip: You could use the method for integrating expressions of the form $f'(x) \times [f(x)]^n$ from page 84 here instead of integration by substitution.

- You can solve this using integration by substitution:

Let $u = \sin\theta$, then $\dfrac{du}{d\theta} = \cos\theta \Rightarrow d\theta = \dfrac{1}{\cos\theta} du$

and $\theta = \dfrac{\pi}{2} \Rightarrow u = 1$, $\theta = 0 \Rightarrow u = 0$

- So $A = 2\displaystyle\int_{0}^{\frac{\pi}{2}} \sin^2\theta\cos\theta \, d\theta$

$$= 2\int_{0}^{1} u^2 \cos\theta \times \frac{1}{\cos\theta} \, du$$
$$= 2\int_{0}^{1} u^2 \, du$$
$$= 2\left[\frac{1}{3}u^3\right]_0^1$$
$$= 2\left[\frac{1}{3}\right] = \frac{2}{3}$$

- Now use the same θ_1, θ_2 and $\frac{dx}{d\theta}$ to find the volume of revolution:

$$V = \pi \int_{\theta_1}^{\theta_2} y^2 \frac{dx}{d\theta} d\theta = \pi \int_{\frac{\pi}{2}}^{0} \sin^2 2\theta \times -\sin\theta \, d\theta$$

$$= \pi \int_{\frac{\pi}{2}}^{0} (2\sin\theta\cos\theta)^2 \times -\sin\theta \, d\theta$$

$$= \pi \int_{\frac{\pi}{2}}^{0} -4\sin^3\theta\cos^2\theta \, d\theta$$

Tip: Here the limits are left with the higher number on the bottom — because the limits actually swap back when you make the substitution below.

- Use integration by substitution again:

Let $u = \cos\theta$, then $\frac{du}{d\theta} = -\sin\theta \Rightarrow d\theta = \frac{-1}{\sin\theta} du$

$\theta = \frac{\pi}{2} \Rightarrow u = 0$, $\theta = 0 \Rightarrow u = 1$

and $\sin^2\theta + \cos^2\theta \equiv 1 \Rightarrow \sin^2\theta = 1 - u^2$

- So $V = \pi \int_{\frac{\pi}{2}}^{0} -4\sin^3\theta\cos^2\theta \, d\theta$

$$= \pi \int_{0}^{1} -4\sin\theta(1 - u^2)u^2 \times \frac{-1}{\sin\theta} du$$

$$= 4\pi \int_{0}^{1} u^2 - u^4 \, du$$

$$= 4\pi \left[\frac{1}{3}u^3 - \frac{1}{5}u^5 \right]_{0}^{1} = 4\pi \left[\frac{2}{15} \right] = \frac{8\pi}{15}$$

Exercise 3.2

Q1 Curve M is defined by the parametric equations $x = 5t - t^2$ and $y = \sqrt{t - 3}$, for $t \geq 3$. Find, to 2 decimal places:

a) the area bounded by M, the x-axis and the lines $x = 0$ and $x = 4$,

b) the volume of the solid formed when the area calculated in a) is rotated 2π radians about the x-axis.

Q2 a) Find the area of region P, which is bounded by the x-axis, the lines $x = 0$ and $x = 1$, and the curve given by $x = t^2$, $y = e^t$, for $t \geq 0$.

b) Find the volume of Q, the solid formed by rotating P 2π radians about the x-axis.

Q3 The region K is enclosed by the x-axis, the lines $x = 1$ and $x = 2$, and the curve C, which is given by $x = \sec\theta$, $y = 1 + \cos\theta$, $0 \leq \theta < \frac{\pi}{2}$. The solid J is formed by rotating K 2π radians about the x-axis. Find the exact area of K and the exact volume of J.

Q4 Region R is enclosed by the lines $x = 0$ and $x = \frac{1}{\sqrt{2}}$, the x-axis and the curve with parametric equations $x = \sin\theta$, $y = 2 + \tan\theta$, for $0 \leq \theta \leq \frac{\pi}{3}$.

a) Find the area of R to 2 decimal places.

b) Find, to 2 decimal places, the volume of the solid formed by rotating R 2π radians about the x-axis.

Q4 Hint: You'll need to use trig identities in this question.

Q5 A curve is given by the equations $x = \ln(t^2 - 1)$ and $y = \frac{1}{2t}$, for $t \geq 1$.

a) Find the area bounded by this curve, the x-axis and the lines $x = \ln 3$ and $x = \ln 8$, to 3 significant figures.

b) Find the volume of the solid formed when this area is rotated 360° about the x-axis, to 3 significant figures.

Q5 Hint: Partial fractions will be useful for this one.

4. Numerical Integration

Learning Objectives:

- Be able to estimate the value of the integral of any of the types of function covered in C3 or C4 using the trapezium rule.
- Understand that the accuracy of an estimate found using the trapezium rule can be increased by using more strips.
- Be able to calculate the percentage error in an estimate found using the trapezium rule.

You've seen the trapezium rule before, so there's not actually a lot that's new in this topic. It's mostly a case of applying the method you already know to the types of function you've been dealing with throughout C3 and C4.

The trapezium rule

You met the trapezium rule in C2. It's a way of approximating the area under a curve by dividing the area up into a number of trapezium-shaped strips.

Here's a reminder of how it works. For an approximation of the area under the curve $y = f(x)$ between $x = a$ and $x = b$, using n strips or intervals, each of width h:

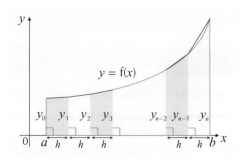

- The area of each trapezium is $A = \frac{h}{2}(y_r + y_{r+1})$
- You can find the width of each strip using $h = \frac{(b-a)}{n}$
- This gives you x-values $x_r = a + rh$ (for r from 0 to n).
- $y_0, y_1, y_2, \ldots, y_n$ are the heights of the sides of the trapeziums — you get these by putting the corresponding x-values into the equation of the curve (so $y_0 = f(x_0)$, etc).
- The area represented by $\int_a^b y \, dx$ is approximately:

$$\int_a^b y \, dx \approx \frac{h}{2}[y_0 + 2(y_1 + y_2 + \ldots + y_{n-1}) + y_n]$$

where n is the number of strips or intervals and h is the width of each strip.

Tip: Some questions might refer to the y-values as 'ordinates' — remember that 5 ordinates is the same as 4 strips.

Example 1

Use the trapezium rule with 3 strips to find an approximate value for $\int_0^{1.5} \sqrt{x^2 + 2x} \, dx$.

- $n = 3$, $a = 0$ and $b = 1.5$, so the width of each strip is $h = \frac{1.5 - 0}{3} = 0.5$.
- This gives x-values of $x_0 = 0$, $x_1 = 0.5$, $x_2 = 1$ and $x_3 = 1.5$.
- Calculate the value of y for each of x_0, x_1, x_2, x_3:

x	$y = \sqrt{x^2 + 2x}$
$x_0 = 0$	$y_0 = 0$
$x_1 = 0.5$	$y_1 = \sqrt{1.25} = 1.118\ldots$
$x_2 = 1$	$y_2 = \sqrt{3} = 1.732\ldots$
$x_3 = 1.5$	$y_3 = \sqrt{5.25} = 2.291\ldots$

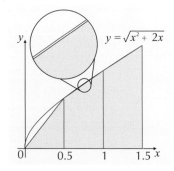

Tip: The graph shows that the estimate here is less than the actual value of the integral — there's a gap between the curve and the top of each strip. Even where it looks like the curve and the top of the trapezium are the same, if you zoom in far enough there will always be a gap.

- Now use the formula to find the approximate value of the integral:

$$\int_0^{1.5} \sqrt{x^2 + 2x}\, dx \approx \frac{h}{2}[y_0 + 2(y_1 + y_2) + y_3]$$

$$= \frac{0.5}{2}[0 + 2(1.118 + 1.732) + 2.291]$$

$$= \frac{1}{4}[7.991]$$

$$= \boxed{2.00 \text{ to 3 s.f.}}$$

Tip: This final answer is smaller than the actual integral — it's an underestimate. Remember from C2 it can be an **underestimate** or an **overestimate**, depending on the shape of the graph:

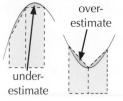

over-estimate

under-estimate

Using **more strips** (i.e. **increasing** n) gives you a **more accurate** approximation.

Example 2

Use the trapezium rule to approximate the area of $\int_0^4 \dfrac{6x^2}{x^3 + 2}\, dx$, using:

a) $n = 2$

- For 2 strips, the width of each strip is $h = \dfrac{4 - 0}{2} = 2$, so the x-values are 0, 2 and 4.

- Calculate the corresponding y-values:

x	$y = \dfrac{6x^2}{x^3 + 2}$
$x_0 = 0$	$y_0 = 0$
$x_1 = 2$	$y_1 = 2.4$
$x_2 = 4$	$y_2 = 1.4545$ (to 4 d.p.)

Tip: If you have to round the y-values, make sure you leave enough decimal places. For example, if your final answer has to be to 3 d.p., find the y-values to at least 4 d.p.

- Putting these values into the formula gives:

$$\int_0^4 \dfrac{6x^2}{x^3 + 2}\, dx \approx \frac{h}{2}[y_0 + 2y_1 + y_2]$$

$$= \frac{2}{2}[0 + 2(2.4) + 1.4545]$$

$$= \boxed{6.255 \text{ to 3 d.p.}}$$

b) $n = 4$

- For 4 strips, the width of each strip is $h = \dfrac{4 - 0}{4} = 1$, so the x-values are 0, 1, 2, 3 and 4.

- Calculate the corresponding y-values:

x	$y = \dfrac{6x^2}{x^3 + 2}$
$x_0 = 0$	$y_0 = 0$
$x_1 = 1$	$y_1 = 2$
$x_2 = 2$	$y_2 = 2.4$
$x_3 = 3$	$y_3 = 1.8621$ (to 4 d.p.)
$x_4 = 4$	$y_4 = 1.4545$ (to 4 d.p.)

Tip: Increasing the number of strips increases the accuracy because the gaps between curve and line are smaller:

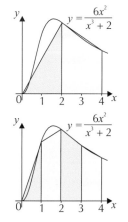

- Putting these values into the formula gives:

$$\int_0^4 \dfrac{6x^2}{x^3 + 2}\, dx \approx \frac{h}{2}[y_0 + 2(y_1 + y_2 + y_3) + y_4]$$

$$= \frac{1}{2}[0 + 2(2 + 2.4 + 1.8621) + 1.4545]$$

$$= \frac{1}{2}[13.9787] = \boxed{6.989 \text{ to 3 d.p.}}$$

Q1 Use the trapezium rule to find approximations of each of the following integrals. Use the given number of intervals in each case. Give your answers to 3 significant figures.

a) $\int_0^2 \sqrt{x+2} \, dx$, 2 intervals

b) $\int_1^3 2(\ln x)^2 \, dx$, 4 intervals

c) $\int_0^{0.4} e^{x^2} \, dx$, 2 intervals

d) $\int_0^{\frac{\pi}{2}} \sqrt{\sin x} \, dx$, 3 intervals

e) $\int_{-\frac{\pi}{4}}^{\frac{\pi}{4}} 4x \tan x \, dx$, 4 intervals

f) $\int_0^{0.3} \sqrt{e^x + 1} \, dx$, 6 intervals

g) $\int_1^4 (1 + \ln x)^4 \, dx$, 3 intervals

h) $\int_0^{\pi} \ln(2 + \sin x) \, dx$, 6 intervals

Q2 Use the trapezium rule with 3 intervals to find an estimate to $\int_0^{\frac{\pi}{2}} \sin^3 \theta \, d\theta$. Give your answer to 3 d.p.

Q3 Use the trapezium rule with 5 intervals to estimate the area enclosed by the curve $y = \sqrt{\ln x}$, the x-axis and the lines $x = 2$ and $x = 7$. Give your answer to 3 d.p.

Q4 a) Complete the following table of values to 3 d.p. for $y = e^{\cos 2x}$.

x	0	$\frac{\pi}{8}$	$\frac{\pi}{4}$	$\frac{3\pi}{8}$	$\frac{\pi}{2}$
y	2.718	2.028	1.000		

b) Using the trapezium rule with 4 intervals, estimate $\int_0^{\frac{\pi}{2}} e^{\cos 2x} \, dx$ to 2 d.p.

Q5 a) Complete the following table of values to 3 d.p. for $y = e^{\sin x}$.

x	0	$\frac{\pi}{8}$	$\frac{\pi}{4}$	$\frac{3\pi}{8}$	$\frac{\pi}{2}$
y	1	1.466			2.718

b) (i) Using the trapezium rule with 2 intervals, estimate $\int_0^{\frac{\pi}{2}} e^{\sin x} \, dx$ to 2 d.p.

(ii) Repeat the calculation using 4 intervals.

c) Which is the better estimate? Explain your answer.

Q6 The diagram below shows part of the curve $y = \frac{3}{\ln x}$.

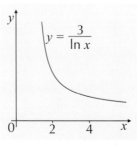

a) Using the trapezium rule with 4 intervals, find an estimate to 2 d.p. for $\int_2^4 \frac{3}{\ln x} \, dx$.

b) Without further calculation, state whether your answer to part a) is an over-estimate or under-estimate of the true area. Explain your answer.

Calculating error

Once you've estimated an integral with the trapezium rule, you can **check** how accurate your answer is by working out the **percentage error**.

To work out the **percentage error**, calculate the **exact value** of the integral, then use this **formula**:

Tip: Sometimes you'll be given the exact value in the question instead of having to calculate it.

$$\% \text{ Error} = \left| \frac{\text{exact value} - \text{approximate value}}{\text{exact value}} \right| \times 100$$

Example

Calculate the percentage error to 2 d.p. for parts a) and b) of Example 2 on p.111.

- First, work out the exact value of the integral:

$$\int_0^4 \frac{6x^2}{x^3 + 2} \, dx = [2\ln|x^3 + 2|]_0^4 = [2\ln 66] - [2\ln 2] = 2\ln 33$$

Tip: The exact integral is calculated using the formula on p.78.

- For part a), the percentage error is $\left| \frac{2\ln 33 - 6.255}{2\ln 33} \right| \times 100 = $ **10.55%**

- And for part b), $\left| \frac{2\ln 33 - 6.989}{2\ln 33} \right| \times 100 = $ **0.06%**

Tip: Don't round your exact answer if you don't have to — here you can just put $2\ln 33$ into your calculator.

The approximation with **more strips** has a **lower percentage error** — so it's a **more accurate** approximation.

Exercise 4.2

Q1 a) Use the trapezium rule with 3 intervals to approximate $\int_0^6 \sqrt{x^2 + 1} \, dx$ to 3 decimal places.

b) Given that the real value of $\int_0^6 \sqrt{x^2 + 1} \, dx$ to 3 d.p. is 19.494, calculate the percentage error for your answer to part a).

Q2 a) Use the trapezium rule and 4 intervals to find an estimate for $\int_1^5 \ln x \, dx$. Give your answer to 3 d.p.

b) Use integration by parts to find the exact value of $\int_1^5 \ln x \, dx$.

c) Hence find the percentage error in the estimate found in a).

d) Explain why the estimate in a) is an underestimate of the true area.

Q3 a) Use the trapezium rule with 4 intervals to estimate the value of $\int_0^{\frac{\pi}{2}} x \sin x \, dx$ to 3 d.p.

b) Use integration by parts to find the exact value of this integral, and hence find the percentage error in the estimate found in a).

Q4 a) Use the trapezium rule with 4 intervals to calculate an estimate of $\int_0^2 \frac{2x}{x^2 + 1} \, dx$ to 3 d.p.

b) Find the exact value of $\int_0^2 \frac{2x}{x^2 + 1} \, dx$, and hence find the percentage error in the estimate found in a).

5. Differential Equations

Learning Objectives:

- Be able to formulate a differential equation for a given situation.
- Be able to find general and particular solutions to differential equations.
- Be able to formulate and solve differential equations that model real-life situations, and interpret the results in context.

Differential equations involve differentiation as well as integration. The differentiation comes in because they always include a derivative term, usually to describe a rate of change, and integration is used to solve them.

Differential equations

- A **differential equation** is an equation that includes a **derivative term** such as $\frac{dy}{dx}$ (or $\frac{dP}{dt}, \frac{ds}{dt}, \frac{dV}{dr}$ etc, depending on the variables), as well as **other variables** (like x and y).
- Before you even think about **solving** them, you have to be able to **set up** ('**formulate**') differential equations.
- Differential equations tend to involve a **rate of change** (giving a derivative term) and a **proportion relation**, where the rate of change will be directly or inversely proportional to some function of the variables.
- It'll help to think about what the derivative **actually means**. $\frac{dy}{dx}$ is defined as 'the **rate of change** of y with respect to x', in other words, it tells you how y changes as x changes.

Tip: One of the variables in a differential equation will often be time, t, — so the question will be about how something changes over time.

Example 1

The number of bacteria in a petri dish, b, is increasing over time, t, at a rate directly proportional to the number of bacteria.
Formulate a differential equation that shows this information.

- The question tells you that you need to write a differential equation, so you know there'll be a **derivative term**. Work out what that is first.
- You're told that the number of bacteria (b) increases as time (t) increases — so that's the rate of change of b with respect to t, or $\frac{db}{dt}$.
- The rate of change, $\frac{db}{dt}$, is proportional to b, so $\frac{db}{dt} \propto b$.
- We're looking for an equation, not a proportion relation, so rewrite it:

  So $\frac{db}{dt} = kb$ for some constant k, $k > 0$.

Tip: Remember — if $a \propto b$, then $a = kb$ for some constant k.

Example 2

The volume of interdimensional space jelly, V, in a container is decreasing over time, t, at a rate inversely proportional to the square of its volume. Show this as a differential equation.

- This time the question tells you how V decreases as t increases — the derivative term is the rate of change of V with respect to t, or $\frac{dV}{dt}$.
- $\frac{dV}{dt}$ is **inversely proportional** to the **square** of V, so $\frac{dV}{dt} \propto \frac{1}{V^2}$.
- The equation needs a minus sign, because V is **decreasing** as t increases.

  $\frac{dV}{dt} = -\frac{k}{V^2}$ for some constant k, $k > 0$.

Tip: 'x is inversely proportional to y' means x is directly proportional to $\frac{1}{y}$.

Example 3

The rate of cooling of a hot liquid is proportional to the difference between the temperature of the liquid and the temperature of the room. Formulate a differential equation to represent this situation.

- Let L = temperature of the liquid, R = room temperature and t = time.

- The derivative term is the rate of change of L with respect to t, or $\dfrac{dL}{dt}$.

- The rate of change is proportional to the difference between L and R, so $\dfrac{dL}{dt} \propto (L - R)$.

- $\dfrac{dL}{dt}$ is the rate of cooling — so the temperature is **decreasing** and you need a minus sign in the equation again.

$$\frac{dL}{dt} = -k(L - R) \text{ for some constant } k,\ k > 0.$$

Tip: If the variables aren't given in the question, you'll have to come up with them for yourself.

Exercise 5.1

Q1 The number of fleas (N) on a cat is increasing over time, t, at a rate directly proportional to the number of fleas. Show this as a differential equation.

Q2 The value of x is increasing over time, t, at a rate inversely proportional to the square of x. Formulate a differential equation to show this.

Q3 The rate of depreciation of the amount (£A) a car is worth is directly proportional to the square root of A. Show this as a differential equation.

Q4 The rate of decrease of y with respect to time, t, is directly proportional to the difference between y and λ where λ is a constant. Formulate a differential equation to show this.

Q5 The volume of water which is being poured into a container is directly proportional to the volume of water (V) in the container. The container has a hole in it from which water flows out at a rate of 20 cm³s⁻¹. Show this as a differential equation.

Q5 Hint: The overall rate of change of V is the difference between the rate at which water is flowing in and the rate at which it's flowing out.

Solving differential equations

- **Solving** a differential equation means using it to find an **equation** in terms of the two variables, **without** a derivative term. To do this, you need to use **integration**.

Tip: Remember — your equation might not be in terms of x and y.

- The only differential equations containing x and y terms that you'll be able to solve in C4 are ones with **separable variables** — where x and y can be separated into functions **f(x)** and **g(y)**.

Here's the method:

- **Step 1:** Write the differential equation in the form $\dfrac{dy}{dx} = \text{f}(x)\text{g}(y)$.

Tip: Like in integration by substitution, you can treat $\dfrac{dy}{dx}$ as if it's a fraction here.

- **Step 2:** **Rearrange** the equation into the form: $\dfrac{1}{\text{g}(y)}dy = \text{f}(x)dx$.

  To do this, get all the terms containing y on the **left-hand side**, and all the terms containing x on the **right-hand side** and split up the $\dfrac{dy}{dx}$.

- **Step 3:** Now **integrate both sides**: $\displaystyle\int \dfrac{1}{\text{g}(y)}dy = \int \text{f}(x)dx$.

  Don't forget the **constant of integration** (you only need one — not one on each side). It might be useful to write the constant as **ln k** rather than **C** (see p.79).

Tip: Sometimes there'll already be another k in the differential equation (e.g. if you've formulated the equation yourself). Obviously, in that case you can't use $\ln k$ as the constant of integration, so pick another letter — you might see examples that use $\ln A$ instead.

- **Step 4:** **Rearrange** your answer to get it in a **nice form** — you might be asked to find it in the form $y = \text{h}(x)$.

- **Step 5:** If you're asked for a **general solution**, leave C (or k) in your answer. If they want a **particular solution**, they'll give you x and y values for a certain point. All you do is put these values into your equation and use them to **find C** (or k).

Example 1

Find the general solution of the differential equation $\dfrac{ds}{dt} = -6t^2$.

Tip: There's no 's' term in this differential equation. When this is the case, you can just integrate 'normally' without separating the variables.

$$s = \int \dfrac{ds}{dt}\, dt$$

- **Step 1** is already done — $\text{f}(t) = -6t^2$, $\text{g}(s) = 1$.

- **Step 2** — rearrange the equation: $ds = -6t^2\, dt$

- **Step 3** — integrate both sides: $\displaystyle\int 1\, ds = \int -6t^2\, dt$

  $\Rightarrow$ $\boxed{s = -2t^3 + C}$

Steps 4 and 5 aren't needed here — the equation doesn't need rearranging, and you're only looking for the general solution, so you're done.

Example 2

Find the particular solution of $\frac{dy}{dx} = 2y(1 + x)^2$ when $x = -1$ and $y = 4$.

- Identify $f(x)$ and $g(y)$: $f(x) = 2(1 + x)^2$ and $g(y) = y$.

- Separate the variables: $\frac{1}{y} dy = 2(1 + x)^2\, dx$

- And integrate: $\int \frac{1}{y} dy = \int 2(1 + x)^2\, dx$

  $$\Rightarrow \quad \ln|y| = \frac{2}{3}(1 + x)^3 + C$$

- Now to find the particular solution, work out the value of C for the given values of x and y:

  $$\ln 4 = \frac{2}{3}(1 + (-1))^3 + C$$

  $$\Rightarrow \quad \ln 4 = C$$

  so $\ln|y| = \frac{2}{3}(1 + x)^3 + \ln 4$

Example 3

Find the general solution of $(x - 2)(2x + 3)\frac{dy}{dx} = xy + 5y$, where $x > 2$. Give your answer in the form $y = f(x)$.

- First, separate the variables: $\frac{dy}{dx} = \frac{x + 5}{(x - 2)(2x + 3)} \times y$

  $$\frac{1}{y} dy = \frac{x + 5}{(x - 2)(2x + 3)}\, dx$$

- To make the right-hand side easier to integrate, write it as partial fractions (see Chapter 1):

  $$\frac{x + 5}{(x - 2)(2x + 3)} \equiv \frac{A}{x - 2} + \frac{B}{2x + 3}$$

  $$\Rightarrow \quad x + 5 \equiv A(2x + 3) + B(x - 2)$$

- Solving for A and B gives $A = 1$, $B = -1$, so $\frac{1}{y} dy = \frac{1}{x - 2} - \frac{1}{2x + 3}\, dx$

- Now you can integrate: $\int \frac{1}{y} dy = \int \frac{1}{x - 2} - \frac{1}{2x + 3}\, dx$

  $$\Rightarrow \quad \ln|y| = \ln|x - 2| - \frac{1}{2}\ln|2x + 3| + \ln k$$

  $$\Rightarrow \quad \ln|y| = \ln\left|\frac{k(x - 2)}{\sqrt{2x + 3}}\right|$$

  You know $x > 2$ so $x - 2$ is positive and the modulus can be removed. $\Rightarrow$

  $$y = \frac{k(x - 2)}{\sqrt{2x + 3}}$$

Tip: Since all the other terms are ln (something), it makes sense to use ln k as the constant of integration here, then you can use the log laws to simplify.

Example 4

Find the particular solution to the differential equation $\dfrac{db}{dt} = 4\sqrt{b}$, given that when $t = 12$, $b = 900$.

Give your answer in the form $b = f(t)$.

- Rearranging $\dfrac{db}{dt} = 4\sqrt{b}$ gives: $\qquad\qquad \dfrac{1}{\sqrt{b}}\,db = 4\,dt$

- Integrate both sides: $\qquad\qquad\qquad \int b^{-\frac{1}{2}}\,db = \int 4\,dt$

$$\Rightarrow \qquad\qquad 2b^{\frac{1}{2}} = 4t + C$$

- In this case, it's easier to find C for the given values of b and t before you rearrange the equation:

$$2\sqrt{b} = 4t + C \quad\Rightarrow\quad 2\sqrt{900} = 4(12) + C$$
$$\Rightarrow\ 60 = 48 + C$$
$$\Rightarrow\ C = 12$$

Tip: Rearranging the equation first, then finding C would give you a quadratic in C to solve, so it's easier to leave the rearrangement till last here.

- Now rearrange to get the form $b = f(t)$:

$$2\sqrt{b} = 4t + 12 \quad\Rightarrow\quad \sqrt{b} = 2t + 6$$
$$\Rightarrow\quad \boxed{b = 4t^2 + 24t + 36}$$

Exercise 5.2

Q1 Find the general solutions of the following differential equations where $x \geq 0$. Give your answers in the form $y = f(x)$.

a) $\dfrac{dy}{dx} = 8x^3$
b) $\dfrac{dy}{dx} = 5y$

c) $\dfrac{dy}{dx} = 6x^2 y$
d) $\dfrac{dy}{dx} = \dfrac{y}{x}$

e) $\dfrac{dy}{dx} = (y + 1)\cos x$
f) $\dfrac{dy}{dx} = \dfrac{(3x - 6)y}{(x - 4)(2x - 5)}$

Q1f) Hint: You'll need to do some work before you can integrate with respect to x.

Q2 Find the particular solutions of the following differential equations at the given conditions:

a) $\dfrac{dy}{dx} = -\dfrac{x}{y}$ $\qquad\qquad x = 0,\ y = 2$

b) $\dfrac{dx}{dt} = \dfrac{2}{\sqrt{x}}$ $\qquad\qquad t = 5,\ x = 9$

c) $\dfrac{dV}{dt} = 3(V - 1)$ $\qquad\quad t = 0,\ V = 5$

d) $\dfrac{dy}{dx} = \dfrac{\tan y}{x}$ $\qquad\qquad x = 2,\ y = \dfrac{\pi}{2}$

e) $\dfrac{dx}{dt} = 10x(x + 1)$ $\qquad\ t = 0,\ x = 1$

Q3 The rate of increase of the variable V at time t satisfies the differential equation $\frac{dV}{dt} = a - bV$, where a and b are positive constants.

   a) Show that $V = \frac{a}{b} - Ae^{-bt}$, where A is a positive constant.

   b) Given that $V = \frac{a}{4b}$ when $t = 0$, find A in terms of a and b.

   c) Find the value V approaches as t gets very large.

Q4 a) Solve the differential equation $\frac{dx}{dt} = (x + 2)(2x + 3)\tan t$, where $x \neq -2, -\frac{3}{2}$, given that $x = 0$ when $t = 0$.

   b) Find x when $t = \frac{\pi}{3}$.

Applying differential equations to real-life problems

- Some questions involve taking **real-life problems** and using differential equations to **model** them.

- **Population** questions come up quite often — the population might be **increasing** or **decreasing**, and you have to find and solve differential equations to show it. In cases like this, one variable will usually be t, **time**.

- You might be given a **starting condition** — e.g. the **initial population**. The important thing to remember is that:

> the starting condition occurs when $t = 0$

Tip: This might seem pretty obvious, but it's really important.

- Once you've solved the differential equation you can use it to **answer questions** about the model. For example, if the equation is for population you might be asked to find the **population** after a certain number of years, or the **number of years** it takes to reach a certain population. Don't forget to relate the answer back to the situation given in the question.

Questions like the ones below can be a bit **overwhelming**, but follow things through **step by step** and they shouldn't be too bad.

Example 1

The population of rabbits in a park is decreasing as winter approaches. The rate of decrease is directly proportional to the current number of rabbits (P).

a) **Explain why this situation can be modelled by the differential equation $\frac{dP}{dt} = -kP$, where t is the time in days and k is a positive constant.**

- The model states that the rate of decrease in the rabbit population (i.e. $\frac{dP}{dt}$) is **proportional** to P. This means $\frac{dP}{dt} \propto P$.

- By introducing a **constant** of proportionality, the model becomes:
$$\frac{dP}{dt} = -kP$$

- The minus sign shows that the population is decreasing.

b) **If the initial population is P_0, solve your differential equation to find P in terms of P_0, k and t.**

- First, solve the differential equation to find the general solution:

$$\frac{dP}{dt} = -kP \implies \frac{1}{P}\,dP = -k\,dt$$
$$\implies \int \frac{1}{P}\,dP = \int -k\,dt$$
$$\implies \ln P = -kt + C$$

Tip: You don't need modulus signs when you integrate to get $\ln P$ here. $P \geq 0$ as you can't have a negative population.

- At $t = 0$, $P = P_0$. Putting these values into the equation gives:

$$\ln P_0 = -k(0) + C \implies \ln P_0 = C$$

- So the equation becomes:

$$\ln P = -kt + \ln P_0 \implies P = e^{(-kt + \ln P_0)} = e^{-kt}e^{\ln P_0}$$
$$\implies P = P_0 e^{-kt}$$

c) **Given that $k = 0.1$, find the time at which the population of rabbits will have halved, to the nearest day.**

- When the population of rabbits has halved, $P = \frac{1}{2}P_0$. You've been told that $k = 0.1$, so substitute these values into the equation above and solve for t:

$$\frac{1}{2}P_0 = P_0 e^{-0.1t} \implies \frac{1}{2} = e^{-0.1t}$$
$$\implies \ln \frac{1}{2} = -0.1t$$
$$\implies -0.6931 = -0.1t$$
$$\implies t = 6.931$$

Tip: Make sure you always link the numbers back to the situation.

- So to the nearest day, $t = 7$.
  This means that it will take $\boxed{7 \text{ days}}$ for the population to halve.

Example 2

Water is leaking from the bottom of a water tank shaped like a vertical cylinder, so that at time t seconds the depth, D, of water in the tank is decreasing at a rate proportional to $\frac{1}{D^2}$.

a) **Explain why the depth of water satisfies the differential equation $\frac{dD}{dt} = -\frac{k}{D^2}$ for some constant $k > 0$.**

The question tells you that the rate at which D decreases (i.e. $\frac{dD}{dt}$) is inversely proportional to D^2. This can be written as :

$$\frac{dD}{dt} \propto \frac{1}{D^2} \implies \frac{dD}{dt} = -\frac{k}{D^2}, \text{ for some } k > 0 .$$

The minus sign indicates that the depth of the water is decreasing.

b) **Given that D is decreasing at a rate of 2 cm s^{-1} when $D = 40$ cm, find k.**

Use the differential equation for D: $\frac{dD}{dt} = -\frac{k}{D^2}$

So $\frac{dD}{dt} = -2$ when $D = 40 \implies -\frac{k}{40^2} = -2$

$$\implies k = 2 \times 40^2 = \boxed{3200}$$

c) **Given that $D = 60$ cm at $t = 0$ s , find a particular solution to the differential equation for D, and hence calculate how long it takes for the tank to empty.**

Tip: There are a few steps to part c) — first you have to find the general solution, then sub in the values given to find the particular solution, then use this solution to answer the question.

■ Solve the differential equation, using the value of k from part b), to find the general solution:

$$\frac{dD}{dt} = -\frac{3200}{D^2} \Rightarrow D^2\,dD = -3200\,dt$$

$$\Rightarrow \int D^2\,dD = \int -3200\,dt$$

$$\Rightarrow \frac{1}{3}D^3 = -3200t + C$$

■ When $t = 0$, $D = 60$. Putting these values into the equation gives:

$$\frac{1}{3}60^3 = -3200(0) + C \Rightarrow C = 72\ 000$$

So $\frac{1}{3}D^3 = 72\ 000 - 3200t$

■ The tank is empty when $D = 0 \Rightarrow 72\ 000 = 3200t$

$$\Rightarrow \boxed{t = 22.5 \text{ s}}$$

d) **Given that the radius of the cylinder is 20 cm, calculate the rate at which the volume of water in the tank is decreasing when $t = 10$ s.**

■ The volume of water in the tank is $V = \pi r^2 h = \pi(20)^2 D = 400\pi D$.

$$\Rightarrow \frac{dV}{dD} = 400\pi$$

■ So using the chain rule:

$$\frac{dV}{dt} = \frac{dV}{dD} \times \frac{dD}{dt} = 400\pi \times -\frac{3200}{D^2} = -\frac{1280000\pi}{D^2}$$

Tip: Part d) is a 'connected rates of change' question — see p.55 if you've forgotten how to tackle them.

■ When $t = 10$, $\frac{1}{3}D^3 = 72000 - 3200(10) = 40000$

$$\Rightarrow D = \sqrt[3]{3 \times 40000} = 49.324 \text{ cm}$$

So $\frac{dV}{dt} = \frac{-1280000\pi}{49.324^2} = -1652.87\text{cm}^3\text{s}^{-1}$

■ So the volume is decreasing at a rate of $\boxed{1650 \text{ cm}^3\text{s}^{-1}}$ (3 s.f.)

Exercise 5.3

Q1 A virus spreads so that t hours after infection, the rate of increase of the number of germs (N) in the body of an infected person is directly proportional to the number of germs in the body.

Q1 Hint: Don't be put off by the amount of information given in the question. Just go through it step by step.

　　a) Given that this can be represented by the differential equation $\frac{dN}{dt} = kN$, show that the general solution of this equation is
$N = Ae^{kt}$, where A and k are positive constants.

　　b) Given that a person catching the virus will initially be infected with 200 germs and that this will double to 400 germs in 8 hours, find the number of infected germs a person has after 24 hours.

Q2 The rate of depreciation of the value (V) of a car at time t after it is first purchased is directly proportional to V.

a) If the initial value of the car is V_0, show that $V = V_0 e^{-kt}$, where k is a positive constant.

b) If the car drops to one half of its initial value in the first year after purchase, how long (to the nearest month) will it take to be worth 5% of its initial value?

Q3 It is thought that the rate of increase of the number of field mice (N) in a given area is directly proportional to N.

a) Formulate a differential equation for N.

b) Given that in 4 weeks the number of mice in a particular field has risen from 20 to 30, find the length of time, to the nearest week, before the field is over-run with 1000 mice.

A biologist believes that the rate of increase of the number field mice is actually directly proportional to the square root of N when natural factors such as predators and disease are taken into account.

c) Repeat parts a) and b) using this new model.

Q4 A cube has side length x. At time t seconds, the side length is increasing at a rate of $\dfrac{1}{x^2(t+1)}$ cm s^{-1}.

a) Show that the volume (V) is increasing at a rate which satisfies the differential equation $\dfrac{dV}{dt} = \dfrac{3}{t+1}$.

b) Given that the volume of the cube is initially 15 cm³, find the length of time, to 3 s.f., for it to reach a volume of 19 cm³.

Q5 A sinister cult has developed a new recruitment strategy. The rate of increase of the number of cult members (y) in a town can be represented by the differential equation $\dfrac{dy}{dt} = k(p - y)$, where p is the population of the town and t is the time in days since the new strategy was introduced in the town.

a) Find the general solution of this equation.

b) The cult tests its strategy in the town of Mathchester. Given that the population of Mathchester is 30 000, the cult initially has 10 000 members in the town, and it takes 5 days for the membership to reach 12 000, how long, to the nearest day, will it take to reach 25 000?

Q5 c) Hint: You just need to sketch the graph of the equation you found in part b).

c) Draw a graph to show this.

d) The Supreme Leader wants 28 000 cult members in Mathchester within 92 days of introducing the new recruitment strategy. According to the model, will he achieve this?

Review Exercise — Chapter 6

Q1 Find the following integrals, using the given substitution in each case.

a) $\int 16x(5 - x^2)^5 \, dx$, using $u = 5 - x^2$

b) $\int 3 \sin\theta \cos^4\theta \, d\theta$, using $u = \cos\theta$

c) $\int e^x(e^x + 1)(e^x - 1)^2 \, dx$, using $u = e^x - 1$

Q2 Find the exact value of each of the following, using the given substitutions.

a) $\int_2^4 x(x^2 - 4)^3 \, dx$, using $u = x^2 - 4$

b) $\int_{\frac{\pi}{4}}^{\frac{\pi}{3}} \sec^4 x \tan x \, dx$, using $u = \sec x$

c) $\int_3^{11} \frac{2x}{\sqrt{3x - 8}} \, dx$, using $u = \sqrt{3x - 8}$

Q3 Find:

a) $\int_0^{\frac{\pi}{2}} \frac{1}{4} \cos x \sin 2x \, dx$, using the substitution $u = \cos x$

b) $\int_1^{\sqrt{3}} \frac{4x}{\sqrt{1 + x^2}} \, dx$, using the substitution $x = \cot\theta$, $-\frac{\pi}{2} \leq \theta \leq \frac{\pi}{2}$

Q4 Use integration by parts to solve:

a) $\int 3x^2 \ln x \, dx$

b) $\int 4x \cos 4x \, dx$

c) $\int_0^4 e^{\frac{x}{2}} x^2 \, dx$

Q5 Region R is enclosed by the x-axis and the lines $y = 2x - 1$, $x = 1$ and $x = 3$.
Find the exact volume of the solid generated when R is rotated 2π radians about the x-axis.

Q6 Find the exact volume of the solid formed when the area bounded by the curve $y = \frac{1}{x}$,
the x-axis and the lines $x = 2$ and $x = 4$ is rotated 2π radians about the x-axis.

Q7 Find the exact volume of the solid formed when the region bounded by the curve $y = 4\sqrt{\ln x}$
and the lines $y = 0$, $x = 1$ and $x = 2$ is rotated 2π radians about the x-axis.

Q8 Curve C is defined by the parametric equations $x = t^2 - 3t$ and $y = \frac{1}{\sqrt{t^3}}$, for $t > 2$.
The region R is bounded by C, the x-axis and the lines $x = 4$ and $x = 54$. Find:
a) the area of R,
b) the volume of the solid formed when R is rotated 2π radians about the x-axis, to 3 d.p.

Q9 The region S is enclosed by the curve given by the equations $x = \cos\theta + \theta$ and $y = \cot\theta$,
the x-axis, and the vertical lines corresponding to $\theta_1 = \frac{\pi}{6}$ and $\theta_2 = \frac{\pi}{2}$.
a) Find the area of S to 3 s.f.
b) Show that V, the volume of revolution formed when S is rotated 2π radians about the
x-axis, is given by $\pi \int_{\frac{\pi}{6}}^{\frac{\pi}{2}} \cosec^2\theta - 1 - \cosec\theta + \sin\theta \, d\theta$.
c) Hence calculate V to 3 s.f.

Q10 a) Use the trapezium rule with 3 intervals to find an approximate value of $\int_1^7 \frac{5}{x} \, dx$.
Give your answers to 3 significant figures.

b) Calculate the exact value of $\int_1^7 \frac{5}{x} \, dx$. Hence find the percentage error in your estimate.

Q11 a) Complete the following table of values to 3 d.p. for $y = \ln(x^3 + 4)$.

x	1	1.1	1.2	1.3	1.4	1.5
y	1.609	1.674	1.745		1.909	

b) Use the trapezium rule and all the values in the table to estimate $\int_1^{1.5} \ln(x^3 + 4)\,dx$ to 2 d.p.

Q12 Use the trapezium rule to estimate the value of $\int_0^6 (6x - 12)(x^2 - 4x + 3)^2 dx$, first using 4 strips and then again with 6 strips. Calculate the percentage error for each answer.

Q13 Formulate differential equations to represent the following:

a) The rate of increase of x as y increases is directly proportional to the square of x.

b) The volume (V) of water in a container is decreasing with time (t) at a rate inversely proportional to the square root of V.

c) The speed, s, of a moving object is decreasing with time at a rate directly proportional to the difference between s and the object's initial speed, s_0.

Q14 Find the general solution to the differential equation $\dfrac{dy}{dx} = \dfrac{1}{y}\cos x$.
Give your answer in the form $y^2 = f(x)$.

Q15 Find the particular solution of the differential equation $\dfrac{dx}{dt} = kte^t$,
given that $x = 0$ when $t = 1$ and $x = -3$ when $t = 0$.

Q16 a) Find the general solution of the equation $\dfrac{dx}{d\theta} = \cos^2 x \cot \theta$.

b) Given that $x = \dfrac{\pi}{4}$ when $\theta = \dfrac{\pi}{2}$, find a particular solution.

c) Hence find the value of x when $\theta = \dfrac{\pi}{6}$, for $0 < x < \dfrac{\pi}{2}$.

Q17 The population of squirrels is increasing suspiciously quickly.
The rate of increase is directly proportional to the current number of squirrels, S.

a) Formulate a differential equation to model the rate of increase in terms of S, t (time in weeks) and k, a positive constant.

b) The squirrels need a population of 150 to successfully take over the forest. If, initially, $S = 30$ and $\dfrac{dS}{dt} = 6$, how long (to the nearest week) will it take before they can overthrow the evil hedgehogs?

Q18 The rate of decrease of temperature ($T\,°C$) of a cup of tea with time (t minutes) satisfies the differential equation $\dfrac{dT}{dt} = -k(T - 21)$, where k is a positive constant.

a) Given that the initial temperature of the tea is 90 °C, and it cools to 80 °C in 5 minutes, find a particular solution for T.

b) Use this solution to find: (i) the temperature of the tea after 15 minutes,
(ii) the time it takes to drop to 40 °C.

c) Sketch the graph of T against t.

1   Find the volume of the solid formed when the region R, bounded by the curve $y = \operatorname{cosec} x$, the x-axis and the lines $x = \frac{\pi}{4}$ and $x = \frac{\pi}{3}$, is rotated 2π radians about the x-axis. Give your answer to 3 decimal places.

(3 marks)

2   **Figure 1** shows the graph of $y = x \sin x$. The region R is bounded by the curve and the x-axis ($0 \leq x \leq \pi$).

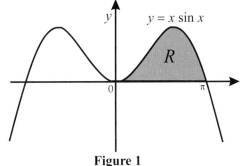

Figure 1

a)   Fill in the missing values of y in the table below. Give your answers to 4 decimal places.

x	0	$\frac{\pi}{4}$	$\frac{\pi}{2}$	$\frac{3\pi}{4}$	π
y	0	0.5554			0

(2 marks)

b)   Hence find an approximation for the area of R, using the trapezium rule. Give your answer to 3 decimal places.

(4 marks)

c)   Find the exact area of R using integration by parts.

(4 marks)

d)   Hence find the percentage error of the approximation.

(2 marks)

3   Find the value of $\int_{1}^{2} \frac{8}{x}(\ln x + 2)^3 \, dx$ using the substitution $u = \ln x$. Give your answer to 4 s.f.

(6 marks)

4   a)   Find $\int \frac{1}{x(2x-3)} \, dx$ using partial fractions.

(4 marks)

     b)   Use integration by parts to calculate the exact value of $\int_{1}^{4} \frac{2\ln x}{(2x-3)^2} \, dx$.

(5 marks)

5 An equilateral triangular prism of material expands when exposed to water.

After t seconds, the side length of the triangular cross section is x mm and the length of the prism is $4x$ mm. The volume of the prism is increasing at a constant rate of 4.2 mm³s⁻¹

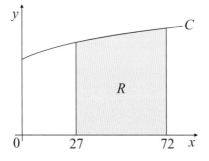

a) Find $\dfrac{\mathrm{d}x}{\mathrm{d}t}$ when the side length of the cross section of the prism is 6 mm. Give your answer correct to 3 s.f.

(4 marks)

b) Find the rate of increase of the cross-sectional area of the prism when $x = 3$. Give your answer correct to 3 s.f.

(3 marks)

6 A solid hemisphere of radius r and surface area S is decreasing in size.

a) Given that r is decreasing at a rate directly proportional to rt,

(i)   formulate a differential equation in terms of r, t and a positive constant k,

(2 marks)

(ii) show that $\dfrac{\mathrm{d}S}{\mathrm{d}t} = -2ktS$

(4 marks)

b) Given that the total surface area of the hemisphere is 200 cm² at time $t = 10$ minutes and 50 cm² at time $t = 30$ mins,

(i)   find the particular solution of the equation $\dfrac{\mathrm{d}S}{\mathrm{d}t} = -2ktS$,

(6 marks)

(ii) hence find the initial surface area of the hemisphere.

(1 mark)

7 The graph below shows part of the curve C, which is defined by the equations $x = t^2 - 6t$, $y = \sqrt{3t}$, for $t > 6$.

The region R is bounded by C, the x-axis and the lines $x = 27$ and $x = 72$. Find the volume of the solid generated when R is rotated 360° about the x-axis.

(5 marks)

8   a)   Find the general solution to the differential equation

$$\frac{dy}{dx} = \frac{\cos x \cos^2 y}{\sin x}.$$

(4 marks)

b)   Given that $y = \pi$ when $x = \frac{\pi}{6}$, solve the differential equation above.

(2 marks)

9   Use integration by parts to find:

a) $\int x \sin 4x \, dx$

(3 marks)

b) $\int x^2 \cos 4x \, dx$

(4 marks)

10   a)   Complete the following table of values for $y = 4xe^{x^2}$.
Give your answers to 4 decimal places.

x	0	0.25	0.5	0.75	1
y	0	1.0645			10.8731

(2 marks)

b)   Use the trapezium rule with 4 intervals to find an
estimate to 4 significant figures for $\int_0^1 4xe^{x^2} \, dx$.

(4 marks)

c)   Use integration by substitution with $u = x^2$
to find the exact value of $\int_0^1 4xe^{x^2} \, dx$.

(4 marks)

d)   Hence find the percentage error in the estimate found in b).

(2 marks)

11   A supermarket sets up an advertising campaign to increase sales on the cheese counter.
After the start of the campaign, the number of kilograms of cheese sold each day, S,
increases over time, t days. The increase in sales is modelled by the differential equation
$\frac{dS}{dt} = k\sqrt{S}$ $(k > 0)$.

a)   At the start of the campaign, the supermarket was selling 81 kg of cheese a day.
Use this information to solve the differential equation,
giving S in terms of k and t.

(4 marks)

b)   Given that $\frac{dS}{dt} = 18$ at the start of the campaign, calculate the number
of kg sold on the fifth day after the start of the campaign $(t = 5)$.

(3 marks)

c)   How many days will it take before the sales reach 225 kg a day?

(2 marks)

1. Vectors

You might have seen vectors before in M1 — they've got a size and a direction. In this section you'll see how they work and what you can do with them.

Learning Objectives:

- Understand what vectors are and how to represent them.
- Be able to add and subtract vectors and multiply them by scalars.
- Be able to show that two vectors are parallel, and that three points are collinear.
- Be able to convert vectors between unit vector form and column vectors.

Introducing vectors

> **Scalars** are quantities **without a direction** — e.g. a speed of 2 m/s.

> **Vectors** have both **size and direction** — e.g. a velocity of 2 m/s on a bearing of 050°.

- Vectors are drawn as **lines** with **arrowheads** on them.

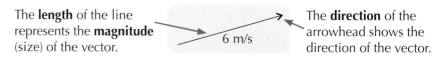

The **length** of the line represents the **magnitude** (size) of the vector.

The **direction** of the arrowhead shows the direction of the vector.

- Sometimes vectors are drawn to **scale**:

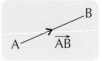

- Vectors are usually **written** using either a **lowercase bold** letter or a **lowercase underlined** letter. When the **endpoints** of a vector are labelled, the vector can also be written by putting an **arrow** over the endpoints:

Tip: When a vector is typed it's usually bold, but if you're handwriting a vector you should always write it underlined, e.g. <u>a</u>.

Adding vectors

- You can **add** vectors together by drawing the arrows **nose to tail**.

Tip: You might also see this referred to as the triangle rule.

- The single vector that goes from the start to the end of the combined vectors is called the **resultant vector**.

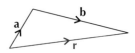

Resultant: $\mathbf{r} = \mathbf{a} + \mathbf{b}$

- This method of adding is called the **parallelogram rule** because **a** and **b** form the sides of a parallelogram which has the resultant vector $\mathbf{r} = \mathbf{a} + \mathbf{b}$ as its diagonal.

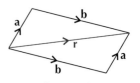

$\mathbf{a} + \mathbf{b} = \mathbf{r} = \mathbf{b} + \mathbf{a}$

When you add two vectors you're really **combining** two **translations**:

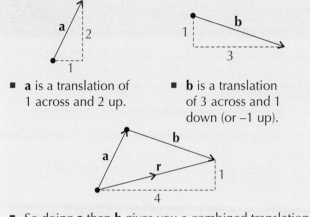

- **a** is a translation of 1 across and 2 up.
- **b** is a translation of 3 across and 1 down (or –1 up).

- So doing **a** then **b** gives you a combined translation of $(1 + 3) = 4$ across and $(2 - 1) = 1$ up.

Subtracting vectors

- The vector –**a** points in the opposite direction to the vector **a**. They're both exactly the **same size**.

- So **subtracting** a vector is the same as **adding the negative vector**:

> To go from Q to P you can't just add the vectors **a** and **b** because the arrows don't run from end to end.
>
> But replace vector **a** with –**a** (which goes in the opposite direction) and now you can add.

So: $\overrightarrow{QP} = \mathbf{b} + (-\mathbf{a}) = \mathbf{b} - \mathbf{a}$

Tip: So when you're adding, going against the arrow on a vector is the same as subtracting that vector.

You can use these rules to find a vector in terms of **other vectors**.

Example

Find $\overrightarrow{WZ}$ and $\overrightarrow{ZX}$ in terms of p, q and r.

- Relabel the vectors on the diagram so that they run from end to end.

- When you do this you can see that $\overrightarrow{WZ}$ is the resultant vector of $-\mathbf{p} + \mathbf{q} + (-\mathbf{r})$.

- So: $\overrightarrow{WZ} = -\mathbf{p} + \mathbf{q} - \mathbf{r}$

- Using the addition and subtraction rules in the same way to find $\overrightarrow{ZX}$ you get: $\overrightarrow{ZX} = \mathbf{r} - \mathbf{q}$

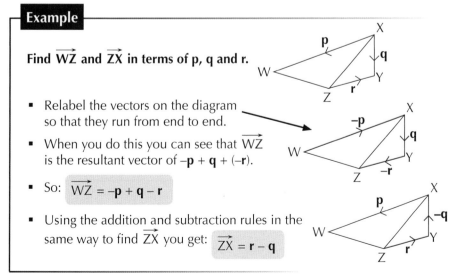

Tip: You don't have to draw this diagram out — it's enough to know that if you want your vector to go from W to X and the vector **p** goes from X to W then you need to use –**p** instead.

Scalar multiplication

- You can **multiply** a vector by a **scalar** (just a number).

- When you do this the **length changes** but the **direction** stays the **same**...

> **Tip:** The number in these expressions is a scalar, the letter is a vector.

$$\mathbf{a} \xrightarrow{\times 3} 3\mathbf{a} \xrightarrow{\times (-1)} -3\mathbf{a}$$

...unless the scalar is **negative**, then the direction's **reversed**.

- You can '**divide**' a vector by a scalar as well, you just **multiply** the vector by the **reciprocal** of the scalar. E.g. $\frac{\mathbf{a}}{3} = \frac{1}{3}\mathbf{a}$.

- **Multiplying** a vector by a **non-zero** scalar always produces a **parallel** vector.

Example 1

X divides BC in the ratio 2:5. Find $\overrightarrow{AX}$ in terms of p and q.

- $\overrightarrow{AX} = \overrightarrow{AB} + \overrightarrow{BX}$. You know $\overrightarrow{AB} = \mathbf{p}$, so you just need to find $\overrightarrow{BX}$ in terms of **p** and **q**.

> **Tip:** 'X divides **BC** in the ratio 2:5' means X is $\frac{2}{7}$ of the way from **B** to **C**. 'X divides **CB** in the ratio 2:5' would mean X is $\frac{2}{7}$ of the way from **C** to **B**.

- X divides BC in the ratio 2:5, so BX is $\frac{2}{2+5} = \frac{2}{7}$ of BC. That means $\overrightarrow{BX} = \frac{2}{7}\overrightarrow{BC}$.

- Now to find $\overrightarrow{BC}$ in terms of **p** and **q**:
$$\overrightarrow{BC} = \overrightarrow{BA} + \overrightarrow{AC} = -\overrightarrow{AB} + \overrightarrow{AC} = -\mathbf{p} + \mathbf{q}$$

- Plugging all this back into your equation for $\overrightarrow{AX}$ gives:
$$\overrightarrow{AX} = \overrightarrow{AB} + \overrightarrow{BX} = \overrightarrow{AB} + \frac{2}{7}\overrightarrow{BC} = \mathbf{p} + \frac{2}{7}(-\mathbf{p} + \mathbf{q}) = \frac{5}{7}\mathbf{p} + \frac{2}{7}\mathbf{q}$$

- All **parallel** vectors are **scalar multiples** of each other, so showing that one vector is a scalar multiple of another is the same as showing they're parallel.

Example 2

Show that the vector 9a + 15b is parallel to the vector 6a + 10b.

- To show that they're **parallel** you need to try and write one as a **scalar multiple** of the other.

- To do this you need to find the **scalar factor** that you multiply by:
$$\frac{9\mathbf{a}}{6\mathbf{a}} = 1.5$$
$$\frac{15\mathbf{b}}{10\mathbf{b}} = 1.5$$

> Each **part** of the vector has the **same** scalar factor

> **Tip:** If you're asked to find whether or not two vectors are parallel then you need to check the scalar factor for each coefficient. If they're all the same then the vectors are parallel, if not then they're not.

- In this case the scalar factor is the **same** for **a** and **b**, so it's possible to write the first vector as a scalar multiple of the second.

- So $9\mathbf{a} + 15\mathbf{b} = 1.5(6\mathbf{a} + 10\mathbf{b})$ and the vectors are parallel.

Example 3

$\vec{CA}$ = p, $\vec{CB}$ = q, point M lies halfway along $\vec{CB}$, point N lies halfway along $\vec{AB}$. Show that $\vec{MN}$ is parallel to $\vec{CA}$.

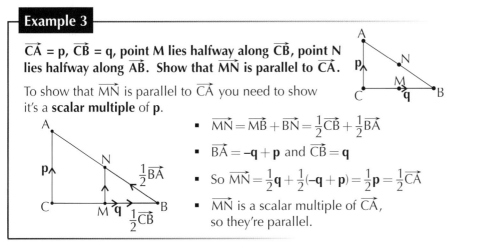

To show that $\vec{MN}$ is parallel to $\vec{CA}$ you need to show it's a **scalar multiple** of **p**.

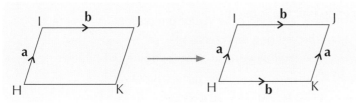

- $\vec{MN} = \vec{MB} + \vec{BN} = \frac{1}{2}\vec{CB} + \frac{1}{2}\vec{BA}$

- $\vec{BA} = -\mathbf{q} + \mathbf{p}$ and $\vec{CB} = \mathbf{q}$

- So $\vec{MN} = \frac{1}{2}\mathbf{q} + \frac{1}{2}(-\mathbf{q} + \mathbf{p}) = \frac{1}{2}\mathbf{p} = \frac{1}{2}\vec{CA}$

- $\vec{MN}$ is a scalar multiple of $\vec{CA}$, so they're parallel.

- A vector can be **anywhere** in **space**.
- This means that vectors of the **same size** which are **parallel** and pointing in the **same direction** are the **same**, even if they're not in the same place.
- E.g. in a parallelogram, opposite sides have the **same vector**, so knowing one means you know the other:

Tip: Look out for questions where you have to recognise that two lines are parallel in order to find a vector.

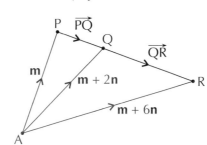

Collinear points

You can also use **vector addition** to show that three points are **collinear**.

- Three or more points are collinear if they all lie on a **single straight line**.
- If vectors $\vec{AB}$ and $\vec{BC}$ are **parallel**, then the points A, B and C must lie on a straight line, i.e. they are **collinear**.

Example

$\vec{AP}$ = **m**, $\vec{AQ}$ = **m** + 2**n**, $\vec{AR}$ = **m** + 6**n**. Show that P, Q and R are collinear.

First find $\vec{PQ}$ and $\vec{QR}$:

- $\vec{PQ} = -\vec{AP} + \vec{AQ}$
  $= -\mathbf{m} + \mathbf{m} + 2\mathbf{n} = 2\mathbf{n}$

- $\vec{QR} = -\vec{AQ} + \vec{AR}$
  $= -\mathbf{m} - 2\mathbf{n} + \mathbf{m} + 6\mathbf{n} = 4\mathbf{n}$

Now show that $\vec{QR}$ is a **scalar multiple** of $\vec{PQ}$:

- $\vec{QR} = 4\mathbf{n} = 2(2\mathbf{n}) = 2(\vec{PQ})$

- $\vec{QR}$ is a scalar multiple of $\vec{PQ}$ so the vectors are parallel, meaning the points P, Q and R lie on a **straight line** — i.e. the points P, Q and R are **collinear**.

Q1 State whether each example described below refers to a scalar quantity, a vector quantity or neither.

a) A pilot flies due south for a distance of 200 kilometres.

b) The time taken to travel from London to Exeter is 3 hours.

c) A force of 20 newtons is required to pull a sledge up the steepest section of a hill – the slope is at an angle of 5° to the horizontal.

Q2 Vectors **a** and **b** are represented by the lines below:

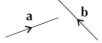

Draw and label sketches that represent the following vectors:

a) −**a**   b) 2**b**   c) **a** + **b**   d) **a** − **b**.

Q3 For the rectangle ABCD shown on the right, write down single vectors that are equivalent to:

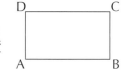

a) $\overrightarrow{AB} + \overrightarrow{BC}$ b) $\overrightarrow{BC} + \overrightarrow{CD} + \overrightarrow{DA}$ c) $\overrightarrow{DC} - \overrightarrow{BC}$

Q4 Hint: It helps to draw the shape out before you start answering the question.

Q4 In the triangle XYZ the vector **p** represents $\overrightarrow{XZ}$ and the vector **q** represents $\overrightarrow{YX}$.

Express the following in terms of **p** or **q** or both:

a) $\overrightarrow{XY}$ b) $\overrightarrow{YZ}$ c) $\overrightarrow{ZY}$

Q5 Group the following into sets of parallel vectors:

$2\mathbf{a} + \mathbf{b}$ $2\mathbf{p} + \mathbf{q}$ $2\mathbf{a} - \mathbf{b}$ $4\mathbf{b} + 8\mathbf{a}$

$5(2\mathbf{a} - \mathbf{b})$ $-\mathbf{b} - 2\mathbf{a}$ $\frac{1}{2}\mathbf{q} + \mathbf{p}$

Q6 In the rectangle ABCD, E is the midpoint of AD and F divides DC in the ratio 2:1.

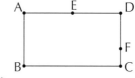

If $\overrightarrow{AB} = \mathbf{b}$ and $\overrightarrow{AD} = \mathbf{d}$, find the following vectors in terms of **b** and **d**.

a) $\overrightarrow{DF}$ b) $\overrightarrow{BE}$ c) $\overrightarrow{EF}$

Q7 Hint: You need to prove that they all lie on the same straight line — which means that the vectors between them will be parallel.

Q7 $\overrightarrow{OA} = \mathbf{a}$, $\overrightarrow{OB} = \mathbf{b}$, $\overrightarrow{OC} = 5\mathbf{a} - 4\mathbf{b}$. Show that A, B and C are collinear.

Q8 In triangle DEF, J and L are midpoints of ED and FD respectively.

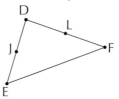

a) Given that $\overrightarrow{EF} = \mathbf{f}$ and $\overrightarrow{ED} = \mathbf{d}$, find $\overrightarrow{JL}$ in terms of **f** and **d**.

b) What can you deduce about JL compared to EF?

Position vectors

You can use a vector to describe the **position** of a point in relation to the **origin**, O. This vector is called a **position vector**.

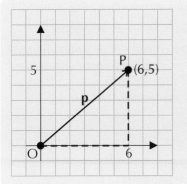

- One way of describing the position of the point P is with its **Cartesian coordinates** which are e.g. (6,5).
- This just tells you how far P is vertically and horizontally from the **origin** O.
- Another way of describing how far P is from the origin is using the **position vector** $\overrightarrow{OP} = \mathbf{p}$ which has **horizontal** and **vertical** components.

Tip: Position vectors always start at the origin and finish at the point they're describing the position of.

The position vector of any point A is $\overrightarrow{OA}$. It's usually called vector **a**.

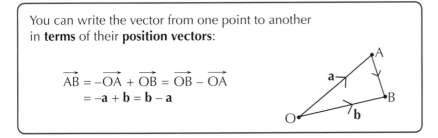

You can write the vector from one point to another in **terms** of their **position vectors**:

$$\overrightarrow{AB} = -\overrightarrow{OA} + \overrightarrow{OB} = \overrightarrow{OB} - \overrightarrow{OA}$$
$$= -\mathbf{a} + \mathbf{b} = \mathbf{b} - \mathbf{a}$$

Tip: This result will be used time after time for finding the vector from one point to another in this chapter.
Make sure you learn it in both its forms:
$$\overrightarrow{AB} = \overrightarrow{OB} - \overrightarrow{OA} = \mathbf{b} - \mathbf{a}$$

i + j units

- A **unit vector** is any vector with a **length of 1 unit**.
- The vectors **i** and **j** are **standard unit vectors**, so they each have a length of 1 unit. **i** is in the direction of the **positive x-axis**, and **j** is in the direction of the **positive y-axis**.

Every vector is made up of **horizontal** and **vertical components**, so you can express any vector as a **sum** of **i** and **j** unit vectors:

- Vector **a** goes from the origin O to the point A.
- To get from O to A you move **4** units **to the right** and **3** units **up**.
- So **a** is the **resultant** vector when you add a **horizontal vector** that goes **4 units** in the positive x direction and a **vertical vector** that goes **3 units** in the positive y direction.
- **i** and **j** are the **standard** unit vectors we use to express horizontal and vertical components. So **a** = 4**i** + 3**j**

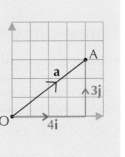

Tip: This only works for vectors which are two-dimensional. Three-dimensional vectors need an extra unit vector to describe them — you'll see more on this later on (p.134).

Example

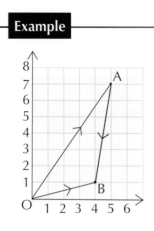

a) **Write down the position vectors of A and B in i + j form.**
- Point A lies 5 units to the right and 7 units above the origin, so the position vector of point A is: $\boxed{\mathbf{a} = 5\mathbf{i} + 7\mathbf{j}}$
- The position vector of point B is:
$$\boxed{\mathbf{b} = 4\mathbf{i} + \mathbf{j}}$$

b) **Hence find $\overrightarrow{AB}$ in terms of i and j.**
To find $\overrightarrow{AB}$:
- You know $\overrightarrow{AB} = -\overrightarrow{OA} + \overrightarrow{OB} = \overrightarrow{OB} - \overrightarrow{OA}$
$$= -\mathbf{a} + \mathbf{b} = \mathbf{b} - \mathbf{a}$$

- Add or subtract the **i** and **j** components **separately**:
Vector $\overrightarrow{AB} = \mathbf{b} - \mathbf{a} = (4\mathbf{i} + \mathbf{j}) - (5\mathbf{i} + 7\mathbf{j}) = \boxed{-\mathbf{i} - 6\mathbf{j}}$

Tip: This means that to go from A to B, you go 1 unit left and 6 units down. It's just like a translation.

Column vectors

Column vectors are another way of writing vectors in terms of their **horizontal** and **vertical components**.

- You just write the **horizontal (i) component** on **top** of the **vertical (j) component** and put a **bracket** around them:

$$x\mathbf{i} + y\mathbf{j} = \begin{pmatrix} x \\ y \end{pmatrix}$$

Tip: Using column vectors is often quicker and easier than working with sums of **i** and **j** components.

- **Calculating** with them is simple. Just add or subtract the **top** row, then add or subtract the **bottom** row **separately**:

$$\mathbf{a} = 5\mathbf{i} + 7\mathbf{j} = \begin{pmatrix} 5 \\ 7 \end{pmatrix} \quad \mathbf{b} = 4\mathbf{i} + \mathbf{j} = \begin{pmatrix} 4 \\ 1 \end{pmatrix}$$
$$\mathbf{b} - \mathbf{a} = \begin{pmatrix} 4 \\ 1 \end{pmatrix} - \begin{pmatrix} 5 \\ 7 \end{pmatrix} = \begin{pmatrix} 4-5 \\ 1-7 \end{pmatrix} = \begin{pmatrix} -1 \\ -6 \end{pmatrix}$$

- When you're **multiplying** a column vector by a **scalar** you multiply **each number** in the column vector by the scalar:

$$2\mathbf{b} - 3\mathbf{a} = 2\begin{pmatrix} 4 \\ 1 \end{pmatrix} - 3\begin{pmatrix} 5 \\ 7 \end{pmatrix} = \begin{pmatrix} 2 \times 4 \\ 2 \times 1 \end{pmatrix} - \begin{pmatrix} 3 \times 5 \\ 3 \times 7 \end{pmatrix} = \begin{pmatrix} 8 \\ 2 \end{pmatrix} - \begin{pmatrix} 15 \\ 21 \end{pmatrix} = \begin{pmatrix} -7 \\ -19 \end{pmatrix}$$

Three-dimensional vectors

Tip: Three-dimensional vectors are used to describe things in three-dimensional space, e.g. an aeroplane moving through the sky.

- **Three-dimensional vectors** have components in the direction of the **x-**, **y-** and **z-axes**. Imagine that the x- and y-axes lie flat on the page. Then imagine a **third axis** sticking straight through the page at right angles to it — this is the **z-axis**.

- The points in three dimensions are given **(x, y, z) coordinates**.

- The **unit vector** in the direction of the z-axis is **k**, so three-dimensional vectors can be written like this: $x\mathbf{i} + y\mathbf{j} + z\mathbf{k}$ or $\begin{pmatrix} x \\ y \\ z \end{pmatrix}$

- Calculating with 3D vectors is just the same as with 2D vectors, as the next example shows.

Example

The diagram below shows the position of the points P and Q.

a) Write the position vectors $\overrightarrow{OP}$ and $\overrightarrow{OQ}$ as column vectors.

$$\overrightarrow{OP} = 4\mathbf{i} + 3\mathbf{j} + 0\mathbf{k} = \begin{pmatrix} 4 \\ 3 \\ 0 \end{pmatrix}$$

$$\overrightarrow{OQ} = 2\mathbf{i} + 5\mathbf{j} + 4\mathbf{k} = \begin{pmatrix} 2 \\ 5 \\ 4 \end{pmatrix}$$

b) Hence find $\overrightarrow{PQ}$ as a column vector.

$$\overrightarrow{PQ} = -\overrightarrow{OP} + \overrightarrow{OQ} = -\begin{pmatrix} 4 \\ 3 \\ 0 \end{pmatrix} + \begin{pmatrix} 2 \\ 5 \\ 4 \end{pmatrix} = \begin{pmatrix} 2-4 \\ 5-3 \\ 4-0 \end{pmatrix} = \begin{pmatrix} -2 \\ 2 \\ 4 \end{pmatrix}$$

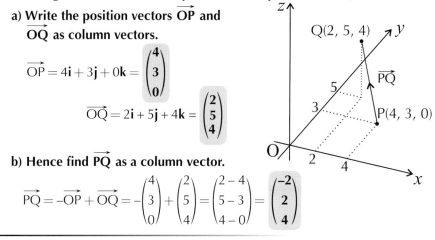

Tip: Don't get confused between a point and its position vector. Points are given by (x, y, z) coordinates and position vectors are the movement needed to get to the point from the origin, given in the form $x\mathbf{i} + y\mathbf{j} + z\mathbf{k}$. You'll need to be able to swap between the forms.

Tip: Just add along each row of the column as you do with 2D column vectors — don't forget that you've multiplied $\overrightarrow{OP}$ by the scalar '−1' so all its entries will change signs.

Exercise 1.2

Q1 A is the point $(2, 3)$ and B is the point $(4, -5)$. Write down the position vectors of A and B, giving your answers as column vectors.

Q2 R is the point $(4, -5, 1)$ and S is the point $(-3, 0, -1)$. Write down the position vectors of R and S, giving your answers in unit vector form.

Q3 C has position vector $-\mathbf{i} + 2\mathbf{j}$ and D has position vector $4\mathbf{i} - 3\mathbf{j}$.
  a) What are the Cartesian coordinates of the points C and D?
  b) Write the vectors $\overrightarrow{CD}$ and $\overrightarrow{DC}$ in unit vector form.

Q3 Hint: Remember the rule for writing the vector from A to B (see p.133):

$$\overrightarrow{AB} = \overrightarrow{OB} - \overrightarrow{OA} = \mathbf{b} - \mathbf{a}$$

Q4 Give $\overrightarrow{GH}$ and $\overrightarrow{HG}$ as column vectors, where $\overrightarrow{OG} = \begin{pmatrix} 2 \\ -3 \\ 4 \end{pmatrix}$ and $\overrightarrow{OH} = \begin{pmatrix} -1 \\ 4 \\ 9 \end{pmatrix}$.

Q5 M is the midpoint of the line PQ, where P has position vector $-3\mathbf{i} + \mathbf{j}$ and M has position vector $2\mathbf{i} - 5\mathbf{j}$.
  What is the position vector of Q?

Q6 Triangle ABC is shown on the right.

  Find the vectors $\overrightarrow{AB}$, $\overrightarrow{BC}$ and $\overrightarrow{CA}$.

C (−1, 3), *A (2, 4)*, *B (0, 1)*

Q6 Hint: The question doesn't mention $\mathbf{i}$ and $\mathbf{j}$ components or column vectors so you can answer it using either.

Q7 Quadrilateral DEFG has vertices at the points D $(-7, -2)$, E $(-3, -1)$, F $(-1, 5)$ and G $(-3, 10)$.
  a) State the vectors $\overrightarrow{DE}$, $\overrightarrow{EF}$, $\overrightarrow{FG}$ and $\overrightarrow{GD}$.
  b) Is this quadrilateral a parallelogram, a trapezium, or neither of these? Explain the reasons for your answer.

Q8 Hint: You answer questions about shapes in 3 dimensions in exactly the same way as shapes in 2 dimensions.

Q8 Triangle JKL has vertices at the points J $(4, 0, -3)$, K $(-1, 3, 0)$, L $(2, 2, 7)$. Find the vectors $\overrightarrow{JK}$, $\overrightarrow{KL}$ and $\overrightarrow{LJ}$.

2. Magnitude of Vectors

Learning Objectives:

- Be able to find the magnitude of any vector in two or three dimensions.
- Be able to find the unit vector in the direction of any vector in two or three dimensions.
- Be able to find the distance between any two two-dimensional or three-dimensional points using vectors.

The magnitude of a vector is a scalar that tells you the vector's length. In this section you'll see how to calculate it and what you can use it for.

Magnitude of two-dimensional vectors

- The **magnitude** of a vector is the **distance** between its start point and end point. It's sometimes called **modulus** instead of magnitude.

> The **magnitude** of a vector **a** is written $|\mathbf{a}|$

> The **magnitude** of a vector $\overrightarrow{AB}$ is written $|\overrightarrow{AB}|$.

- Magnitude is a **scalar**, and it's **always positive**.
- The **i** and **j** components of a vector form a convenient **right-angled triangle**, so you can use **Pythagoras' theorem** to find a vector's magnitude.

Example 1

Find the magnitude of the vector a = 5i + 3j.

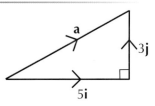

- You know the length of two sides of the right-angled triangle formed by **a** and its **horizontal** and **vertical** components.
- The magnitude of **a** is the length of the **hypotenuse** of this triangle.
- So find $|\mathbf{a}|$ using **Pythagoras**:

$$|\mathbf{a}| = \sqrt{5^2 + 3^2} = \sqrt{34} = \boxed{5.83} \text{ to 3 s.f.}$$

Tip: You don't need to draw the triangle out every time, just plug the coefficients of **i** and **j** into the Pythagoras formula.

You can use a vector's magnitude to find the **distance** between two **points**:

Example 2

$\overrightarrow{JK} = \begin{pmatrix} 4 \\ -7 \end{pmatrix}$ **Find the distance between J and K. Give your answer in surd form.**

The distance between J and K is $|\overrightarrow{JK}|$. Find the magnitude using **Pythagoras**:

$$|\overrightarrow{JK}| = \sqrt{4^2 + (-7)^2} = \boxed{\sqrt{65}}$$

You can find **missing components** of the vector using its magnitude:

Example 3

$\overrightarrow{OP} = \begin{pmatrix} 3 \\ 5 \end{pmatrix}$, $\overrightarrow{OQ} = \begin{pmatrix} -2 \\ b \end{pmatrix}$, **given that** $|\overrightarrow{PQ}| = \sqrt{29}$ **and** $|\overrightarrow{OQ}| = \sqrt{13}$**, find** b**.**

- First find $\overrightarrow{PQ}$: $\overrightarrow{PQ} = \overrightarrow{OQ} - \overrightarrow{OP} = \begin{pmatrix} -2 \\ b \end{pmatrix} - \begin{pmatrix} 3 \\ 5 \end{pmatrix} = \begin{pmatrix} -5 \\ b-5 \end{pmatrix}$

- Now find the magnitude of $\overrightarrow{PQ}$ in terms of b and compare it with the value given:

$$|\overrightarrow{PQ}| = \sqrt{25 + (b-5)^2}$$
$$\Rightarrow 29 = 25 + (b-5)^2$$
$$\Rightarrow \quad 4 = (b-5)^2$$
$$\Rightarrow \pm 2 = b - 5$$
$$\Rightarrow b = 3 \text{ or } b = 7$$

- Do the same with $\overrightarrow{OQ}$:

$$|\overrightarrow{OQ}| = \sqrt{(-2)^2 + b^2}$$
$$\Rightarrow 13 = 4 + b^2$$
$$\Rightarrow \;\; 9 = b^2$$
$$\Rightarrow \;\; b = \pm\, 3$$

- Both statements '$b = \pm 3$' and '$b = 3$ or $b = 7$' must hold, so $\boxed{b = 3}$

- To find a **unit vector** in the direction of a particular vector you just **divide** the vector by its **magnitude** (i.e. multiply by the magnitude's reciprocal).

- So the unit vector in the direction of the vector **a** is: $\dfrac{1}{|\mathbf{a}|}\mathbf{a} = \dfrac{\mathbf{a}}{|\mathbf{a}|}$.

- Its magnitude is $\dfrac{1}{|\mathbf{a}|} \times |\mathbf{a}| = 1$.

Tip: Remember, a unit vector always has a magnitude of 1.

- It's a **positive scalar multiple** of **a** (because magnitude is always positive), so it has the **same direction** as **a**.

Tip: Positive scalar multiples of **a** are parallel to **a** and have the same direction as **a**. Negative scalar multiples of **a** are parallel to **a** and have the opposite direction (the direction of –**a**).

Example 4

Find the unit vector in the direction of q = 5i – 12j.

- First find the magnitude of **q**:

$$|\mathbf{q}| = \sqrt{5^2 + (-12)^2} = \sqrt{169} = 13$$

- So the unit vector is:

$$\frac{\mathbf{q}}{|\mathbf{q}|} = \frac{1}{13}(5\mathbf{i} - 12\mathbf{j}) = \boxed{\frac{5}{13}\mathbf{i} - \frac{12}{13}\mathbf{j}}$$

Exercise 2.1

Q1 Find the exact magnitude of each of the following vectors.

a) $6\mathbf{i} + 8\mathbf{j}$

b) $12\mathbf{i} - 5\mathbf{j}$

c) $\begin{pmatrix} 2 \\ 4 \end{pmatrix}$

d) $\begin{pmatrix} -3 \\ -1 \end{pmatrix}$

e) $\begin{pmatrix} 24 \\ -7 \end{pmatrix}$

f) $\begin{pmatrix} -\sqrt{13} \\ 6 \end{pmatrix}$

g) $3\mathbf{i} + \sqrt{7}\,\mathbf{j}$

h) $-7\mathbf{j}$

Q1-3 Hint: Remember 'exact magnitude' or 'exact length' suggests some of the answers will include surds.

Q2 S has position vector $10\mathbf{i} + 5\mathbf{j}$.
Find the exact length of the line that joins point S to the origin.

Q3 For each of the pairs of vectors given below, find the exact magnitude of the resultant when the two vectors are added together.

a) $\mathbf{a} = 2\mathbf{i} + \mathbf{j}$ and $\mathbf{b} = 2\mathbf{i} - 4\,\mathbf{j}$

b) $\mathbf{u} = -5\mathbf{i} + \mathbf{j}$ and $\mathbf{v} = 9\mathbf{i} - 5\mathbf{j}$

c) $\mathbf{f} = \begin{pmatrix} 7 \\ 2 \end{pmatrix}$ and $\mathbf{g} = \begin{pmatrix} 17 \\ -12 \end{pmatrix}$

d) $\mathbf{d} = \begin{pmatrix} 4 \\ -2 \end{pmatrix}$ and $\mathbf{e} = \begin{pmatrix} -1 \\ -4 \end{pmatrix}$

Q4 $\overrightarrow{AB} = 3\mathbf{i} - 2\mathbf{j}$ and $\overrightarrow{BC} = \mathbf{i} + 5\mathbf{j}$. Find $|\overrightarrow{AC}|$.

Q5 If **a** = 4**i** + 12**j** and **b** = 13**i**, find the magnitude of **b** – **a**.

Q6 M has position vector 32**i** – 48**j** and N has position vector 21**i** + 12**j**. Find the distance between points M and N.

Q7 Find the unit vector in the direction of the vector $\begin{pmatrix} 16 \\ -12 \end{pmatrix}$.

Q8 Find the unit vector in the direction of $\overrightarrow{TU}$ where T has position vector **t** = 3**i** – 7**j** and U has position vector **u** = –5**i** – **j**.

Q9 $|\overrightarrow{FG}| = 13$. Given that $\overrightarrow{OF} = \begin{pmatrix} 4 \\ 7 \end{pmatrix}$ and $\overrightarrow{OG} = \begin{pmatrix} a \\ -5 \end{pmatrix}$, find the 2 possible values of a.

Magnitude of three-dimensional vectors

Pythagoras' theorem works in **three dimensions** too:

> The **distance** of point (**a, b, c**) from the origin is:
> $$\sqrt{a^2 + b^2 + c^2}$$

Tip: Remember the position vector of the point (a, b, c) is $a\mathbf{i} + b\mathbf{j} + c\mathbf{k}$, or as a column vector: $\begin{pmatrix} a \\ b \\ c \end{pmatrix}$

You can **derive** this formula from the **two-dimensional** Pythagoras' theorem:

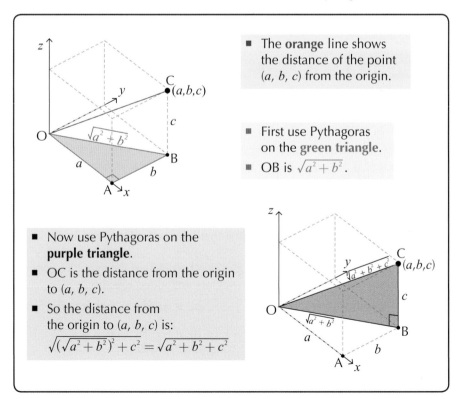

- The **orange** line shows the distance of the point (a, b, c) from the origin.

- First use Pythagoras on the **green triangle**.
- OB is $\sqrt{a^2 + b^2}$.

- Now use Pythagoras on the **purple triangle**.
- OC is the distance from the origin to (a, b, c).
- So the distance from the origin to (a, b, c) is:
$$\sqrt{(\sqrt{a^2 + b^2})^2 + c^2} = \sqrt{a^2 + b^2 + c^2}$$

The **magnitude** of the position vector $a\mathbf{i} + b\mathbf{j} + c\mathbf{k}$ is the same as the distance of point (a, b, c) from the origin:

$$|a\mathbf{i} + b\mathbf{j} + c\mathbf{k}| = \sqrt{a^2 + b^2 + c^2}$$

Example 1

The diagram below shows the position of point Q.
Find $|\overrightarrow{OQ}|$, giving your answer in reduced surd form.

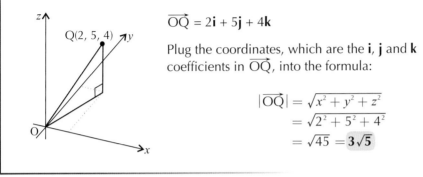

$\overrightarrow{OQ} = 2\mathbf{i} + 5\mathbf{j} + 4\mathbf{k}$

Plug the coordinates, which are the $\mathbf{i}$, $\mathbf{j}$ and $\mathbf{k}$ coefficients in $\overrightarrow{OQ}$, into the formula:

$$\begin{aligned} |\overrightarrow{OQ}| &= \sqrt{x^2 + y^2 + z^2} \\ &= \sqrt{2^2 + 5^2 + 4^2} \\ &= \sqrt{45} = \mathbf{3\sqrt{5}} \end{aligned}$$

Tip: As in two dimensions, there's no need to draw a triangle out to use Pythagoras — you can just plug the coordinates into the formula.

The formula can also be used to find the **distance** between **two points**:

The **distance** between any **two points** (x_1, y_1, z_1) and (x_2, y_2, z_2) is:
$$\sqrt{(x_2 - x_1)^2 + (y_2 - y_1)^2 + (z_2 - z_1)^2}$$

You can **prove** this formula as follows:

- The **distance** between the two points $P(x_1, y_1, z_1)$ and $Q(x_2, y_2, z_2)$ is the **magnitude** of the vector $\overrightarrow{PQ}$.

- $\overrightarrow{PQ} = \overrightarrow{OQ} - \overrightarrow{OP} = (x_2\mathbf{i} + y_2\mathbf{j} + z_2\mathbf{k}) - (x_1\mathbf{i} + y_1\mathbf{j} + z_1\mathbf{k})$
  $= (x_2 - x_1)\mathbf{i} + (y_2 - y_1)\mathbf{j} + (z_2 - z_1)\mathbf{k}$

- So the magnitude of the vector $\overrightarrow{PQ} = (x_2 - x_1)\mathbf{i} + (y_2 - y_1)\mathbf{j} + (z_2 - z_1)\mathbf{k}$
  is $\sqrt{(x_2 - x_1)^2 + (y_2 - y_1)^2 + (z_2 - z_1)^2}$, by Pythagoras' theorem.

Tip: To see visually why this formula works draw a diagram with two right-angled triangles like the one on the opposite page. The triangles will have sides whose lengths are the distances between the two points in the x, y and z directions.

Example 2

The position vector of point A is $3\mathbf{i} + 2\mathbf{j} + 4\mathbf{k}$,
and the position vector of point B is $2\mathbf{i} + 6\mathbf{j} - 5\mathbf{k}$.
Find $|\overrightarrow{AB}|$ to 1 decimal place.

- A has the coordinates $(3, 2, 4)$, B has the coordinates $(2, 6, -5)$.

- $\begin{aligned} |\overrightarrow{AB}| &= \sqrt{(x_2 - x_1)^2 + (y_2 - y_1)^2 + (z_2 - z_1)^2} \\ &= \sqrt{(2 - 3)^2 + (6 - 2)^2 + (-5 - 4)^2} \\ &= \sqrt{1 + 16 + 81} \\ &= \sqrt{98} = \mathbf{9.9} \text{ to 1d.p.} \end{aligned}$

Example 3

A = (−3, −6, 4), B = (2t, 1, −t). $|\vec{AB}| = 3\sqrt{11}$.
Find the possible values of t.

$$|\vec{AB}| = \sqrt{(2t+3)^2 + (1+6)^2 + (-t-4)^2}$$

So: $\sqrt{(2t+3)^2 + (1+6)^2 + (-t-4)^2} = 3\sqrt{11}$

$\Rightarrow 4t^2 + 12t + 9 + 49 + t^2 + 8t + 16 = 99$

$\Rightarrow \qquad\qquad 5t^2 + 20t + 74 = 99$

$\Rightarrow \qquad\qquad 5t^2 + 20t - 25 = 0$

$\Rightarrow \qquad\qquad t^2 + 4t - 5 = 0$

$\Rightarrow \qquad\qquad (t+5)(t-1) = 0$

$\Rightarrow \qquad\qquad \boxed{t = -5 \text{ or } t = 1}$

Exercise 2.2

Unless specified, give each answer in this exercise as an integer or as a simplified surd.

Q1 Find the magnitude of each of the following vectors.

a) $\mathbf{i} + 4\mathbf{j} + 8\mathbf{k}$ b) $\begin{pmatrix} 4 \\ 2 \\ 4 \end{pmatrix}$ c) $\begin{pmatrix} -4 \\ -5 \\ 20 \end{pmatrix}$ d) $7\mathbf{i} + \mathbf{j} - 7\mathbf{k}$ e) $\begin{pmatrix} -2 \\ 4 \\ -6 \end{pmatrix}$

Q2 Find the magnitude of the resultant of each pair of vectors.
a) $\mathbf{i} + \mathbf{j} + 2\mathbf{k}$ and $\mathbf{i} + 2\mathbf{j} + 4\mathbf{k}$ b) $2\mathbf{i} + 11\mathbf{j} + 25\mathbf{k}$ and $3\mathbf{j} - 2\mathbf{k}$

c) $\begin{pmatrix} 4 \\ 2 \\ 8 \end{pmatrix}$ and $\begin{pmatrix} -2 \\ 4 \\ 1 \end{pmatrix}$ d) $\begin{pmatrix} 3 \\ 0 \\ 10 \end{pmatrix}$ and $\begin{pmatrix} -1 \\ 5 \\ 4 \end{pmatrix}$ e) $\begin{pmatrix} 8 \\ 4 \\ 10 \end{pmatrix}$ and $\begin{pmatrix} 2 \\ -2 \\ 4 \end{pmatrix}$

Q3 Find the distances between each of the following pairs of points.
   a) (3, 4, 5), (5, 6, 6)   b) (7, 2, 9), (−11, 1, 15)
   c) (10, −2, −1), (6, 10, −4)   d) (0, −4, 10), (7, 0, 14)
   e) (−4, 7, 10), (2, 4, −12)   f) (7, −1, 4), (30, 9, −6)

Q4 $\mathbf{m} = \begin{pmatrix} -5 \\ -2 \\ 6 \end{pmatrix}$ and $\mathbf{n} = \begin{pmatrix} -4 \\ 1 \\ 2 \end{pmatrix}$, find $|2\mathbf{m} - \mathbf{n}|$ to 4 significant figures.

Q5 $\vec{OA} = \mathbf{i} - 4\mathbf{j} + 3\mathbf{k}$ and $\vec{OB} = -\mathbf{i} - 3\mathbf{j} + 5\mathbf{k}$. Find $|\vec{AO}|$, $|\vec{BO}|$ and $|\vec{BA}|$.
Show that triangle AOB is right-angled.

Q5 Hint: If the lengths of a triangle's sides satisfy Pythagoras' theorem then the triangle must be right-angled.

Q6 Find the unit vector in the direction of $\mathbf{v}$ where $\mathbf{v} = 4\mathbf{i} - 4\mathbf{j} - 7\mathbf{k}$.

Q7 P is the point (2, −1, 4) and Q is the point (q − 2, 5, 2q + 1).
Given that the length of the line PQ is 11,
find the possible coordinates of the point Q.

3. Vector Equations of Lines

You can use vectors to give the equation of a straight line. In this section you'll see how to convert between the Cartesian equation of a line (y = mx + c) and a vector equation, as well as how to work with lines written in vector form.

Vector equations of lines in 2D

You've seen straight lines represented in **Cartesian coordinates** by an **equation** '$y = mx + c$' that includes the **gradient** (m) of the line and a **point** that it passes through (the y-intercept, c).

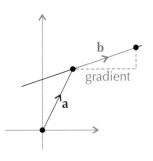

You can also use **vectors** to give the equation of a line. Just like the Cartesian equation, the **vector equation** uses the **gradient** of the line and a **point** it passes through.

The **position** of a point on the line is given as a **position vector**, usually called vector **a**.

The **gradient** is given by a **vector in the direction of the line**, usually called vector **b**.

- The vector **a** goes from the origin to the line and the vector **b** goes along the line, so you can reach any point on the line by following **a** then some scalar multiple of **b**.

- For example, by following vector **a** then vector **b** you get to point P, which has position vector **p** = **a** + **b**.

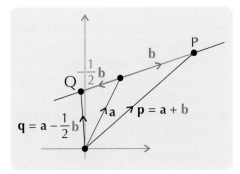

- And by following vector **a** then $-\frac{1}{2}$**b** you get to point Q which has position vector **q** = **a** $- \frac{1}{2}$**b**.

- The equation **r** = **a** + *t***b** gives the **position vector** of any point, R, on the line, just as $y = mx + c$ gives the **coordinates** of any point on the line. So **r** = **a** + *t***b** is the vector equation of the **whole line**.

The **vector equation of a straight line** through point A and parallel to vector **b** is:

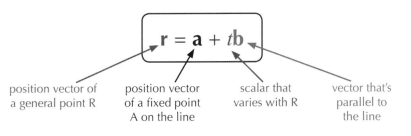

position vector of a general point R

position vector of a fixed point A on the line

scalar that varies with R

vector that's parallel to the line

Learning Objectives:

- Be able to find the vector equation of a 2D line from its Cartesian equation.

- Be able to find the vector equation of a line from a point on the line and a parallel vector.

- Be able to find the vector equation of a line from two points on the line.

- Be able to find the intersection point of two lines from their vector equations.

- Be able to show whether two lines are parallel, skew or intersecting.

Tip: Vector equations of lines aren't unique — you can use any point on the line for **a** and any vector parallel to the line for **b**.

Example

The diagram on the right shows the positions of points
P and Q on a line with vector equation r = a + *t*b.
Find *t* when: a)   r = $\overrightarrow{OP}$ b)   r = $\overrightarrow{OQ}$

a)   The position vector of P is $\overrightarrow{OP}$ = **a** − **b**,
     so when r = $\overrightarrow{OP}$, *t* =   **−1**

b)   The position vector of Q is $\overrightarrow{OQ}$ = **a** + 2**b**,
     so when r = $\overrightarrow{OQ}$, *t* =   **2**

Finding vector a

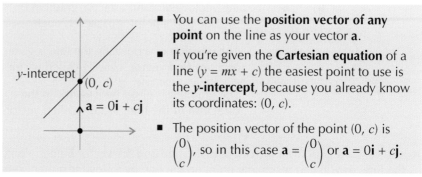

- You can use the **position vector of any point** on the line as your vector **a**.
- If you're given the **Cartesian equation** of a line ($y = mx + c$) the easiest point to use is the **y-intercept**, because you already know its coordinates: $(0, c)$.
- The position vector of the point $(0, c)$ is $\binom{0}{c}$, so in this case **a** = $\binom{0}{c}$ or **a** = $0\mathbf{i} + c\mathbf{j}$.

Finding vector b

- You can use any **vector that's parallel to the line** for vector **b**.
- A vector parallel to the line (i.e. with the same direction as the line) will have the **same gradient** as the line itself. The vector **b** isn't unique because **any scalar multiple** of **b** (i.e. any parallel vector) will have the same gradient.

Tip: It doesn't matter whether **b** is pointing up or down the line because this includes negative scalar multiples (i.e. vectors that are parallel but pointing in the opposite direction).

- If you're given the **Cartesian equation** of a line you can use the **gradient** *m* to find a vector pointing in the same direction as the line. Remember $m = \dfrac{\text{change in } y}{\text{change in } x}$, you can use this to find the horizontal (**i**) and vertical (**j**) components of the vector **b**:

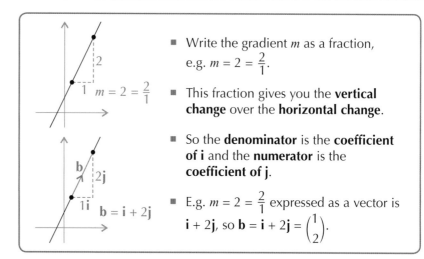

- Write the gradient *m* as a fraction, e.g. $m = 2 = \dfrac{2}{1}$.
- This fraction gives you the **vertical change** over the **horizontal change**.
- So the **denominator** is the **coefficient of i** and the **numerator** is the **coefficient of j**.
- E.g. $m = 2 = \dfrac{2}{1}$ expressed as a vector is $\mathbf{i} + 2\mathbf{j}$, so **b** = $\mathbf{i} + 2\mathbf{j} = \binom{1}{2}$.

So you can find a **vector equation** of a line from its **Cartesian equation**.

Example 1

Line *l* has Cartesian equation $y = \frac{1}{2}x + 2$.

a) **Express as a vector**

   (i) **the position of the *y* intercept**

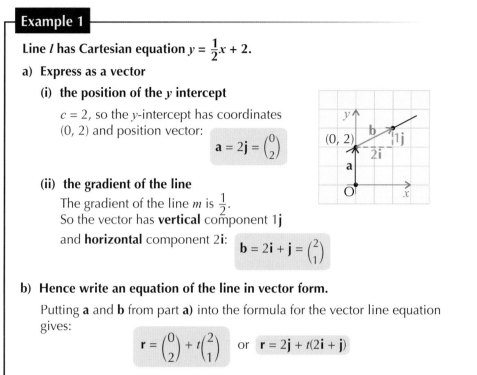

      $c = 2$, so the *y*-intercept has coordinates
      (0, 2) and position vector:

$$\mathbf{a} = 2\mathbf{j} = \begin{pmatrix} 0 \\ 2 \end{pmatrix}$$

   (ii) **the gradient of the line**

      The gradient of the line *m* is $\frac{1}{2}$.
      So the vector has **vertical** component $1\mathbf{j}$
      and **horizontal** component $2\mathbf{i}$:

$$\mathbf{b} = 2\mathbf{i} + \mathbf{j} = \begin{pmatrix} 2 \\ 1 \end{pmatrix}$$

b) **Hence write an equation of the line in vector form.**

   Putting **a** and **b** from part **a)** into the formula for the vector line equation
   gives:

$$\mathbf{r} = \begin{pmatrix} 0 \\ 2 \end{pmatrix} + t\begin{pmatrix} 2 \\ 1 \end{pmatrix} \quad \text{or} \quad \mathbf{r} = 2\mathbf{j} + t(2\mathbf{i} + \mathbf{j})$$

> **Tip:** You could also express this line as a single column vector — just add up along each row of the columns:
> $$\mathbf{r} = \begin{pmatrix} 2t \\ 2 + t \end{pmatrix}$$

You can also find the **Cartesian equation** of a line from its **vector equation**.

Example 2

The vector equation of line *l* is $\mathbf{r} = \begin{pmatrix} 3 \\ 2 \end{pmatrix} + t\begin{pmatrix} -2 \\ 7 \end{pmatrix}$.

Find the Cartesian equation of line *l* in the form $y = mx + c$.

You need to find the gradient *m* and the *y*-intercept *c*.

- You work out the gradient by putting the **j** component
  of vector **b** over the **i** component, so $m = \frac{7}{-2} = -\frac{7}{2}$

- So the Cartesian equation of the line is $y = -\frac{7}{2}x + c$.

- $\begin{pmatrix} 3 \\ 2 \end{pmatrix}$ is the position vector of a point on the line, so (3, 2) lies on the line.

  This means that when $x = 3$, $y = 2$.
  So plug these values into the equation $y = -\frac{7}{2}x + c$:

$$2 = -\frac{7}{2}(3) + c \;\Rightarrow\; \frac{4}{2} + \frac{21}{2} = c$$

$$\Rightarrow\; \frac{25}{2} = c$$

So the Cartesian equation of the line is: $y = -\frac{7}{2}x + \frac{25}{2}$

> **Tip:** If the vector **a** had zero in the top row (i.e. the **i** component 0) you'd already have the position vector of the *y*-intercept and you'd just read the value of *c* from the bottom row.

You can use the **position vectors** of **two points C** and **D** on a line to find the line's **equation**:

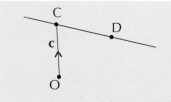 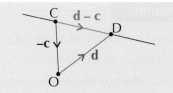

- You take one of the position vectors (e.g. **c**) as your vector for a point on the line (**a**).

- Then you take the vector $\overrightarrow{CD} = \mathbf{d} - \mathbf{c}$ as your direction vector (**b**).

Plugging these vectors into the formula $\mathbf{r} = \mathbf{a} + t\mathbf{b}$ gives you a **formula** for the line in **terms of the position vectors** of **C** and **D**:

$$\boxed{\mathbf{r} = \mathbf{c} + t(\mathbf{d} - \mathbf{c})}$$

You can use this formula to **quickly find the equation** of a line from two points, without having to work out which vectors to use each time.

Tip: In fact you could use **c** or **d** as the position vector and (**c** – **d**) or (**d** – **c**) as the direction vector. Using different combinations will give you different vector equations of the same line.

Tip: You can use column vectors or unit vector form to give the vector equation of a line, but column vectors are usually quicker to work with.

Tip: This is a different method of finding c to the one on p.143.

Example 3

M and N have position vectors m = 3i – 4j and n = –2i + 3j.

a) Find a vector equation of the line that passes through M and N.

Using the formula:
$$\mathbf{r} = \mathbf{m} + t(\mathbf{n} - \mathbf{m}) = \begin{pmatrix} 3 \\ -4 \end{pmatrix} + t\left(\begin{pmatrix} -2 \\ 3 \end{pmatrix} - \begin{pmatrix} 3 \\ -4 \end{pmatrix}\right) = \boxed{\begin{pmatrix} 3 \\ -4 \end{pmatrix} + t\begin{pmatrix} -5 \\ 7 \end{pmatrix}}$$

b) Write the Cartesian equation of this line in the form $y = mx + c$.

- First find the gradient: $m = \dfrac{\mathbf{j} \text{ component of direction vector}}{\mathbf{i} \text{ component of direction vector}} = \dfrac{7}{-5} = -\dfrac{7}{5}$

- Now the y-intercept:
$$\begin{pmatrix} 0 \\ c \end{pmatrix} = \begin{pmatrix} 3 \\ -4 \end{pmatrix} + t\begin{pmatrix} -5 \\ 7 \end{pmatrix} \Rightarrow 0 = 3 - 5t \Rightarrow 5t = 3 \Rightarrow t = \frac{3}{5}$$
$$c = -4 + 7t = -4 + 7\left(\frac{3}{5}\right) = \frac{-20 + 21}{5} = \frac{1}{5}$$

- So the equation is: $\boxed{y = -\frac{7}{5}x + \frac{1}{5}}$

Exercise 3.1

Q1 State the gradient and the y-intercept of each straight line below.

    a) $\mathbf{r} = \begin{pmatrix} 0 \\ 2 \end{pmatrix} + t\begin{pmatrix} 1 \\ 3 \end{pmatrix}$ b) $\mathbf{r} = \begin{pmatrix} 0 \\ -5 \end{pmatrix} - t\begin{pmatrix} 1 \\ 2 \end{pmatrix}$ c) $\mathbf{r} = \begin{pmatrix} 0 \\ 0 \end{pmatrix} + t\begin{pmatrix} 3 \\ 15 \end{pmatrix}$

Q2 Write equations for the following straight lines in vector form.

    a) $y = x + 2$ b) $y = 7$ c) $y = -4x$ d) $y = -3x + 5$

Q3 Hint: This is like using the Cartesian equation to find a vector equation, but vector **a** won't be $\begin{pmatrix} 0 \\ c \end{pmatrix}$.

Q3 For each of the following write a vector equation of the straight line with gradient m passing through point A.

    a) $m = -3$, A (2, 6)   b) $m = \frac{1}{2}$, A (2, 2)   c) $m = 0$, A (1, –5)

Q4 Write equations for the following straight lines in the form $y = mx + c$.

a) $\mathbf{r} = \begin{pmatrix} 0 \\ 0 \end{pmatrix} + t\begin{pmatrix} 1 \\ 1 \end{pmatrix}$

b) $\mathbf{r} = \begin{pmatrix} 0 \\ -4 \end{pmatrix} + t\begin{pmatrix} -1 \\ 2 \end{pmatrix}$

c) $\mathbf{r} = \begin{pmatrix} 6 \\ 0 \end{pmatrix} + t\begin{pmatrix} 2 \\ 1 \end{pmatrix}$

d) $\mathbf{r} = \begin{pmatrix} 1 \\ 2 \end{pmatrix} + t\begin{pmatrix} 3 \\ 0 \end{pmatrix}$

e) $\mathbf{r} = \begin{pmatrix} -2 \\ 3 \end{pmatrix} + t\begin{pmatrix} 2 \\ 5 \end{pmatrix}$

f) $\mathbf{r} = \begin{pmatrix} 5 \\ 0 \end{pmatrix} + t\begin{pmatrix} 0 \\ 1 \end{pmatrix}$

Q5 For each of the following write a vector equation of the straight line that passes through point A and is parallel to vector **b**. Give your answers in **i** + **j** form.

a) A (2, 5), $\mathbf{b} = -\mathbf{i} + 2\mathbf{j}$

b) A (–1, 0), $\mathbf{b} = 3\mathbf{i} + 4\mathbf{j}$

c) A (–3, –1), $\mathbf{b} = 6\mathbf{i} - \mathbf{j}$

d) A (0, 4), $\mathbf{b} = -3\mathbf{i} - 5\mathbf{j}$

Q6 For each of the following, find a vector equation of the straight line that passes through the two points whose position vectors are given. Give your answers in **i** + **j** form.

a) $\mathbf{p} = \mathbf{i}$, $\mathbf{q} = 2\mathbf{i} + \mathbf{j}$

b) $\mathbf{f} = 3\mathbf{i} - 4\mathbf{j}$, $\mathbf{g} = 2\mathbf{i} + 5\mathbf{j}$

c) $\mathbf{n} = -\mathbf{i} + 3\mathbf{j}$, $\mathbf{m} = -5\mathbf{i} - \frac{3}{2}\mathbf{j}$

Vector equations of lines in 3D

You've seen that the vector equation of a line passing **through point A** in the **direction** of **vector b** is $\mathbf{r} = \mathbf{a} + t\mathbf{b}$, where t is a variable scalar.

This isn't just true for 2D lines — it works in **three dimensions** as well.

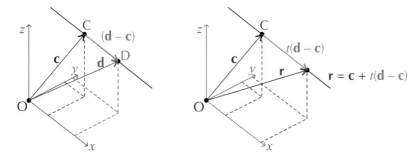

So just like in 2D you can find the vector equation of a line in 3D from a **point** on the line and a **parallel vector**.

You've also seen that the equation for a 2D line passing through **two points** C and D is $\mathbf{r} = \mathbf{c} + t(\mathbf{d} - \mathbf{c})$ — this works just the **same** in **three dimensions** too:

Tip: What it means for lines to be parallel in 3D is covered in more detail on page 148.

- C and D have position vectors **c** and **d** respectively.
- **c** is the position vector of a point on the line.
- $\overrightarrow{CD} = \mathbf{d} - \mathbf{c}$ is a vector in the direction of the line.

So you can also find the vector equation of a 3D line from the position vectors of **two points** on the line.

All this is exactly the same as in two dimensions — the only difference is that the vectors **r**, **a** and **b** (or **r**, **c** and **d**) have three components instead of two.

Example 1

A line passes through points with the coordinates (3, 2, 4) and (2, –2, 0). Find a vector equation for this line.

Call (3, 2, 4) point C and (2, –2, 0) point D.

Then $\mathbf{c} = \begin{pmatrix} 3 \\ 2 \\ 4 \end{pmatrix}$, and $\mathbf{d} = \begin{pmatrix} 2 \\ -2 \\ 0 \end{pmatrix}$.

Plugging these vectors into the equation
$\mathbf{r} = \mathbf{c} + t(\mathbf{d} - \mathbf{c})$ gives:

$$\mathbf{r} = \begin{pmatrix} 3 \\ 2 \\ 4 \end{pmatrix} + t\left(\begin{pmatrix} 2 \\ -2 \\ 0 \end{pmatrix} - \begin{pmatrix} 3 \\ 2 \\ 4 \end{pmatrix}\right) \Rightarrow \mathbf{r} = \begin{pmatrix} 3 \\ 2 \\ 4 \end{pmatrix} + t\begin{pmatrix} -1 \\ -4 \\ -4 \end{pmatrix}$$

Tip: You don't need to draw a diagram to answer the question, but it's a good idea to sketch one if it helps you picture what's going on.

Given a point P with position vector $\mathbf{p}$ you can show that P lies on the line $\mathbf{r} = \mathbf{a} + t\mathbf{b}$ if you can **solve** the equation $\mathbf{p} = \mathbf{a} + t\mathbf{b}$ to find t.

Example 2

Show that the point M (–1, 3, –1) lies on the line $\mathbf{r} = \begin{pmatrix} 2 \\ -6 \\ 5 \end{pmatrix} + \mu\begin{pmatrix} -1 \\ 3 \\ -2 \end{pmatrix}$.

Tip: The variable in a vector line equation isn't always represented by t. Sometimes other letters are used, including Greek letters λ (lambda) and μ (mu).

We want to solve:
$$\mathbf{m} = \begin{pmatrix} -1 \\ 3 \\ -1 \end{pmatrix} = \begin{pmatrix} 2 \\ -6 \\ 5 \end{pmatrix} + \mu\begin{pmatrix} -1 \\ 3 \\ -2 \end{pmatrix} = \begin{pmatrix} 2 - \mu \\ -6 + 3\mu \\ 5 - 2\mu \end{pmatrix}$$

Solve along each row to find μ:

first row: $-1 = 2 - \mu \Rightarrow -3 = -\mu \Rightarrow \mu = 3$

second row: $3 = -6 + 3\mu \Rightarrow 9 = 3\mu \Rightarrow \mu = 3$

third row: $-1 = 5 - 2\mu \Rightarrow -6 = -2\mu \Rightarrow \mu = 3$

All of the equations give the same μ value so there is a solution:

$$\mathbf{m} = \begin{pmatrix} -1 \\ 3 \\ -1 \end{pmatrix} = \begin{pmatrix} 2 \\ -6 \\ 5 \end{pmatrix} + 3\begin{pmatrix} -1 \\ 3 \\ -2 \end{pmatrix}$$ so M lies on the line $\mathbf{r} = \begin{pmatrix} 2 \\ -6 \\ 5 \end{pmatrix} + \mu\begin{pmatrix} -1 \\ 3 \\ -2 \end{pmatrix}$.

Example 3

The point with coordinates (–4, 10, b) lies on the line $\mathbf{r} = \begin{pmatrix} 2 \\ 0 \\ 1 \end{pmatrix} + t\begin{pmatrix} 3 \\ a \\ 1 \end{pmatrix}$. Find a and b.

You know that $\begin{pmatrix} -4 \\ 10 \\ b \end{pmatrix} = \begin{pmatrix} 2 \\ 0 \\ 1 \end{pmatrix} + t\begin{pmatrix} 3 \\ a \\ 1 \end{pmatrix} = \begin{pmatrix} 2 + 3t \\ ta \\ 1 + t \end{pmatrix}$, for some value of t.

Tip: In this example you have to solve along the top row to find t first because both of the other rows have more than one unknown.

- Solve along the top row to find t:
  $$-4 = 2 + 3t \Rightarrow -6 = 3t \Rightarrow t = -2$$

- Now replace t with –2 in the second and third rows to find a and b:

  $10 = -2a \Rightarrow \boxed{a = -5}$ $b = 1 - 2 \Rightarrow \boxed{b = -1}$

Q1 Line L passes through point A and is parallel to vector **b**.
The vectors **a** and **b** are given by

$$\mathbf{a} = \begin{pmatrix} 4 \\ -3 \\ -2 \end{pmatrix} \text{ and } \mathbf{b} = \begin{pmatrix} 1 \\ 2 \\ 3 \end{pmatrix}$$

a) Find the position vectors of points
X, Y, Z and Q, where:
$\overrightarrow{OX} = \mathbf{a} + \mathbf{b}$, $\overrightarrow{OY} = \mathbf{a} + 2\mathbf{b}$,
$\overrightarrow{OZ} = \mathbf{a} + 3\mathbf{b}$, $\overrightarrow{OQ} = \mathbf{a} - \mathbf{b}$

b) Write a vector equation for line L.

Q2 Points C, D, E and F lie on the line with equation $\mathbf{r} = \begin{pmatrix} 2 \\ 1 \\ 3 \end{pmatrix} + \lambda \begin{pmatrix} 1 \\ -1 \\ 4 \end{pmatrix}$
and correspond to $\lambda = 0$, $\lambda = 1$, $\lambda = 4$ and $\lambda = -2$
respectively. Write down the coordinates of each point.

Q3 Give the coordinates of any 3 points on the line $\mathbf{r} = 3\mathbf{j} - 4\mathbf{k} + t(-\mathbf{i} + 2\mathbf{j})$.

Q4 Point S (−1, 4, 5) lies on a straight line that passes through the origin O.
a) Give a vector equation of this line.
b) State the coordinates of 2 other points that lie on the line.

Q4 Hint: The origin is
(0, 0, 0) so you've got
the coordinates of two
points on the line.

Q5 a) Find a vector equation for the straight line that passes through the
point with position vector **a**, and which is parallel to vector **b**,
where:

(i) $\mathbf{a} = \begin{pmatrix} 4 \\ 2 \\ -1 \end{pmatrix}$, $\mathbf{b} = \begin{pmatrix} -2 \\ 0 \\ 3 \end{pmatrix}$ (ii) $\mathbf{a} = \begin{pmatrix} 0 \\ 0 \\ 1 \end{pmatrix}$, $\mathbf{b} = \begin{pmatrix} 1 \\ -1 \\ 0 \end{pmatrix}$

(iii) $\mathbf{a} = 2\mathbf{i} + \mathbf{j}$, $\mathbf{b} = 5\mathbf{i} - \mathbf{k}$

b) Each of the points P (−2, 2, 1), Q (2, 2, 2) and R (−3, 1, 1)
lies on just one of the lines from part a).
Determine which point lies on which line.

Q6 Line L has equation $\mathbf{r} = -6\mathbf{i} - \mathbf{j} + \mathbf{k} + t(\mathbf{i} - 3\mathbf{k})$. Write down an
equation for the line parallel to L that passes through (5, −1, 3).

Q7 Points P (−4, a, 10) and Q (b, c, −11) lie on a line $\mathbf{r} = \begin{pmatrix} -2 \\ 5 \\ 4 \end{pmatrix} + s \begin{pmatrix} 1 \\ 2 \\ -3 \end{pmatrix}$.
Find the values of a, b and c.

Q7 Hint: For each
point find s first by
solving along a line with
no other unknowns,
then find the missing
coordinates.

Q8 $\mathbf{r} = \begin{pmatrix} -4 \\ 0 \\ 1 \end{pmatrix} + s \begin{pmatrix} 3 \\ 2 \\ -1 \end{pmatrix}$ is an equation for line L.

Write an equation for the line L in the form $\mathbf{r} = \mathbf{a} + t\mathbf{b}$, where:

a) **b** is not $\begin{pmatrix} 3 \\ 2 \\ -1 \end{pmatrix}$ b) **a** is not $\begin{pmatrix} -4 \\ 0 \\ 1 \end{pmatrix}$

Q9 Find equations for the lines that pass through the following pairs of points:
a) (7, 0, −3) and (−1, 1, −3) b) (−1, 1, 4) and (−4, 1, 0)
c) (2, 5, 0) and (−2, −1, 2)

Intersecting, parallel and skew lines

Tip: 'Two distinct lines' just means two lines that aren't exactly the same.

In **two dimensions**, given **two distinct lines** there are only **two possibilities**:

1. The lines are **intersecting** — they **meet** at a single **point**.

2. The lines are **parallel** — they never intersect and the shortest **distance** between them is always the **same**.

In **three dimensions** there are **three possibilities**:

1. The lines are **intersecting**.

2. The lines are **parallel**.

Tip: It's enough to say that parallel lines in 2D are lines that don't intersect because all lines are either intersecting or parallel. This isn't true in three-dimensions so we have to be more specific.

In 2D, parallel lines are lines that never intersect. **Parallel** lines in **3D** are similar, but not all non-intersecting lines are parallel in 3D.

- In three-dimensional space two lines are parallel when the **smallest distance** from one line to the other is **constant** along the line.

- 3D **parallel lines** are **translations** of each other in the x, y and z directions, just like 2D parallel lines are translations of each other in the x and y directions.

- Another way to think of it is that any two lines that lie in the **same plane** and **don't intersect** are parallel.

- The **purple** and **blue** lines on the left are parallel because they both lie in the **blue plane** and they don't intersect.

- The **purple** and **orange** lines are also parallel — they lie in the **orange plane** and don't intersect.

- Just like in 2D, **two lines** that are both **parallel to a third line** are **parallel** to each other, so the blue and orange lines are also parallel to each other.

Tip: Also if two lines are both parallel to the same vector then they must be parallel to each other.

Tip: Skew lines must lie in different planes, otherwise they would have to either be parallel or intersect.

3. The lines are **neither parallel nor intersecting**. These lines are called **skew**. The two lines shown on the right are skew.

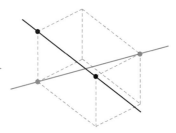

You can **work out** whether two lines are parallel, intersecting or skew from their **vector equations**.

Intersecting lines

- **Intersecting lines** meet somewhere, so they must **share a point**.
- For lines with equations $\mathbf{r} = \mathbf{c} + \lambda\mathbf{d}$ and $\mathbf{r} = \mathbf{e} + \mu\mathbf{f}$ this means that there's a value for λ and a value for μ so that $\mathbf{c} + \lambda\mathbf{d} = \mathbf{e} + \mu\mathbf{f}$, i.e. you get the same point for each line. This point is the **point of intersection**.

Tip: To prove that two lines intersect you just solve this equation to show that they have a point in common.

Example

Determine whether Line 1, $\mathbf{r} = \begin{pmatrix} 5 \\ 2 \\ -1 \end{pmatrix} + \mu\begin{pmatrix} 1 \\ -2 \\ -3 \end{pmatrix}$ and Line 2, $\mathbf{r} = \begin{pmatrix} 2 \\ 0 \\ 4 \end{pmatrix} + \lambda\begin{pmatrix} 1 \\ 2 \\ -1 \end{pmatrix}$ intersect.

If they do, find the coordinates of the point of intersection.

If the two lines intersect then at the point of intersection we'll have:

$$\begin{pmatrix} 5 \\ 2 \\ -1 \end{pmatrix} + \mu\begin{pmatrix} 1 \\ -2 \\ -3 \end{pmatrix} = \begin{pmatrix} 2 \\ 0 \\ 4 \end{pmatrix} + \lambda\begin{pmatrix} 1 \\ 2 \\ -1 \end{pmatrix}$$

So take the equation from **each row**:

① $5 + \mu = 2 + \lambda$
② $2 - 2\mu = 0 + 2\lambda$
③ $-1 - 3\mu = 4 - \lambda$

If you can find a value for μ and a value for λ which **solve all** of these equations **at once** then there's a **point** that lies on **both lines**. If not then there's no intersection point.

- Solve the first two **simultaneously**:
  $2 \times$ ①: $10 + 2\mu = 4 + 2\lambda$ ④
  ④ − ②: $8 + 4\mu = 4 \Rightarrow \mu = -1$

- Now **substitute** μ into equation ②: $2 - 2(-1) = 0 + 2\lambda \Rightarrow \lambda = 2$

- If these values of μ and λ also solve equation ③ then the lines intersect. So substitute the values for μ and λ into equation ③:
  $-1 - (3 \times -1) = 4 - 2 \Rightarrow 2 = 2$
  — this is **true**, so the lines **do intersect** .

Tip: If you've got two equations that describe the same line then there'll be a solution to this equation for every value of the two variables, because they intersect everywhere. You show that two lines are the same by giving a solution for an intersection point and showing their direction vectors are parallel.

Now you can find the **intersection point** by plugging the value for μ into the **equation of Line 1**:

$$\mathbf{r} = \begin{pmatrix} 5 \\ 2 \\ -1 \end{pmatrix} + \mu\begin{pmatrix} 1 \\ -2 \\ -3 \end{pmatrix} = \begin{pmatrix} 5 \\ 2 \\ -1 \end{pmatrix} - 1\begin{pmatrix} 1 \\ -2 \\ -3 \end{pmatrix} \Rightarrow \mathbf{r} = \begin{pmatrix} 4 \\ 4 \\ 2 \end{pmatrix} = 4\mathbf{i} + 4\mathbf{j} + 2\mathbf{k}$$

This is the **position vector** of the intersection point.

The **coordinates** are **(4, 4, 2)** .

Tip: You could plug the value for λ into the equation of Line 2 instead, either will give you the position vector of the intersection point.

Parallel lines

- Every line with equation $\mathbf{r} = \mathbf{a} + t\mathbf{b}$ is parallel to any scalar multiple of the vector $\mathbf{b}$.
- If two lines are both parallel to a third line then they must be parallel to each other, so to prove that the **two lines $\mathbf{r} = \mathbf{c} + \lambda\mathbf{d}$ and $\mathbf{r} = \mathbf{e} + \mu\mathbf{f}$** are parallel you just need to show that the **vectors $\mathbf{d}$ and $\mathbf{f}$ are parallel**.

Show that the lines L$_1$: r = $\begin{pmatrix} 0 \\ 3 \\ -5 \end{pmatrix} + \lambda \begin{pmatrix} -1 \\ 0 \\ 2 \end{pmatrix}$ **and L$_2$: r =** $\begin{pmatrix} -2 \\ 3 \\ 1 \end{pmatrix} + \mu \begin{pmatrix} -2 \\ 0 \\ 4 \end{pmatrix}$
are parallel.

- Let **b$_1$** = $\begin{pmatrix} -1 \\ 0 \\ 2 \end{pmatrix}$ and **b$_2$** = $\begin{pmatrix} -2 \\ 0 \\ 4 \end{pmatrix}$, then **b$_2$** = 2**b$_1$**.

- So the direction vectors of L$_1$ and L$_2$ (**b$_1$** and **b$_2$**) are scalar multiples of one another, which means they're parallel.

- Therefore L$_1$ and L$_2$ are parallel as they're parallel, respectively, to their direction vectors **b$_1$** and **b$_2$**.

Skew lines

To prove that two lines are **skew** you just show that they're **not parallel** and they **don't intersect**.

Example

Lines l_1 and l_2 are given by l_1: r = (−1 + 2λ)**i** + (4 + λ)**j** + (1 − 2λ)**k**
                                          l_2: r = (2 + 3μ)**i** + (−5 − 2μ)**j** + (−4 + 3μ)**k**

Prove that l_1 and l_2 are skew.

Rewrite the equations in **column vector** form:

$$\mathbf{r} = \begin{pmatrix} -1 \\ 4 \\ 1 \end{pmatrix} + \lambda \begin{pmatrix} 2 \\ 1 \\ -2 \end{pmatrix} \text{ and } \mathbf{r} = \begin{pmatrix} 2 \\ -5 \\ -4 \end{pmatrix} + \mu \begin{pmatrix} 3 \\ -2 \\ 3 \end{pmatrix}$$

First show that l_1 and l_2 **don't intersect**:

- You need to show that there's no solution to the equation:

$$\begin{pmatrix} -1 \\ 4 \\ 1 \end{pmatrix} + \lambda \begin{pmatrix} 2 \\ 1 \\ -2 \end{pmatrix} = \begin{pmatrix} 2 \\ -5 \\ -4 \end{pmatrix} + \mu \begin{pmatrix} 3 \\ -2 \\ 3 \end{pmatrix}$$

- The three rows give the equations: $-1 + 2\lambda = 2 + 3\mu$
                                          $4 + \lambda = -5 - 2\mu$
                                          $1 - 2\lambda = -4 + 3\mu$

- Solve the first two **simultaneously**:
  $-1 + 2\lambda = 2 + 3\mu \Rightarrow -1 + \frac{2}{3}\lambda = \mu$
  $4 + \lambda = -5 - 2\mu \Rightarrow 4 + \lambda = -5 - 2\left(-1 + \frac{2}{3}\lambda\right) \Rightarrow 7 = -\frac{7}{3}\lambda \Rightarrow \lambda = -3$
  $\Rightarrow \mu = -1 + \frac{2}{3}(-3) = -3$

- Now plug these values into the third equation:
  $1 - 2\lambda = -4 + 3\mu \Rightarrow 1 - 2(-3) = -4 + 3(-3) \Rightarrow 1 + 6 = -4 - 9 \Rightarrow 7 = -13$

- This is false so l_1 and l_2 **don't intersect**.

Now show that they're **not parallel**:

- If l_1 and l_2 are parallel then their direction vectors are parallel, i.e. scalar multiples of one another.

- In that case their **i**, **j** and **k** components will have a common scalar factor, so $\frac{2}{3} = \frac{1}{-2} = \frac{-2}{3}$ will hold. This isn't true so l_1 and l_2 **aren't parallel**.

As they're **neither intersecting nor parallel** l_1 and l_2 are **skew**.

Tip: For questions where the line equation is given in a different form you'll probably find it easier to write it in the standard column vector form before you answer the question.

Tip: Note that the direction vectors of l_1 and l_2 are:

$\mathbf{b}_1 = \begin{pmatrix} 2 \\ 1 \\ -2 \end{pmatrix}$ and $\mathbf{b}_2 = \begin{pmatrix} 3 \\ -2 \\ 3 \end{pmatrix}$

So for the **i**, **j** and **k** components to share a common factor you'll need $\frac{2}{3} = \frac{1}{-2} = \frac{-2}{3}$.

Exercise 3.3

Q1 State whether or not each of the following pairs of lines are parallel.

a) $\mathbf{r} = \begin{pmatrix} 1 \\ 0 \\ 1 \end{pmatrix} + p\begin{pmatrix} 0 \\ 7 \\ 0 \end{pmatrix}$, $\mathbf{r} = \begin{pmatrix} 2 \\ -4 \\ 1 \end{pmatrix} + q\begin{pmatrix} 0 \\ -2 \\ 0 \end{pmatrix}$

b) $\mathbf{r} = (\mathbf{i} + \mathbf{k}) + \lambda(\mathbf{j} + \mathbf{k})$
$\mathbf{r} = (\mathbf{j} + \mathbf{k}) + \lambda(2\mathbf{i} + 2\mathbf{k})$

Q2 Find the values of a, b, c and d, given that each pair of lines is parallel.

a) $\mathbf{r} = \begin{pmatrix} -5 \\ 4 \\ 2 \end{pmatrix} + s\begin{pmatrix} a \\ 0 \\ -1 \end{pmatrix}$, $\mathbf{r} = \begin{pmatrix} 9 \\ 8 \\ -4 \end{pmatrix} + t\begin{pmatrix} 10 \\ b \\ -5 \end{pmatrix}$

b) $\mathbf{r} = (3\mathbf{i} - \mathbf{j}) + \lambda(2\mathbf{i} + c\mathbf{j} - 4\mathbf{k})$, $\mathbf{r} = (5\mathbf{i} + \mathbf{j} - \mathbf{k}) + \mu(d\mathbf{i} + 3\mathbf{j} + 2\mathbf{k})$

> **Q2 Hint:** You don't need to worry about s and t in this question — so just focus on the direction vectors.

Q3 Show that each pair of lines below intersects at a point, and find the coordinates of the point of intersection.

a) $\mathbf{r} = (2\mathbf{i} + \mathbf{j}) + \lambda(\mathbf{i} - 2\mathbf{j} + \mathbf{k})$, $\mathbf{r} = (-3\mathbf{i} - \mathbf{k}) + \mu(4\mathbf{i} + 3\mathbf{j})$

b) $\mathbf{r} = \begin{pmatrix} -1 \\ 7 \\ 1 \end{pmatrix} + \lambda\begin{pmatrix} 2 \\ -2 \\ 1 \end{pmatrix}$, $\mathbf{r} = \begin{pmatrix} 1 \\ 3 \\ 2 \end{pmatrix} + \mu\begin{pmatrix} 2 \\ -1 \\ 1 \end{pmatrix}$

c) $\mathbf{r} = (5\mathbf{i} + 7\mathbf{j} - 3\mathbf{k}) + s(\mathbf{i} + 3\mathbf{j} - 2\mathbf{k})$, $\mathbf{r} = (-4\mathbf{i} + 15\mathbf{j} - 10\mathbf{k}) + t(\mathbf{i} - 4\mathbf{j} + 3\mathbf{k})$

Q4 Lines L_1 and L_2 have equations $\mathbf{r} = \begin{pmatrix} 1 \\ 0 \\ a \end{pmatrix} + \lambda\begin{pmatrix} -1 \\ b \\ 2 \end{pmatrix}$ and $\mathbf{r} = \begin{pmatrix} 0 \\ c \\ 3 \end{pmatrix} + \mu\begin{pmatrix} 2 \\ 1 \\ d \end{pmatrix}$.
L_1 meets L_2 at $(2, -3, 2)$.
Find the values of a, b, c and d.

> **Q4 Hint:** Use the intersection point to find λ and μ first, then find the other unknowns.

Q5 Show that each pair of lines is skew:

a) $\mathbf{r} = \begin{pmatrix} 4 \\ 0 \\ 1 \end{pmatrix} + \lambda\begin{pmatrix} 1 \\ 2 \\ 1 \end{pmatrix}$, $\mathbf{r} = \begin{pmatrix} -1 \\ 3 \\ 2 \end{pmatrix} + \mu\begin{pmatrix} -1 \\ 1 \\ 0 \end{pmatrix}$

b) $\mathbf{r} = (\mathbf{i} + \mathbf{j} - \mathbf{k}) + \lambda(-\mathbf{i} + 2\mathbf{j} + 3\mathbf{k})$, $\mathbf{r} = (-2\mathbf{i} + 4\mathbf{j} + \mathbf{k}) + \mu(\mathbf{i} - \mathbf{j} + 3\mathbf{k})$

c) $\mathbf{r} = (3\mathbf{i} + \mathbf{j} + \mathbf{k}) + s(-\mathbf{i} + 2\mathbf{j} + \mathbf{k})$, $\mathbf{r} = (2\mathbf{i} - 2\mathbf{j}) + t(\mathbf{i} + \mathbf{j} - 3\mathbf{k})$

Q6 Determine whether the pair of equations $\mathbf{r} = (3\mathbf{i} + 4\mathbf{j}) + \lambda(-\mathbf{i} + \mathbf{j} - \mathbf{k})$ and $\mathbf{r} = (-6\mathbf{i} - 8\mathbf{j}) + \mu(-\mathbf{i} + \mathbf{j} - \mathbf{k})$ represent two different parallel lines, or the same line written in two different ways.

Q7 Find whether each pair of non-parallel lines below are intersecting or skew. Give the position vector of their intersection where possible.

a) $\mathbf{r} = \begin{pmatrix} 4 \\ -5 \\ 1 \end{pmatrix} + p\begin{pmatrix} 2 \\ 4 \\ 3 \end{pmatrix}$, $\mathbf{r} = \begin{pmatrix} 2 \\ -1 \\ 0 \end{pmatrix} + q\begin{pmatrix} 1 \\ 3 \\ 2 \end{pmatrix}$

b) $\mathbf{r} = (\mathbf{i} - \mathbf{j} + 4\mathbf{k}) + \lambda(\mathbf{i} - \mathbf{j} + \mathbf{k})$, $\mathbf{r} = (2\mathbf{i} + 4\mathbf{j} + 7\mathbf{k}) + \mu(2\mathbf{i} + \mathbf{j} + 3\mathbf{k})$

Q8 Quadrilateral ABCD is shown on the right.
a) Obtain vector equations for the lines containing diagonals AC and BD.
b) The diagonals meet at point E. Find the coordinates of E.

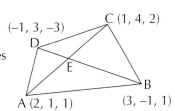

$(-1, 3, -3)$ D
C $(1, 4, 2)$
E
A $(2, 1, 1)$
B
$(3, -1, 1)$

4. Scalar Product

Learning Objectives:

- Be able to find the scalar product of two vectors.
- Be able to find the angle between two vectors using the scalar product.
- Be able to find the angle between two lines from their vector equations.
- Be able to use the scalar product to find if two lines are parallel or perpendicular.
- Be able to find the shortest distance between a line and a point (and other complex vector problems).

The scalar product of two vectors is a method that combines (or 'multiplies') together two vectors to get a scalar. There is another method of 'multiplying' vectors, the cross product, which gives a vector instead. This section only covers finding the scalar product of two vectors, as well as how to use the scalar product to calculate the angle between two lines.

The scalar product

The **scalar product** of two vectors **a** and **b** is written **a.b** (you read this as 'a dot b'). The scalar product is sometimes called the **dot product**.

The **scalar product** of two vectors is **always** a **scalar** quantity, it's never a vector.

Given two vectors **a** and **b** the definition of the **scalar product** is:

$$\mathbf{a}.\mathbf{b} = |\mathbf{a}||\mathbf{b}|\cos\theta$$

where θ is the angle between **a** and **b**.

- For **position vectors** it's clear what we mean by the angle between **a** and **b**.

- For other vectors θ is the angle between the vectors when **drawn away** from the **same point**.

Tip: Make sure you know which angle θ is when you've got two vectors — the correct angle might not always be obvious.

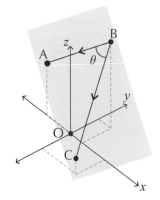

- When you're working with two **3D vectors** there'll be some **plane** that they **both lie in**.
- The **angle** between the two vectors (e.g. angle ABC) is just the **angle in this plane**.
- Because you're working in a plane the angle between 3D vectors is just like the angle between 2D vectors.

Tip: This means that when you're finding the angle between two 3D vectors you can draw a 2D diagram to help you see what's going on.

Tip: It's really important you write the dot in **a.b** to make it clear you mean scalar product (instead of cross product — you don't need to know about the cross product for C4).

Example

The diagram on the right shows the vectors a and b.
Given that |a| = 7 and |b| = 6,
find the scalar product of a and b.
Give your answer to 1 decimal place.

Using the formula for the scalar product you get:

$$\mathbf{a}.\mathbf{b} = |\mathbf{a}||\mathbf{b}|\cos\theta = 7 \times 6 \times \cos 30° = \boxed{\mathbf{36.4}} \text{ to 1 decimal place.}$$

Parallel vectors don't intersect, but you can still find their scalar product. The **scalar product** of two **parallel** vectors is **plus or minus** the **product** of the **magnitudes** of the vectors:

- If two vectors are **parallel**, the angle between them is **0° or 180°**:

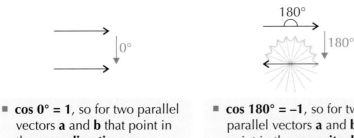

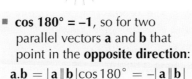

> **Tip:** The angle between parallel vectors is 180° when one is a negative scalar multiple of the other, so they have opposite directions.

- **cos 0° = 1**, so for two parallel vectors **a** and **b** that point in the **same direction**:
  $$\mathbf{a}.\mathbf{b} = |\mathbf{a}||\mathbf{b}|\cos 0° = |\mathbf{a}||\mathbf{b}|$$

- **cos 180° = –1**, so for two parallel vectors **a** and **b** that point in the **opposite direction**:
  $$\mathbf{a}.\mathbf{b} = |\mathbf{a}||\mathbf{b}|\cos 180° = -|\mathbf{a}||\mathbf{b}|$$

So for any two **parallel** vectors **a** and **b**:

> $\mathbf{a}.\mathbf{b} = |\mathbf{a}||\mathbf{b}|$ when the vectors point in the **same** direction.
> $\mathbf{a}.\mathbf{b} = -|\mathbf{a}||\mathbf{b}|$ when the vectors point in **opposite** directions.

If the **scalar product** of two vectors is **zero** then the vectors are **perpendicular** (or one of the vectors is zero).

- **Perpendicular** vectors are at **90°** to each other.
- **Cos 90° = 0**, so for perpendicular vectors **a** and **b**:
  $$\mathbf{a}.\mathbf{b} = |\mathbf{a}||\mathbf{b}|\cos 90° = 0$$

So for any two **perpendicular** vectors **a** and **b**: $\boxed{\mathbf{a}.\mathbf{b} = 0}$

- Having $|\mathbf{a}| = 0$ or $|\mathbf{b}| = 0$ is the only other way to make the scalar product 0, and this can only happen if the vector itself is **zero**.
- So if the **scalar product** of two vectors is **zero** either one of the vectors is zero or the two vectors are **perpendicular**.

> **Tip:** This means that if you can show the scalar product of two non-zero vectors is zero then you've proved they're perpendicular.

Example

Find the following scalar products

a) $\mathbf{j}.\mathbf{j}$

Two identical vectors are **parallel** and point in the **same direction**, so:
$$\mathbf{j}.\mathbf{j} = |\mathbf{j}| \times |\mathbf{j}| = 1 \times 1 = \boxed{1}$$

b) $3\mathbf{k}.-4\mathbf{k}$

$3\mathbf{k}$ is **parallel** to $-4\mathbf{k}$, but they're pointing in **opposite directions**, so:
$$3\mathbf{k}.-4\mathbf{k} = -|3\mathbf{k}| \times |-4\mathbf{k}| = -(3 \times 4) = \boxed{-12}$$

c) $\mathbf{i}.\mathbf{j}$

i and **j** are **perpendicular** to one another, so: $\mathbf{i}.\mathbf{j} = \boxed{0}$

d) $3\mathbf{j}.-4\mathbf{k}$

j and **k** are **perpendicular** to one another, so: $3\mathbf{j}.-4\mathbf{k} = \boxed{0}$

> **Tip:** The unit vectors **i**, **j** and **k** are all perpendicular to each other.

Q1 Each diagram below shows the magnitudes of two vectors and an angle between them. For each diagram find the scalar product of the two vectors in exact form.

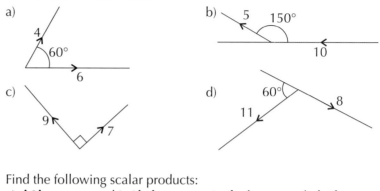

a)

b)

c)

d)

Q2 Find the following scalar products:
   a) $\mathbf{i}.3\mathbf{j}$ b) $2\mathbf{j}.-\mathbf{j}$ c) $4\mathbf{k}.-\mathbf{i}$ d) $\mathbf{k}.6\mathbf{k}$

Q3 Each diagram below show the magnitudes of two vectors whose scalar product is 3. In each case find θ to the nearest degree.

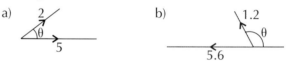

a)

b)

Scalar product from vector components

Tip: You can only use the formula
$\mathbf{a}.\mathbf{b} = |\mathbf{a}||\mathbf{b}|\cos\theta$
to find $\mathbf{a}.\mathbf{b}$ if you already know the angle between $\mathbf{a}$ and $\mathbf{b}$.

The formula $\mathbf{a}.\mathbf{b} = |\mathbf{a}||\mathbf{b}|\cos\theta$ tells you what the scalar product is, but to work it out straight from the vectors $\mathbf{a}$ and $\mathbf{b}$ you need another formula.

Scalar products work like multiplication, so the normal laws of multiplication apply to scalar products:

- The **commutative** law: $\mathbf{a}.\mathbf{b} = \mathbf{b}.\mathbf{a}$
- The **distributive** law: $\mathbf{a}.(\mathbf{b} + \mathbf{c}) = \mathbf{a}.\mathbf{b} + \mathbf{a}.\mathbf{c}$

You can apply these laws to find a formula for working out the scalar product.

The scalar product of vectors $\mathbf{a} = a_1\mathbf{i} + a_2\mathbf{j} + a_3\mathbf{k}$ and $\mathbf{b} = b_1\mathbf{i} + b_2\mathbf{j} + b_3\mathbf{k}$ is:
$$\mathbf{a}.\mathbf{b} = (a_1\mathbf{i} + a_2\mathbf{j} + a_3\mathbf{k}) . (b_1\mathbf{i} + b_2\mathbf{j} + b_3\mathbf{k})$$

Applying the **distributive law** to **multiply** out the brackets gives:

$$= (a_1\mathbf{i}) . (b_1\mathbf{i}) + (a_1\mathbf{i}) . (b_2\mathbf{j}) + (a_1\mathbf{i}) . (b_3\mathbf{k}) + (a_2\mathbf{j}) . (b_1\mathbf{i}) + (a_2\mathbf{j}) . (b_2\mathbf{j})$$
$$+ (a_2\mathbf{j}) . (b_3\mathbf{k}) + (a_3\mathbf{k}) . (b_1\mathbf{i}) + (a_3\mathbf{k}) . (b_2\mathbf{j}) + (a_3\mathbf{k}) . (b_3\mathbf{k})$$

Now use the **scalar product** definition to work out each of these terms. Unit vectors $\mathbf{i}$, $\mathbf{j}$ and $\mathbf{k}$ are all **perpendicular** to each other, so their scalar product is always **zero**:

$$= (a_1\mathbf{i}) . (b_1\mathbf{i}) + 0 + 0 + 0 + (a_2\mathbf{j}) . (b_2\mathbf{j}) + 0 + 0 + 0 + (a_3\mathbf{k}) . (b_3\mathbf{k})$$

$$= (a_1\mathbf{i}) . (b_1\mathbf{i}) + (a_2\mathbf{j}) . (b_2\mathbf{j}) + (a_3\mathbf{k}) . (b_3\mathbf{k})$$

Use the scalar product definition on each term that's left:

$$(a_1\mathbf{i}).(b_1\mathbf{i}) = |a_1\mathbf{i}||b_1\mathbf{i}|\cos\theta = |a_1|\,|\mathbf{i}|\,|b_1|\,|\mathbf{i}|\cos\theta = |a_1 b_1|\cos\theta$$

Now either a_1 and b_1 have the same sign, so $\theta = 0°$
$$\Rightarrow\ (a_1\mathbf{i}).(b_1\mathbf{i}) = |a_1 b_1|\cos 0° = |a_1 b_1| = a_1 b_1\ (a_1 b_1 \text{ is positive}),$$

or a_1 and b_1 have opposite signs, so $\theta = 180°$
$$\Rightarrow (a_1\mathbf{i}).(b_1\mathbf{i}) = |a_1 b_1|\cos 180° = -|a_1 b_1| = a_1 b_1\ (a_1 b_1 \text{ is negative}).$$

Either way $(a_1\mathbf{i}) . (b_1\mathbf{i}) = a_1 b_1$, and the same is true for the $\mathbf{j}$ and $\mathbf{k}$ vectors. So, going back to the formula for the scalar product:

$$\mathbf{a.b} = (a_1\mathbf{i}) . (b_1\mathbf{i}) + (a_2\mathbf{j}) . (b_2\mathbf{j}) + (a_3\mathbf{k}) . (b_3\mathbf{k})$$
$$= a_1 b_1 + a_2 b_2 + a_3 b_3$$

Tip: Remember, the magnitude of unit vectors is always 1.

Tip: The rules $|ab| = |a||b|$ and $|c\mathbf{d}| = |c||\mathbf{d}|$ are used here. You might not have been formally introduced to them before, but they make sense if you think about the value of each magnitude.

So we've got another formula for the scalar product:
For two vectors $\mathbf{a} = a_1\mathbf{i} + a_2\mathbf{j} + a_3\mathbf{k}$ and $\mathbf{b} = b_1\mathbf{i} + b_2\mathbf{j} + b_3\mathbf{k}$, the scalar product of $\mathbf{a}$ and $\mathbf{b}$ is:

$$\mathbf{a.b} = a_1 b_1 + a_2 b_2 + a_3 b_3$$

Tip: For 2D vectors the formula is just:
$$\mathbf{a.b} = a_1 b_1 + a_2 b_2$$
because 2D vectors have no $\mathbf{k}$ components.

Examples

a) **Find** $\begin{pmatrix} 3 \\ -4 \\ 2 \end{pmatrix} . \begin{pmatrix} -5 \\ -1 \\ 5 \end{pmatrix}$

Use the formula $\mathbf{a.b} = a_1 b_1 + a_2 b_2 + a_3 b_3$:

$$\begin{pmatrix} 3 \\ -4 \\ 2 \end{pmatrix} . \begin{pmatrix} -5 \\ -1 \\ 5 \end{pmatrix} = (3 \times (-5)) + ((-4) \times (-1)) + (2 \times 5) = -15 + 4 + 10 = \boxed{-1}$$

b) **$(2\mathbf{i} + 3\mathbf{j} + \mathbf{k}) . (\alpha\mathbf{i} - \mathbf{j} - 5\mathbf{k}) = -12$. Find the value of α.**

- Let $\mathbf{a} = 2\mathbf{i} + 3\mathbf{j} + \mathbf{k}$ and $\mathbf{b} = \alpha\mathbf{i} - \mathbf{j} - 5\mathbf{k}$.
- Work out their scalar product $\mathbf{a.b}$ in terms of α using the formula $\mathbf{a.b} = a_1 b_1 + a_2 b_2 + a_3 b_3$:
$$\mathbf{a.b} = (2 \times \alpha) + (3 \times (-1)) + (1 \times (-5)) = 2\alpha - 8$$
- So: $-12 = \mathbf{a.b} = 2\alpha - 8 \Rightarrow -4 = 2\alpha \Rightarrow \boxed{\alpha = -2}$

Knowing that the **scalar product** of **perpendicular** vectors is always **zero** gives you an easy way to check if vectors are perpendicular.

You could also check if vectors are **parallel** using the scalar product.
If $\mathbf{a.b} = |\mathbf{a}||\mathbf{b}|$ or $-|\mathbf{a}||\mathbf{b}|$ then the vectors $\mathbf{a}$ and $\mathbf{b}$ are parallel, but if $\mathbf{a.b} \neq |\mathbf{a}||\mathbf{b}|$ or $-|\mathbf{a}||\mathbf{b}|$ they're not.

Tip: It's usually quicker to find out if two vectors are parallel by checking if they're scalar multiples of one another, but this is a handy check if you already know the vectors' magnitudes and scalar product.

a) Determine if vectors a = 5i – 7k and b = –2i – 4j – 3k are perpendicular to one another.

Find the scalar product of the two vectors — if they're **perpendicular**, the scalar product will be **zero**.

$$\mathbf{a}.\mathbf{b} = a_1b_1 + a_2b_2 + a_3b_3 = (5 \times -2) + (0 \times -4) + (-7 \times -3)$$
$$= -10 + 0 + 21 = 11 \neq 0$$

The scalar product **isn't zero**, so the vectors are **not perpendicular**.

b) Calculate the scalar product of 2i + 3j – k and 4i – 6j + 2k, and hence show that they are neither parallel nor perpendicular.

- Let $\mathbf{a} = 2\mathbf{i} + 3\mathbf{j} - \mathbf{k}$ and $\mathbf{b} = 4\mathbf{i} - 6\mathbf{j} + 2\mathbf{k}$
$$\mathbf{a}.\mathbf{b} = a_1b_1 + a_2b_2 + a_3b_3 = (2 \times 4) + (3 \times -6) + (-1 \times 2)$$
$$= 8 - 18 - 2 = -12 \neq 0$$

- So **a** and **b** are **not perpendicular** as $\mathbf{a}.\mathbf{b} \neq 0$.

- Now prove they're not parallel by showing $\mathbf{a}.\mathbf{b} \neq \pm|\mathbf{a}||\mathbf{b}|$
$$|\mathbf{a}| = \sqrt{2^2 + 3^2 + (-1)^2} = \sqrt{14}$$
$$|\mathbf{b}| = \sqrt{4^2 + (-6)^2 + 2^2} = \sqrt{56} = \sqrt{4}\sqrt{14} = 2\sqrt{14}$$
So $|\mathbf{a}||\mathbf{b}| = 2\sqrt{14}\sqrt{14} = 28$
Then $\mathbf{a}.\mathbf{b} = -12 \neq |\mathbf{a}||\mathbf{b}|$ or $-|\mathbf{a}||\mathbf{b}|$

- So **a** and **b** are **not parallel** as $\mathbf{a}.\mathbf{b} \neq |\mathbf{a}||\mathbf{b}|$ or $-|\mathbf{a}||\mathbf{b}|$

Tip: The question says 'hence show', which is a hint that you're meant to use the scalar product you've just worked out to show the vectors aren't parallel or perpendicular.

Exercise 4.2

Q1 Find the scalar product of these pairs of vectors.

a) $\begin{pmatrix} 1 \\ 4 \end{pmatrix}, \begin{pmatrix} -2 \\ 1 \end{pmatrix}$

b) $2\mathbf{i} - \mathbf{j}, \mathbf{i} + 3\mathbf{j}$

c) $-2\mathbf{i} - 6\mathbf{j} + \mathbf{k}, -\mathbf{i} + 2\mathbf{j} + 9\mathbf{k}$

d) $\begin{pmatrix} 3 \\ 1 \\ -4 \end{pmatrix}, \begin{pmatrix} 2 \\ 3 \\ 1 \end{pmatrix}$

e) $5\mathbf{j} - 6\mathbf{k}, 6\mathbf{i} + 5\mathbf{k}$

Q2 These pairs of vectors all have scalar products that are equal to 8. Find the values of e, f and g.

a) $\begin{pmatrix} 4 \\ e \end{pmatrix}, \begin{pmatrix} -2 \\ 4 \end{pmatrix}$

b) $7\mathbf{i} + f\mathbf{j} - 3\mathbf{k}, -2\mathbf{i} - \mathbf{j} - 5\mathbf{k}$

c) $\begin{pmatrix} -2 \\ 5 \\ 1 \end{pmatrix}, \begin{pmatrix} g \\ -2 \\ 12 \end{pmatrix}$

Q3 Determine which pairs of vectors are perpendicular to one another.

a) $4\mathbf{i} - 5\mathbf{j}, 10\mathbf{i} - 8\mathbf{j}$

b) $\begin{pmatrix} 4 \\ 0 \\ -5 \end{pmatrix}, \begin{pmatrix} 0 \\ 2 \\ 0 \end{pmatrix}$

c) $\begin{pmatrix} 3 \\ 6 \\ -5 \end{pmatrix}, \begin{pmatrix} -2 \\ 4 \\ 2 \end{pmatrix}$

d) $-\mathbf{i} - 2\mathbf{j} + \mathbf{k}, 2\mathbf{i} + \mathbf{j} + 4\mathbf{k}$

e) $5\mathbf{j} + 2\mathbf{k}, -4\mathbf{i} + 10\mathbf{j}$

Q4 The following pairs of vectors are perpendicular.
Find the values of a, b, c and d.

a) $4\mathbf{i} + a\mathbf{j}$, $5\mathbf{i} - 10\mathbf{j}$

b) $5b\mathbf{i} - 6\mathbf{j} + 9\mathbf{k}$, $2\mathbf{i} - \mathbf{j} - 4\mathbf{k}$

c) $\begin{pmatrix} 2 \\ 3 \\ 1 \end{pmatrix}$, $\begin{pmatrix} -1 \\ 1 \\ c \end{pmatrix}$

d) $\begin{pmatrix} -3 \\ 9 \\ 8 \end{pmatrix} \begin{pmatrix} d \\ 3 \\ -6 \end{pmatrix}$

Q5 Use the scalar product to show that $\begin{pmatrix} 4 \\ -1 \\ 3 \end{pmatrix}$ and $\begin{pmatrix} -12 \\ 3 \\ -9 \end{pmatrix}$ are parallel.

Q6 Find 3 non-parallel vectors that are perpendicular to $3\mathbf{i} - \mathbf{j} - 2\mathbf{k}$.

> **Q6 Hint:** Start by finding an equation for the scalar product of the vector $3\mathbf{i} - \mathbf{j} - 2\mathbf{k}$ and a vector with unknown coefficients.

Finding angles between vectors

$\mathbf{a.b} = |\mathbf{a}||\mathbf{b}|\cos\theta$ can be rearranged to get:

$$\cos\theta = \frac{\mathbf{a.b}}{|\mathbf{a}||\mathbf{b}|}$$

Using this formula you can work out the angle θ between two vectors $\mathbf{a}$ and $\mathbf{b}$ straight from their $\mathbf{i}$, $\mathbf{j}$ and $\mathbf{k}$ components:

- Find the scalar product using the formula: $\mathbf{a.b} = a_1b_1 + a_2b_2 + a_3b_3$.

- Find the magnitude of $\mathbf{a}$ and of $\mathbf{b}$ using Pythagoras: $|\mathbf{a}| = \sqrt{a_1^2 + a_2^2 + a_3^2}$.

- Plug these values into the formula $\cos\theta = \frac{\mathbf{a.b}}{|\mathbf{a}||\mathbf{b}|}$.

Example 1

Find the angle between the vectors $-\mathbf{i} - 6\mathbf{j}$ and $4\mathbf{i} + 2\mathbf{j} + 8\mathbf{k}$.

Let $\mathbf{a} = -\mathbf{i} - 6\mathbf{j}$ and $\mathbf{b} = 4\mathbf{i} + 2\mathbf{j} + 8\mathbf{k}$.

We're looking for θ, where $\cos\theta = \frac{\mathbf{a.b}}{|\mathbf{a}||\mathbf{b}|}$.

- Find the **scalar product** of the vectors:

$$\mathbf{a.b} = a_1b_1 + a_2b_2 + a_3b_3 = (-1 \times 4) + (-6 \times 2) + (0 \times 8)$$
$$= -4 - 12 + 0 = \boxed{-16}$$

- Find the **magnitude** of each vector:

$$|\mathbf{a}| = \sqrt{(-1)^2 + (-6)^2 + (0)^2} = \boxed{\sqrt{37}}$$
$$|\mathbf{b}| = \sqrt{(4)^2 + (2)^2 + (8)^2} = \boxed{\sqrt{84}}$$

- Now put these values into the formula and find the **angle**:

$$\cos\theta = \frac{\mathbf{a.b}}{|\mathbf{a}||\mathbf{b}|} = \frac{-16}{\sqrt{37}\sqrt{84}} \Rightarrow \boxed{\theta = 106.7°} \text{ to 1 d.p.}$$

> **Tip:** It's good to give your vectors names, it'll save you having to write them out every time you want to refer to them.

Tip: It usually helps to draw a picture so you can see what's going on.

You can also use this formula for answering **geometric questions**, the key is figuring out which vectors you need to use:

Example 2

The coordinates of A, B and C are (–2, 0, 3), (1, 5, 2) and (3, –2, 1) respectively. Find the size of angle ABC to one decimal place.

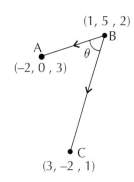

(1, 5 , 2)

B

A

θ

(–2, 0 , 3)

C

(3, –2 , 1)

- The **angle** you're looking for is ABC, so it's the angle **between** lines **AB and BC**.
- Both vectors need to be directed **away from the angle** so the vectors you need are $\vec{BA}$ and $\vec{BC}$.
- You can then use the formula $\cos\theta = \dfrac{\vec{BA}.\vec{BC}}{|\vec{BA}||\vec{BC}|}$ to **find** θ.
- Find the vectors first:

Tip: Even though these are 3D vectors you only need a 2D diagram to see what angle you're looking for.

$$\vec{BA} = \vec{OA} - \vec{OB} = \begin{pmatrix} -2 \\ 0 \\ 3 \end{pmatrix} - \begin{pmatrix} 1 \\ 5 \\ 2 \end{pmatrix} = \begin{pmatrix} -3 \\ -5 \\ 1 \end{pmatrix}$$

$$\vec{BC} = \vec{OC} - \vec{OB} = \begin{pmatrix} 3 \\ -2 \\ 1 \end{pmatrix} - \begin{pmatrix} 1 \\ 5 \\ 2 \end{pmatrix} = \begin{pmatrix} 2 \\ -7 \\ -1 \end{pmatrix}$$

- Now find the scalar product and the magnitudes as before:

$$\vec{BA}.\vec{BC} = (-3 \times 2) + (-5 \times (-7)) + (1 \times (-1)) = -6 + 35 - 1 = \boxed{28}$$

$$|\vec{BA}| = \sqrt{(-3)^2 + (-5)^2 + 1^2} = \boxed{\sqrt{35}}$$

$$|\vec{BC}| = \sqrt{2^2 + (-7)^2 + (-1)^2} = \boxed{\sqrt{54}}$$

- Stick these values into the formula to find θ:

$$\cos\theta = \frac{\vec{BA}.\vec{BC}}{|\vec{BA}||\vec{BC}|} = \frac{28}{\sqrt{35}\sqrt{54}} \Rightarrow \boxed{\theta = 49.9°} \text{ to 1 d.p.}$$

Exercise 4.3

Q1 Find the angle between each of the following pairs of vectors. In each case, give your answer in degrees correct to 1 d.p.

a) $p = 4i + 3j,$ $q = 12i + 5j$

b) $r = \begin{pmatrix} 2 \\ -1 \end{pmatrix}$, $s = \begin{pmatrix} -6 \\ 3 \end{pmatrix}$

c) $a = \begin{pmatrix} -2 \\ -4 \end{pmatrix}$, $b = \begin{pmatrix} 3 \\ -1 \end{pmatrix}$

Q2 Find the angle between each of the following pairs of vectors. In each case, give your answer in degrees correct to 1 d.p.

a) $a = \begin{pmatrix} 2 \\ -2 \\ 1 \end{pmatrix}$, $b = \begin{pmatrix} 6 \\ 3 \\ 2 \end{pmatrix}$

b) $c = \begin{pmatrix} -7 \\ -4 \\ 4 \end{pmatrix}$, $d = \begin{pmatrix} -6 \\ 7 \\ 6 \end{pmatrix}$

c) $e = 9i + 6j - 2k,$ $f = i + 4j - 8k$

d) $g = 7i + j - k,$ $h = i - 18j - 6k$

e) $t = \begin{pmatrix} 23 \\ -10 \\ 10 \end{pmatrix}$, $u = \begin{pmatrix} 2 \\ -4 \\ 4 \end{pmatrix}$

Q3 Triangle ABC has vertices at the points A (–4, –1), B (–1, 3) and C (4, 5).

Q3 Hint: Draw a diagram if it helps you to see what's going on.

  a) Find the vectors $\overrightarrow{AB}$ and $\overrightarrow{AC}$.

  b) Find $|\overrightarrow{AB}|$ and $|\overrightarrow{AC}|$.

  c) Find $(\overrightarrow{AB}) \cdot (\overrightarrow{AC})$.

  d) Hence calculate angle BAC, correct to the nearest degree.

Q4 Points P, Q and R have position vectors $\mathbf{p} = -4\mathbf{i} - 7\mathbf{j} - 9\mathbf{k}$, $\mathbf{q} = -2\mathbf{i} + 2\mathbf{j} + 5\mathbf{k}$ and $\mathbf{r} = -2\mathbf{i} - \mathbf{j} - 11\mathbf{k}$ respectively.

  a) Find the vectors $\overrightarrow{PQ}$ and $\overrightarrow{PR}$.

  b) Find the magnitudes $|\overrightarrow{PQ}|$ and $|\overrightarrow{PR}|$.

  c) Find $(\overrightarrow{PQ}) \cdot (\overrightarrow{PR})$.

  d) Hence find the angle QPR,
     giving your answer in degrees correct to 3 s.f.

Q5 The isosceles triangle TRU shown has TR = TU.

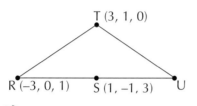

  a) Find $(\overrightarrow{TS}) \cdot (\overrightarrow{RS})$.

  b) Show that S is the midpoint of RU.

  c) Write down the coordinates of U.

Q6 ABCD is a parallelogram where A, B and C have position vectors $\mathbf{a} = -4\mathbf{i} + 5\mathbf{j} - 6\mathbf{k}$, $\mathbf{b} = 4\mathbf{j} + 2\mathbf{k}$ and $\mathbf{c} = 6\mathbf{i} + 13\mathbf{j}$ respectively.

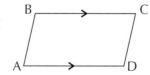

  a) Write down the position vector of D.

  b) Find the vectors $\overrightarrow{AB}$ and $\overrightarrow{AD}$ in $\mathbf{i}$, $\mathbf{j}$, $\mathbf{k}$ form.

  c) Find the magnitudes of $\overrightarrow{AB}$ and $\overrightarrow{AD}$.

  d) Hence find the angle BAD,
     giving your answer in degrees correct to 4 s.f.

Q7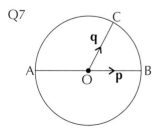

AB is the diameter of a circle centre O, radius r. C is a point on the circumference of the circle.
$\overrightarrow{OB} = \mathbf{p}$ and $\overrightarrow{OC} = \mathbf{q}$.

  a) Find the vectors $\overrightarrow{AC}$ and $\overrightarrow{CB}$ in terms of $\mathbf{p}$ and $\mathbf{q}$.

  b) Show that $(\overrightarrow{AC}) \cdot (\overrightarrow{CB}) = \mathbf{p} \cdot \mathbf{p} - \mathbf{q} \cdot \mathbf{q}$.

  c) Hence explain why angle ACB = 90°.

Q7 b) Hint: Remember the commutative and distributive laws (p.154) and you'll also need to know that:
$(c_1\mathbf{d}) \cdot (c_2\mathbf{b}) = c_1c_2(\mathbf{d} \cdot \mathbf{b})$

Finding the angle between two lines

You can find the **angle between two lines** from the **vector equations** of the lines, or from **two points** on each line.

If you're given the **vector equations** you just use the **b** vectors in the equations $\mathbf{r}_1 = \mathbf{a}_1 + s\mathbf{b}_1$ and $\mathbf{r}_2 = \mathbf{a}_2 + t\mathbf{b}_2$ (the 'parallel to' or the 'direction' bits), and find the angle between them using $\cos\theta = \dfrac{\mathbf{b}_1 . \mathbf{b}_2}{|\mathbf{b}_1||\mathbf{b}_2|}$.

- This formula gives you the **angle** that both vectors are **pointing away from**, which could be up to 180°.

- The **angle between two lines** is the **smallest angle** you can rotate one line by to get it onto the other line, so it **can't be more than 90°**.

Tip: If you rotate a line by more than 90° clockwise it's the same as a rotation of less than 90° anticlockwise.

- So you might have to **subtract** the angle you get from the formula **from 180°** to find the angle between the lines:

If the angle θ that comes out of the formula is **90° or less** then the angle between the direction vectors is the angle between the lines and **you're done**.

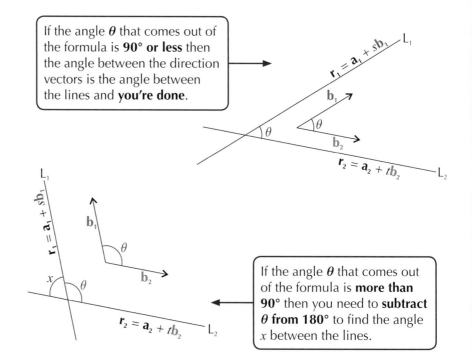

If the angle θ that comes out of the formula is **more than 90°** then you need to **subtract** θ from 180° to find the angle x between the lines.

If you're given **two points** on a line you'll have to **find a vector parallel to the line** before you can plug it into the formula.

Tip: This is what you do when you're finding the vector equation of a line from two points. If you're only asked to find the angle there's no need to write the whole equation out (though you can do if it helps).

This is nice and simple because the vector that joins the two points is parallel to the line, so given two points P and Q with position vectors **p** and **q** you just use the vector $\overrightarrow{PQ} = \mathbf{q} - \mathbf{p}$.

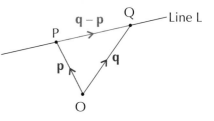

Example 1

Line *l* has the equation r = (2i + 4k) + λ(i + 2j –k).
Point A and point B have coordinates (4, 4, 2) and (1, 0, 3) respectively.
Point A lies on *l*.

a) **Find the acute angle between *l* and line segment AB.**

- First draw a **diagram**, it'll make everything clearer:

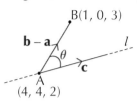

B(1, 0, 3)

b – a

l

θ

c

A
(4, 4, 2)

Tip: Don't worry about drawing everything accurately, it's just to give you an idea of what's going on.

- Find the vectors that you want to **know the angle** between.
  The vector parallel to line segment AB is $\overrightarrow{AB}$.

$$\overrightarrow{AB} = \mathbf{b} - \mathbf{a} = \begin{pmatrix} 1 \\ 0 \\ 3 \end{pmatrix} - \begin{pmatrix} 4 \\ 4 \\ 2 \end{pmatrix} = \begin{pmatrix} -3 \\ -4 \\ 1 \end{pmatrix}$$

The direction vector of *l* (which we've called **c**) is: $\mathbf{c} = \begin{pmatrix} 1 \\ 2 \\ -1 \end{pmatrix}$

- Next you need to find the scalar product of your two vectors:

$$\overrightarrow{AB} \cdot \mathbf{c} = (-3 \times 1) + (-4 \times 2) + (1 \times -1) = -3 - 8 - 1 = \boxed{-12}$$

- And the magnitudes of each vector:

$$|\overrightarrow{AB}| = \sqrt{(-3)^2 + (-4)^2 + (1)^2} = \boxed{\sqrt{26}}$$
$$|\mathbf{c}| = \sqrt{(1)^2 + (2)^2 + (-1)^2} = \boxed{\sqrt{6}}$$

- Now plug these values into the equation and find the angle:

$$\cos \theta = \frac{\overrightarrow{AB} \cdot \mathbf{c}}{|\overrightarrow{AB}||\mathbf{c}|} = \frac{-12}{\sqrt{26}\sqrt{6}} \Rightarrow \theta = 163.897...°$$

- The formula's given us the **obtuse angle**, so the situation must have been more like this: ⟶

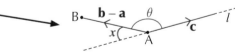

B

b – a

θ

c

l

x

A

Tip: Remember, the vectors always point away from the angle θ that the formula gives you.

- So you just **subtract this angle from 180°** to get the acute angle (that's *x*) between the lines:

$$180° - 163.897...° = \mathbf{16.1°} \text{ to 1 d.p.}$$

b) **P is the point on *l* such that BP is the shortest distance from B to *l*.
   Find the distance BP to two decimal places.**

Draw a diagram.
BP is the shortest distance from B to *l*,
so it must be perpendicular to *l*: ⟶

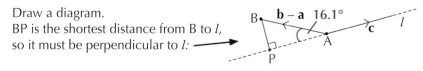

B

b – a   16.1°

c   *l*

A

P

Tip: The shortest distance between a point and a line is always the perpendicular line segment.

APB is a right-angled triangle, so you can find the length of BP using trig.

- You know from part **a)** that the vector $\overrightarrow{AB}$ is $\begin{pmatrix} -3 \\ -4 \\ 1 \end{pmatrix}$, and $|\overrightarrow{AB}| = \sqrt{26}$
- Angle PAB is 16.1°.
- You want to find side BP, the side opposite PAB.
  opposite $= \sin\theta \times$ hypotenuse, so:

$$BP = \sin(16.1...) \times \sqrt{26} = \boxed{\textbf{1.41}} \text{ to 2 d.p.}$$

You can prove **lines are perpendicular** by showing that their direction vectors are perpendicular, i.e. by showing the **scalar product** of their direction vectors is **zero**:

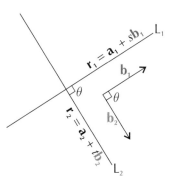

L_1 and L_2 are **perpendicular** if $\mathbf{b}_1 . \mathbf{b}_2 = 0$

Example 2

Show that the lines $\mathbf{r}_1 = (\mathbf{i} + 6\mathbf{j} + 2\mathbf{k}) + \lambda(\mathbf{i} + 2\mathbf{j} + 2\mathbf{k})$ and $\mathbf{r}_2 = (3\mathbf{i} - \mathbf{j} + \mathbf{k}) + \mu(4\mathbf{i} - 3\mathbf{j} + \mathbf{k})$ are perpendicular.

- $\mathbf{r}_1$ and $\mathbf{r}_2$ are **parallel** to their direction vectors $\mathbf{b}_1 = \mathbf{i} + 2\mathbf{j} + 2\mathbf{k}$ and $\mathbf{b}_2 = 4\mathbf{i} - 3\mathbf{j} + \mathbf{k}$ respectively.
- The **scalar product** of $\mathbf{b}_1$ and $\mathbf{b}_2$ is:
$$(\mathbf{i} + 2\mathbf{j} + 2\mathbf{k}).(4\mathbf{i} - 3\mathbf{j} + \mathbf{k}) = 4 - 6 + 2 = 0$$
- So $\mathbf{b}_1$ and $\mathbf{b}_2$ are perpendicular, therefore $\mathbf{r}_1$ and $\mathbf{r}_2$ are **perpendicular**.

Exercise 4.4

Q1 Hint: You don't need to use the scalar product to decide if the lines are parallel or not.

Q1 For each pair of lines whose equations are given below, state whether the lines are parallel, perpendicular or neither.

a) $\mathbf{r} = (\mathbf{i} - 2\mathbf{j} + \mathbf{k}) + s(2\mathbf{i} - 4\mathbf{j} - 6\mathbf{k})$, $\mathbf{r} = (2\mathbf{i} + 3\mathbf{j} + 4\mathbf{k}) + t(-\mathbf{i} + 2\mathbf{j} + 3\mathbf{k})$

b) $\mathbf{r} = \begin{pmatrix} -5 \\ 3 \\ 2 \end{pmatrix} + p\begin{pmatrix} 4 \\ -1 \\ 1 \end{pmatrix}$, $\mathbf{r} = \begin{pmatrix} 2 \\ 1 \\ 0 \end{pmatrix} + q\begin{pmatrix} 1 \\ -4 \\ 0 \end{pmatrix}$

c) $\mathbf{r} = \lambda(2\mathbf{j} - 7\mathbf{k})$, $\mathbf{r} = 3\mathbf{k} + \mu(2\mathbf{i} - 7\mathbf{k})$

d) $\mathbf{r} = (\mathbf{j} + \mathbf{k}) + p(\mathbf{i} + \mathbf{j})$, $\mathbf{r} = (\mathbf{i} + \mathbf{k}) + q(\mathbf{i} - \mathbf{j} + 2\mathbf{k})$

e) $\mathbf{r} = \begin{pmatrix} 1 \\ 0 \\ 0 \end{pmatrix} + \lambda\begin{pmatrix} 0 \\ 0 \\ 4 \end{pmatrix}$, $\mathbf{r} = \begin{pmatrix} 0 \\ 1 \\ 0 \end{pmatrix} + \mu\begin{pmatrix} -4 \\ 8 \\ 0 \end{pmatrix}$

Q2 Find the acute angle between each pair of intersecting lines below.

a) $\mathbf{r} = \begin{pmatrix} 4 \\ 0 \\ 4 \end{pmatrix} + \lambda \begin{pmatrix} 2 \\ 2 \\ 1 \end{pmatrix}$, $\mathbf{r} = \begin{pmatrix} 1 \\ -4 \\ 3 \end{pmatrix} + \mu \begin{pmatrix} 2 \\ 3 \\ 6 \end{pmatrix}$

b) $\mathbf{r} = (-\mathbf{i} - \mathbf{j} - 3\mathbf{k}) + p(4\mathbf{i} + 4\mathbf{j} - 7\mathbf{k})$, $\mathbf{r} = (2\mathbf{i} + 4\mathbf{j} + \mathbf{k}) + q(8\mathbf{i} + \mathbf{j} - 4\mathbf{k})$

c) $\mathbf{r} = \begin{pmatrix} 5 \\ -7 \\ 11 \end{pmatrix} + s \begin{pmatrix} 6 \\ -7 \\ 5 \end{pmatrix}$, $\mathbf{r} = \begin{pmatrix} 9 \\ 0 \\ -9 \end{pmatrix} + t \begin{pmatrix} 2 \\ 1 \\ -1 \end{pmatrix}$

d) $\mathbf{r} = 4\mathbf{i} + \alpha(7\mathbf{i} - 6\mathbf{j} + 6\mathbf{k})$, $\mathbf{r} = 4\mathbf{j} + \beta(-4\mathbf{i} + 2\mathbf{j} - 2\mathbf{k})$

e) $\mathbf{r} = (4\mathbf{i} - \mathbf{j}) + u(-3\mathbf{i} - 5\mathbf{j} + 2\mathbf{k})$, $\mathbf{r} = 5\mathbf{k} + v(2\mathbf{i} + \mathbf{k})$

Q3 The lines given by equations $\mathbf{r} = (4\mathbf{i} + \mathbf{j} + 2\mathbf{k}) + \lambda(4\mathbf{i} + 6\mathbf{j} - \mathbf{k})$ and $\mathbf{r} = (4\mathbf{i} + \mathbf{j} + 2\mathbf{k}) + \mu(5\mathbf{i} - 2\mathbf{j} + z\mathbf{k})$ are perpendicular. Find z.

Q4 A $(-1, -2, 6)$, B $(p, -1, 3)$ and C $(-1, 0, 2)$ are the vertices of a triangle where angle ABC is $90°$.

a) Write down vector equations for the lines containing AB and BC in terms of p.

b) Find 2 possible values of p.

Q5 The position vectors of points A and B are $\begin{pmatrix} 4 \\ 2 \\ -2 \end{pmatrix}$ and $\begin{pmatrix} -1 \\ 3 \\ 1 \end{pmatrix}$ respectively.

The points C and D are such that $\overrightarrow{OD} = 2\overrightarrow{OB}$ and $\overrightarrow{OC} = \frac{3}{2}\overrightarrow{OA}$.

a) Write down the position vectors of C and D.

b) Line L_1 passes through A and D, line L_2 passes through B and C. Write down vector equations for L_1 and L_2.

c) Determine whether the lines are skew or intersecting.

d) Find the acute angle between the directions of the 2 lines, correct to 1 decimal place.

Q6 a) Find an equation for the line L which passes through A $(3, 8, -5)$ and B $(8, -2, 0)$.

b) Find the co-ordinates of the point P, lying on line L, such that OP is perpendicular to line L.

c) Find the distance of P from O in the form $m\sqrt{n}$.

Q7 Points A, B and C have position vectors $(4\mathbf{i} - 6\mathbf{j} + 2\mathbf{k})$, $(-3\mathbf{i} + 2\mathbf{j} + 4\mathbf{k})$ and $(5\mathbf{i} - \mathbf{j} - \mathbf{k})$ respectively. The line l passes through B and C.

a) Find a vector equation for the line l.

b) Find the acute angle between the line segment AB and line l to 1 d.p.

c) Find the shortest distance from the point A to the line l to 2 d.p.

Q7 c) Hint:
You're looking for the perpendicular line segment.

Review Exercise — Chapter 7

Q1 Give two vectors that are parallel to each of the following:

    a) 2**a**   b) 3**i** + 4**j** − 2**k**   c) $\begin{pmatrix} 1 \\ 2 \\ -1 \end{pmatrix}$

Q2 Using the diagram on the right find these vectors in terms of vectors **a**, **b** and **c**.

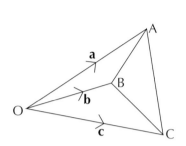

    a) $\overrightarrow{AB}$ b) $\overrightarrow{BA}$ c) $\overrightarrow{CB}$ d) $\overrightarrow{AC}$

Q3 CDEFGH is a regular hexagon whose centre is O.

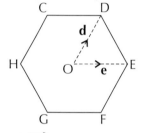

If $\overrightarrow{OE} = $ **e** and $\overrightarrow{OD} = $ **d**, express in terms of **e** and **d**:

    a) $\overrightarrow{HE}$ b) $\overrightarrow{DG}$ c) $\overrightarrow{ED}$ d) $\overrightarrow{CE}$ e) $\overrightarrow{DF}$

Q4 Give, in unit vector form, the position vector of point P, which has the coordinates (2, −4, 5).

Q5 X is the point (6, −1, 0) and Y is the point (4, −4, 7).
Write the vectors $\overrightarrow{XO}$ and $\overrightarrow{YO}$ in unit vector form and in column vector form.

Q6 R has position vector $\begin{pmatrix} 3 \\ -1 \end{pmatrix}$ and S has position vector $\begin{pmatrix} -5 \\ -7 \end{pmatrix}$.
Find the magnitude of $\overrightarrow{RS}$.

Q7 Find the magnitudes of these vectors: a) 3**i** + 4**j** − 2**k**   b) $\begin{pmatrix} 1 \\ 2 \\ -1 \end{pmatrix}$

Q8 If A is (1, 2, 3) and B is (3, −1, −2), find: a) $\left| \overrightarrow{OA} \right|$ b) $\left| \overrightarrow{OB} \right|$ c) $\left| \overrightarrow{AB} \right|$

Q9 X is the point (−2, 1, 0).

The distance between X and Y is 6. The unit vector in the direction $\overrightarrow{XY}$ is $\begin{pmatrix} \frac{2}{3} \\ \frac{2}{3} \\ -\frac{1}{3} \end{pmatrix}$.

Find the coordinates of Y.

Q10 Find vector equations for the following lines in unit and in column vector form.
    a) a straight line through (4, 1, 2), parallel to vector 3**i** + **j** − **k**.
    b) a straight line through (2, −1, 1) and (0, 2, 3).

Q11 Find three points that lie on the line with vector equation $\mathbf{r} = \begin{pmatrix} 3 \\ 2 \\ 4 \end{pmatrix} + t \begin{pmatrix} -1 \\ 3 \\ 0 \end{pmatrix}$.

Q12 Line L passes through the origin and contains the point A whose position vector is $2\mathbf{i} + 8\mathbf{j} - 4\mathbf{k}$. Points B, C and D also lie on the line, where B is the midpoint of OA, A is the midpoint of OC and O is the midpoint of DA.
a) Draw a sketch of the positions of O, A, B, C and D on the line.
b) Write down the position vectors of B, C and D.
c) Give a vector equation for line L.

Q13 Point P has position vector $\begin{pmatrix} 3 \\ -5 \\ 2 \end{pmatrix}$ and point Q has position vector $\begin{pmatrix} 5 \\ -2 \\ -1 \end{pmatrix}$.
a) Write down the vector $\overrightarrow{PQ}$ in column vector form.
b) Find a vector equation for the straight line that passes through P and Q.

Q14 Points A and B have coordinates (1, 1, 3) and (9, –3, 9) respectively.
Line m passes through A and is parallel to the vector $3\mathbf{i} - \mathbf{j} + 4\mathbf{k}$.
Line n passes through B and is parallel to the vector $-\mathbf{i} + \mathbf{j} + \mathbf{k}$.
a) Show that line m and line n intersect,
and find the coordinates of the point of intersection C.
b) Show that triangle ABC is right-angled.

Q15 Find $\mathbf{a} \cdot \mathbf{b}$ if: a) $\mathbf{a} = 3\mathbf{i} + 4\mathbf{j}$ and $\mathbf{b} = \mathbf{i} - 2\mathbf{j} + 3\mathbf{k}$ b) $\mathbf{a} = \begin{pmatrix} 4 \\ 2 \\ 1 \end{pmatrix}$ and $\mathbf{b} = \begin{pmatrix} 3 \\ -4 \\ -3 \end{pmatrix}$

Q16

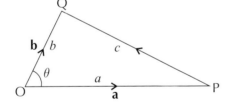

O is the origin and points P and Q have position vectors $\mathbf{a}$ and $\mathbf{b}$ respectively.
Triangle OPQ has sides whose lengths are given by OP = a, OQ = b, PQ = c. Angle POQ = θ.
a) Write down the vector $\overrightarrow{PQ}$ in terms of $\mathbf{a}$ and $\mathbf{b}$.
b) Obtain an expression for $(\mathbf{b} - \mathbf{a}) \cdot (\mathbf{b} - \mathbf{a})$ in terms of $\mathbf{a}$, $\mathbf{b}$ and θ.
c) Hence deduce that $c^2 = a^2 + b^2 - 2ab\cos\theta$.

Q17 $\mathbf{r}_1 = \begin{pmatrix} 2 \\ -1 \\ 2 \end{pmatrix} + t \begin{pmatrix} -4 \\ 6 \\ -2 \end{pmatrix}$ and $\mathbf{r}_2 = \begin{pmatrix} 3 \\ 2 \\ 4 \end{pmatrix} + u \begin{pmatrix} -1 \\ 3 \\ 0 \end{pmatrix}$
a) Show that these lines intersect and find the position vector of their intersection point.
b) Find the angle between these lines.

Q18 Find a vector that is perpendicular to $3\mathbf{i} + 4\mathbf{j} - 2\mathbf{k}$.

Q19 Two lines L_1 and L_2 have vector equations $\mathbf{r}_1 = (x\mathbf{i} + \mathbf{j} + 5\mathbf{k}) + \lambda(2\mathbf{i} + 2\mathbf{j} + 3\mathbf{k})$ and $\mathbf{r}_2 = (-\mathbf{i} - 2\mathbf{j} + 3\mathbf{k}) + \mu(3\mathbf{i} - \mathbf{j} - 2\mathbf{k})$. Given that the two lines intersect:
a) Find the value of x.
b) Find the coordinates of the point of intersection.
c) Find the acute angle between the two lines.

Exam-Style Questions — Chapter 7

1 The quadrilateral ABCD has vertices A(1, 5, 9), B(3, 2, 1), C(–2, 4, 3) and D(5, –1, –7).

a) Find the vector $\overrightarrow{AB}$.

(2 marks)

b) C and D lie on line l_1. Using the parameter μ, find the vector equation of l_1.

(2 marks)

c) Find the coordinates of the intersection point of l_1 and the line that passes through AB.

(5 marks)

d) (i) Find the acute angle between l_1 and AB. Give your answer to 1 decimal place.

(4 marks)

(ii) Find the shortest distance from point A to l_1.

(4 marks)

2 The lines l_1 and l_2 are given by the vector equations:

$$l_1: \quad \mathbf{r} = (3\mathbf{i} - 3\mathbf{j} - 2\mathbf{k}) + \mu(\mathbf{i} - 4\mathbf{j} + 2\mathbf{k})$$
$$l_2: \quad \mathbf{r} = (10\mathbf{i} - 21\mathbf{j} + 11\mathbf{k}) + \lambda(-3\mathbf{i} + 12\mathbf{j} - 6\mathbf{k})$$

a) Show that l_1 and l_2 are parallel.

(1 mark)

b) Show that point A(2, 1, –4) lies on l_1.

(2 marks)

c) Point B lies on l_2 and is such that the line segment AB is perpendicular to l_1 and l_2. Find the position vector of point B.

(6 marks)

d) Find $|\overrightarrow{AB}|$.

(2 marks)

3 Point A has the position vector $3\mathbf{i} + 2\mathbf{j} + \mathbf{k}$ and point B has position vector $3\mathbf{i} - 4\mathbf{j} - \mathbf{k}$.

a) Show that AOB is a right-angled triangle.

(3 marks)

b) Find angle ABO in the triangle using the scalar product definition.

(5 marks)

c) (i) Point C has the position vector $3\mathbf{i} - \mathbf{j}$. Show that triangle OAC is isosceles.

(3 marks)

(ii) Calculate the area of triangle OAC.

(4 marks)

d) (i) Find the vector equation for line l, which passes through points A and B.

(2 marks)

(ii) The point D lies on line l and has the position vector $a\mathbf{i} + b\mathbf{j}$. Find a and b.

(3 marks)

4   The point A has coordinates $(-5, -4, 6)$, the point B has coordinates $(-1, 1, 8)$ and the point D has coordinates $(-7, 0, 5)$.

Given that ABCD is a parallelogram, find

a)   the position vector of point C

(3 marks)

b)   a vector equation for the line L_1 that contains the line segment DC

(2 marks)

c)   a vector equation for the line L_2 that contains the points A and C

(3 marks)

d)   the shortest distance between L_1 and the origin, to 3 significant figures.

(6 marks)

5   The line l passes through points J and K, where J has position vector $2\mathbf{i} - 2\mathbf{j} + \mathbf{k}$ and K has position vector $3\mathbf{i} + \mathbf{j} - \mathbf{k}$.

a)   Obtain a vector equation for the line l.

(2 marks)

b)   Find the acute angle between the line l and the line segment OJ.

Give your answer to the nearest degree.

(4 marks)

Determine, showing your reasons clearly, whether the following sets of points are collinear

c)   J, K and G, where point G has coordinates $(1, -5, 3)$

(2 marks)

d)   J, K and H, where point H has coordinates $(5, 11, -2)$

(2 marks)

6   The lines l_1 and l_2 are given by the equations:

$$l_1 : \mathbf{r} = \begin{pmatrix} 3 \\ 0 \\ -2 \end{pmatrix} + \lambda \begin{pmatrix} 1 \\ 3 \\ -2 \end{pmatrix} \qquad l_2 : \mathbf{r} = \begin{pmatrix} 0 \\ 2 \\ 1 \end{pmatrix} + \mu \begin{pmatrix} 2 \\ -5 \\ -3 \end{pmatrix}$$

a)   Show that l_1 and l_2 do not intersect.

(4 marks)

b)   Point P has coordinates $(5, 8, -3)$.

Point Q is the image of point P after reflection in line l_1.

Points P and Q both lie on the line which has equation $\mathbf{r} = \begin{pmatrix} 5 \\ 4 \\ -9 \end{pmatrix} + t \begin{pmatrix} 0 \\ 2 \\ 3 \end{pmatrix}$.

(i)   Find the intersection point of line segment PQ and line l_1.

(4 marks)

(ii)   Show that the line segment PQ and line l_1 are perpendicular.

(2 marks)

(iii) Find the position vector of point Q.

(3 marks)

Answers

Chapter 1: Algebra and Functions

1. Partial Fractions

Exercise 1.1 — Expressing in partial fractions

Q1
$$\frac{3x+3}{(x-1)(x-4)} \equiv \frac{A}{(x-1)} + \frac{B}{(x-4)}$$
$$\Rightarrow \frac{3x+3}{(x-1)(x-4)} \equiv \frac{A(x-4)+B(x-1)}{(x-1)(x-4)}$$
$$\Rightarrow 3x+3 \equiv A(x-4)+B(x-1)$$

Substitution:
$x = 4 \Rightarrow 15 = 3B \Rightarrow B = 5$
$x = 1 \Rightarrow 6 = -3A \Rightarrow A = -2$

This gives: $\dfrac{3x+3}{(x-1)(x-4)} \equiv -\dfrac{2}{(x-1)} + \dfrac{5}{(x-4)}$

Q2
$$\frac{5x-1}{x(2x+1)} \equiv \frac{A}{x} + \frac{B}{(2x+1)}$$
$$\Rightarrow 5x-1 \equiv A(2x+1)+Bx$$

Equating coefficients:
x terms: $\quad 5 = 2A + B$
constants: $\quad -1 = A$
$A = -1$, putting this into the first equation gives:
$5 = -2 + B \Rightarrow B = 7$

This gives: $\dfrac{5x-1}{x(2x+1)} \equiv -\dfrac{1}{x} + \dfrac{7}{(2x+1)}$

Q3
$$\frac{3x-2}{x^2+x-12} \equiv \frac{3x-2}{(x+4)(x-3)} \equiv \frac{A}{(x+4)} + \frac{B}{(x-3)}$$
$$\Rightarrow \frac{3x-2}{(x+4)(x-3)} \equiv \frac{A(x-3)+B(x+4)}{(x+4)(x-3)}$$
$$\Rightarrow 3x-2 \equiv A(x-3)+B(x+4)$$

Equating coefficients:
x terms: $\quad 3 = A + B$
constants: $-2 = -3A + 4B$
Solving simultaneously gives: $A = 2$, $B = 1$

This gives: $\dfrac{3x-2}{x^2+x-12} \equiv \dfrac{2}{(x+4)} + \dfrac{1}{(x-3)}$

Q4
$$\frac{2}{x^2-16} \equiv \frac{2}{(x+4)(x-4)} \equiv \frac{A}{(x+4)} + \frac{B}{(x-4)}$$
$$\Rightarrow 2 \equiv A(x-4)+B(x+4)$$

Substitution:
$x = 4 \Rightarrow 2 = 8B \Rightarrow B = \dfrac{1}{4}$
$x = -4 \Rightarrow 2 = -8A \Rightarrow A = -\dfrac{1}{4}$

This gives: $\dfrac{2}{x^2-16} \equiv -\dfrac{1}{4(x+4)} + \dfrac{1}{4(x-4)}$

Don't worry if you get fractions for your coefficients — just put the numerator on the top of your partial fraction and the denominator on the bottom.

Q5 $x^2 - x - 6 = (x-3)(x+2)$
$$\frac{5}{(x-3)(x+2)} \equiv \frac{A}{(x-3)} + \frac{B}{(x+2)}$$
$$\Rightarrow 5 \equiv A(x+2)+B(x-3)$$

Equating coefficients:
x terms: $\quad 0 = A + B$
constants: $5 = 2A - 3B$
Solving simultaneously gives: $A = 1$, $B = -1$

This gives: $\dfrac{5}{x^2-x-6} \equiv \dfrac{1}{(x-3)} - \dfrac{1}{(x+2)}$

Q6
$$\frac{11x}{2x^2+5x-12} \equiv \frac{11x}{(2x-3)(x+4)} \equiv \frac{A}{(2x-3)} + \frac{B}{(x+4)}$$
$$\Rightarrow 11x \equiv A(x+4)+B(2x-3)$$

Equating coefficients:
x terms: $\quad 11 = A + 2B$
constants: $0 = 4A - 3B$
Solving simultaneously gives: $A = 3$, $B = 4$

This gives $\dfrac{11x}{2x^2+5x-12} \equiv \dfrac{3}{(2x-3)} + \dfrac{4}{(x+4)}$

Q7 a) $x^3 - 9x = x(x^2-9) = x(x+3)(x-3)$

b)
$$\frac{x^2-3x+2}{x(x+3)(x-3)} \equiv \frac{A}{x} + \frac{B}{(x+3)} + \frac{C}{(x-3)}$$
$$\Rightarrow x^2-3x+2$$
$$\equiv A(x+3)(x-3)+Bx(x-3)+Cx(x+3)$$

Equating coefficients:
x^2 terms: $\quad 1 = A + B + C$
x terms: $\quad -3 = -3B + 3C$
constants: $\quad 2 = -9A$
The third equation gives that $A = -\dfrac{2}{9}$
Then solving the first two simultaneously gives:
$B = \dfrac{10}{9}$, $C = \dfrac{1}{9}$

This gives: $\dfrac{x^2-3x+2}{x^3-9x} \equiv -\dfrac{2}{9x} + \dfrac{10}{9(x+3)} + \dfrac{1}{9(x-3)}$

Q8
$$\frac{4x^2-14}{x^3-36x} \equiv \frac{4x^2-14}{x(x^2-36)} \equiv \frac{4x^2-14}{x(x+6)(x-6)}$$
$$\frac{4x^2-14}{x(x+6)(x-6)} \equiv \frac{A}{x} + \frac{B}{(x+6)} + \frac{C}{(x-6)}$$
$$\Rightarrow 4x^2-14 \equiv A(x+6)(x-6)+Bx(x-6)+Cx(x+6)$$

Substitution:
$x = 0 \Rightarrow -14 = -36A \Rightarrow A = \dfrac{14}{36} = \dfrac{7}{18}$
$x = 6 \Rightarrow 130 = 72C \Rightarrow C = \dfrac{130}{72} = \dfrac{65}{36}$
$x = -6 \Rightarrow 130 = 72B \Rightarrow B = \dfrac{130}{72} = \dfrac{65}{36}$

This gives: $\dfrac{4x^2-14}{x^3-36x} \equiv \dfrac{7}{18x} + \dfrac{65}{36(x+6)} + \dfrac{65}{36(x-6)}$

Q9 a) $f(x) = x^3 - 7x - 6$
$f(-1) = -1 + 7 - 6 = 0 \Rightarrow (x+1)$ is a factor
Once you've found one factor using the factor theorem you can use this method:
$(x + 1)$ is a factor of $x^3 - 7x - 6$, so:
$x^3 - 7x - 6 = (x+1)(\qquad\qquad)$

There's an x^3 on the LHS, so there's an x^2 term in the bracket:
$$x^3 - 7x - 6 = (x + 1)(x^2 \qquad)$$
There's -6 on the LHS, so you need -6 in the bracket to multiply with the 1 in $(x + 1)$ and give -6:
$$x^3 - 7x - 6 = (x + 1)(x^2 \qquad -6)$$
Now you've got $-7x$ on the LHS and $-6x$ (from multiplying x by -6) on the RHS. So you need $-x$ in the middle of the bracket to get another $-x$ on the RHS (from multiplying 1 by $-x$):
$$x^3 - 7x - 6 = (x + 1)(x^2 - x - 6)$$
When you multiply out the RHS you get the LHS (the terms in x^2 cancel), so this is the right quadratic. Finally, factorise the quadratic:
$$x^3 - 7x - 6 = (x + 1)(x^2 - x - 6) = (x + 1)(x + 2)(x - 3)$$
This method looks a bit involved, but it's just laid out like this to show you what's going on — if you did it yourself you'd just write:
'$x^3 - 7x - 6 = (x + 1)(x^2 - x - 6) = (x + 1)(x + 2)(x - 3)$'
So $x^3 - 7x - 6 = (x + 1)(x - 3)(x + 2)$
Or you can keep using trial and error to find the other factors, but this could take a while:
$f(3) = 27 - 21 - 6 = 0 \Rightarrow (x - 3)$ is a factor
$f(-2) = -8 + 14 - 6 = 0 \Rightarrow (x + 2)$ is a factor
So $x^3 - 7x - 6 = (x + 1)(x - 3)(x + 2)$

b) $\dfrac{5x^2 - 7x - 4}{x^3 - 7x - 6} \equiv \dfrac{5x^2 - 7x - 4}{(x + 1)(x - 3)(x + 2)}$

$\dfrac{5x^2 - 7x - 4}{(x + 1)(x - 3)(x + 2)} \equiv \dfrac{A}{(x + 1)} + \dfrac{B}{(x - 3)} + \dfrac{C}{(x + 2)}$

$\Rightarrow 5x^2 - 7x - 4$
$\equiv A(x - 3)(x + 2) + B(x + 1)(x + 2)$
$\qquad\qquad\qquad + C(x + 1)(x - 3)$

Substitution:
$x = -1 \Rightarrow 8 = -4A \Rightarrow A = -2$
$x = 3 \Rightarrow 20 = 20B \Rightarrow B = 1$
$x = -2 \Rightarrow 30 = 5C \Rightarrow C = 6$
This gives:
$$\dfrac{5x^2 - 7x - 4}{x^3 - 7x - 6} \equiv -\dfrac{2}{(x + 1)} + \dfrac{1}{(x - 3)} + \dfrac{6}{(x + 2)}$$

Q10 $\dfrac{6x^2 - x + 5}{(x + 4)(x - 1)(x + 1)} \equiv \dfrac{A}{(x + 4)} + \dfrac{B}{(x - 1)} + \dfrac{C}{(x + 1)}$

$\Rightarrow 6x^2 - x + 5$
$\equiv A(x - 1)(x + 1) + B(x + 4)(x + 1) + C(x + 4)(x - 1)$
$x = 1 \Rightarrow 10 = 10B \Rightarrow B = 1$
$x = -1 \Rightarrow 12 = -6C \Rightarrow C = -2$
$x = -4 \Rightarrow 105 = 15A \Rightarrow A = 7$
This gives:
$$\dfrac{6x^2 - x + 5}{(x + 4)(x - 1)(x + 1)} \equiv \dfrac{7}{(x + 4)} + \dfrac{1}{(x - 1)} - \dfrac{2}{(x + 1)}$$

Q11 $\dfrac{3x^2 - 6x + 3}{x^3 - 6x^2 + 3x + 10} \equiv \dfrac{3x^2 - 6x + 3}{(x + 1)(x - 2)(x - 5)}$

You get this by using the factor theorem, as in Q9.

$\dfrac{3x^2 - 6x + 3}{(x + 1)(x - 2)(x - 5)} \equiv \dfrac{A}{(x + 1)} + \dfrac{B}{(x - 2)} + \dfrac{C}{(x - 5)}$

$\Rightarrow 3x^2 - 6x + 3$
$\equiv A(x - 2)(x - 5) + B(x + 1)(x - 5) + C(x + 1)(x - 2)$

Substitution:
$x = 2 \Rightarrow 3 = -9B \Rightarrow B = -\dfrac{1}{3}$

$x = 5 \Rightarrow 48 = 18C \Rightarrow C = \dfrac{8}{3}$

$x = -1 \Rightarrow 12 = 18A \Rightarrow A = \dfrac{2}{3}$

This gives:
$$\dfrac{3x^2 - 6x + 3}{x^3 - 6x^2 + 3x + 10} \equiv \dfrac{2}{3(x + 1)} - \dfrac{1}{3(x - 2)} + \dfrac{8}{3(x - 5)}$$

Exercise 1.2 — Repeated factors

Q1 $\dfrac{3x}{(x + 5)^2} \equiv \dfrac{A}{(x + 5)} + \dfrac{B}{(x + 5)^2} \equiv \dfrac{A(x + 5) + B}{(x + 5)^2}$

$\Rightarrow \quad 3x \equiv A(x + 5) + B$

Equating coefficients:
x terms: $\quad 3 = A$
constants: $\quad 0 = 5A + B$
The first equation gives $A = 3$, putting this into the second equation gives $B = -15$.

This gives: $\dfrac{3x}{(x + 5)^2} \equiv \dfrac{3}{(x + 5)} - \dfrac{15}{(x + 5)^2}$

Q2 $\dfrac{x^2 - 5x + 2}{x^2(x + 1)} \equiv \dfrac{A}{x} + \dfrac{B}{x^2} + \dfrac{C}{(x + 1)}$

$\Rightarrow x^2 - 5x + 2 \equiv Ax(x + 1) + B(x + 1) + Cx^2$

Equating coefficients:
x^2 terms: $\quad 1 = A + C$
x terms: $\quad -5 = A + B$
constants: $\quad 2 = B$
The third equation gives $B = 2$, putting this into the second equation gives $A = -7$, putting this into the first equation gives $C = 8$.

This gives: $\dfrac{x^2 - 5x + 2}{x^2(x + 1)} \equiv -\dfrac{7}{x} + \dfrac{2}{x^2} + \dfrac{8}{(x + 1)}$

Q3 $\dfrac{x^2 + 5x - 1}{(x - 2)^3} \equiv \dfrac{A}{(x - 2)} + \dfrac{B}{(x - 2)^2} + \dfrac{C}{(x - 2)^3}$

$\Rightarrow x^2 + 5x - 1 \equiv A(x - 2)^2 + B(x - 2) + C$

Substitution: $x = 2 \Rightarrow 13 = C$
Equating coefficients:
x^2 terms: $\quad 1 = A$
x terms: $\quad 5 = -4A + B \Rightarrow B = 9$

This gives: $\dfrac{x^2 + 5x - 1}{(x - 2)^3} \equiv \dfrac{1}{(x - 2)} + \dfrac{9}{(x - 2)^2} + \dfrac{13}{(x - 2)^3}$

Q4 a) $\dfrac{2x - 7}{(x - 3)^2} \equiv \dfrac{A}{(x - 3)} + \dfrac{B}{(x - 3)^2}$

$\Rightarrow 2x - 7 \equiv A(x - 3) + B$

Substitution: $\quad x = 3 \Rightarrow -1 = B$
Equating coefficients of the x terms: $2 = A$

This gives: $\dfrac{2x - 7}{(x - 3)^2} \equiv \dfrac{2}{(x - 3)} - \dfrac{1}{(x - 3)^2}$

b) $\dfrac{x + 4}{(x + 2)^2} \equiv \dfrac{A}{(x + 2)} + \dfrac{B}{(x + 2)^2}$

$\Rightarrow x + 4 \equiv A(x + 2) + B$

Substitution: $x = -2 \Rightarrow 2 = B$
Equating coefficients of x: $A = 1$

This gives: $\dfrac{x + 4}{(x + 2)^2} \equiv \dfrac{1}{(x + 2)} + \dfrac{2}{(x + 2)^2}$

c) $\dfrac{2x^2-9x+5}{(x-4)^2(x+2)} \equiv \dfrac{A}{(x-4)} + \dfrac{B}{(x-4)^2} + \dfrac{C}{(x+2)}$

$\Rightarrow 2x^2-9x+5 \equiv A(x-4)(x+2)$
$$+ B(x+2)+C(x-4)^2$$

Substitution:

$x=4 \Rightarrow 1=6B \Rightarrow B=\dfrac{1}{6}$

$x=-2 \Rightarrow 31=36C \Rightarrow C=\dfrac{31}{36}$

Equating coefficients: x^2 terms:

$2=A+C \Rightarrow A=\dfrac{41}{36}$

This gives:

$\dfrac{2x^2-9x+5}{(x-4)^2(x+2)} \equiv \dfrac{41}{36(x-4)} + \dfrac{1}{6(x-4)^2} + \dfrac{31}{36(x+2)}$

d) $\dfrac{3x^2-7x-25}{x(x-5)^2} \equiv \dfrac{A}{x} + \dfrac{B}{(x-5)} + \dfrac{C}{(x-5)^2}$

$\Rightarrow 3x^2-7x-25 \equiv A(x-5)^2 + Bx(x-5)^2 + Cx$

Substituting:

$x=5 \Rightarrow 15=5C \Rightarrow C=3$

$x=0 \Rightarrow -25=25A \Rightarrow A=-1$

Equating the coefficients of x^2:

$3=A+B=-1+B \Rightarrow B=4$

This gives:

$\dfrac{3x^2-7x-25}{x(x-5)^2} \equiv -\dfrac{1}{x} + \dfrac{4}{(x-5)} + \dfrac{3}{(x-5)^2}$

Q5 $x^3-10x^2+25x = x(x^2-10x+25) = x(x-5)(x-5)$

So $\dfrac{5x^2-10x-5}{x^3-10x^2+25x} = \dfrac{5x^2-10x-5}{x(x-5)^2}$

$\dfrac{5x^2-10x-5}{x(x-5)^2} \equiv \dfrac{A}{x} + \dfrac{B}{(x-5)} + \dfrac{C}{(x-5)^2}$

$\Rightarrow 5x^2-10x-5 \equiv A(x-5)^2 + Bx(x-5) + Cx$

Substitution: $x=0 \Rightarrow -5=25A \Rightarrow A=-\dfrac{1}{5}$

Equating coefficients:

x^2 terms: $\quad 5=A+B=-\dfrac{1}{5}+B \Rightarrow B=\dfrac{26}{5}$

x terms: $\quad -10=-10A-5B+C=2-26+C$
$$\Rightarrow C=14$$

This gives: $\dfrac{5x^2-10x-5}{x^3-10x^2+25x} \equiv -\dfrac{1}{5x} + \dfrac{26}{5(x-5)} + \dfrac{14}{(x-5)^2}$

Exercise 1.3 — Improper fractions as partial fractions

Q1 a) $(x-3)(x+1) = x^2-2x-3$

$$x^2-2x-3 \overline{\smash{\big)}\, 2x^2-4x+6} \quad \overset{\displaystyle 2}{}$$
$$\underline{-(2x^2-4x-6)}$$
$$12$$

So: $\dfrac{2x^2-4x+6}{(x-3)(x+1)} \equiv 2 + \dfrac{12}{(x-3)(x+1)}$

Here $q(x)=2$, $r(x)=12$ and $d(x)=(x-3)(x+1)$.

b) $\dfrac{12}{(x-3)(x+1)} \equiv \dfrac{A}{(x-3)} + \dfrac{B}{(x+1)}$

$\Rightarrow \qquad 12 \equiv A(x+1) + B(x-3)$

Substitution: $\quad x=-1 \Rightarrow 12=-4B \Rightarrow B=-3$
$\qquad\qquad\qquad x=3 \Rightarrow 12=4A \Rightarrow A=3$

This gives: $\dfrac{12}{(x-3)(x+1)} \equiv \dfrac{3}{(x-3)} - \dfrac{3}{(x+1)}$

So: $\dfrac{2x^2-4x+6}{(x-3)(x+1)} \equiv 2 + \dfrac{3}{(x-3)} - \dfrac{3}{(x+1)}$

Q2 $(x+2)(x+3) \equiv x^2+5x+6$

$$x^2+5x+6 \overline{\smash{\big)}\, 3x^3+4x^2+2x-5} \quad \overset{\displaystyle 3x-11}{}$$
$$\underline{-(3x^3+15x^2+18x)}$$
$$-11x^2-16x-5$$
$$\underline{-(-11x^2-55x-66)}$$
$$39x+61$$

So: $\dfrac{3x^3+4x^2+2x-5}{(x+2)(x+3)} \equiv 3x-11 + \dfrac{39x+61}{(x+2)(x+3)}$

Here $q(x)=3x-11$, $r(x)=39x+61$ and $d(x)=(x+2)(x+3)$.

Now, converting to partial fractions:

$\dfrac{39x+61}{(x+2)(x+3)} \equiv \dfrac{A}{(x+2)} + \dfrac{B}{(x+3)}$

$\Rightarrow \quad 39x+61 \equiv A(x+3) + B(x+2)$

Substitution:

$x=-3 \Rightarrow -56=-B \Rightarrow B=56$

$x=-2 \Rightarrow -17=A \Rightarrow A=-17$

This gives: $\dfrac{39x+61}{(x+2)(x+3)} \equiv -\dfrac{17}{(x+2)} + \dfrac{56}{(x+3)}$

So: $\dfrac{3x^3+4x^2+2x-5}{(x^2+5x+6)} \equiv 3x-11 - \dfrac{17}{(x+2)} + \dfrac{56}{(x+3)}$

Q3 By algebraic division:

$\dfrac{2x^2+4x+7}{(x-1)(x+2)} \equiv 2 + \dfrac{2x+11}{(x-1)(x+2)}$

Just use the same method you've used in Q1 and Q2 for this first bit.

$\dfrac{2x+11}{(x-1)(x+2)} \equiv \dfrac{B}{(x-1)} + \dfrac{C}{(x+2)}$

$\Rightarrow \quad 2x+11 \equiv B(x+2) + C(x-1)$

Substitution:

$x=1 \Rightarrow 13=3B \Rightarrow B=\dfrac{13}{3}$

$x=-2 \Rightarrow 7=-3C \Rightarrow C=-\dfrac{7}{3}$

This gives: $\dfrac{2x+11}{(x-1)(x+2)} \equiv \dfrac{13}{3(x-1)} - \dfrac{7}{3(x+2)}$

So: $\dfrac{2x^2+4x+7}{(x-1)(x+2)} \equiv 2 + \dfrac{13}{3(x-1)} - \dfrac{7}{3(x+2)}$

Q4 By algebraic division:

$\dfrac{3x^2-5x+2}{(x-3)^2} \equiv 3 + \dfrac{13x-25}{(x-3)^2}$

$\dfrac{13x-25}{(x-3)^2} \equiv \dfrac{B}{(x-3)} + \dfrac{C}{(x-3)^2}$

$\Rightarrow 13x-25 \equiv B(x-3) + C$

Substitution: $x=3 \Rightarrow 14=C$

Equating coefficients of the x terms: $13=B$

This gives: $\dfrac{13x-25}{(x-3)^2} \equiv \dfrac{13}{(x-3)} + \dfrac{14}{(x-3)^2}$

So: $\dfrac{3x^2-5x+2}{(x-3)^2} \equiv 3 + \dfrac{13}{(x-3)} + \dfrac{14}{(x-3)^2}$

Q5 By algebraic division:

$\dfrac{x^3-3x^2-3x+9}{x^2+3x-4} \equiv x-6 + \dfrac{19x-15}{(x+4)(x-1)}$

So $A=1$ and $B=-6$.

The remainder can be split as follows:

$\dfrac{19x-15}{(x+4)(x-1)} \equiv \dfrac{C}{(x+4)} + \dfrac{D}{(x-1)}$

$\Rightarrow\ 19x-15 \equiv C(x-1) + D(x+4)$

Substitution:

$x = 1 \Rightarrow 4 = 5D \Rightarrow D = \dfrac{4}{5}$

$x = -4 \Rightarrow -91 = -5C \Rightarrow C = \dfrac{91}{5}$

This gives: $\dfrac{19x-15}{(x+4)(x-1)} \equiv \dfrac{91}{5(x+4)} + \dfrac{4}{5(x-1)}$

So: $\dfrac{x^3-3x^2-3x+9}{x^2+3x-4} \equiv x - 6 + \dfrac{91}{5(x+4)} + \dfrac{4}{5(x-1)}$

Q6 By algebraic division:

$\dfrac{x^3+4x^2-3x+8}{x^2(x-2)} \equiv 1 + \dfrac{6x^2-3x+8}{x^2(x-2)}$

$\dfrac{6x^2-3x+8}{x^2(x-2)} \equiv \dfrac{A}{x} + \dfrac{B}{x^2} + \dfrac{C}{(x-2)}$

$\Rightarrow 6x^2-3x+8 \equiv Ax(x-2) + B(x-2) + Cx^2$

Substitution:

$x = 0 \Rightarrow 8 = -2B \Rightarrow B = -4$

$x = 2 \Rightarrow 26 = 4C \Rightarrow C = \dfrac{13}{2}$

Equate coefficients of the x^2 terms:

$6 = A + C \Rightarrow 6 = A + \dfrac{13}{2} \Rightarrow A = -\dfrac{1}{2}$

This gives: $\dfrac{6x^2-3x+8}{x^2(x-2)} \equiv -\dfrac{1}{2x} - \dfrac{4}{x^2} + \dfrac{13}{2(x-2)}$

So: $\dfrac{x^3+4x^2-3x+8}{x^2(x-2)} \equiv 1 - \dfrac{1}{2x} - \dfrac{4}{x^2} + \dfrac{13}{2(x-2)}$

Review Exercise — Chapter 1

For these questions you can use the substitution method or the equating coefficients method, but only one method has been shown for each.

Q1 $\dfrac{2x}{(x-5)(x+5)} \equiv \dfrac{A}{(x-5)} + \dfrac{B}{(x+5)}$

$\Rightarrow\ \ 2x \equiv A(x+5) + B(x-5)$

Substitution:

$x = -5 \Rightarrow -10 = -10B \Rightarrow B = 1$

$x = 5 \Rightarrow 10 = 10A \Rightarrow A = 1$

This gives: $\dfrac{2x}{(x-5)(x+5)} \equiv \dfrac{1}{(x-5)} + \dfrac{1}{(x+5)}$

Q2 $\dfrac{2-x}{(3x+2)(x+1)} \equiv \dfrac{A}{(3x+2)} + \dfrac{B}{(x+1)}$

$\Rightarrow\ \ 2-x \equiv A(x+1) + B(3x+2)$

Substitution:

$x = -1 \Rightarrow 3 = -B \Rightarrow B = -3$

$x = -\dfrac{2}{3} \Rightarrow \dfrac{8}{3} = \dfrac{1}{3}A \Rightarrow A = 8$

This gives: $\dfrac{2-x}{(3x+2)(x+1)} \equiv \dfrac{8}{(3x+2)} - \dfrac{3}{(x+1)}$

Q3 $\dfrac{x^2-3x-8}{x^3+3x^2+2x} \equiv \dfrac{x^2-3x-8}{x(x+1)(x+2)}$

$\equiv \dfrac{A}{x} + \dfrac{B}{(x+1)} + \dfrac{C}{(x+2)}$

$\Rightarrow x^2-3x-8$

$\equiv A(x+1)(x+2) + Bx(x+2) + Cx(x+1)$

Equating coefficients:

x^2 terms: $1 = A + B + C$

x terms: $-3 = 3A + 2B + C$

constants: $-8 = 2A$

the equation for the constant terms gives $A = -4$.

Then solving simultaneously gives: $B = 4$, $C = 1$

This gives: $\dfrac{x^2-3x-8}{x^3+3x^2+2x} \equiv -\dfrac{4}{x} + \dfrac{4}{(x+1)} + \dfrac{1}{(x+2)}$

Q4 **a)** $\dfrac{2}{(x+1)(x-1)} \equiv \dfrac{A}{x+1} + \dfrac{B}{x-1}$

$\Rightarrow 2 \equiv A(x-1) + B(x+1)$

Substitution:

$x = 1 \Rightarrow 2 = 2B \Rightarrow 1 = B$

$x = -1 \Rightarrow 2 = -2A \Rightarrow -1 = A$

This gives: $\dfrac{2}{(x+1)(x-1)} \equiv -\dfrac{1}{x+1} + \dfrac{1}{x-1}$

b) $\dfrac{4}{x^2+x} \equiv \dfrac{4}{x(x+1)} \equiv \dfrac{A}{x} + \dfrac{B}{(x+1)}$

$\Rightarrow 4 \equiv A(x+1) + Bx$

Substitution:

$x = 0 \Rightarrow 4 = A$

$x = -1 \Rightarrow 4 = -B \Rightarrow -4 = B$

This gives: $\dfrac{4}{x^2+x} \equiv \dfrac{4}{x} - \dfrac{4}{(x+1)}$

c) $\dfrac{4x+5}{(x+4)(2x-3)} \equiv \dfrac{A}{(x+4)} + \dfrac{B}{(2x-3)}$

$\Rightarrow\ \ \ \ \ \ \ 4x+5 \equiv A(2x-3) + B(x+4)$

Substitution:

$x = -4 \Rightarrow -11 = -11A \Rightarrow A = 1$

$x = 1.5 \Rightarrow 11 = 5.5B \Rightarrow B = 2$

This gives: $\dfrac{4x+5}{(x+4)(2x-3)} \equiv \dfrac{1}{(x+4)} + \dfrac{2}{(2x-3)}$

d) $\dfrac{-7x-7}{(3x+1)(x-2)} \equiv \dfrac{A}{(3x+1)} + \dfrac{B}{(x-2)}$

$\Rightarrow\ \ \ \ \ \ \ -7x-7 \equiv A(x-2) + B(3x+1)$

Equating coefficients:

x terms: $-7 = A + 3B$

constants: $-7 = -2A + B$

Solving simultaneously gives: $A = 2$, $B = -3$

This gives: $\dfrac{-7x-7}{(3x+1)(x-2)} \equiv \dfrac{2}{(3x+1)} - \dfrac{3}{(x-2)}$

e) $\dfrac{x-18}{(x+4)(3x-4)} \equiv \dfrac{A}{(x+4)} + \dfrac{B}{(3x-4)}$

$\Rightarrow\ \ \ \ \ \ \ x-18 \equiv A(3x-4) + B(x+4)$

Substitution:

$x = -4 \Rightarrow -22 = -16A \Rightarrow A = \dfrac{11}{8}$.

Equating coefficients of the x terms:

$1 = 3A + B \Rightarrow B = 1 - \dfrac{33}{8} = -\dfrac{25}{8}$.

This gives:

$\dfrac{x-18}{(x+4)(3x-4)} \equiv \dfrac{11}{8(x+4)} - \dfrac{25}{8(3x-4)}$

f) $\dfrac{5x}{x^2+x-6} \equiv \dfrac{5x}{(x+3)(x-2)} \equiv \dfrac{A}{(x+3)} + \dfrac{B}{(x-2)}$

$\Rightarrow 5x \equiv A(x-2) + B(x+3)$

Substitution:

$x = -3 \Rightarrow -15 = -5A \Rightarrow A = 3$

$x = 2 \Rightarrow 10 = 5B \Rightarrow B = 2$

This gives: $\dfrac{5x}{x^2+x-6} \equiv \dfrac{3}{(x+3)} + \dfrac{2}{(x-2)}$

g) $\dfrac{6+4y}{9-y^2} \equiv \dfrac{6+4y}{(3-y)(3+y)} \equiv \dfrac{A}{(3-y)} + \dfrac{B}{(3+y)}$

$\Rightarrow 6+4y \equiv A(3+y) + B(3-y)$

Substitution:

$y = 3 \Rightarrow 18 = 6A \Rightarrow A = 3$

$y = -3 \Rightarrow -6 = 6B \Rightarrow B = -1$

This gives: $\dfrac{6+4y}{9-y^2} \equiv \dfrac{3}{(3-y)} - \dfrac{1}{(3+y)}$

h) $\dfrac{10x^2 + 32x + 16}{(x+3)(2x+4)(x-2)}$

$\equiv \dfrac{A}{(x+3)} + \dfrac{B}{(2x+4)} + \dfrac{C}{(x-2)}$

$\Rightarrow 10x^2 + 32x + 16$

$\equiv A(2x+4)(x-2) + B(x+3)(x-2)$
$+ C(x+3)(2x+4)$

Substitution:

$x = 2 \Rightarrow 120 = 40C \Rightarrow C = 3$

$x = -3 \Rightarrow 10 = 10A \Rightarrow A = 1$

$x = -2 \Rightarrow -8 = -4B \Rightarrow B = 2$

This gives: $\dfrac{10x^2 + 32x + 16}{(x+3)(2x+4)(x-2)}$

$\equiv \dfrac{1}{(x+3)} + \dfrac{2}{(2x+4)} + \dfrac{3}{(x-2)}$

$\equiv \dfrac{1}{(x+3)} + \dfrac{1}{(x+2)} + \dfrac{3}{(x-2)}$

You could have spotted at the beginning that the whole fraction could be divided by 2 on the top and bottom

to get $\dfrac{5x^2 + 16x + 8}{(x+3)(x+2)(x-2)}$.

i) $\dfrac{-11x^2 + 6x + 11}{(2x+1)(3-x)(x+2)}$

$\equiv \dfrac{A}{(2x+1)} + \dfrac{B}{(3-x)} + \dfrac{C}{(x+2)}$

$\Rightarrow -11x^2 + 6x + 11$

$\equiv A(3-x)(x+2) + B(2x+1)(x+2)$
$+ C(2x+1)(3-x)$

Substitution:

$x = 3 \Rightarrow -70 = 35B \Rightarrow B = -2$

$x = -2: -45 = -15C \Rightarrow C = 3$

$x = -0.5: 5.25 = 5.25A \Rightarrow A = 1$

This gives: $\dfrac{-11x^2 + 6x + 11}{(2x+1)(3-x)(x+2)}$

$\equiv \dfrac{1}{(2x+1)} - \dfrac{2}{(3-x)} + \dfrac{3}{(x+2)}$

j) $\dfrac{4x^2 + 12x + 6}{x^3 + 3x^2 + 2x} \equiv \dfrac{4x^2 + 12x + 6}{x(x^2 + 3x + 2)}$

$\equiv \dfrac{4x^2 + 12x + 6}{x(x+1)(x+2)} \equiv \dfrac{A}{x} + \dfrac{B}{(x+1)} + \dfrac{C}{(x+2)}$

$\Rightarrow 4x^2 + 12x + 6$

$\equiv A(x+1)(x+2) + Bx(x+2) + Cx(x+1)$

Substitution:

$x = -1 \Rightarrow -2 = -B \Rightarrow B = 2$

$x = 0 \Rightarrow 6 = 2A \Rightarrow A = 3$

$x = -2 \Rightarrow -2 = 2C \Rightarrow C = -1$

This gives:

$\dfrac{4x^2 + 12x + 6}{x^3 + 3x^2 + 2x} \equiv \dfrac{3}{x} + \dfrac{2}{(x+1)} - \dfrac{1}{(x+2)}$

Q5 $\dfrac{2x^2 - 3x + 1}{(x-3)^2(x-8)} \equiv \dfrac{A}{(x-3)} + \dfrac{B}{(x-3)^2} + \dfrac{C}{(x-8)}$

$\Rightarrow 2x^2 - 3x + 1 \equiv A(x-3)(x-8) + B(x-8) + C(x-3)^2$

Substitution:

$x = 3 \Rightarrow 10 = -5B \Rightarrow B = -2$

$x = 8 \Rightarrow 105 = 25C \Rightarrow C = \dfrac{21}{5}$

Equating coefficients of the x^2 terms:

$2 = A + C \Rightarrow A = -\dfrac{11}{5}$

This gives:

$\dfrac{2x^2 - 3x + 1}{(x-3)^2(x-8)} \equiv -\dfrac{11}{5(x-3)} - \dfrac{2}{(x-3)^2} + \dfrac{21}{5(x-8)}$

Q6 $\dfrac{2x^2 + 2x - 5}{x(x-5)^2} \equiv \dfrac{A}{x} + \dfrac{B}{(x-5)} + \dfrac{C}{(x-5)^2}$

$\Rightarrow 2x^2 + 2x - 5 \equiv A(x-5)^2 + Bx(x-5) + Cx$

Substitution:

$x = 5 \Rightarrow 55 = 5C \Rightarrow C = 11$

$x = 0 \Rightarrow -5 = 25A \Rightarrow A = -\dfrac{1}{5}$

Equating coefficients of the x^2 terms:

$2 = A + B \Rightarrow B = \dfrac{11}{5}$

This gives: $\dfrac{2x^2 + 2x - 5}{x(x-5)^2} \equiv -\dfrac{1}{5x} + \dfrac{11}{5(x-5)} + \dfrac{11}{(x-5)^2}$

Q7 a) $\dfrac{2x+2}{(x+3)^2} \equiv \dfrac{A}{(x+3)} + \dfrac{B}{(x+3)^2}$

$\Rightarrow 2x + 2 \equiv A(x+3) + B$

Substitution:

$x = -3 \Rightarrow -4 = B$

$x = 0 \Rightarrow 2 = 3A - 4 \Rightarrow A = 2$

This gives: $\dfrac{2x+2}{(x+3)^2} \equiv \dfrac{2}{(x+3)} - \dfrac{4}{(x+3)^2}$

b) $\dfrac{6x^2 + 17x + 5}{x(x+2)^2} \equiv \dfrac{A}{x} + \dfrac{B}{(x+2)} + \dfrac{C}{(x+2)^2}$

$\Rightarrow 6x^2 + 17x + 5 \equiv A(x+2)^2 + Bx(x+2) + Cx$

Substitution:

$x = -2 \Rightarrow -5 = -2C \Rightarrow C = \dfrac{5}{2}$

$x = 0 \Rightarrow 5 = 4A \Rightarrow A = \dfrac{5}{4}$

Equating coefficients of the x^2 terms:

$6 = A + B \Rightarrow 6 = \dfrac{5}{4} + B \Rightarrow B = \dfrac{19}{4}$

This gives:

$\dfrac{6x^2 + 17x + 5}{x(x+2)^2} \equiv \dfrac{5}{4x} + \dfrac{19}{4(x+2)} + \dfrac{5}{2(x+2)^2}$

c) $\dfrac{-18x + 14}{(2x-1)^2(x+2)}$

$\equiv \dfrac{A}{(2x-1)} + \dfrac{B}{(2x-1)^2} + \dfrac{C}{(x+2)}$

$\Rightarrow -18x + 14$

$\equiv A(2x-1)(x+2) + B(x+2) + C(2x-1)^2$

Substitution:

$x = -2 \Rightarrow 50 = 25C \Rightarrow C = 2$

$x = 0.5 \Rightarrow 5 = 2.5B \Rightarrow B = 2$

Equating coefficients of the x^2 terms:

$0 = 2A + 4C \Rightarrow 0 = 2A + 8 \Rightarrow A = -4$

This gives:

$\dfrac{-18x + 14}{(2x-1)^2(x+2)} \equiv \dfrac{-4}{(2x-1)} + \dfrac{2}{(2x-1)^2} + \dfrac{2}{(x+2)}$

d) $\dfrac{8x^2 - x - 5}{x^3 - x^2} \equiv \dfrac{8x^2 - x - 5}{x^2(x - 1)} \equiv \dfrac{A}{x} + \dfrac{B}{x^2} + \dfrac{C}{(x - 1)}$

$\Rightarrow 8x^2 - x - 5 \equiv Ax(x - 1) + B(x - 1) + Cx^2$

Equating coefficients:

x^2 terms: $\quad 8 = A + C$

x terms: $\quad -1 = -A + B$

constants: $-5 = -B$

The third equation gives $B = 5$, putting this into the second equation gives $A = 6$, putting this into the first equation gives $C = 2$.

This gives: $\dfrac{8x^2 - x - 5}{x^3 - x^2} \equiv \dfrac{6}{x} + \dfrac{5}{x^2} + \dfrac{2}{(x - 1)}$

Q8 Using algebraic division gives:

$\dfrac{5x^2 - 10x + 42}{(5x - 1)(x + 2)} \equiv 1 + \dfrac{-19x + 44}{(5x - 1)(x + 2)}$

$\dfrac{-19x + 44}{(5x - 1)(x + 2)} \equiv \dfrac{B}{(5x - 1)} + \dfrac{C}{(x + 2)}$

$\Rightarrow -19x + 44 \equiv B(x + 2) + C(5x - 1)$

Substitution:

$x = -2 \Rightarrow 82 = -11C \Rightarrow C = -\dfrac{82}{11}$

$x = \dfrac{1}{5} \Rightarrow \dfrac{201}{5} = \dfrac{11}{5}B \Rightarrow B = \dfrac{201}{11}$

This gives: $\dfrac{-19x + 44}{(5x - 1)(x + 2)} \equiv \dfrac{201}{11(5x - 1)} - \dfrac{82}{11(x + 2)}$

So: $\dfrac{5x^2 - 10x + 42}{(5x - 1)(x + 2)} \equiv 1 + \dfrac{201}{11(5x - 1)} - \dfrac{82}{11(x + 2)}$

Q9 By algebraic division:

$\dfrac{4x^3 + 12x^2 - x - 5}{(x + 1)(2x - 1)} \equiv 2x + 5 - \dfrac{4x}{(x + 1)(2x - 1)}$

Have a look at Q1 and Q2 in Exercise 1.3 for methods for doing the division.

Writing the remainder as partial fractions:

$\dfrac{-4x}{(x + 1)(2x - 1)} \equiv \dfrac{A}{(x + 1)} + \dfrac{B}{(2x - 1)}$

$\Rightarrow -4x \equiv A(2x - 1) + B(x + 1)$

Substitution:

$x = -1 \Rightarrow -4 = -3A \Rightarrow A = \dfrac{4}{3}$

$x = \dfrac{1}{2} \Rightarrow -2 = \dfrac{3}{2}B \Rightarrow B = -\dfrac{4}{3}$

This gives: $\dfrac{-4x}{(x + 1)(2x - 1)} \equiv \dfrac{4}{3(x + 1)} - \dfrac{4}{3(2x - 1)}$

So: $\dfrac{4x^3 + 12x^2 - x - 5}{(x + 1)(2x - 1)} \equiv 2x + 5 + \dfrac{4}{3(x + 1)} - \dfrac{4}{3(2x - 1)}$

Q10 a) By algebraic division:

$\dfrac{2x^2 + 18x + 26}{(x + 2)(x + 4)} \equiv 2 + \dfrac{6x + 10}{(x + 2)(x + 4)}$

$\dfrac{6x + 10}{(x + 2)(x + 4)} \equiv \dfrac{A}{(x + 2)} + \dfrac{B}{(x + 4)}$

$\Rightarrow 6x + 10 \equiv A(x + 4) + B(x + 2)$

Substitution:

$x = -4 \Rightarrow -14 = -2B \Rightarrow B = 7$

$x = -2 \Rightarrow -2 = 2A \Rightarrow A = -1$

This gives: $\dfrac{6x + 10}{(x + 2)(x + 4)} \equiv -\dfrac{1}{(x + 2)} + \dfrac{7}{(x + 4)}$

So: $\dfrac{2x^2 + 18x + 26}{(x + 2)(x + 4)} \equiv 2 - \dfrac{1}{(x + 2)} + \dfrac{7}{(x + 4)}$

b) By algebraic division:

$\dfrac{3x^2 + 9x + 2}{x(x + 1)} \equiv 3 + \dfrac{6x + 2}{x(x + 1)}$

$\dfrac{6x + 2}{x(x + 1)} \equiv \dfrac{A}{x} + \dfrac{B}{(x + 1)}$

$\Rightarrow 6x + 2 \equiv A(x + 1) + Bx$

Substitution:

$x = -1 \Rightarrow -4 = -B \Rightarrow B = 4$

$x = 0 \Rightarrow 2 = A$

This gives: $\dfrac{6x + 2}{x(x + 1)} \equiv \dfrac{2}{x} + \dfrac{4}{(x + 1)}$

So: $\dfrac{3x^2 + 9x + 2}{x(x + 1)} \equiv 3 + \dfrac{2}{x} + \dfrac{4}{(x + 1)}$

c) By algebraic division:

$\dfrac{3x^3 - 2x^2 - 2x - 3}{(x + 1)(x - 2)} \equiv 3x + 1 + \dfrac{5x - 1}{(x + 1)(x - 2)}$

$\dfrac{5x - 1}{(x + 1)(x - 2)} \equiv \dfrac{A}{(x + 1)} + \dfrac{B}{(x - 2)}$

$\Rightarrow 5x - 1 \equiv A(x - 2) + B(x + 1)$

Substitution:

$x = 2 \Rightarrow 9 = 3B \Rightarrow B = 3$

$x = -1 \Rightarrow -6 = -3A \Rightarrow A = 2$

This gives: $\dfrac{5x - 1}{(x + 1)(x - 2)} \equiv \dfrac{2}{(x + 1)} + \dfrac{3}{(x - 2)}$

So:

$\dfrac{3x^3 - 2x^2 - 2x - 3}{(x + 1)(x - 2)} \equiv 3x + 1 + \dfrac{2}{(x + 1)} + \dfrac{3}{(x - 2)}$

d) By algebraic division:

$\dfrac{24x^2 - 70x + 53}{(2x - 3)^2} \equiv 6 + \dfrac{2x - 1}{(2x - 3)^2}$

$\dfrac{2x - 1}{(2x - 3)^2} \equiv \dfrac{A}{(2x - 3)} + \dfrac{B}{(2x - 3)^2}$

$\Rightarrow 2x - 1 \equiv A(2x - 3) + B$

Substitution:

$x = 1.5 \Rightarrow 2 = B$

$x = 0 \Rightarrow -1 = -3A + B \Rightarrow A = 1$

This gives: $\dfrac{2x - 1}{(2x - 3)^2} \equiv \dfrac{1}{(2x - 3)} + \dfrac{2}{(2x - 3)^2}$

So: $\dfrac{24x^2 - 70x + 53}{(2x - 3)^2} \equiv 6 + \dfrac{1}{(2x - 3)} + \dfrac{2}{(2x - 3)^2}$

Exam-Style Questions — Chapter 1

Q1 Add the partial fractions and equate the numerators:

$5 + 9x \equiv A + B(1 + 3x)$ *[1 mark]*

Substitution:

$x = -\dfrac{1}{3}: \ 2 = A \ \Rightarrow \ A = 2$ *[1 mark]*

$x = 0: \ 5 = 2 + B \ \Rightarrow \ B = 3$ *[1 mark]*

Q2 To use algebraic long division, first expand the denominator:

$\dfrac{18x^2 - 15x - 62}{(3x + 4)(x - 2)} \equiv \dfrac{18x^2 - 15x - 62}{3x^2 - 2x - 8}$

Then divide the fraction:

$$3x^2 - 2x - 8 \overline{\smash{\big)}\, \begin{array}{l} 6 \\ 18x^2 - 15x - 62 \\ \underline{-(18x^2 - 12x - 48)} \\ -3x - 14 \end{array}}$$

Watch out for the negative signs here. You're subtracting the bottom line from the top, so be sure to get it right. You could use alternative methods for the division. You'll still get the marks, so use the one you're happiest with unless they tell you otherwise.

$$\frac{18x^2 - 15x - 62}{(3x+4)(x-2)} \equiv 6 + \frac{-3x-14}{(3x+4)(x-2)}$$

So $A = 6$ *[1 mark]*

$$\frac{-3x-14}{(3x+4)(x-2)} \equiv \frac{B}{(3x+4)} + \frac{C}{(x-2)}$$

$\Rightarrow \quad -3x - 14 \equiv B(x-2) + C(3x+4)$ *[1 mark]*

Substitution:

$$x = 2 \Rightarrow -20 = 10C \Rightarrow C = -2 \ \textit{[1 mark]}$$

You could carry on using the substitution method for the last bit but you'd need to substitute $-\frac{4}{3}$ in for x, so it's easier to equate coefficients.

Equating coefficients of the x terms:

$$-3 = B + 3C \quad \Rightarrow \quad -3 = B - 6 \quad \Rightarrow \quad B = 3 \ \textit{[1 mark]}$$

Q3 $5x^2 + 3x + 6 \equiv A(2x-1)^2 + B(3-x) + C(2x-1)(3-x)$

[1 mark]

Substitution:

$$x = 3 \Rightarrow 60 = 25A \Rightarrow A = \frac{12}{5} \ \textit{[1 mark]}$$

$$x = \frac{1}{2} \Rightarrow \frac{35}{4} = \frac{5}{2}B \Rightarrow B = \frac{7}{2} \ \textit{[1 mark]}$$

Equating coefficients of the x^2 terms:
$$5 = 4A - 2C$$

$$\Rightarrow 5 = \frac{48}{5} - 2C \Rightarrow -\frac{23}{5} = -2C \Rightarrow C = \frac{23}{10} \ \textit{[1 mark]}$$

Q4 To use algebraic long division, first expand the denominator:

$$\frac{-80x^2 + 49x - 9}{(5x-1)(2-4x)} \equiv \frac{-80x^2 + 49x - 9}{-20x^2 + 14x - 2}$$

Then divide the fraction:

$$\begin{array}{r} 4 \\ -20x^2 + 14x - 2 \overline{)\ -80x^2 + 49x - 9} \\ -(-80x^2 + 56x - 8) \\ \hline -7x - 1 \end{array}$$

$$\frac{-80x^2 + 49x - 9}{(5x-1)(2-4x)} \equiv 4 + \frac{-7x-1}{(5x-1)(2-4x)} \ \textit{[1 mark]}$$

$$\frac{-7x-1}{(5x-1)(2-4x)} \equiv \frac{A}{(5x-1)} + \frac{B}{(2-4x)}$$

$-7x - 1 \equiv A(2-4x) + B(5x-1)$ *[1 mark]*

Substitution:

$$x = 0.5 \quad \Rightarrow \quad -4.5 = 1.5B \quad \Rightarrow \quad B = -3 \ \textit{[1 mark]}$$

Equating coefficients of the x terms: $-7 = -4A + 5B$

$\Rightarrow -7 = -4A - 15 \Rightarrow 8 = -4A \Rightarrow A = -2$ *[1 mark]*

Q5 a) Expand the denominator:

$$\frac{3x^2 + 12x - 11}{(x+3)(x-1)} \equiv \frac{3x^2 + 12x - 11}{x^2 + 2x - 3}$$

Divide the fraction:

$$\begin{array}{r} 3 \\ x^2 + 2x - 3 \overline{)\ 3x^2 + 12x - 11} \\ -(3x^2 + 6x - 9) \\ \hline 6x - 2 = -2 + 6x \end{array}$$

$$\frac{3x^2 + 12x - 11}{(x+3)(x-1)} \equiv 3 + \frac{-2+6x}{(x+3)(x-1)} \ \textit{[1 mark]}$$

You can also answer this part of the question without using division — use the same method you'd use to find the constants for partial fractions:

$$\frac{3x^2 + 12x - 11}{(x+3)(x-1)} \equiv A + \frac{B+Cx}{(x+3)(x-1)}$$

$$\Rightarrow 3x^2 + 12x - 11 = A(x+3)(x-1) + B + Cx$$

Equating coefficients:

x^2 terms: $\quad 3 = A$

x terms: $\quad 12 = 2A + C = 6 + C \Rightarrow C = 6$

constants: $-11 = -3A + B = -9 + B \Rightarrow B = -2$

$$\frac{3x^2 + 12x - 11}{(x+3)(x-1)} \equiv 3 + \frac{-2+6x}{(x+3)(x-1)} \ \textit{[1 mark]}$$

b) $$\frac{3x^2 + 12x - 11}{(x+3)(x-1)} \equiv 3 + \frac{-2+6x}{(x+3)(x-1)}$$

$$\frac{-2+6x}{(x+3)(x-1)} \equiv \frac{D}{(x+3)} + \frac{E}{(x-1)}$$

$-2 + 6x \equiv D(x-1) + E(x+3)$ *[1 mark]*

Substitution:

$x = 1 \Rightarrow 4 = 4E \Rightarrow E = 1$ *[1 mark]*

$x = -3 \Rightarrow -20 = -4D \Rightarrow D = 5$ *[1 mark]*

So overall:

$$\frac{3x^2 + 12x - 11}{(x+3)(x-1)} \equiv 3 + \frac{5}{(x+3)} + \frac{1}{(x-1)}$$

[1 mark]

Q6 $$\frac{x^2 - 2x - 9}{x(x+1)(x-5)} \equiv \frac{A}{x} + \frac{B}{(x+1)} + \frac{C}{(x-5)}$$

$$\Rightarrow x^2 - 2x - 9$$
$$\equiv A(x+1)(x-5) + Bx(x-5) + Cx(x+1)$$

[1 mark]

Substitution:

$x = -1 \Rightarrow -6 = 6B \Rightarrow B = -1$ *[1 mark]*

$x = 0 \Rightarrow -9 = -5A \Rightarrow A = \frac{9}{5}$ *[1 mark]*

$x = 5 \Rightarrow 6 = 30C \Rightarrow C = \frac{1}{5}$ *[1 mark]*

This gives: $\frac{x^2 - 2x - 9}{x(x+1)(x-5)} \equiv \frac{9}{5x} - \frac{1}{(x+1)} + \frac{1}{5(x-5)}$

Q7 $$\frac{6x-1}{x^2 + 4x + 4} \equiv \frac{6x-1}{(x+2)^2} \equiv \frac{A}{(x+2)} + \frac{B}{(x+2)^2}$$

$\Rightarrow \quad 6x - 1 \equiv A(x+2) + B$ *[1 mark]*

Equating coefficients:

x terms: $\quad 6 = A$ *[1 mark]*

constants: $-1 = 2A + B \Rightarrow B = -13$ *[1 mark]*

This gives: $\frac{6x-1}{x^2 + 4x + 4} \equiv \frac{6}{(x+2)} - \frac{13}{(x+2)^2}$ *[1 mark]*

Q8 Divide the fraction:

$$\begin{array}{r} -2x \\ x^2 + 2x - 3 \overline{)\ -2x^3 - 4x^2 + 18x + 6} \\ -(-2x^3 - 4x^2 + 6x) \\ \hline 12x + 6 \end{array}$$

$$\frac{-2x^3 - 4x^2 + 18x + 6}{x^2 + 2x - 3} \equiv -2x + \frac{12x+6}{x^2 + 2x - 3}$$

$$\equiv -2x + \frac{12x+6}{(x+3)(x-1)}$$

So $A = -2$ *[1 mark]* and $B = 0$ *[1 mark]*

$$\frac{12x+6}{(x+3)(x-1)} \equiv \frac{C}{(x+3)} + \frac{D}{(x-1)}$$

$\Rightarrow \quad 12x + 6 \equiv C(x-1) + D(x+3)$ *[1 mark]*

Substitution:

$x = 1 \Rightarrow 18 = 4D \Rightarrow D = \frac{9}{2}$ *[1 mark]*

$x = -3 \Rightarrow -30 = -4C \Rightarrow C = \frac{15}{2}$ *[1 mark]*

You could also answer this question using the method without division shown in Question 5 a).

Q9 a) Using the factor theorem from C2:

$f(x) = 2x^3 - 19x^2 + 32x + 21$

$f(3) = 0 \Rightarrow (x - 3)$ is a factor *[1 mark]*

$$
\begin{aligned}
2x^3 - 19x^2 + 32x + 21 &= (x - 3)(2x^2 \qquad\qquad) \\
&= (x - 3)(2x^2 \qquad -7) \\
&= (x - 3)(2x^2 - 13x - 7) \\
&= (x - 3)(2x + 1)(x - 7)
\end{aligned}
$$

[1 mark]

This method is explained in Exercise 1.1, Question 9 a) — your other option is to use the factor theorem to find the other factors.

b) $\dfrac{x^2 - 9x - 21}{2x^3 - 19x^2 + 32x + 21} \equiv \dfrac{A}{(x - 3)} + \dfrac{B}{(x - 7)} + \dfrac{C}{(2x + 1)}$

$\Rightarrow x^2 - 9x - 21$
$\equiv A(x - 7)(2x + 1) + B(x - 3)(2x + 1)$
$\qquad\qquad\qquad + C(x - 3)(x - 7)$

[1 mark]

Substitution:

$x = 7 \Rightarrow -35 = 60B \Rightarrow B = -\frac{7}{12}$ *[1 mark]*

$x = -\frac{1}{2} \Rightarrow -\frac{65}{4} = \frac{105}{4}C \Rightarrow C = \frac{-13}{21}$ *[1 mark]*

$x = 3 \Rightarrow -39 = -28A \Rightarrow A = \frac{39}{28}$ *[1 mark]*

So:

$\dfrac{x^2 - 9x - 21}{2x^3 - 19x^2 + 32x + 21}$

$\equiv \dfrac{39}{28(x - 3)} - \dfrac{7}{12(x - 7)} - \dfrac{13}{21(2x + 1)}$

Q10 $\dfrac{7x^2 - 34x + 10}{(2x - 4)^2(x + 3)} \equiv \dfrac{A}{(2x - 4)} + \dfrac{B}{(2x - 4)^2} + \dfrac{C}{(x + 3)}$

$\Rightarrow 7x^2 - 34x + 10 \equiv$
$\qquad A(2x - 4)(x + 3) + B(x + 3) + C(2x - 4)^2$

[1 mark]

Substitution:

$x = -3 \Rightarrow 175 = 100C \Rightarrow C = \frac{7}{4}$ *[1 mark]*

$x = 2 \Rightarrow -30 = 5B \Rightarrow B = -6$ *[1 mark]*

Equating coefficients of the x^2 terms:

$7 = 2A + 4C \Rightarrow 7 = 2A + 7 \Rightarrow 2A = 0 \Rightarrow A = 0$

[1 mark]

This gives: $\dfrac{7x^2 - 34x + 10}{(2x - 4)^2(x + 3)} \equiv -\dfrac{6}{(2x - 4)^2} + \dfrac{7}{4(x + 3)}$

Q11

$$
\begin{array}{r}
4x - 3 \\
x^2 - 9\overline{)4x^3 - 3x^2 + 12x - 16} \\
-(4x^3 + 0x^2 - 36x) \\
\hline
-3x^2 + 48x - 16 \\
-(-3x^2 + 0x + 27) \\
\hline
48x - 43
\end{array}
$$

So: $\dfrac{4x^3 - 3x^2 + 12x - 16}{(x^2 - 9)} \equiv 4x - 3 + \dfrac{48x - 43}{(x^2 - 9)}$

[1 mark]

$\dfrac{48x - 43}{(x^2 - 9)} \equiv \dfrac{48x - 43}{(x + 3)(x - 3)} \equiv \dfrac{A}{(x + 3)} + \dfrac{B}{(x - 3)}$

$\Rightarrow \qquad 48x - 43 \equiv A(x - 3) + B(x + 3)$

Substitution:

$x = 3 \Rightarrow 101 = 6B \Rightarrow B = \frac{101}{6}$ *[1 mark]*

$x = -3 \Rightarrow -187 = -6A \Rightarrow A = \frac{187}{6}$ *[1 mark]*

This gives that: $\dfrac{48x - 43}{(x^2 - 9)} \equiv \dfrac{187}{6(x + 3)} + \dfrac{101}{6(x - 3)}$

So: $\dfrac{4x^3 - 3x^2 + 12x - 16}{(x^2 - 9)} \equiv 4x - 3 + \dfrac{187}{6(x + 3)} + \dfrac{101}{6(x - 3)}$

[1 mark]

Q12 $\dfrac{18x^3 - 57x^2 + 0x + 38}{3x^2 - 7x - 6} \equiv \dfrac{18x^3 - 57x^2 + 0x + 38}{(x - 3)(3x + 2)}$

$$
\begin{array}{r}
6x - 5 \\
3x^2 - 7x - 6\overline{)18x^3 - 57x^2 + 0x + 38} \\
-(18x^3 - 42x^2 - 36x) \\
\hline
-15x^2 + 36x + 38 \\
-(-15x^2 + 35x + 30) \\
\hline
x + 8
\end{array}
$$

So: $\dfrac{18x^3 - 57x^2 + 0x + 38}{(x - 3)(3x + 2)} \equiv 6x - 5 + \dfrac{x + 8}{(x - 3)(3x + 2)}$

So $A = 6$ *[1 mark]* and $B = -5$ *[1 mark]*

$\dfrac{x + 8}{(x - 3)(3x + 2)} \equiv \dfrac{C}{(x - 3)} + \dfrac{D}{(3x + 2)}$

$\Rightarrow \qquad x + 8 \equiv C(3x + 2) + D(x - 3)$ *[1 mark]*

Substitution:

$x = 3 \Rightarrow 11 = 11C \Rightarrow C = 1$ *[1 mark]*

Equating coefficients of constant terms:

$8 = 2C - 3D \Rightarrow 8 = 2 - 3D \Rightarrow 6 = -3D \Rightarrow D = -2$

[1 mark]

You could also answer this question using the method without division shown in question 5 a).

Chapter 2: Coordinate Geometry in the (x, y) Plane

1. Parametric Equations of Curves
Exercise 1.1 — Finding coordinates from parametric equations

Q1 a) $x = 3t = 3 \times 5 = 15$
$y = t^2 = 5^2 = 25$
So coordinates are (15, 25).

b) $18 = 3t \Rightarrow t = 6$

c) $36 = t^2 \Rightarrow t = \pm 6 \Rightarrow x = \pm 18$

Q2 a) $x = 2t - 1 = (2 \times 7) - 1 = 13$
$y = 4 - t^2 = 4 - 7^2 = -45$
So coordinates are (13, -45).

b) $2t - 1 = 15 \Rightarrow t = 8$

c) $4 - t^2 = -5 \Rightarrow t = \pm 3 \Rightarrow x = -7$ or 5

Q3 a) $x = 2 + \sin\theta = 2 + \sin\dfrac{\pi}{4} = \dfrac{4 + \sqrt{2}}{2}$

$y = -3 + \cos\theta = -3 + \cos\dfrac{\pi}{4} = \dfrac{\sqrt{2} - 6}{2}$

So coordinates are $\left(\dfrac{4 + \sqrt{2}}{2}, \dfrac{\sqrt{2} - 6}{2}\right)$.

b) $2 + \sin\theta = \dfrac{4 + \sqrt{3}}{2} = 2 + \dfrac{\sqrt{3}}{2}$

$\Rightarrow \sin\theta = \dfrac{\sqrt{3}}{2} \Rightarrow \theta = \dfrac{\pi}{3}$

c) $-3 + \cos \theta = -\frac{7}{2} \Rightarrow \cos \theta = -\frac{1}{2} \Rightarrow \theta = \frac{2\pi}{3}$

The angle in a) was given in radians so make sure you use radians for b) and c). They're both cos values you should know an angle for off by heart. The cos value in part c) is negative so you can use the CAST diagram (see C2) to figure out which angle you need (cos is negative in the 2nd and 3rd quadrants).

Q4 a) $5 \cos 2t = \frac{5\sqrt{3}}{2} \Rightarrow \cos 2t = \frac{\sqrt{3}}{2}$

You'd normally double the domain when solving for 2t. In this case the domain for t is $O < t < \frac{\pi}{2}$, so $O < 2t < \pi$. There is only one positive solution for cos in this domain, as given below:

$2t = \frac{\pi}{6} \Rightarrow t = \frac{\pi}{12}$

b) $3 \sin t = -\frac{3\sqrt{3}}{2} \Rightarrow \sin t = -\frac{\sqrt{3}}{2}$

There are two values of t in the domain $O \le t \le 2\pi$ that have $\sin t = -\frac{\sqrt{3}}{2}$ — you can find these using the CAST diagram (sin is negative in the 3rd and 4th quadrants).

Since $\sin \frac{\pi}{3} = \frac{\sqrt{3}}{2}$, then $t = \pi + \frac{\pi}{3} = \frac{4\pi}{3}$
and $t = 2\pi - \frac{\pi}{3} = \frac{5\pi}{3}$, are two possible solutions.
There are other possible solutions outside of the range $O \le t \le 2\pi$.

Q5

t	-5	-4	-3	-2	-1	0	1	2	3	4	5
x	-25	-20	-15	-10	-5	0	5	10	15	20	25
y	$-\frac{2}{5}$	$-\frac{1}{2}$	$-\frac{2}{3}$	-1	-2	—	2	1	$\frac{2}{3}$	$\frac{1}{2}$	$\frac{2}{5}$

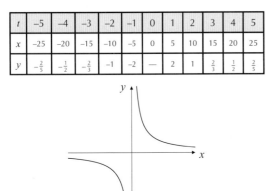

When t = O, y is undefined, so there must be an asymptote.

Q6

t	-5	-4	-3	-2	-1	0	1	2	3	4	5
x	25	16	9	4	1	0	1	4	9	16	25
y	-4	-3	-2	-1	0	1	2	3	4	5	6

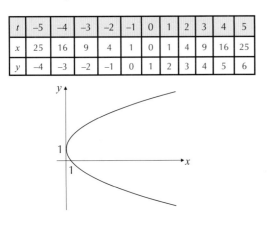

Q7

θ	0	$\frac{\pi}{4}$	$\frac{\pi}{3}$	$\frac{\pi}{2}$	$\frac{2\pi}{3}$	$\frac{3\pi}{4}$	π	$\frac{4\pi}{3}$	$\frac{3\pi}{2}$	$\frac{5\pi}{3}$	2π
x	1	1.71	1.87	2	1.87	1.71	1	0.13	0	0.13	1
y	3	2.71	2.5	2	1.5	1.29	1	1.5	2	2.5	3

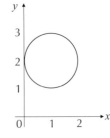

Q8

t	0	$\frac{\pi}{4}$	$\frac{\pi}{2}$	$\frac{3\pi}{4}$	π	$\frac{5\pi}{4}$	$\frac{3\pi}{2}$	$\frac{7\pi}{4}$	2π
x	0	2.12	3	2.12	0	-2.12	-3	-2.12	0
y	5	3.54	0	-3.54	-5	-3.54	0	3.54	5

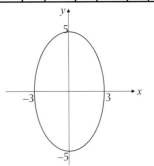

Q9 E.g.

t	-5	-4	-3	-2	-1	0	1	2	3	4	5
x	-6	-5	-4	-3	-2	-1	0	1	2	3	4
y	-9	0	7	12	15	16	15	12	7	0	-9

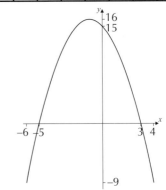

Exercise 1.2 — Finding intersections

Q1 At A: $y = 0 \Rightarrow -2 + t = 0 \Rightarrow t = 2$
$x = 3 + t = 3 + 2 = 5$
At B: $x = 0 \Rightarrow 3 + t = 0 \Rightarrow t = -3$
$y = -2 + (-3) = -5$
So the coordinates are A(5, 0) and B(0, –5).

Q2 **a)** The curve meets the x-axis when $y = 0$, so:
$3t^3 - 24 = 0$
$\Rightarrow 3(t^3 - 8) = 0$
$\Rightarrow t^3 = 8 \Rightarrow t = 2$

b) The curve meets the y-axis when $x = 0$, so:
$2t^2 - 50 = 0$
$\Rightarrow 2(t^2 - 25) = 0$
$\Rightarrow t^2 = 25 \Rightarrow t = \pm 5$

If you'd have been asked to give the coordinates you would then just put the t values into the parametric equations.

Q3 The curve meets the y-axis when $x = 0$, so:
$64 - t^3 = 0 \Rightarrow t^3 = 64 \Rightarrow t = 4$
$y = \frac{1}{t} = \frac{1}{4}$, so P is $\left(0, \frac{1}{4}\right)$.

Q4 $y = x - 3$
$\Rightarrow 4t = (2t + 1) - 3$
$\Rightarrow 2t = -2 \Rightarrow t = -1$

To find the coordinates when t = –1, just put this value back into the parametric equations...

$x = (2 \times -1) + 1 = -1$
$y = 4 \times -1 = -4$
So P is (–1, –4).

Q5 $y = x^2 + 32$
$\Rightarrow 6t^2 = (2t)^2 + 32$
$\Rightarrow 6t^2 = 4t^2 + 32$
$\Rightarrow 2t^2 = 32$
$\Rightarrow t^2 = 16 \Rightarrow t = \pm 4$

When $t = 4$:
$x = 2 \times 4 = 8$
$y = 6 \times 4^2 = 96$
So one point of intersection is (8, 96).

When $t = -4$:
$x = 2 \times -4 = -8$
$y = 6 \times (-4)^2 = 96$
So the other point of intersection is (–8, 96).

Q6 $x^2 + y^2 = 32$
$\Rightarrow (t^2)^2 + (2t)^2 = 32$
$\Rightarrow t^4 + 4t^2 - 32 = 0$
$\Rightarrow (t^2 - 4)(t^2 + 8) = 0$
$\Rightarrow t^2 = 4 \Rightarrow t = \pm 2$
(there are no real solutions to $t^2 = -8$).

When $t = 2$:
$x = 2^2 = 4$
$y = 2 \times 2 = 4$
So one point of intersection is (4, 4).

When $t = -2$:
$x = (-2)^2 = 4$
$y = 2 \times -2 = -4$
So the other point of intersection is (4, –4).

Q7 **a)** At the point (0, 4):
$x = 0 \Rightarrow a(t - 2) = 0 \Rightarrow t = 2$ (as $a \neq 0$)
$y = 4 \Rightarrow 2at^2 + 3 = 4 \Rightarrow 2a(2^2) + 3 = 4$
$\Rightarrow 8a + 3 = 4 \Rightarrow a = \frac{1}{8}$.

b) The curve would meet the x-axis when $y = 0$.
$y = 2at^2 + 3 = \frac{2t^2}{8} + 3 = \frac{t^2}{4} + 3$
So at the x-axis, $\frac{t^2}{4} + 3 = 0 \Rightarrow t^2 = -12$.
This has no real solutions, so the curve does not meet the x-axis.

Q8 **a)** The curve crosses the x-axis when $y = 0$.
$t^2 - 9 = 0 \Rightarrow t = \pm 3$
When $t = 3$, $x = \frac{2}{3}$, so one point is $\left(\frac{2}{3}, 0\right)$.
When $t = -3$, $x = -\frac{2}{3}$, so the other point is $\left(-\frac{2}{3}, 0\right)$.

b) The curve would meet the y-axis when $x = 0$, i.e. when $\frac{2}{t} = 0$. This has no solutions, so the curve does not meet the y-axis.

c) $y = \frac{10}{x} - 3$
$\Rightarrow t^2 - 9 = \frac{10t}{2} - 3$
$\Rightarrow t^2 - 5t - 6 = 0$
$\Rightarrow (t + 1)(t - 6) = 0$
$\Rightarrow t = -1$ and $t = 6$

When $t = -1$:
$x = -2$
$y = (-1)^2 - 9 = -8$
So one point of intersection is (–2, –8).

When $t = 6$:
$x = \frac{2}{6} = \frac{1}{3}$
$y = 6^2 - 9 = 27$
So the other point of intersection is $\left(\frac{1}{3}, 27\right)$.

Q9 **a)** The curve meets the x-axis when $y = 0$.
$5 \cos t = 0 \Rightarrow \cos t = 0$
$\Rightarrow t = -\frac{3\pi}{2}, -\frac{\pi}{2}, \frac{\pi}{2}$ and $\frac{3\pi}{2}$.

It's easiest to check the symmetry of the cos t graph below to find all these solutions in the domain.

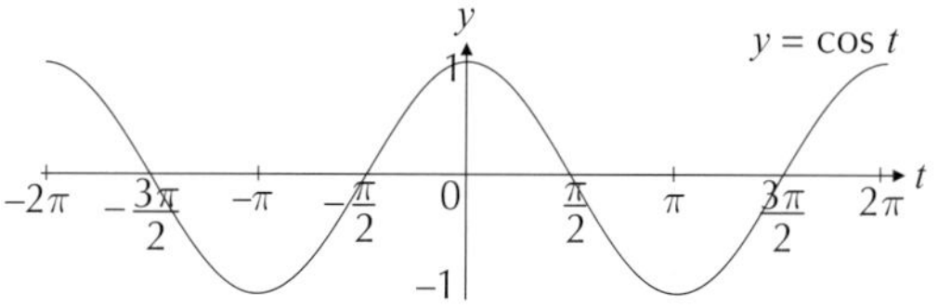

When $t = -\frac{3\pi}{2}$, $x = 3 \sin\left(-\frac{3\pi}{2}\right) = 3$, so (3, 0).

When $t = -\frac{\pi}{2}$, $x = 3 \sin\left(-\frac{\pi}{2}\right) = -3$, so (–3, 0).

When $t = \frac{\pi}{2}$, $x = 3 \sin\left(\frac{\pi}{2}\right) = 3$, so (3, 0).

When $t = \frac{3\pi}{2}$, $x = 3 \sin\left(\frac{3\pi}{2}\right) = -3$, so (–3, 0).

So the curve crosses the x-axis twice in the domain $-2\pi \leq t \leq 2\pi$, at (–3, 0) and (3, 0).

The curve meets the y-axis when $x = 0$.

$3 \sin t = 0 \Rightarrow \sin t = 0$
$\Rightarrow t = -2\pi, -\pi, 0, \pi$ and 2π.

Again, look at the symmetry of the sin t graph...

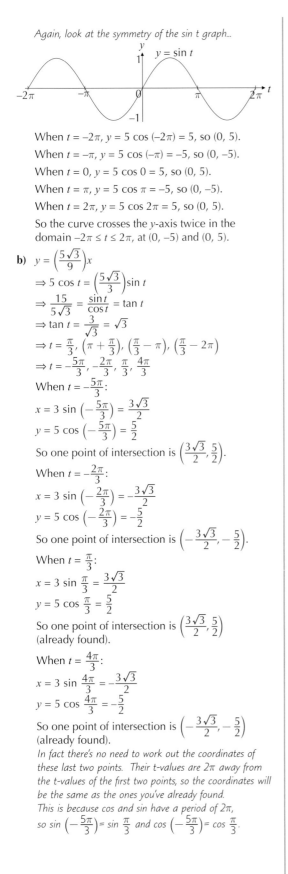

When $t = -2\pi$, $y = 5\cos(-2\pi) = 5$, so $(0, 5)$.

When $t = -\pi$, $y = 5\cos(-\pi) = -5$, so $(0, -5)$.

When $t = 0$, $y = 5\cos 0 = 5$, so $(0, 5)$.

When $t = \pi$, $y = 5\cos \pi = -5$, so $(0, -5)$.

When $t = 2\pi$, $y = 5\cos 2\pi = 5$, so $(0, 5)$.

So the curve crosses the y-axis twice in the domain $-2\pi \leq t \leq 2\pi$, at $(0, -5)$ and $(0, 5)$.

b) $y = \left(\dfrac{5\sqrt{3}}{9}\right)x$

$\Rightarrow 5\cos t = \left(\dfrac{5\sqrt{3}}{3}\right)\sin t$

$\Rightarrow \dfrac{15}{5\sqrt{3}} = \dfrac{\sin t}{\cos t} = \tan t$

$\Rightarrow \tan t = \dfrac{3}{\sqrt{3}} = \sqrt{3}$

$\Rightarrow t = \dfrac{\pi}{3}, \left(\pi + \dfrac{\pi}{3}\right), \left(\dfrac{\pi}{3} - \pi\right), \left(\dfrac{\pi}{3} - 2\pi\right)$

$\Rightarrow t = -\dfrac{5\pi}{3}, -\dfrac{2\pi}{3}, \dfrac{\pi}{3}, \dfrac{4\pi}{3}$

When $t = -\dfrac{5\pi}{3}$:

$x = 3\sin\left(-\dfrac{5\pi}{3}\right) = \dfrac{3\sqrt{3}}{2}$

$y = 5\cos\left(-\dfrac{5\pi}{3}\right) = \dfrac{5}{2}$

So one point of intersection is $\left(\dfrac{3\sqrt{3}}{2}, \dfrac{5}{2}\right)$.

When $t = -\dfrac{2\pi}{3}$:

$x = 3\sin\left(-\dfrac{2\pi}{3}\right) = -\dfrac{3\sqrt{3}}{2}$

$y = 5\cos\left(-\dfrac{2\pi}{3}\right) = -\dfrac{5}{2}$

So one point of intersection is $\left(-\dfrac{3\sqrt{3}}{2}, -\dfrac{5}{2}\right)$.

When $t = \dfrac{\pi}{3}$:

$x = 3\sin\dfrac{\pi}{3} = \dfrac{3\sqrt{3}}{2}$

$y = 5\cos\dfrac{\pi}{3} = \dfrac{5}{2}$

So one point of intersection is $\left(\dfrac{3\sqrt{3}}{2}, \dfrac{5}{2}\right)$ (already found).

When $t = \dfrac{4\pi}{3}$:

$x = 3\sin\dfrac{4\pi}{3} = -\dfrac{3\sqrt{3}}{2}$

$y = 5\cos\dfrac{4\pi}{3} = -\dfrac{5}{2}$

So one point of intersection is $\left(-\dfrac{3\sqrt{3}}{2}, -\dfrac{5}{2}\right)$ (already found).

In fact there's no need to work out the coordinates of these last two points. Their t-values are 2π away from the t-values of the first two points, so the coordinates will be the same as the ones you've already found. This is because cos and sin have a period of 2π, so $\sin\left(-\dfrac{5\pi}{3}\right) = \sin\dfrac{\pi}{3}$ and $\cos\left(-\dfrac{5\pi}{3}\right) = \cos\dfrac{\pi}{3}$.

2. Parametric and Cartesian Equations

Exercise 2.1 — Converting parametric equations to Cartesian equations

Q1 a) $x = t + 3 \Rightarrow t = x - 3$, so $y = t^2 = (x-3)^2 = x^2 - 6x + 9$

$y = x^2 - 6x + 9$

b) $x = 3t \Rightarrow t = \dfrac{x}{3}$ so $y = \dfrac{6}{t} = \dfrac{18}{x}$

$y = \dfrac{18}{x}$

c) $x = 2t^3 \Rightarrow t = \left(\dfrac{x}{2}\right)^{\frac{1}{3}}$, so $y = t^2 = \left(\dfrac{x}{2}\right)^{\frac{2}{3}}$

$y = \left(\dfrac{x}{2}\right)^{\frac{2}{3}}$

d) $x = t + 7 \Rightarrow t = x - 7$,

so $y = 12 - 2t = 12 - 2(x-7) = 26 - 2x$

$y = 26 - 2x$

e) $x = t + 4 \Rightarrow t = x - 4$,

so $y = t^2 - 9 = (x-4)^2 - 9 = x^2 - 8x + 7$

$y = x^2 - 8x + 7$

f) $x = \sin\theta$, $y = \cos\theta$

Use trig identities here rather than rearranging...

$\sin^2\theta + \cos^2\theta \equiv 1$

$\Rightarrow x^2 + y^2 = 1$

g) $x = 1 + \sin\theta \Rightarrow \sin\theta = x - 1$

$y = 2 + \cos\theta \Rightarrow \cos\theta = y - 2$

$\sin^2\theta + \cos^2\theta \equiv 1 \Rightarrow (x-1)^2 + (y-2)^2 = 1$

You can leave this equation in the form it's in — it's the equation of a circle radius 1, centre (1, 2).

h) $x = \sin\theta$, $y = \cos 2\theta$

The 2θ should make you think of the double angle formulae...

$\cos 2\theta \equiv 1 - 2\sin^2\theta \Rightarrow y = 1 - 2x^2$

i) $x = \cos\theta$, $y = \cos 2\theta$

$\cos 2\theta \equiv 2\cos^2\theta - 1 \Rightarrow y = 2x^2 - 1$

j) $x = \cos\theta - 5 \Rightarrow \cos\theta = x + 5$

$y = \cos 2\theta$

$\cos 2\theta \equiv 2\cos^2\theta - 1$

$\Rightarrow y = 2(x+5)^2 - 1 = 2x^2 + 20x + 49$

$y = 2x^2 + 20x + 49$

Q2 $x = \tan\theta$, $y = \sec\theta$

Using the identity $\sec^2\theta \equiv 1 + \tan^2\theta$ gives:

$y^2 = 1 + x^2$

Q3 $x = 2\cot\theta \Rightarrow \cot\theta = \dfrac{x}{2}$

$y = 3\text{ cosec }\theta \Rightarrow \text{cosec }\theta = \dfrac{y}{3}$

Using the identity $\text{cosec}^2\theta \equiv 1 + \cot^2\theta$ gives:

$\dfrac{y^2}{9} = 1 + \dfrac{x^2}{4} \Rightarrow y^2 = 9 + \dfrac{9x^2}{4}$

Q4 a) From the parametric equations the centre of the circle is $(5, -3)$, and the radius is 1.

b) $x = 5 + \sin\theta \Rightarrow \sin\theta = x - 5$

$y = -3 + \cos\theta \Rightarrow \cos\theta = y + 3$

Using the identity $\sin^2\theta + \cos^2\theta \equiv 1$ gives:

$(x - 5)^2 + (y + 3)^2 = 1$

Q5 a) $x = \dfrac{1 + 2t}{t} \Rightarrow xt = 1 + 2t \Rightarrow xt - 2t = 1$

$\Rightarrow t(x - 2) = 1 \Rightarrow t = \dfrac{1}{(x-2)}$.

b) $y = \dfrac{3 + t}{t^2} = \dfrac{3 + \dfrac{1}{(x-2)}}{\dfrac{1}{(x-2)^2}} = 3(x-2)^2 + (x-2)$

$= 3(x^2 - 4x + 4) + x - 2$
$= 3x^2 - 11x + 10$
$= (3x - 5)(x - 2)$

c)

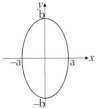

Q6 $x = \dfrac{2 - 3t}{1 + t} \Rightarrow x(1 + t) = 2 - 3t \Rightarrow x + xt = 2 - 3t$

$\Rightarrow xt + 3t = 2 - x \Rightarrow t(x + 3) = 2 - x \Rightarrow t = \dfrac{2 - x}{x + 3}$

$y = \dfrac{5 - t}{4t + 1} = \dfrac{5 - \left(\dfrac{2 - x}{x + 3}\right)}{4\left(\dfrac{2 - x}{x + 3}\right) + 1} = \dfrac{5(x + 3) - (2 - x)}{4(2 - x) + (x + 3)}$

$\Rightarrow y = \dfrac{6x + 13}{11 - 3x}$

You could also write this as $6x - 11y + 3xy + 13 = 0$

Q7 $x = 5\sin^2\theta \Rightarrow \sin^2\theta = \dfrac{x}{5}$
$y = \cos\theta$

Using the identity $\sin^2\theta + \cos^2\theta \equiv 1$ gives:
$\dfrac{x}{5} + y^2 = 1 \Rightarrow y^2 = 1 - \dfrac{x}{5}$

Q8 a) $x = a\sin\theta \Rightarrow \sin\theta = \dfrac{x}{a}$
$y = b\cos\theta \Rightarrow \cos\theta = \dfrac{y}{b}$
Using the identity $\sin^2\theta + \cos^2\theta \equiv 1$ gives:
$\left(\dfrac{x}{a}\right)^2 + \left(\dfrac{y}{b}\right)^2 = 1$

b) To sketch the graph, find the x- and y-intercepts.

When $x = 0$, $\left(\dfrac{y}{b}\right)^2 = 1 \Rightarrow y = \pm b$.

When $y = 0$, $\left(\dfrac{x}{a}\right)^2 = 1 \Rightarrow x = \pm a$.
So the curve looks like this:

c) An ellipse.
If a and b were equal it would be a circle.

Q9 a) $y = 2t - 1 \Rightarrow t = \dfrac{y + 1}{2}$

$x = 3t^2 = 3\left(\dfrac{y + 1}{2}\right)^2 = \dfrac{3}{4}(y + 1)^2$

b) Substitute $y = 4x - 3$ into the equation above:
$x = \dfrac{3}{4}(4x - 3 + 1)^2$
$4x = 3(4x - 2)^2$
$4x = 3(16x^2 - 16x + 4)$
$4x = 48x^2 - 48x + 12$
$12x^2 - 13x + 3 = 0$
$(3x - 1)(4x - 3) = 0$
$x = \dfrac{1}{3}$ and $x = \dfrac{3}{4}$
$y = 4\left(\dfrac{1}{3}\right) - 3 = -\dfrac{5}{3}$ and $y = 4\left(\dfrac{3}{4}\right) - 3 = 0$
So the curve and the line intersect at $\left(\dfrac{1}{3}, -\dfrac{5}{3}\right)$
and $\left(\dfrac{3}{4}, 0\right)$.

Q10 $x = 7t + 2 \quad t = \dfrac{x - 2}{7}$

$y = \dfrac{5}{t} = \dfrac{5}{\left(\dfrac{x - 2}{7}\right)} = \dfrac{35}{x - 2}$

This is the graph of $y = \dfrac{1}{x}$ stretched vertically by a
factor of 35 and translated right by 2.
The y-intercept is at $x = 0$, so $y = \dfrac{35}{-2} = -17.5$.

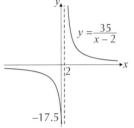

3. Parametric Integration
Exercise 3.1 — The area under a curve

Q1 a) $x = 3t^{-1} \Rightarrow \dfrac{dx}{dt} = -3t^{-2} = -\dfrac{3}{t^2}$
$y = 4t^2$

$\displaystyle\int y\,dx = \int y\,\dfrac{dx}{dt}\,dt = \int (4t^2) \times \left(-\dfrac{3}{t^2}\right) dt$

$\displaystyle = \int -12\,dt$

*For lots of these you could take the constant outside the
integral — e.g. this could be written as $-12\int 1\,dt$.*

b) $x = \sqrt{t} = t^{\frac{1}{2}} \Rightarrow \dfrac{dx}{dt} = \dfrac{1}{2}t^{-\frac{1}{2}} = \dfrac{1}{2\sqrt{t}}$
$y = 3t^2 - 4$

$\displaystyle\int y\,dx = \int y\,\dfrac{dx}{dt}\,dt = \int (3t^2 - 4) \times \left(\dfrac{1}{2\sqrt{t}}\right) dt$

$\displaystyle = \int \dfrac{3t^2 - 4}{2\sqrt{t}}\,dt$

*You could also write this as $\int \left(\dfrac{3}{2}t^{\frac{3}{2}} - \dfrac{4}{2}t^{-\frac{1}{2}}\right)dt$,
or $\dfrac{1}{2}\int \left(3t^{\frac{3}{2}} - 4t^{-\frac{1}{2}}\right)dt$.*

c) $x = \sin^2\theta \Rightarrow \dfrac{dx}{d\theta} = 2\sin\theta\cos\theta$
$y = \cos\theta$

$\displaystyle\int y\,dx = \int y\,\dfrac{dx}{d\theta}\,d\theta = \int (\cos\theta)(2\sin\theta\cos\theta)\,d\theta$

$\displaystyle = \int 2\sin\theta\cos^2\theta\,d\theta$

d) $x = \tan 5\theta \Rightarrow \dfrac{dx}{d\theta} = 5\sec^2 5\theta$

$y = \sec^2 5\theta$

$\int y\, dx = \int y\dfrac{dx}{d\theta}\, d\theta = \int (\sec^2 5\theta)(5\sec^2 5\theta)\, d\theta$

$\qquad\qquad\qquad\qquad = \int 5\sec^4 5\theta\, d\theta$

Q2 a) $x = t - 2 \Rightarrow \dfrac{dx}{dt} = 1$

$y = 4t + 3$

$\int y\, dx = \int y\dfrac{dx}{dt}\, dt = \int (4t + 3) \times 1\, dt$

$\qquad\qquad\qquad\qquad = \int (4t + 3)\, dt$

$\qquad\qquad\qquad\qquad = 2t^2 + 3t + C$

b) $x = 3t^2 \Rightarrow \dfrac{dx}{dt} = 6t$

$y = 5t - 1$

$\int y\, dx = \int y\dfrac{dx}{dt}\, dt = \int (5t - 1) \times (6t)\, dt$

$\qquad\qquad\qquad\qquad = \int (30t^2 - 6t)\, dt$

$\qquad\qquad\qquad\qquad = 10t^3 - 3t^2 + C$

c) $x = (4t - 5)^2 \Rightarrow \dfrac{dx}{dt} = 2(4t - 5) \times 4 = 32t - 40$

$y = t^2 - 3t$

$\int y\, dx = \int y\dfrac{dx}{dt}\, dt = \int (t^2 - 3t) \times (32t - 40)\, dt$

$\qquad\qquad\qquad\qquad = \int (32t^3 - 136t^2 + 120t)\, dt$

$\qquad\qquad\qquad\qquad = 8t^4 - \dfrac{136}{3}t^3 + 60t^2 + C$

d) $x = t^2 + 3 \Rightarrow \dfrac{dx}{dt} = 2t$

$y = 4t - 1$

$\int y\, dx = \int y\dfrac{dx}{dt}\, dt = \int (4t - 1) \times (2t)\, dt$

$\qquad\qquad\qquad\qquad = \int (8t^2 - 2t)\, dt$

$\qquad\qquad\qquad\qquad = \dfrac{8}{3}t^3 - t^2 + C$

Q3 $x = \cos 3\theta + 4 \Rightarrow \dfrac{dx}{d\theta} = -3\sin 3\theta$

$y = 2\cos 3\theta$

$\int y\, dx = \int y\dfrac{dx}{d\theta}\, d\theta = \int (2\cos 3\theta)(-3\sin 3\theta)\, d\theta$

$\qquad\qquad\qquad\qquad = \int -6\sin 3\theta \cos 3\theta\, d\theta$

$\qquad\qquad\qquad\qquad = \int -3(2\sin 3\theta \cos 3\theta)\, d\theta$

$\qquad\qquad\qquad\qquad = \int -3\sin 6\theta\, d\theta$

(using the double angle formula for sin).

Q4 $x = 3t + 6 \Rightarrow \dfrac{dx}{dt} = 3$

$y = 2t - 8$

So $y\dfrac{dx}{dt} = 3(2t - 8)$

$\int_{-2}^{2} y\dfrac{dx}{dt}\, dt = \int_{-2}^{2} 3(2t - 8)\, dt = 3\int_{-2}^{2}(2t - 8)\, dt$

$\qquad\qquad\qquad\quad = 3[t^2 - 8t]_{-2}^{2}$

$\qquad\qquad\qquad\quad = 3((4 - 16) - (4 + 16))$

$\qquad\qquad\qquad\quad = -96$

So the area is 96 but it is negative so it lies below the x-axis.

Q5 $x = 3t^2 \Rightarrow \dfrac{dx}{dt} = 6t$

$y = \dfrac{5}{t}$

So $y\dfrac{dx}{dt} = \dfrac{5}{t} \times 6t = 30$

When $x = 75$, $3t^2 = 75 \Rightarrow t = 5$ (since $t > 0$).

When $x = 3$, $3t^2 = 3 \Rightarrow t = 1$ (since $t > 0$).

$\int_{3}^{75} y\, dx = \int_{1}^{5} y\dfrac{dx}{dt}\, dt = \int_{1}^{5} 30\, dt = 30\int_{1}^{5} 1\, dt$

$\qquad\qquad\qquad\qquad\qquad = 30[t]_{1}^{5}$

$\qquad\qquad\qquad\qquad\qquad = 30(5 - 1)$

$\qquad\qquad\qquad\qquad\qquad = 120$

Q6 a) When $x = 8$:

$4t(t + 1) = 8 \Rightarrow t(t + 1) = 2 \Rightarrow t^2 + t - 2 = 0$

$(t - 1)(t + 2) = 0 \Rightarrow t = 1$ $(t > 0)$.

When $x = 120$:

$4t(t + 1) = 120 \Rightarrow t(t + 1) = 30 \Rightarrow t^2 + t - 30 = 0$

$(t - 5)(t + 6) = 0 \Rightarrow t = 5$ $(t > 0)$.

b) $x = 4t^2 + 4t \Rightarrow \dfrac{dx}{dt} = 8t + 4$

$y = 3t^3$

So $y\dfrac{dx}{dt} = 24t^4 + 12t^3$

$\int_{8}^{120} y\, dx = \int_{1}^{5} y\dfrac{dx}{dt}\, dt$

$\qquad\qquad\quad = \int_{1}^{5} 24t^4 + 12t^3\, dt$

$\qquad\qquad\quad = \left[\dfrac{24t^5}{5} + 3t^4\right]_{1}^{5}$

$\qquad\qquad\quad = (15000 + 1875) - \left(\dfrac{24}{5} + 3\right)$

$\qquad\qquad\quad = \dfrac{84336}{5} = 16\,867.2$

Review Exercise — Chapter 2

Q1 a) $\dfrac{1}{t} = \dfrac{1}{4} \Rightarrow t = 4$

$y = \dfrac{2}{t^2} = \dfrac{2}{16} = \dfrac{1}{8}$

b) $\dfrac{1}{50} = \dfrac{2}{t^2} \Rightarrow t^2 = 100 \;\; t = \pm 10$

Q2 a) Substitute the values of t into the parametric equations to find the corresponding values of x and y:

$t = 0 \Rightarrow x = \dfrac{6 - 0}{2} = 3,\; y = 2(0)^2 + 0 + 4 = 4$

$t = 1 \Rightarrow x = \dfrac{6 - 1}{2} = 2.5,\; y = 2(1)^2 + 1 + 4 = 7$

$t = 2 \Rightarrow x = \dfrac{6 - 2}{2} = 2,\; y = 2(2)^2 + 2 + 4 = 14$

$t = 3 \Rightarrow x = \dfrac{6 - 3}{2} = 1.5,\; y = 2(3)^2 + 3 + 4 = 25$

b) Use the given values in the parametric equations and solve for t:

(i) $\dfrac{6 - t}{2} = -7 \Rightarrow t = 20$

(ii) $2t^2 + t + 4 = 19$

$\qquad \Rightarrow 2t^2 + t - 15 = 0$

$\qquad \Rightarrow (2t - 5)(t + 3) = 0$

$\qquad \Rightarrow t = 2.5,\; t = -3$

c) Rearrange the parametric equation for x to make t the subject:
$$x = \frac{6-t}{2} \Rightarrow 2x = 6-t \Rightarrow t = 6-2x$$
Now substitute this into the parametric equation for y:
$$y = 2t^2 + t + 4$$
$$= 2(6-2x)^2 + (6-2x) + 4$$
$$= 2(36 - 24x + 4x^2) + 10 - 2x$$
$$y = 8x^2 - 50x + 82.$$

Q3 a) Substitute the values of θ into the parametric equations to find the corresponding values of x and y:

(i) $x = 2\sin\frac{\pi}{4} = \frac{2}{\sqrt{2}} = \sqrt{2}$
$$y = \cos^2\frac{\pi}{4} + 4 = \left(\cos\frac{\pi}{4}\right)^2 + 4 = \left(\frac{1}{\sqrt{2}}\right)^2 + 4$$
$$= \frac{1}{2} + 4 = \frac{9}{2}$$
So the coordinates are $\left(\sqrt{2}, \frac{9}{2}\right)$.

(ii) $x = 2\sin\frac{\pi}{6} = 2 \times \frac{1}{2} = 1$
$$y = \cos^2\frac{\pi}{6} + 4 = \left(\cos\frac{\pi}{6}\right)^2 + 4 = \left(\frac{\sqrt{3}}{2}\right)^2 + 4$$
$$= \frac{3}{4} + 4 = \frac{19}{4}$$
So the coordinates are $\left(1, \frac{19}{4}\right)$.

b) Use the identity $\cos^2\theta \equiv 1 - \sin^2\theta$ in the equation for y so both equations are in terms of $\sin\theta$:
$$y = \cos^2\theta + 4$$
$$= 1 - \sin^2\theta + 4$$
$$= 5 - \sin^2\theta$$
Rearrange the equation for x to get $\sin^2\theta$ in terms of x:
$$x = 2\sin\theta \Rightarrow \frac{x}{2} = \sin\theta \Rightarrow \sin^2\theta = \frac{x^2}{4}$$
So $y = 5 - \sin^2\theta \Rightarrow y = 5 - \frac{x^2}{4}$

c) $x = 2\sin\theta$, and $-1 \le \sin\theta \le 1$ so $-2 \le x \le 2$.

Q4 Use the identity $\cos 2\theta \equiv 1 - 2\sin^2\theta$ in the equation for y:
$$y = 3 + 2\cos 2\theta$$
$$= 3 + 2(1 - 2\sin^2\theta)$$
$$= 5 - 4\sin^2\theta$$
Rearrange the equation for x to get $\sin^2\theta$ in terms of x:
$$x = \frac{\sin\theta}{3} \Rightarrow 3x = \sin\theta \Rightarrow \sin^2\theta = 9x^2$$
So $y = 5 - 4\sin^2\theta$
$$\Rightarrow y = 5 - 4(9x^2)$$
$$\Rightarrow y = 5 - 36x^2$$

Q5 a) (i) On the y-axis:
$$x = 0 \Rightarrow t^2 - 1 = 0 \Rightarrow t = \pm 1$$
If $t = 1$, $y = 4 + \frac{3}{1} = 7$
If $t = -1$, $y = 4 + \frac{3}{-1} = 1$
So the curve crosses the y-axis at $(0, 1)$ and $(0, 7)$.

(ii) Substitute the parametric equations into the equation of the line:
$$x + 2y = 14$$
$$\Rightarrow (t^2 - 1) + 2(4 + \frac{3}{t}) = 14$$
$$\Rightarrow t^2 - 1 + 8 + \frac{6}{t} = 14$$
$$\Rightarrow t^2 - 7 + \frac{6}{t} = 0$$
$$\Rightarrow t^3 - 7t + 6 = 0$$
$$\Rightarrow (t - 1)(t^2 + t - 6) = 0$$
$$\Rightarrow (t - 1)(t - 2)(t + 3) = 0$$
$$\Rightarrow t = 1, t = 2, t = -3$$
When $t = 1$, $x = 0$, $y = 7$ (from part (i))
When $t = 2$, $x = 2^2 - 1 = 3$, $y = 4 + \frac{3}{2} = 5.5$
When $t = -3$, $x = (-3)^2 - 1 = 8$,
$$y = 4 + \frac{3}{-3} = 3$$
So the curve crosses the line $x + 2y = 14$ at $(0, 7)$, $(3, 5.5)$ and $(8, 3)$.

b) Use $\int y\,dx = \int y\frac{dx}{dt}\,dt$
$$\frac{dx}{dt} = 2t, \text{ so}$$
$$\int y\,dx = \int\left(4 + \frac{3}{t}\right)2t\,dt = \int 8t + 6\,dt$$

Q6 a) $x = t^2 + 3 \Rightarrow t = \sqrt{x - 3}$
(t is the positive root since $t > 0$)
When $x = 4$, $t = \sqrt{4 - 3} = 1$.
When $x = 12$, $t = \sqrt{12 - 3} = 3$.

b) $y = 4t - 1$ and $\frac{dx}{dt} = 2t$
$$\int_4^{12} y\,dx = \int_1^3 y\frac{dx}{dt}\,dt = \int_1^3 (4t - 1)(2t)\,dt$$
$$= \int_1^3 8t^2 - 2t\,dt$$
$$= \left[\frac{8t^3}{3} - t^2\right]_1^3$$
$$= \left[(72 - 9) - \left(\frac{8}{3} - 1\right)\right]$$
$$= 61\frac{1}{3}$$

Q7 $x = 2t^3 \Rightarrow t = \sqrt[3]{\frac{x}{2}}$
When $x = 2$, $t = \sqrt[3]{\frac{2}{2}} = 1$.
When $x = 54$, $t = \sqrt[3]{\frac{54}{2}} = 3$.
$y = \frac{2}{t}$ and $\frac{dx}{dt} = 6t^2$
$$\int_2^{54} y\,dx = \int_1^3 y\frac{dx}{dt}\,dt = \int_1^3 \left(\frac{2}{t}\right)(6t^2)\,dt$$
$$= \int_1^3 12t\,dt$$
$$= \left[6t^2\right]_1^3$$
$$= 54 - 6$$
$$= 48$$

Exam-Style Questions — Chapter 2

Q1 a) Substitute the given value of θ into the parametric equations:

$\theta = \frac{\pi}{3} \Rightarrow x = 1 - \tan\frac{\pi}{3} = 1 - \sqrt{3}$

$y = \frac{1}{2}\sin\left(\frac{2\pi}{3}\right) = \frac{1}{2}\left(\frac{\sqrt{3}}{2}\right) = \frac{\sqrt{3}}{4}$

So $P = \left(1 - \sqrt{3}, \frac{\sqrt{3}}{4}\right)$

[2 marks available — 1 mark for substituting $\theta = \frac{\pi}{3}$ into the parametric equations, 1 mark for both coordinates of P correct.]

b) Use $y = -\frac{1}{2}$ to find the value of θ:

$-\frac{1}{2} = \frac{1}{2}\sin 2\theta \Rightarrow \sin 2\theta = -1$

$\Rightarrow 2\theta = -\frac{\pi}{2}$

$\Rightarrow \theta = -\frac{\pi}{4}$

You can also find θ using the parametric equation for x, with x = 2.

[2 marks available — 1 mark for substituting given x- or y-value into the correct parametric equation, 1 mark for finding the correct value of θ.]

c) $x = 1 - \tan\theta \Rightarrow \tan\theta = 1 - x$

$y = \frac{1}{2}\sin 2\theta$

$= \frac{1}{2}\left(\frac{2\tan\theta}{1 + \tan^2\theta}\right)$

$= \frac{\tan\theta}{1 + \tan^2\theta}$

$= \frac{(1 - x)}{1 + (1 - x)^2}$

$= \frac{1 - x}{1 + 1 - 2x + x^2}$

$= \frac{1 - x}{x^2 - 2x + 2}$

[3 marks available — 1 mark for using the given identity to rearrange one of the parametric equations, 1 mark for eliminating θ from the parametric equation for y, 1 mark for correctly expanding to give the Cartesian equation given in the question.]

Q2 a) Substitute $y = 1$ into the parametric equation for y:

$t^2 - 2t + 2 = 1$

$\Rightarrow t^2 - 2t + 1 = 0$

$\Rightarrow (t - 1)^2 = 0$

$\Rightarrow t = 1$ *[1 mark]*

So a is the value of x when $t = 1$.

$a = t^3 + t = 1^3 + 1 = 2$ *[1 mark]*

b) Substitute the parametric equations for x and y into the equation of the line:

$8y = x + 6$

$\Rightarrow 8(t^2 - 2t + 2) = (t^3 + t) + 6$ *[1 mark]*

$\Rightarrow 8t^2 - 16t + 16 = t^3 + t + 6$

$\Rightarrow t^3 - 8t^2 + 17t - 10 = 0$

We know that this line passes through K, and from a) we know that $t = 1$ at K, so $t = 1$ is a solution of this equation, and $(t - 1)$ is a factor:

$\Rightarrow (t - 1)(t^2 - 7t + 10) = 0$ *[1 mark]*

$\Rightarrow (t - 1)(t - 2)(t - 5) = 0$

So $t = 2$ at L and $t = 5$ at M. *[1 mark]*

Substitute $t = 2$ and $t = 5$ back into the parametric equations: *[1 mark]*

If $t = 2$, then $x = 2^3 + 2 = 10$

and $y = 2^2 - 2(2) + 2 = 2$

If $t = 5$, then $x = 5^3 + 5 = 130$

and $y = 5^2 - 2(5) + 2 = 17$

So $L = (10, 2)$ *[1 mark]*

and $M = (130, 17)$ *[1 mark]*

Q3 a) At A, $y = 4$, so $4\cos\theta = 4 \Rightarrow \cos\theta = 1$

$\Rightarrow \theta = 0$, as $0 \leq \theta \leq \frac{\pi}{2}$.

At B, $x = 3$, so $3\sin\theta = 3 \Rightarrow \sin\theta = 1$

$\Rightarrow \theta = \frac{\pi}{2}$, as $0 \leq \theta \leq \frac{\pi}{2}$.

[2 marks available — 1 mark for each value of θ]

b) $y = 4\cos\theta$

$\frac{dx}{d\theta} = 3\cos\theta$ *[1 mark]*

$\int_0^3 y\,dx = \int_0^{\frac{\pi}{2}} y\frac{dx}{d\theta}\,d\theta = \int_0^{\frac{\pi}{2}}(4\cos\theta)(3\cos\theta)\,d\theta$

$= \int_0^{\frac{\pi}{2}}12\cos^2\theta\,d\theta$ *[1 mark]*

Now use the identity $2\cos^2\theta - 1 \equiv \cos 2\theta$

$\Rightarrow \int_0^{\frac{\pi}{2}}12\cos^2\theta\,d\theta = 6\int_0^{\frac{\pi}{2}}2\cos^2\theta\,d\theta$

$= 6\int_0^{\frac{\pi}{2}}(\cos 2\theta + 1)\,d\theta$ *[1 mark]*

Q4 a) The area $R = \int_4^{18} y\,dx$ *[1 mark]*

$\frac{dx}{dt} = 2t + 3$ *[1 mark]*

Change the limits of the integral:

$x = 18 \Rightarrow t^2 + 3t - 18 = 0 \Rightarrow (t - 3)(t + 6) = 0$

$\Rightarrow t = 3, t = -6$

$x = 4 \Rightarrow t^2 + 3t - 4 = 0 \Rightarrow (t - 1)(t + 4) = 0$

$\Rightarrow t = 1, t = -4$

$t > 0$, so we can ignore the negative values of t, so the limits are $t = 3$ and $t = 1$. *[1 mark]*

So $R = \int_4^{18} y\,dx = \int_1^3 y\frac{dx}{dt}\,dt$

$= \int_1^3\left(t^2 + \frac{1}{t^3}\right)(2t + 3)\,dt$

$= \int_1^3\left(\frac{t^5 + 1}{t^3}\right)(2t + 3)\,dt$

$= \int_1^3\frac{(t^5 + 1)(2t + 3)}{t^3}\,dt$ *[1 mark]*

b) $R = \int_1^3\frac{(t^5 + 1)(2t + 3)}{t^3}\,dt$

$= \int_1^3\frac{2t^6 + 3t^5 + 2t + 3}{t^3}\,dt$

$= \int_1^3\frac{2t^6}{t^3} + \frac{3t^5}{t^3} + \frac{2t}{t^3} + \frac{3}{t^3}\,dt$

$= \int_1^3 2t^3 + 3t^2 + 2t^{-2} + 3t^{-3}\,dt$ *[1 mark]*

$$= \left[\frac{t^4}{2} + t^3 - 2t^{-1} - \frac{3}{2}t^{-2} \right]_1^3 \quad \textbf{[1 mark]}$$

$$= \left(\frac{81}{2} + 27 - \frac{2}{3} - \frac{1}{6} \right) - \left(\frac{1}{2} + 1 - 2 - \frac{3}{2} \right)$$

[1 mark]

$$= \frac{200}{3} - (-2) = \frac{206}{3} \quad \textbf{[1 mark]}$$

Q5 a) Use the x- or y-coordinate of H in the relevant parametric equation to find θ:

At H, $3 + 4 \sin\theta = 5$

$\Rightarrow 4 \sin\theta = 2$

$\Rightarrow \sin\theta = \frac{1}{2}$

$\Rightarrow \theta = \frac{\pi}{6}$

OR

At H, $\dfrac{1 + \cos 2\theta}{3} = \dfrac{1}{2}$

$\Rightarrow 1 + \cos 2\theta = \frac{3}{2}$

$\Rightarrow \cos 2\theta = \frac{1}{2}$

$\Rightarrow 2\theta = \frac{\pi}{3}$

$\Rightarrow \theta = \frac{\pi}{6}$

[2 marks available — 1 mark for substituting one coordinate of H into the correct parametric equation, 1 mark finding the correct value of θ.]

b) $R = \displaystyle\int_{-1}^{5} y \, dx$

To get the integral with respect to θ, we need to use $\int y \, dx = \int y \dfrac{dx}{d\theta} \, d\theta$ **[1 mark]**

$\dfrac{dx}{d\theta} = 4\cos\theta$ **[1 mark]**

Change the limits of the integral:

$x = 5 \Rightarrow \theta = \dfrac{\pi}{6}$, from part a)

$x = -1 \Rightarrow 3 + 4\sin\theta = -1$

$\Rightarrow 4\sin\theta = -4$

$\Rightarrow \sin\theta = -1$

$\Rightarrow \theta = -\dfrac{\pi}{2}$ **[1 mark]**

So $R = \displaystyle\int_{-1}^{5} y \, dx = \int_{-\frac{\pi}{2}}^{\frac{\pi}{6}} y \dfrac{dx}{d\theta} \, d\theta$

$= \displaystyle\int_{-\frac{\pi}{2}}^{\frac{\pi}{6}} \left(\dfrac{1 + \cos 2\theta}{3} \right)(4\cos\theta) \, d\theta$ **[1 mark]**

$= \displaystyle\int_{-\frac{\pi}{2}}^{\frac{\pi}{6}} \dfrac{4}{3}(1 + \cos 2\theta)(\cos\theta) \, d\theta$

$= \displaystyle\int_{-\frac{\pi}{2}}^{\frac{\pi}{6}} \dfrac{4}{3}(2\cos^2\theta)(\cos\theta) \, d\theta$

(Using $\cos 2\theta \equiv 2\cos^2\theta - 1$) **[1 mark]**

$= \dfrac{8}{3}\displaystyle\int_{-\frac{\pi}{2}}^{\frac{\pi}{6}} \cos^3\theta \, d\theta$

c) Rearrange the parametric equation for x to make $\sin\theta$ the subject:

$x = 3 + 4\sin\theta \Rightarrow \sin\theta = \dfrac{x - 3}{4}$ **[1 mark]**

Use the identity $\cos 2\theta \equiv 1 - 2\sin^2\theta$ to rewrite the parametric equation for y in terms of $\sin\theta$:

$y = \dfrac{1 + \cos 2\theta}{3}$

$= \dfrac{1 + (1 - 2\sin^2\theta)}{3}$ **[1 mark]**

$= \dfrac{2 - 2\sin^2\theta}{3}$

$= \dfrac{2}{3}(1 - \sin^2\theta)$

$= \dfrac{2}{3}\left(1 - \left(\dfrac{x - 3}{4}\right)^2\right)$ **[1 mark]**

$= \dfrac{2}{3}\left(1 - \dfrac{(x - 3)^2}{16}\right)$

$= \dfrac{2}{3}\left(\dfrac{16 - (x^2 - 6x + 9)}{16}\right)$

$= \dfrac{2}{3}\left(\dfrac{-x^2 + 6x + 7}{16}\right)$

$= \dfrac{-x^2 + 6x + 7}{24}$ **[1 mark]**

d) $-\dfrac{\pi}{2} \leq \theta \leq \dfrac{\pi}{2} \Rightarrow -1 \leq \sin\theta \leq 1$

$\Rightarrow -4 \leq 4\sin\theta \leq 4$

$\Rightarrow -1 \leq 3 + 4\sin\theta \leq 7$

$\Rightarrow -1 \leq x \leq 7$ **[1 mark]**

Chapter 3:
Sequences and Series

1. The Binomial Expansion
Exercise 1.1 — Expansions where n is a positive integer

Q1 $(1 + x)^3 = 1 + 3x + \dfrac{3(3 - 1)}{1 \times 2}x^2 + \dfrac{3(3 - 1)(3 - 2)}{1 \times 2 \times 3}x^3$

$= 1 + 3x + 3x^2 + x^3$

Q2 $(1 + x)^7 = 1 + 7x + \dfrac{7(7 - 1)}{1 \times 2}x^2 + \dfrac{7(7 - 1)(7 - 2)}{1 \times 2 \times 3}x^3 + \ldots$

$= 1 + 7x + 21x^2 + 35x^3 + \ldots$

This isn't the full expansion, so keep the dots at the end to show it carries on.

Q3 $(1 - x)^4 = 1 + 4(-x) + \dfrac{4(4 - 1)}{1 \times 2}(-x)^2$

$+ \dfrac{4(4 - 1)(4 - 2)}{1 \times 2 \times 3}(-x)^3$

$+ \dfrac{4(4 - 1)(4 - 2)(4 - 3)}{1 \times 2 \times 3 \times 4}(-x)^4$

$= 1 - 4x + 6x^2 - 4x^3 + x^4$

Q4 $(1 + 3x)^6 = 1 + 6(3x) + \dfrac{6(6 - 1)}{1 \times 2}(3x)^2 + \ldots$

$= 1 + 6(3x) + 15(9x^2) + \ldots$

$= 1 + 18x + 135x^2 + \ldots$

Q5 $(1 + 2x)^8 = 1 + 8(2x) + \dfrac{8(8 - 1)}{1 \times 2}(2x)^2$

$+ \dfrac{8(8 - 1)(8 - 2)}{1 \times 2 \times 3}(2x)^3 + \ldots$

$= 1 + 8(2x) + 28(4x^2) + 56(8x^3) + \ldots$

$= 1 + 16x + 112x^2 + 448x^3 + \ldots$

Q6 $(1 - 5x)^5 = 1 + 5(-5x) + \dfrac{5(5 - 1)}{1 \times 2}(-5x)^2 + \ldots$

$= 1 + 5(-5x) + 10(25x^2) + \ldots$

$= 1 - 25x + 250x^2 - \ldots$

Q7 $(1 - 4x)^3 = 1 + 3(-4x) + \dfrac{3(3 - 1)}{1 \times 2}(-4x)^2$

$\qquad + \dfrac{3(3 - 1)(3 - 2)}{1 \times 2 \times 3}(-4x)^3$

$\qquad = 1 + 3(-4x) + 3(16x^2) + (-64x^3)$

$\qquad = 1 - 12x + 48x^2 - 64x^3$

Q8 $(1 + 6x)^6 = 1 + 6(6x) + \dfrac{6(6 - 1)}{1 \times 2}(6x)^2$

$\qquad + \dfrac{6(6 - 1)(6 - 2)}{1 \times 2 \times 3}(6x)^3 + \dots$

$\qquad = 1 + 6(6x) + 15(36x^2) + 20(216x^3)$

$\qquad = 1 + 36x + 540x^2 + 4320x^3 + \dots$

Exercise 1.2 — Expansions where n is negative or a fraction

Q1 $(1 + x)^{-4} = 1 + (-4)x + \dfrac{-4(-4 - 1)}{1 \times 2}x^2$

$\qquad + \dfrac{-4(-4 - 1)(-4 - 2)}{1 \times 2 \times 3}x^3 + \dots$

$\qquad = 1 + (-4)x + \dfrac{-4 \times -5}{2}x^2$

$\qquad\qquad + \dfrac{-4 \times -5 \times -6}{6}x^3 + \dots$

$\qquad = 1 - 4x + 10x^2 - 20x^3 + \dots$

Q2 a) $(1 - 6x)^{-3} = 1 + (-3)(-6x) + \dfrac{-3(-3 - 1)}{1 \times 2}(-6x)^2$

$\qquad + \dfrac{-3(-3 - 1)(-3 - 2)}{1 \times 2 \times 3}(-6x)^3 + \dots$

$\qquad = 1 + 18x + \dfrac{-3 \times -4}{2}(36x^2)$

$\qquad\qquad + \dfrac{-3 \times -4 \times -5}{6}(-216x^3) + \dots$

$\qquad = 1 + 18x + 6(36x^2) + (-10)(-216x^3) + \dots$

$\qquad = 1 + 18x + 216x^2 + 2160x^3 + \dots$

b) The expansion is valid for $\left|\dfrac{-6x}{1}\right| < 1$, so $|x| < \dfrac{1}{6}$.

Q3 a) $(1 + 4x)^{\frac{1}{3}} = 1 + \dfrac{1}{3}(4x) + \dfrac{\frac{1}{3}\left(\frac{1}{3} - 1\right)}{1 \times 2}(4x)^2 + \dots$

$\qquad = 1 + \dfrac{1}{3}(4x) + \dfrac{\frac{1}{3} \times -\frac{2}{3}}{2}(16x^2) + \dots$

$\qquad = 1 + \dfrac{1}{3}(4x) + \left(-\dfrac{1}{9}\right)(16x^2) + \dots$

$\qquad = 1 + \dfrac{4x}{3} - \dfrac{16x^2}{9} + \dots$

b) $(1 + 4x)^{-\frac{1}{2}} = 1 + \left(-\dfrac{1}{2}\right)(4x) + \dfrac{-\frac{1}{2}\left(-\frac{1}{2} - 1\right)}{1 \times 2}(4x)^2 + \dots$

$\qquad = 1 - \dfrac{1}{2}(4x) + \dfrac{-\frac{1}{2} \times -\frac{3}{2}}{2}(16x^2) + \dots$

$\qquad = 1 - \dfrac{1}{2}(4x) + \left(\dfrac{3}{8}\right)(16x^2) + \dots$

$\qquad = 1 - 2x + 6x^2 - \dots$

c) Both a) and b) are valid for $|x| < \dfrac{1}{4}$.

Q4 a) $\dfrac{1}{(1 - 4x)^2} = (1 - 4x)^{-2}$

$\qquad = 1 + (-2)(-4x) + \dfrac{-2(-2 - 1)}{1 \times 2}(-4x)^2$

$\qquad + \dfrac{-2(-2 - 1)(-2 - 2)}{1 \times 2 \times 3}(-4x)^3 + \dots$

$\qquad = 1 + (-2)(-4x) + \dfrac{-2 \times -3}{2}(16x^2)$

$\qquad + \dfrac{-2 \times -3 \times -4}{6}(-64x^3) + \dots$

$\qquad = 1 + 8x + 3(16x^2) + (-4)(-64x^3) + \dots$

$\qquad = 1 + 8x + 48x^2 + 256x^3 + \dots$

b) $\sqrt{1 + 6x} = (1 + 6x)^{\frac{1}{2}}$

$\qquad = 1 + \dfrac{1}{2}(6x) + \dfrac{\frac{1}{2}\left(\frac{1}{2} - 1\right)}{1 \times 2}(6x)^2$

$\qquad + \dfrac{\frac{1}{2}\left(\frac{1}{2} - 1\right)\left(\frac{1}{2} - 2\right)}{1 \times 2 \times 3}(6x)^3 + \dots$

$\qquad = 1 + \dfrac{1}{2}(6x) + \dfrac{\frac{1}{2} \times -\frac{1}{2}}{2}(36x^2)$

$\qquad + \dfrac{\frac{1}{2} \times -\frac{1}{2} \times -\frac{3}{2}}{6}(216x^3) + \dots$

$\qquad = 1 + \dfrac{1}{2}(6x) + \left(-\dfrac{1}{8}\right)(36x^2) + \dfrac{1}{16}(216x^3) + \dots$

$\qquad = 1 + 3x - \dfrac{9x^2}{2} + \dfrac{27x^3}{2} - \dots$

c) $\dfrac{1}{\sqrt{1 - 3x}} = (1 - 3x)^{-\frac{1}{2}}$

$\qquad = 1 + \left(-\dfrac{1}{2}\right)(-3x) + \dfrac{-\frac{1}{2}\left(-\frac{1}{2} - 1\right)}{1 \times 2}(-3x)^2$

$\qquad + \dfrac{-\frac{1}{2}\left(-\frac{1}{2} - 1\right)\left(-\frac{1}{2} - 2\right)}{1 \times 2 \times 3}(-3x)^3 + \dots$

$\qquad = 1 + \left(-\dfrac{1}{2}\right)(-3x) + \dfrac{-\frac{1}{2} \times -\frac{3}{2}}{2}(9x^2)$

$\qquad + \dfrac{-\frac{1}{2} \times -\frac{3}{2} \times -\frac{5}{2}}{6}(-27x^3) + \dots$

$\qquad = 1 + \dfrac{3x}{2} + \dfrac{3}{8}(9x^2) + \left(-\dfrac{5}{16}\right)(-27x^3) + \dots$

$\qquad = 1 + \dfrac{3x}{2} + \dfrac{27x^2}{8} + \dfrac{135x^3}{16} + \dots$

d) $\sqrt[3]{1 + \dfrac{x}{2}} = \left(1 + \dfrac{1}{2}x\right)^{\frac{1}{3}}$

$\qquad = 1 + \dfrac{1}{3}\left(\dfrac{x}{2}\right) + \dfrac{\frac{1}{3}\left(\frac{1}{3} - 1\right)}{1 \times 2}\left(\dfrac{x}{2}\right)^2$

$\qquad + \dfrac{\frac{1}{3}\left(\frac{1}{3} - 1\right)\left(\frac{1}{3} - 2\right)}{1 \times 2 \times 3}\left(\dfrac{x}{2}\right)^3 \dots$

$\qquad = 1 + \dfrac{1}{3}\left(\dfrac{x}{2}\right) + \dfrac{\frac{1}{3} \times -\frac{2}{3}}{2}\left(\dfrac{x}{2}\right)^2$

$\qquad + \dfrac{\frac{1}{3} \times -\frac{2}{3} \times -\frac{5}{3}}{6}\left(\dfrac{x}{2}\right)^3 \dots$

$\qquad = 1 + \dfrac{1}{3}\left(\dfrac{x}{2}\right) + \left(-\dfrac{1}{9}\right)\left(\dfrac{x}{2}\right)^2 + \dfrac{5}{81}\left(\dfrac{x}{2}\right)^3 \dots$

$\qquad = 1 + \dfrac{x}{6} - \dfrac{x^2}{36} + \dfrac{5x^3}{648} \dots$

Q5 a) $\dfrac{1}{(1 + 7x)^4} = (1 + 7x)^{-4}$

The x^3 term is $\dfrac{-4(-4 - 1)(-4 - 2)}{1 \times 2 \times 3}(7x)^3$

$\qquad = \dfrac{-4 \times -5 \times -6}{6}(343x^3)$

$\qquad = -20(343x^3) = -6860x^3$

So the coefficient of the x^3 term is -6860.

b) The expansion is valid for $|x| < \dfrac{1}{7}$.

Q6 a) $\sqrt[4]{1-4x} = (1-4x)^{\frac{1}{4}}$

The x^5 term is :

$$\frac{\frac{1}{4}\left(\frac{1}{4}-1\right)\left(\frac{1}{4}-2\right)\left(\frac{1}{4}-3\right)\left(\frac{1}{4}-4\right)}{1\times2\times3\times4\times5}(-4x)^5$$

$$=\frac{\frac{1}{4}\times-\frac{3}{4}\times-\frac{7}{4}\times-\frac{11}{4}\times-\frac{15}{4}}{120}(-4)^5x^5$$

$$=\frac{1\times-3\times-7\times-11\times-15}{120}\times\left(\frac{-4}{4}\right)^5\times x^5$$

$$=\frac{3465}{120}\times-1\times x^5 = -\frac{231x^5}{8}$$

So the coefficient of the x^5 term is $-\frac{231}{8}$.

b) The expansion is valid for $|x|<\frac{1}{4}$.

Q7 a) $(1-5x)^{\frac{1}{6}} = 1 + \frac{1}{6}(-5x) + \frac{\frac{1}{6}\left(\frac{1}{6}-1\right)}{1\times2}(-5x)^2 + \dots$

$$= 1 + \frac{1}{6}(-5x) + \frac{\frac{1}{6}\times-\frac{5}{6}}{2}(25x^2) + \dots$$

$$= 1 - \frac{5x}{6} + \left(-\frac{5}{72}\right)(25x^2) + \dots$$

$$= 1 - \frac{5x}{6} - \frac{125x^2}{72} - \dots$$

b) $(1+4x)^4 = 1 + 16x + 96x^2 + \dots$

So $(1+4x)^4(1-5x)^{\frac{1}{6}}$

$$= (1 + 16x + 96x^2 + \dots)(1 - \frac{5x}{6} - \frac{125x^2}{72} + \dots)$$

$$= 1(1 + 16x + 96x^2) - \frac{5x}{6}(1+16x) - \frac{125x^2}{72}(1) + \dots$$

$$= 1 + 16x + 96x^2 - \frac{5x}{6} - \frac{40x^2}{3} - \frac{125x^2}{72} + \dots$$

$$= 1 + \frac{91x}{6} + \frac{5827x^2}{72} + \dots$$

c) The expansion of $(1-5x)^{\frac{1}{6}}$ is valid for $|x|<\frac{1}{5}$.
The expansion of $(1+4x)^4$ is valid for all values of x, since n is a positive integer.

So overall, the expansion of $(1+4x)^4(1-5x)^{\frac{1}{6}}$ is valid for the narrower of these ranges, i.e. $|x|<\frac{1}{5}$.

Q8 a) $\frac{(1+3x)^4}{(1+x)^3} = (1+3x)^4(1+x)^{-3}$

$(1+3x)^4 = 1 + 12x + 54x^2 + \dots$

$(1+x)^{-3} = 1 - 3x + 6x^2 - \dots$

So $(1+3x)^4(1+x)^{-3}$
$= 1 - 3x + 6x^2 + [12x(1-3x)] + 54x^2 + \dots$
$= 1 - 3x + 6x^2 + 12x - 36x^2 + 54x^2 + \dots$
$= 1 + 9x + 24x^2 + \dots$

b) The expansion of $(1+3x)^4$ is valid for all values of x, since n is a positive integer.

The expansion of $(1+x)^{-3}$ is valid for $|x|<1$.

So overall, the expansion of $\frac{(1+3x)^4}{(1+x)^3}$ is valid for the narrower of these ranges, i.e. $|x|<1$.

Exercise 1.3 — Expanding $(p+qx)^n$

Q1 a) $(2+4x)^3 = 2^3(1+2x)^3 = 8(1+2x)^3$

$$(1+2x)^3 = 1 + 3(2x) + \frac{3\times2}{1\times2}(2x)^2 + \frac{3\times2\times1}{1\times2\times3}(2x)^3$$

$$= 1 + 6x + 3(4x^2) + 8x^3$$

$$= 1 + 6x + 12x^2 + 8x^3$$

So $(2+4x)^3 = 8(1 + 6x + 12x^2 + 8x^3)$

$$= 8 + 48x + 96x^2 + 64x^3$$

b) $(3+4x)^5 = 3^5\left(1+\frac{4}{3}x\right)^5 = 243\left(1+\frac{4}{3}x\right)^5$

$$\left(1+\frac{4}{3}x\right)^5 = 1 + 5\left(\frac{4}{3}x\right) + \frac{5\times4}{1\times2}\left(\frac{4}{3}x\right)^2$$

$$+ \frac{5\times4\times3}{1\times2\times3}\left(\frac{4}{3}x\right)^3 + \dots$$

$$= 1 + \frac{20x}{3} + \frac{160x^2}{9} + \frac{640x^3}{27} + \dots$$

$$(3+4x)^5 = 243(1 + \frac{20x}{3} + \frac{160x^2}{9} + \frac{640x^3}{27} + \dots)$$

$$= 243 + 1620x + 4320x^2 + 5760x^3 + \dots$$

c) $(4+x)^{\frac{1}{2}} = 4^{\frac{1}{2}}\left(1+\frac{x}{4}\right)^{\frac{1}{2}} = 2\left(1+\frac{x}{4}\right)^{\frac{1}{2}}$

$$\left(1+\frac{x}{4}\right)^{\frac{1}{2}} = 1 + \frac{1}{2}\left(\frac{x}{4}\right) + \frac{\frac{1}{2}\times-\frac{1}{2}}{1\times2}\left(\frac{x}{4}\right)^2$$

$$+ \frac{\frac{1}{2}\times-\frac{1}{2}\times-\frac{3}{2}}{1\times2\times3}\left(\frac{x}{4}\right)^3 + \dots$$

$$= 1 + \frac{x}{8} - \frac{x^2}{128} + \frac{x^3}{1024} - \dots$$

$$(4+x)^{\frac{1}{2}} = 2\left(1+\frac{x}{4}\right)^{\frac{1}{2}}$$

$$= 2(1 + \frac{x}{8} - \frac{x^2}{128} + \frac{x^3}{1024} - \dots)$$

$$= 2 + \frac{x}{4} - \frac{x^2}{64} + \frac{x^3}{512} - \dots$$

d) $(8+2x)^{-\frac{1}{3}} = 8^{-\frac{1}{3}}\left(1+\frac{2x}{8}\right)^{-\frac{1}{3}} = \frac{1}{2}\left(1+\frac{x}{4}\right)^{-\frac{1}{3}}$

$$\left(1+\frac{x}{4}\right)^{-\frac{1}{3}} = 1 + \left(-\frac{1}{3}\right)\left(\frac{x}{4}\right) + \frac{-\frac{1}{3}\times-\frac{4}{3}}{1\times2}\left(\frac{x}{4}\right)^2$$

$$+ \frac{-\frac{1}{3}\times-\frac{4}{3}\times-\frac{7}{3}}{1\times2\times3}\left(\frac{x}{4}\right)^3 + \dots$$

$$= 1 - \frac{x}{12} + \frac{x^2}{72} - \frac{7x^3}{2592} + \dots$$

$$(8+2x)^{-\frac{1}{3}} = \frac{1}{2}\left(1+\frac{x}{4}\right)^{-\frac{1}{3}}$$

$$= \frac{1}{2}(1 - \frac{x}{12} + \frac{x^2}{72} - \frac{7x^3}{2592} + \dots)$$

$$= \frac{1}{2} - \frac{x}{24} + \frac{x^2}{144} - \frac{7x^3}{5184} + \dots$$

Q2 $(a+5x)^5 = a^5\left(1+\frac{5}{a}x\right)^5$

So the x^2 term is:

$$a^5\left(\frac{5\times4}{1\times2}\right)\left(\frac{5}{a}x\right)^2 = 10a^5\left(\frac{25}{a^2}x^2\right) = \left(\frac{250a^5}{a^2}\right)x^2 = 250a^3x^2$$

So $250a^3 = 2000 \Rightarrow a^3 = 8 \Rightarrow a = 2$.

Q3 a) $(2-5x)^7 = 2^7\left(1-\frac{5}{2}x\right)^7 = 128\left(1-\frac{5}{2}x\right)^7$

$$\left(1-\frac{5}{2}x\right)^7 = 1 + 7\left(-\frac{5}{2}x\right) + \frac{7\times6}{1\times2}\left(-\frac{5}{2}x\right)^2 + \dots$$

$$= 1 - \frac{35x}{2} + \frac{525x^2}{4} - \dots$$

$$(2-5x)^7 = 128(1 - \frac{35x}{2} + \frac{525x^2}{4} - \dots)$$

$$= 128 - 2240x + 16800x^2 - \dots$$

b) $(1 + 6x)^3 = 1 + 18x + 108x^2 + ...$

So $(1 + 6x)^3(2 - 5x)^7 =$

$128 - 2240x + 16800x^2 + 18x(128 - 2240x)$
$+ 108x^2(128) + ...$

$= 128 + 64x - 9696x^2 + ...$

Q4 a) $\left(1 + \frac{6}{5}x\right)^{-\frac{1}{2}} = 1 + \left(-\frac{1}{2}\right)\left(\frac{6}{5}x\right)$

$+ \frac{\left(-\frac{1}{2}\right) \times \left(-\frac{3}{2}\right)}{1 \times 2}\left(\frac{6}{5}x\right)^2$

$+ \frac{\left(-\frac{1}{2}\right) \times \left(-\frac{3}{2}\right) \times \left(-\frac{5}{2}\right)}{1 \times 2 \times 3}\left(\frac{6}{5}x\right)^3 + ...$

$= 1 - \frac{3x}{5} + \frac{27x^2}{50} - \frac{27x^3}{50} + ...$

The expansion is valid for $\left|\frac{6x}{5}\right| < 1$, so $|x| < \frac{5}{6}$.

b) $\sqrt{\frac{20}{5 + 6x}} = \frac{\sqrt{20}}{\sqrt{5 + 6x}} = 20^{\frac{1}{2}}(5 + 6x)^{-\frac{1}{2}}$

$= (20^{\frac{1}{2}})(5^{-\frac{1}{2}})\left(1 + \frac{6}{5}x\right)^{-\frac{1}{2}}$

$= \left(\frac{20^{\frac{1}{2}}}{5^{\frac{1}{2}}}\right)\left(1 + \frac{6}{5}x\right)^{-\frac{1}{2}}$

$= \left(\frac{20}{5}\right)^{\frac{1}{2}}\left(1 + \frac{6}{5}x\right)^{-\frac{1}{2}}$

$= 4^{\frac{1}{2}}\left(1 + \frac{6}{5}x\right)^{-\frac{1}{2}}$

$= 2\left(1 + \frac{6}{5}x\right)^{-\frac{1}{2}}$

So, using the expansion in part a):

$\sqrt{\frac{20}{5 + 6x}} = 2(1 - \frac{3x}{5} + \frac{27x^2}{50} - \frac{27x^3}{50} + ...)$

$= 2 - \frac{6x}{5} + \frac{27x^2}{25} - \frac{27x^3}{25} + ...$

Q5 a) $\frac{1}{\sqrt{5 - 2x}} = (5 - 2x)^{-\frac{1}{2}} = 5^{-\frac{1}{2}}\left(1 - \frac{2}{5}x\right)^{-\frac{1}{2}}$

$\left(1 - \frac{2}{5}x\right)^{-\frac{1}{2}} = 1 + \left(-\frac{1}{2}\right)\left(-\frac{2}{5}x\right)$

$+ \frac{\left(-\frac{1}{2}\right) \times \left(-\frac{3}{2}\right)}{1 \times 2}\left(-\frac{2}{5}x\right)^2 + ...$

$= 1 + \frac{x}{5} + \left(\frac{3}{8}\right)\left(\frac{4}{25}x^2\right) + ...$

$= 1 + \frac{x}{5} + \frac{3x^2}{50} + ...$

So $\frac{1}{\sqrt{5 - 2x}} = 5^{-\frac{1}{2}}\left(1 - \frac{2}{5}x\right)^{-\frac{1}{2}}$

$= \frac{1}{\sqrt{5}}(1 + \frac{x}{5} + \frac{3x^2}{50} ...)$

$= \frac{1}{\sqrt{5}} + \frac{x}{5\sqrt{5}} + \frac{3x^2}{50\sqrt{5}} + ...$

b) $\frac{3 + x}{\sqrt{5 - 2x}} \approx (3 + x)\left(\frac{1}{\sqrt{5}} + \frac{x}{5\sqrt{5}} + \frac{3x^2}{50\sqrt{5}}\right)$

$\approx 3\left(\frac{1}{\sqrt{5}} + \frac{x}{5\sqrt{5}} + \frac{3x^2}{50\sqrt{5}}\right)$

$+ x\left(\frac{1}{\sqrt{5}} + \frac{x}{5\sqrt{5}}\right)$

$= \frac{3}{\sqrt{5}} + \frac{3x}{5\sqrt{5}} + \frac{9x^2}{50\sqrt{5}} + \frac{x}{\sqrt{5}} + \frac{x^2}{5\sqrt{5}}$

$= \frac{3}{\sqrt{5}} + \frac{8x}{5\sqrt{5}} + \frac{19x^2}{50\sqrt{5}}$

Q6 a) $(9 + 4x)^{-\frac{1}{2}} = 9^{-\frac{1}{2}}\left(1 + \frac{4}{9}x\right)^{-\frac{1}{2}}$

$\left(1 + \frac{4}{9}x\right)^{-\frac{1}{2}} = 1 + \left(-\frac{1}{2}\right)\left(\frac{4}{9}x\right)$

$+ \frac{\left(-\frac{1}{2}\right) \times \left(-\frac{3}{2}\right)}{1 \times 2}\left(\frac{4}{9}x\right)^2 + ...$

$= 1 - \frac{2x}{9} + \frac{2x^2}{27} - ...$

So $(9 + 4x)^{-\frac{1}{2}} = \frac{1}{\sqrt{9}}\left(1 - \frac{2x}{9} + \frac{2x^2}{27} - ...\right)$

$= \frac{1}{3} - \frac{2x}{27} + \frac{2x^2}{81} - ...$

b) $(1 + 6x)^4 = 1 + 24x + 216x^2 + ...$

So $\frac{(1 + 6x)^4}{\sqrt{9 + 4x}} = (1 + 6x)^4(9 + 4x)^{-\frac{1}{2}}$

$\approx (1 + 24x + 216x^2)\left(\frac{1}{3} - \frac{2x}{27} + \frac{2x^2}{81}\right)$

$\approx \frac{1}{3} - \frac{2x}{27} + \frac{2x^2}{81} + 24x\left(\frac{1}{3} - \frac{2x}{27}\right) + 216x^2\left(\frac{1}{3}\right)$

$= \frac{1}{3} - \frac{2x}{27} + \frac{2x^2}{81} + 8x - \frac{16x^2}{9} + 72x^2$

$= \frac{1}{3} + \frac{214x}{27} + \frac{5690x^2}{81}$

2. Using the Binomial Expansion as an Approximation
Exercise 2.1 — Approximating with binomial expansions

Q1 a) $(1 + 6x)^{-1} = 1 + (-1)(6x) + \frac{-1 \times -2}{1 \times 2}(6x)^2 + ...$
$= 1 - 6x + 36x^2 - ...$

b) The expansion is valid if $|x| < \frac{1}{6}$.

c) $\frac{100}{106} = \frac{1}{1.06} = \frac{1}{1 + 0.06} = (1 + 0.06)^{-1}$

This is the same as $(1 + 6x)^{-1}$ with $x = 0.01$.
$0.01 < \frac{1}{6}$ so the approximation is valid.
$(1 + 6(0.01))^{-1} \approx 1 - 6(0.01) + 36(0.01^2)$
$= 1 - 0.06 + 0.0036 = 0.9436$

d) $\left|\frac{\left(\frac{100}{106}\right) - 0.9436}{\left(\frac{100}{106}\right)}\right| \times 100 = 0.02 \%$ (to 1 s.f.)

In the answers that follow, the expansions will just be stated. Look back at the previous sections of this chapter to check how to set out the working if you need to.

Q2 a) $(1 + 3x)^{\frac{1}{4}} = 1 + \frac{3x}{4} - \frac{27x^2}{32} + \frac{189x^3}{128} - ...$

b) The expansion is valid if $|x| < \frac{1}{3}$.

c) $\sqrt[4]{1.9} = 1.9^{\frac{1}{4}} = (1 + 0.9)^{\frac{1}{4}}$

This is the same as $(1 + 3x)^{\frac{1}{4}}$ with $x = 0.3$.
$0.3 < \frac{1}{3}$ so the approximation is valid.
$(1 + 3(0.3))^{\frac{1}{4}} \approx 1 + \frac{3(0.3)}{4} - \frac{27(0.3^2)}{32} + \frac{189(0.3^3)}{128}$
$= 1.1889$ (to 4 d.p.)

d) $\left| \dfrac{(\sqrt[4]{1.9}) - 1.1889}{(\sqrt[4]{1.9})} \right| \times 100 = 1.26\%$ (to 3 s.f.)

Q3 a) $(1 - 2x)^{-\frac{1}{2}} = 1 + x + \dfrac{3x^2}{2} + \dfrac{5x^3}{2} + ...$

b) The expansion is valid if $|x| < \dfrac{1}{2}$.

c) Using $x = \dfrac{1}{10}$ gives:

$\left(1 - \dfrac{2}{10}\right)^{-\frac{1}{2}} \approx 1 + \dfrac{1}{10} + \dfrac{3}{200} + \dfrac{5}{2000}$

$\left(\dfrac{4}{5}\right)^{-\frac{1}{2}} \approx 1 + 0.1 + 0.015 + 0.0025$

$\left(\dfrac{5}{4}\right)^{\frac{1}{2}} \approx 1.1175$

$\sqrt{\dfrac{5}{4}} \approx 1.1175$

$\dfrac{\sqrt{5}}{\sqrt{4}} \approx 1.1175$

$\dfrac{\sqrt{5}}{2} \approx 1.1175$

$\sqrt{5} \approx 2 \times 1.1175 = 2.235$

d) $\left| \dfrac{\sqrt{5} - 2.235}{\sqrt{5}} \right| \times 100 = 0.048\%$ (to 2 s.f.)

Q4 a) $(2 - 5x)^6 = 2^6\left(1 - \dfrac{5}{2}x\right)^6$

$= 64\left(1 - 15x + \dfrac{375x^2}{4} - ... \right)$

$= 64 - 960x + 6000x^2 - ...$

b) $1.95^6 = (2 - 0.05)^6$
This is the same as $(2 - 5x)^6$ with $x = 0.01$.
$(2 - 5(0.01))^6 \approx 64 - 960(0.01) + 6000(0.01)^2$
$= 64 - 9.6 + 0.6 = 55$

c) $\left| \dfrac{1.95^6 - 55}{1.95^6} \right| \times 100 = 0.036\%$ (to 2 s.f.)

Q5 a) $\sqrt{3 - 4x} = (3 - 4x)^{\frac{1}{2}} = \sqrt{3}\left(1 - \dfrac{4}{3}x\right)^{\frac{1}{2}}$

$= \sqrt{3}\left(1 - \dfrac{2x}{3} - \dfrac{2x^2}{9} - ...\right)$

$= \sqrt{3} - \dfrac{2\sqrt{3}x}{3} - \dfrac{2\sqrt{3}x^2}{9} - ...$

Remember to factorise the original expression to get it in the form $(1 + ax)^n$.

b) The expansion is valid if $|x| < \dfrac{3}{4}$.

c) $\sqrt{3 - 4\left(\dfrac{3}{40}\right)} \approx \sqrt{3} - \dfrac{2\sqrt{3} \times 3}{3 \times 40} - \dfrac{2\sqrt{3} \times 9}{9 \times 1600}$

$\sqrt{3 - \dfrac{3}{10}} \approx \sqrt{3} - \dfrac{\sqrt{3}}{20} - \dfrac{\sqrt{3}}{800}$

$\sqrt{\dfrac{27}{10}} \approx \dfrac{759\sqrt{3}}{800}$

$\dfrac{3\sqrt{3}}{\sqrt{10}} \approx \dfrac{759\sqrt{3}}{800}$

$\dfrac{3}{\sqrt{10}} \approx \dfrac{759}{800}$

d) $\left| \dfrac{\left(\dfrac{3}{\sqrt{10}}\right) - \left(\dfrac{759}{800}\right)}{\left(\dfrac{3}{\sqrt{10}}\right)} \right| \times 100 = 0.007\%$ (to 1 s.f.)

3. Binomial Expansion and Partial Fractions

Exercise 3.1 — Finding binomial expansions using partial fractions

Q1 a) $5 - 12x \equiv A(4 + 3x) + B(1 + 6x)$

Using the substitution method:

Let $x = -\dfrac{4}{3}$, then $5 + 16 = -7B \Rightarrow B = -3$.

Let $x = -\dfrac{1}{6}$, then $5 + 2 = \dfrac{7A}{2} \Rightarrow A = 2$.

You could also use the 'equating coefficients' method if you prefer.

b) (i) $(1 + 6x)^{-1} = 1 - 6x + 36x^2 - ...$

(ii) $(4 + 3x)^{-1} = 4^{-1}\left(1 + \dfrac{3}{4}x\right)^{-1}$

$= \dfrac{1}{4}\left(1 - \dfrac{3x}{4} + \dfrac{9x^2}{16} - ...\right)$

$= \dfrac{1}{4} - \dfrac{3x}{16} + \dfrac{9x^2}{64} - ...$

c) From a):

$\dfrac{5 - 12x}{(1 + 6x)(4 + 3x)} \equiv \dfrac{2}{(1 + 6x)} - \dfrac{3}{(4 + 3x)}$

$\equiv 2(1 + 6x)^{-1} - 3(4 + 3x)^{-1}$

$2(1 + 6x)^{-1} - 3(4 + 3x)^{-1} \approx$
$2(1 - 6x + 36x^2) - 3\left(\dfrac{1}{4} - \dfrac{3x}{16} + \dfrac{9x^2}{64}\right)$

$= 2 - 12x + 72x^2 - \dfrac{3}{4} + \dfrac{9x}{16} - \dfrac{27x^2}{64}$

$= \dfrac{5}{4} - \dfrac{183x}{16} + \dfrac{4581x^2}{64}$

d) $(1 + 6x)^{-1}$ is valid if $|x| < \dfrac{1}{6}$.

$(4 + 3x)^{-1}$ is valid if $|x| < \dfrac{4}{3}$.

So the full expansion is valid if $|x| < \dfrac{1}{6}$.

Q2 a) $\dfrac{60x^2 + 5x + 7}{(4 - 3x)(1 + 4x)^2} \equiv$

$\dfrac{A}{(4 - 3x)} + \dfrac{B}{(1 + 4x)} + \dfrac{C}{(1 + 4x)^2}$

$60x^2 + 5x + 7 \equiv$
$A(1 + 4x)^2 + B(4 - 3x)(1 + 4x) + C(4 - 3x)$

Equating coefficients:
x^2 terms: $60 = 16A - 12B$
x terms: $5 = 8A + 13B - 3C$
constant terms: $7 = A + 4B + 4C$

Solving simultaneously gives:
$A = 3, B = -1, C = 2$.

Putting these values back into the expression gives:

$\dfrac{60x^2 + 5x + 7}{(4 - 3x)(1 + 4x)^2} \equiv$

$\dfrac{3}{(4 - 3x)} - \dfrac{1}{(1 + 4x)} + \dfrac{2}{(1 + 4x)^2}$

b) $f(x)$ can also be expressed as:
$3(4 - 3x)^{-1} - (1 + 4x)^{-1} + 2(1 + 4x)^{-2}$
Expanding these three parts separately:
$(4 - 3x)^{-1} = 4^{-1}\left(1 - \dfrac{3}{4}x\right)^{-1}$

$= \dfrac{1}{4}\left(1 + \dfrac{3x}{4} + \dfrac{9x^2}{16} + ...\right)$

$$= \frac{1}{4} + \frac{3x}{16} + \frac{9x^2}{64} + \dots$$

$(1 + 4x)^{-1} = 1 - 4x + 16x^2 + \dots$

$(1 + 4x)^{-2} = 1 - 8x + 48x^2 + \dots$

So $f(x) \approx 3\left(\frac{1}{4} + \frac{3x}{16} + \frac{9x^2}{64}\right) - (1 - 4x + 16x^2)$
$$+ 2(1 - 8x + 48x^2)$$

$$= \frac{3}{4} + \frac{9x}{16} + \frac{27x^2}{64} - 1 + 4x - 16x^2 + 2 - 16x + 96x^2$$

$$= \frac{7}{4} - \frac{183x}{16} + \frac{5147x^2}{64}$$

c) $f(0.01) = \dfrac{60(0.01^2) + 5(0.01) + 7}{(4 - 3(0.01))(1 + 4(0.01))^2} = 1.64324\dots$

From the expansion:

$f(0.01) \approx \dfrac{7}{4} - \dfrac{183(0.01)}{16} + \dfrac{5147(0.01^2)}{64}$
$$= 1.64367 \text{ (to 5 d.p.)}$$

So the % error is:

$\left|\dfrac{1.64324 - 1.64367}{1.64324}\right| \times 100 = 0.026\%$ (to 2 s.f.)

Q3 a) $6x^3 + 11x^2 + 4x = x(3x + 4)(2x + 1)$

b) $\dfrac{22x^2 + 40x + 12}{6x^3 + 11x^2 + 4x} \equiv \dfrac{22x^2 + 40x + 12}{x(3x + 4)(2x + 1)}$

$$\equiv \frac{A}{x} + \frac{B}{(3x + 4)} + \frac{C}{(2x + 1)}$$

$22x^2 + 40x + 12 \equiv A(3x + 4)(2x + 1) + Bx(2x + 1)$
$$+ Cx(3x + 4)$$

Equating coefficients:
constant terms: $12 = 4A \Rightarrow A = 3$
x^2 terms: $22 = 18 + 2B + 3C \Rightarrow 4 = 2B + 3C$
x terms: $40 = 33 + B + 4C \Rightarrow 7 = B + 4C$
Solving simultaneously gives: $B = -1$ and $C = 2$.

So $\dfrac{22x^2 + 40x + 12}{6x^3 + 11x^2 + 4x} \equiv \dfrac{3}{x} - \dfrac{1}{(3x + 4)} + \dfrac{2}{(2x + 1)}$

c) $(3x + 4)^{-1} = (4 + 3x)^{-1} = \dfrac{1}{4} - \dfrac{3x}{16} + \dfrac{9x^2}{64} + \dots$
This expansion has been done in question 1.

$(2x + 1)^{-1} = (1 + 2x)^{-1} = 1 - 2x + 4x^2 + \dots$

$\dfrac{22x^2 + 40x + 12}{6x^3 + 11x^2 + 4x} \equiv \dfrac{3}{x} - (3x + 4)^{-1} + 2(2x + 1)^{-1}$

$\approx \dfrac{3}{x} - \left(\dfrac{1}{4} - \dfrac{3x}{16} + \dfrac{9x^2}{64}\right) + 2(1 - 2x + 4x^2)$

$= \dfrac{3}{x} - \dfrac{1}{4} + \dfrac{3x}{16} - \dfrac{9x^2}{64} + 2 - 4x + 8x^2$

$= \dfrac{3}{x} + \dfrac{7}{4} - \dfrac{61x}{16} + \dfrac{503x^2}{64}$

d) $(3x + 4)^{-1}$ is valid if $|x| < \dfrac{4}{3}$.

$(2x + 1)^{-1}$ is valid if $|x| < \dfrac{1}{2}$.

$\dfrac{3}{x}$ is valid for $x \neq 0$.
So the full expansion is valid if $|x| < \dfrac{1}{2}$ and $x \neq 0$.
Make sure you don't get caught out here — the brackets are in the form $(qx + p)^n$, not $(p + qx)^n$.

Q4 a) $\dfrac{12x^2 - 27x - 33}{(3x + 1)(2x - 5)} = \dfrac{12x^2 - 27x - 33}{6x^2 - 13x - 5}$

Dividing gives:

2
$6x^2 - 13x - 5\overline{)12x^2 - 27x - 33}$
$\underline{-(12x^2 - 26x - 10)}$
$ - x - 23$

i.e. $2 + \dfrac{-x - 23}{6x^2 - 13x - 5}$ or $2 + \dfrac{-x - 23}{(3x + 1)(2x - 5)}$

So $A = 2$.
Splitting the rest into partial fractions and multiplying out the denominator gives:
$-x - 23 \equiv B(2x - 5) + C(3x + 1)$

Equating coefficients:
constant terms: $-23 = C - 5B$
x terms: $-1 = 2B + 3C$
Solving simultaneously gives: $B = 4$ and $C = -3$.

Putting these values into the partial fractions:

$f(x) = 2 + \left(\dfrac{B}{(3x + 1)} + \dfrac{C}{(2x - 5)}\right)$

$= 2 + \dfrac{4}{(3x + 1)} - \dfrac{3}{(2x - 5)}$

b) $(3x + 1)^{-1} = 1 - 3x + 9x^2 + \dots$

$(2x - 5)^{-1} = -\dfrac{1}{5}\left(1 - \dfrac{2}{5}x\right)^{-1}$

$= -\dfrac{1}{5}\left(1 + \dfrac{2x}{5} + \dfrac{4x^2}{25} + \dots\right)$

$= -\dfrac{1}{5} - \dfrac{2x}{25} - \dfrac{4x^2}{125} - \dots$

$f(x) = 2 + 4(3x + 1)^{-1} - 3(2x - 5)^{-1}$

$\approx 2 + 4(1 - 3x + 9x^2) - 3\left(-\dfrac{1}{5} - \dfrac{2x}{25} - \dfrac{4x^2}{125}\right)$

$= 2 + 4 - 12x + 36x^2 + \dfrac{3}{5} + \dfrac{6x}{25} + \dfrac{12x^2}{125}$

$= \dfrac{33}{5} - \dfrac{294x}{25} + \dfrac{4512x^2}{125}$

Review Exercise — Chapter 3

Q1 a) $(1 + 2x)^3$

$= 1 + 3(2x) + \dfrac{3 \times 2}{1 \times 2}(2x)^2 + \dfrac{3 \times 2 \times 1}{1 \times 2 \times 3}(2x)^3$

$= 1 + 6x + 12x^2 + 8x^3$

b) $(1 - x)^5 = 1 + 5(-x) + \dfrac{5 \times 4}{1 \times 2}(-x)^2 + \dfrac{5 \times 4 \times 3}{1 \times 2 \times 3}(-x)^3$

$+ \dfrac{5 \times 4 \times 3 \times 2}{1 \times 2 \times 3 \times 4}(-x)^4 + \dfrac{5 \times 4 \times 3 \times 2 \times 1}{1 \times 2 \times 3 \times 4 \times 5}(-x)^5$

$= 1 - 5x + 10x^2 - 10x^3 + 5x^4 - x^5$

c) $(1 - 4x)^4 = 1 + 4(-4x) + \dfrac{4 \times 3}{1 \times 2}(-4x)^2$

$+ \dfrac{4 \times 3 \times 2}{1 \times 2 \times 3}(-4x)^3 + \dfrac{4 \times 3 \times 2 \times 1}{1 \times 2 \times 3 \times 4}(-4x)^4$

$= 1 - 16x + 96x^2 - 256x^3 + 256x^4$

Be careful with terms like $(-4x)^2$ — remember to square everything in the brackets (the x, the 4 and the minus).

Q2 Positive integer values (and zero).

Q3 a) The x^2 term for $(1 + ax)^7$ is:

$\left(\dfrac{7 \times 6}{1 \times 2}\right)(ax)^2 = 21a^2x^2$

So $21a^2 = 189 \Rightarrow a^2 = 9 \Rightarrow a = 3$.
You're told that a is a positive integer, so take the positive root.

b) The x^4 term for $(1 - ax)^6$ is:

$\left(\dfrac{6 \times 5 \times 4 \times 3}{1 \times 2 \times 3 \times 4}\right)(-ax)^4 = 15a^4x^4$

So $15a^4 = 240 \Rightarrow a^4 = 16 \Rightarrow a = 2$.
Again, you're told that a is positive, so take the positive root.

Q4 $\left|\frac{dx}{c}\right| < 1$ (or $|x| < \left|\frac{c}{d}\right|$)

Q5 a) $(1 + x)^{-5} = 1 + (-5)x + \frac{-5 \times -6}{1 \times 2}x^2$

$$+ \frac{-5 \times -6 \times -7}{1 \times 2 \times 3}x^3 + ...$$

$$= 1 - 5x + 15x^2 - 35x^3 + ...$$

b) $(1 - 3x)^{-3} = 1 + (-3)(-3x) + \frac{-3 \times -4}{1 \times 2}(-3x)^2$

$$+ \frac{-3 \times -4 \times -5}{1 \times 2 \times 3}(-3x)^3 + ...$$

$$= 1 + 9x + 54x^2 + 270x^3 + ...$$

c) $(1 - 5x)^{\frac{1}{2}} = 1 + \frac{1}{2}(-5x) + \frac{\frac{1}{2} \times -\frac{1}{2}}{1 \times 2}(-5x)^2$

$$+ \frac{\frac{1}{2} \times -\frac{1}{2} \times -\frac{3}{2}}{1 \times 2 \times 3}(-5x)^3 + ...$$

$$= 1 - \frac{5x}{2} - \frac{25x^2}{8} - \frac{125x^3}{16} + ...$$

Q6 Q5 a): expansion valid for $|x| < 1$.

Q5 b): expansion valid for $|-3x| < 1 \Rightarrow |x| < \frac{1}{3}$

Q5 c): expansion valid for $|-5x| < 1 \Rightarrow |x| < \frac{1}{5}$

Q7 a) (i) $(3 + 2x)^{-2} = \left(3\left(1 + \frac{2}{3}x\right)\right)^{-2} = \frac{1}{9}\left(1 + \frac{2}{3}x\right)^{-2}$

$$\approx \frac{1}{9}\left(1 + (-2)\left(\frac{2}{3}x\right) + \frac{-2 \times -3}{1 \times 2}\left(\frac{2}{3}x\right)^2\right)$$

$$= \frac{1}{9}\left(1 - \frac{4}{3}x + \frac{4}{3}x^2\right)$$

$$= \frac{1}{9} - \frac{4}{27}x + \frac{4}{27}x^2$$

This expansion is valid for $\left|\frac{2x}{3}\right| < 1 \Rightarrow |x| < \frac{3}{2}$.

(ii) $(8 - x)^{\frac{1}{3}} = \left(8\left(1 - \frac{1}{8}x\right)\right)^{\frac{1}{3}} = 2\left(1 - \frac{1}{8}x\right)^{\frac{1}{3}}$

$$\approx 2\left(1 + \frac{1}{3}\left(-\frac{1}{8}x\right) + \frac{\frac{1}{3} \times -\frac{2}{3}}{1 \times 2}\left(-\frac{1}{8}x\right)^2\right)$$

$$= 2\left(1 - \frac{1}{24}x - \frac{1}{576}x^2\right)$$

$$= 2 - \frac{1}{12}x - \frac{1}{288}x^2$$

This expansion is valid for $\left|\frac{-x}{8}\right| < 1 \Rightarrow |x| < 8$.

b) $\frac{\sqrt[3]{8 - x}}{(3 + 2x)^2} = (8 - x)^{\frac{1}{3}}(3 + 2x)^{-2}$

$$\approx \left(2 - \frac{1}{12}x - \frac{1}{288}x^2\right)\left(\frac{1}{9} - \frac{4}{27}x + \frac{4}{27}x^2\right)$$

$$= 2\left(\frac{1}{9} - \frac{4}{27}x + \frac{4}{27}x^2\right) - $$

$$\frac{1}{12}x\left(\frac{1}{9} - \frac{4}{27}x\right) - \frac{1}{288}x^2\left(\frac{1}{9}\right)$$

$$= \frac{2}{9} - \frac{8x}{27} + \frac{8x^2}{27} - \frac{x}{108} + \frac{x^2}{81} - \frac{x^2}{2592}$$

$$= \frac{2}{9} - \frac{11x}{36} + \frac{799x^2}{2592}$$

The combined expansion is valid for the smaller of the individual valid ranges, i.e. $|x| < \frac{3}{2}$.

c) (i) $\sqrt[3]{8 - x} \approx 2 - \frac{1}{12}x - \frac{1}{288}x^2$

To find an approximation to $\sqrt[3]{7}$ use $x = 1$.

The validity for this expansion is $|x| < 8$ so you're fine to use $x = 1$.

$$\sqrt[3]{7} \approx 2 - \frac{1}{12} - \frac{1}{288} = \frac{551}{288}$$

(ii) The % error is:

$$\left|\frac{\sqrt[3]{7} - \frac{551}{288}}{\sqrt[3]{7}}\right| \times 100 = 0.014\% \text{ (to 2 s.f.)}$$

Q8 a) Write as an identity:

$$\frac{5 - 10x}{(1 + 2x)(2 - x)} \equiv \frac{A}{(1 + 2x)} + \frac{B}{(2 - x)}$$

So $5 - 10x \equiv A(2 - x) + B(1 + 2x)$

Let $x = 2$, then $5 - 20 = 5B \Rightarrow B = -3$

Let $x = -0.5$, then $5 + 5 = 2.5A \Rightarrow A = 4$

So $\frac{5 - 10x}{(1 + 2x)(2 - x)} \equiv \frac{4}{(1 + 2x)} - \frac{3}{(2 - x)}$

b) $(1 + 2x)^{-1} \approx 1 - 2x + 4x^2$

$(2 - x)^{-1} = 2^{-1}\left(1 - \frac{1}{2}x\right)^{-1} = \frac{1}{2}\left(1 - \frac{1}{2}x\right)^{-1}$

$$\approx \frac{1}{2}\left(1 + \frac{1}{2}x + \frac{1}{4}x^2\right)$$

$$= \frac{1}{2} + \frac{x}{4} + \frac{x^2}{8}$$

Using the result from a), this means that:

$$\frac{5 - 10x}{(1 + 2x)(2 - x)} \approx 4(1 - 2x + 4x^2) - 3\left(\frac{1}{2} + \frac{x}{4} + \frac{x^2}{8}\right)$$

$$\approx 4 - 8x + 16x^2 - \frac{3}{2} - \frac{3x}{4} - \frac{3x^2}{8}$$

$$\approx \frac{5}{2} - \frac{35x}{4} + \frac{125x^2}{8}$$

c) First, check that $x = 0.1$ is valid for the expansion.

$(1 + 2x)^{-1}$ is valid when $|x| < \frac{1}{2}$.

$(2 - x)^{-1}$ is valid when $|x| < 2$.

$x = 0.1$ is within both of these ranges so it is valid for the combined expansion.

Putting $x = 0.1$ into both sides of the expansion gives:

$$\frac{5 - 10(0.1)}{(1 + 2(0.1))(2 - (0.1))} \approx \frac{5}{2} - \frac{35(0.1)}{4} + \frac{125(0.01)}{8}$$

$$\frac{5 - 1}{(1 + 0.2)(2 - 0.1)} \approx \frac{5}{2} - \frac{3.5}{4} + \frac{1.25}{8}$$

$$\frac{4}{1.2 \times 1.9} \approx 2.5 - 0.875 + 0.15625$$

$$\approx 1.78125$$

So the % error when using this approximation is:

$$\left|\frac{\left(\frac{4}{1.2 \times 1.9}\right) - 1.78125}{\left(\frac{4}{1.2 \times 1.9}\right)}\right| \times 100 = 1.5\% \text{ (to 2 s.f.)}$$

Exam-Style Questions — Chapter 3

Q1 a) $f(x) = (9 - 4x)^{-\frac{1}{2}} = (9)^{-\frac{1}{2}}\left(1 - \frac{4}{9}x\right)^{-\frac{1}{2}} = \frac{1}{3}\left(1 - \frac{4}{9}x\right)^{-\frac{1}{2}}$

$$\left(1 - \frac{4}{9}x\right)^{-\frac{1}{2}} = 1 + \left(-\frac{1}{2}\right)\left(-\frac{4}{9}x\right)$$

$$+ \left(\frac{-\frac{1}{2} \times -\frac{3}{2}}{1 \times 2}\right)\left(-\frac{4}{9}x\right)^2$$

$$+ \left(\frac{-\frac{1}{2} \times -\frac{3}{2} \times -\frac{5}{2}}{1 \times 2 \times 3}\right)\left(-\frac{4}{9}x\right)^3 + ...$$

$$= 1 + \frac{2x}{9} + \left(\frac{3}{8}\right)\left(\frac{16}{81}x^2\right)$$

$$+ \left(-\frac{5}{16}\right)\left(-\frac{64}{729}x^3\right) + ...$$

$$= 1 + \frac{2x}{9} + \frac{2x^2}{27} + \frac{20x^3}{729} + \ldots$$

So $f(x) = \frac{1}{3}\left(1 - \frac{4}{9}x\right)^{-\frac{1}{2}}$

$$= \frac{1}{3}\left(1 + \frac{2x}{9} + \frac{2x^2}{27} + \frac{20x^3}{729} + \ldots\right)$$

$$= \frac{1}{3} + \frac{2x}{27} + \frac{2x^2}{81} + \frac{20x^3}{2187} + \ldots$$

[5 marks available in total:
- *1 mark for factorising out $(9)^{-\frac{1}{2}}$ or $\frac{1}{3}$*
- *1 mark for expansion of an expression of the form $(1 + ax)^{-\frac{1}{2}}$*
- *2 marks for the penultimate line of working —*
  1 for the first two terms in brackets correct,
  1 for the 3rd and 4th terms in brackets correct.
- *1 mark for the final answer correct]*

Multiplying out those coefficients can be pretty tricky.
Don't try to do things all in one go — you won't be
penalised for writing an extra line of working, but you
probably will lose marks if your final answer's wrong.

b) $\frac{2 - x}{\sqrt{(9 - 4x)}} = (2 - x)\left(\frac{1}{3} + \frac{2x}{27} + \frac{2x^2}{81} + \frac{20x^3}{2187} + \ldots\right)$

You only need the first three terms of the expansion, so just write the terms up to x^2 when you multiply out the brackets:

$$\frac{2 - x}{\sqrt{(9 - 4x)}} \approx 2\left(\frac{1}{3} + \frac{2x}{27} + \frac{2x^2}{81}\right) - x\left(\frac{1}{3} + \frac{2x}{27}\right)$$

$$= \frac{2}{3} + \frac{4x}{27} + \frac{4x^2}{81} - \frac{x}{3} - \frac{2x^2}{27}$$

$$= \frac{2}{3} - \frac{5x}{27} - \frac{2x^2}{81}$$

[4 marks available in total:
- *1 mark for multiplying your answer to part (a) by (2 – x)*
- *1 mark for multiplying out brackets to find constant term, two x-terms and two x^2-terms*
- *1 mark for correct constant and x-terms in final answer*
- *1 mark for correct x^2-term in final answer]*

Q2 a) $36x^2 + 3x - 10 \equiv$

$A(1 - 3x)^2 + B(4 + 3x)(1 - 3x) + C(4 + 3x)$ *[1 mark]*

Let $x = \frac{1}{3}$, then:

$4 + 1 - 10 = 5C \Rightarrow -5 = 5C \Rightarrow C = -1$ *[1 mark]*

Let $x = -\frac{4}{3}$, then:

$64 - 4 - 10 = 25A \Rightarrow 50 = 25A \Rightarrow A = 2$ *[1 mark]*

Equating the coefficients of the x^2 terms:
$36 = 9A - 9B = 18 - 9B \Rightarrow -18 = 9B \Rightarrow B = -2$
[1 mark]

b) $f(x) = \frac{2}{(4 + 3x)} - \frac{2}{(1 - 3x)} - \frac{1}{(1 - 3x)^2}$

$$= 2(4 + 3x)^{-1} - 2(1 - 3x)^{-1} - (1 - 3x)^{-2}$$

Expand each bracket separately:

$$(4 + 3x)^{-1} = 4^{-1}\left(1 + \frac{3}{4}x\right)^{-1} = \frac{1}{4}\left(1 + \frac{3}{4}x\right)^{-1}$$

$$= \frac{1}{4}\left(1 + (-1)\left(\frac{3}{4}x\right) + \frac{-1 \times -2}{1 \times 2}\left(\frac{3}{4}x\right)^2 + \ldots\right)$$

$$= \frac{1}{4}\left(1 - \frac{3}{4}x + \frac{9}{16}x^2 + \ldots\right) = \frac{1}{4} - \frac{3x}{16} + \frac{9x^2}{64} + \ldots$$

$$(1 - 3x)^{-1} = 1 + (-1)(-3x) + \frac{-1 \times -2}{1 \times 2}(-3x)^2 + \ldots$$

$$= 1 + 3x + 9x^2 + \ldots$$

$$(1 - 3x)^{-2} = 1 + (-2)(-3x) + \frac{-2 \times -3}{1 \times 2}(-3x)^2 + \ldots$$

$$= 1 + 6x + 27x^2 + \ldots$$

Putting it all together gives:

$$f(x) \approx 2\left(\frac{1}{4} - \frac{3x}{16} + \frac{9x^2}{64}\right) - 2(1 + 3x + 9x^2)$$
$$- (1 + 6x + 27x^2)$$

$$f(x) \approx \frac{1}{2} - \frac{3x}{8} + \frac{9x^2}{32} - 2 - 6x - 18x^2 - 1 - 6x - 27x^2$$

$$= -\frac{5}{2} - \frac{99x}{8} - \frac{1431x^2}{32}$$

[6 marks available in total:
- *1 mark for rewriting f(x) in the form $A(4 + 3x)^{-1} + B(1 - 3x)^{-1} + C(1 - 3x)^{-2}$*
- *1 mark for correct expansion of $(4 + 3x)^{-1}$*
- *1 mark for correct expansion of $(1 - 3x)^{-1}$*
- *1 mark for correct expansion of $(1 - 3x)^{-2}$*
- *1 mark for correct constant and x-terms in final answer*
- *1 mark for correct x^2-term in final answer]*

c) Expansion of $(4 + 3x)^{-1}$ is valid for

$$\left|\frac{3x}{4}\right| < 1 \Rightarrow \frac{3|x|}{4} < 1 \Rightarrow |x| < \frac{4}{3}$$

Expansions of $(1 - 3x)^{-1}$ and $(1 - 3x)^{-2}$ are valid for

$$\left|\frac{-3x}{1}\right| < 1 \Rightarrow \frac{|-3\|x|}{1} < 1 \Rightarrow |x| < \frac{1}{3}$$

The combined expansion is valid for the narrower of these two ranges.

So the expansion of $f(x)$ is valid for $|x| < \frac{1}{3}$.

[2 marks available in total:
- *1 mark for identifying the valid range of the expansion of f(x) as being the narrower of the two valid ranges shown*
- *1 mark for correct answer]*

Q3 a) $(16 + 3x)^{\frac{1}{4}} = 16^{\frac{1}{4}}\left(1 + \frac{3}{16}x\right)^{\frac{1}{4}} = 2\left(1 + \frac{3}{16}x\right)^{\frac{1}{4}}$

$$\approx 2\left[1 + \left(\frac{1}{4}\right)\left(\frac{3}{16}x\right) + \frac{\frac{1}{4} \times -\frac{3}{4}}{1 \times 2}\left(\frac{3}{16}x\right)^2\right]$$

$$= 2\left[1 + \left(\frac{1}{4}\right)\left(\frac{3}{16}x\right) + \left(-\frac{3}{32}\right)\left(\frac{9}{256}x^2\right)\right]$$

$$= 2\left(1 + \frac{3x}{64} - \frac{27x^2}{8192}\right)$$

$$= 2 + \frac{3x}{32} - \frac{27x^2}{4096}$$

[5 marks available in total:
- *1 mark for factorising out $16^{\frac{1}{4}}$ or 2*
- *1 mark for expansion of an expression of the form $(1 + ax)^{\frac{1}{4}}$*
- *2 marks for the penultimate line of working —*
  1 for the first two terms in brackets correct,
  1 for the 3rd term in brackets correct.
- *1 mark for the final answer correct]*

b) (i) $16 + 3x = 12.4 \Rightarrow x = -1.2$

This lies within $|x| < \frac{16}{3}$, so it's a valid approximation.

So $(12.4)^{\frac{1}{4}} \approx 2 + \frac{3}{32}(-1.2) - \frac{27}{4096}(-1.2)^2$

$= 2 - 0.1125 - 0.0094921875$

$= 1.878008$ (to 6 d.p.)

[2 marks available in total:
- *1 mark for substituting $x = -1.2$ into the expansion from part (a)*
- *1 mark for correct answer]*

(ii) Percentage error

$= \left| \dfrac{\text{real value} - \text{estimate}}{\text{real value}} \right| \times 100$

$= \left| \dfrac{\sqrt[4]{12.4} - 1.878008}{\sqrt[4]{12.4}} \right| \times 100$ *[1 mark]*

$= \dfrac{|1.876529... - 1.878008|}{1.876529...} \times 100$

$= 0.0788\%$ (to 3 s.f.) *[1 mark]*

Q4 a) $\left(1 - \frac{4}{3}x\right)^{-\frac{1}{2}}$

$\approx 1 + \left(-\frac{1}{2}\right)\left(-\frac{4}{3}x\right) + \dfrac{-\frac{1}{2} \times -\frac{3}{2}}{1 \times 2}\left(-\frac{4}{3}x\right)^2$

$\qquad + \dfrac{-\frac{1}{2} \times -\frac{3}{2} \times -\frac{5}{2}}{1 \times 2 \times 3}\left(-\frac{4}{3}x\right)^3$

$= 1 + \frac{2x}{3} + \frac{3}{8}\left(\frac{16}{9}x^2\right) + \left(-\frac{15}{48}\right)\left(-\frac{64}{27}x^3\right)$

$= 1 + \frac{2x}{3} + \frac{2x^2}{3} + \frac{20x^3}{27}$

[4 marks available in total:
- *1 mark for writing out binomial expansion formula with $n = -\frac{1}{2}$*
- *1 mark for writing out binomial expansion formula substituting $-\frac{4}{3}x$ for x*
- *1 mark for correct constant and x-terms in final answer*
- *1 mark for correct x^2- and x^3-terms in final answer]*

b) $\sqrt{\dfrac{27}{(3 - 4x)}} = \sqrt{\dfrac{27}{3\left(1 - \frac{4}{3}x\right)}} = \sqrt{\dfrac{9}{\left(1 - \frac{4}{3}x\right)}}$

$= \dfrac{3}{\sqrt{\left(1 - \frac{4}{3}x\right)}}$

$= 3\left(1 - \frac{4}{3}x\right)^{-\frac{1}{2}}$

$\approx 3\left(1 + \frac{2}{3}x + \frac{2}{3}x^2\right)$

$= 3 + 2x + 2x^2$

So $a = 3$, $b = 2$, $c = 2$.

Expansion is valid for:

$\left|-\frac{4}{3}x\right| < 1 \Rightarrow \left|-\frac{4}{3}\right||x| < 1 \Rightarrow |x| < \frac{3}{4}$

[3 marks available in total:
- *1 mark for showing expression is equal to $3\left(1 - \frac{4}{3}x\right)^{-\frac{1}{2}}$*

- *1 mark for using expansion from part (b) to find the correct values of a, b and c.*
- *1 mark for correct valid range]*

Q5 a) (i) $\sqrt{\dfrac{1 + 2x}{1 - 3x}} = \dfrac{\sqrt{1 + 2x}}{\sqrt{1 - 3x}}$

$= (1 + 2x)^{\frac{1}{2}}(1 - 3x)^{-\frac{1}{2}}$ *[1 mark]*

$(1 + 2x)^{\frac{1}{2}} \approx 1 + \frac{1}{2}(2x) + \dfrac{\frac{1}{2} \times -\frac{1}{2}}{1 \times 2}(2x)^2$

$= 1 + x - \frac{x^2}{2}$ *[1 mark]*

$(1 - 3x)^{-\frac{1}{2}}$

$\approx 1 + \left(-\frac{1}{2}\right)(-3x) + \dfrac{-\frac{1}{2} \times -\frac{3}{2}}{1 \times 2}(-3x)^2$

$= 1 + \frac{3x}{2} + \frac{27x^2}{8}$ *[1 mark]*

$\sqrt{\dfrac{1 + 2x}{1 - 3x}} \approx \left(1 + x - \frac{x^2}{2}\right)\left(1 + \frac{3x}{2} + \frac{27x^2}{8}\right)$
[1 mark]

$\approx 1 + \frac{3x}{2} + \frac{27x^2}{8} + x + \frac{3x^2}{2} - \frac{x^2}{2}$

(ignoring any terms in x^3 or above)

$= 1 + \frac{5x}{2} + \frac{35x^2}{8}$ *[1 mark]*

(ii) Expansion of $(1 + 2x)^{\frac{1}{2}}$ is valid for:

$|2x| < 1 \Rightarrow |x| < \frac{1}{2}$.

Expansion of $(1 - 3x)^{-\frac{1}{2}}$ is valid for:

$|-3x| < 1 \Rightarrow |-3||x| < 1 \Rightarrow |x| < \frac{1}{3}$.

The combined expansion is valid for the narrower of these two ranges.

So the expansion of $\sqrt{\dfrac{1 + 2x}{1 - 3x}}$ is valid for:

$|x| < \frac{1}{3}$.

[2 marks available in total:
- *1 mark for identifying the valid range of the expansion as being the narrower of the two valid ranges shown*
- *1 mark for correct answer]*

b) $x = \frac{2}{15} \Rightarrow$

$\sqrt{\dfrac{1 + 2x}{1 - 3x}} = \sqrt{\dfrac{1 + \frac{4}{15}}{1 - \frac{6}{15}}}$

$= \sqrt{\dfrac{\left(\frac{19}{15}\right)}{\left(\frac{9}{15}\right)}} = \sqrt{\dfrac{19}{9}} = \frac{1}{3}\sqrt{19}$ *[1 mark]*

$\sqrt{19} \approx 3\left(1 + \frac{5}{2}\left(\frac{2}{15}\right) + \frac{35}{8}\left(\frac{2}{15}\right)^2\right)$

$= 3\left(1 + \frac{1}{3} + \frac{7}{90}\right)$

$= 3\left(\frac{127}{90}\right)$

$= \frac{127}{30}$ *[1 mark]*

Q6 a) $13x - 17 \equiv A(2x - 1) + B(5 - 3x)$ *[1 mark]*

Let $x = \frac{1}{2}$, then:

$\frac{13}{2} - 17 = B\left(5 - \frac{3}{2}\right) \Rightarrow -\frac{21}{2} = \frac{7}{2}B \Rightarrow B = -3$
[1 mark]

Let $x = \frac{5}{3}$, then:

$\frac{65}{3} - 17 = A\left(\frac{10}{3} - 1\right) \Rightarrow \frac{14}{3} = \frac{7}{3}A \Rightarrow A = 2$
[1 mark]

b) (i) $(2x - 1)^{-1} = -(1 - 2x)^{-1}$ *[1 mark]*

$\approx -\left(1 + (-1)(-2x) + \frac{-1 \times -2}{1 \times 2}(-2x)^2\right)$

$= -(1 + 2x + 4x^2)$

$= -1 - 2x - 4x^2$ *[1 mark]*

(ii) $(5 - 3x)^{-1} = 5^{-1}\left(1 - \frac{3}{5}x\right)^{-1} = \frac{1}{5}\left(1 - \frac{3}{5}x\right)^{-1}$

$\approx \frac{1}{5}\left(1 + (-1)\left(-\frac{3}{5}x\right) + \frac{-1 \times -2}{1 \times 2}\left(-\frac{3}{5}x\right)^2\right)$

$= \frac{1}{5}\left(1 + \frac{3}{5}x + \frac{9}{25}x^2\right)$

$= \frac{1}{5} + \frac{3x}{25} + \frac{9x^2}{125}$

[5 marks available in total:
- *1 mark for factorising out 5^{-1} or $\frac{1}{5}$*
- *1 mark for expansion of an expression of the form $(1 + ax)^{-1}$*
- *2 marks for the penultimate line of working — 1 mark for the first two terms in brackets correct, 1 mark for the 3rd term in brackets correct.*
- *1 mark for the final answer correct]*

c) $\frac{13x - 17}{(5 - 3x)(2x - 1)} = \frac{2}{(5 - 3x)} - \frac{3}{(2x - 1)}$

$= 2(5 - 3x)^{-1} - 3(2x - 1)^{-1}$ *[1 mark]*

$\approx 2\left(\frac{1}{5} + \frac{3}{25}x + \frac{9}{125}x^2\right) - 3(-1 - 2x - 4x^2)$

$= \frac{2}{5} + \frac{6x}{25} + \frac{18x^2}{125} + 3 + 6x + 12x^2$

$= \frac{17}{5} + \frac{156x}{25} + \frac{1518x^2}{125}$ *[1 mark]*

Chapter 4: Differentiation

1. Differentiation with Parametric Equations
Exercise 1.1 — Differentiating parametric equations

Q1 a) $\frac{dx}{dt} = 2t$, $\frac{dy}{dt} = 3t^2 - 1$.

Using the chain rule, $\frac{dy}{dx} = \frac{dy}{dt} \div \frac{dx}{dt}$

so $\frac{dy}{dx} = \frac{3t^2 - 1}{2t}$

b) $\frac{dx}{dt} = 3t^2 + 1$, $\frac{dy}{dt} = 4t$, so $\frac{dy}{dx} = \frac{4t}{3t^2 + 1}$

c) $\frac{dx}{dt} = 4t^3$, $\frac{dy}{dt} = 3t^2 - 2t$,

so $\frac{dy}{dx} = \frac{3t^2 - 2t}{4t^3} = \frac{3t - 2}{4t^2}$

d) $\frac{dx}{dt} = -\sin t$, $\frac{dy}{dt} = 4 - 2t$, so $\frac{dy}{dx} = \frac{2t - 4}{\sin t}$

Q2 a) $\frac{dx}{dt} = 2t$, $\frac{dy}{dt} = 2e^{2t}$, so $\frac{dy}{dx} = \frac{e^{2t}}{t}$

b) When $t = 1$, $\frac{dy}{dx} = e^2$.

Q3 a) $\frac{dy}{dt} = 12t^2 - 4t$, $\frac{dx}{dt} = 3e^{3t}$, so $\frac{dy}{dx} = \frac{12t^2 - 4t}{3e^{3t}}$

b) When $t = 0$, $\frac{dy}{dx} = 0$.

Q4 a) $\frac{dx}{dt} = 3t^2$, $\frac{dy}{dt} = 2t \cos t - t^2 \sin t$,

so $\frac{dy}{dx} = \frac{2t \cos t - t^2 \sin t}{3t^2} = \frac{2 \cos t - t \sin t}{3t}$

b) When $t = \pi$, $\frac{dy}{dx} = -\frac{2}{3\pi}$.

Q5 a) $\frac{dx}{dt} = 2t \sin t + t^2 \cos t$,

$\frac{dy}{dt} = t^3 \cos t + 3t^2 \sin t - \sin t$,

so $\frac{dy}{dx} = \frac{t^3 \cos t + (3t^2 - 1)\sin t}{2t \sin t + t^2 \cos t}$

b) When $t = \pi$, $\frac{dy}{dx} = \pi$.

Q6 a) $\frac{dx}{dt} = \frac{1}{t}$, $\frac{dy}{dt} = 6t - 3t^2$, so $\frac{dy}{dx} = 6t^2 - 3t^3$

b) When $t = -1$, $\frac{dy}{dx} = 9$.

c) At the turning points $6t^2 - 3t^3 = 3t^2(2 - t) = 0$, so the turning points occur at $t = 0$ and $t = 2$.
At $t = 0$, x is not defined.
At $t = 2$, the coordinates are $(\ln 2, 4)$.

Exercise 1.2 — Finding tangents and normals

Q1 $\frac{dx}{dt} = 2t$, $\frac{dy}{dt} = 3t^2 - 6$.

Using the chain rule, $\frac{dy}{dx} = \frac{dy}{dt} \div \frac{dx}{dt}$,

so $\frac{dy}{dx} = \frac{3t^2 - 6}{2t}$.

When $t = 3$:

$\frac{dy}{dx} = \frac{21}{6} = \frac{7}{2}$, $x = 3^2 = 9$ and $y = 3^3 - 6(3) = 9$.

Putting this into $y = mx + c$ gives:

$9 = \frac{7}{2}(9) + c \Rightarrow c = -\frac{45}{2}$

So the equation of the tangent is:

$y = \frac{7}{2}x - \frac{45}{2} \Rightarrow 7x - 2y - 45 = 0$.

Q2 $\frac{dy}{dx} = \frac{3t^2 - 2t + 5}{3t^2 - 4t}$

When $t = -1$:

$\frac{dy}{dx} = \frac{10}{7}$, $x = -3$ and $y = -7$.

Putting this into $y = mx + c$ gives:

$-7 = \frac{10}{7}(-3) + c \Rightarrow c = -\frac{19}{7}$

So the equation of the tangent is $10x - 7y - 19 = 0$.

Q3 $\dfrac{dy}{dx} = \dfrac{3\cos t - t\sin t}{2\cos 2t}$

When $t = \pi$:

$\dfrac{dy}{dx} = -\dfrac{3}{2}$, $x = 0$ and $y = -\pi$.

The gradient of the normal is $\dfrac{2}{3}$.

Putting this into $y = mx + c$ gives:

$-\pi = \dfrac{2}{3}(0) + c \Rightarrow c = -\pi$

So the equation of the normal is $y = \dfrac{2}{3}x - \pi$.

Q4 $\dfrac{dy}{dx} = \dfrac{3t^2 - 2t}{1 + \ln t}$

When $t = 1$:

$\dfrac{dy}{dx} = \dfrac{3 - 2}{1 + 0} = 1$, $x = 0$ and $y = 3$.

Putting this into $y = mx + c$ gives:

$3 = 0 + c \Rightarrow c = 3$

So the equation of the tangent is: $y = x + 3$

Q5 $\dfrac{dy}{dx} = \dfrac{2\theta + \cos\theta - \theta\sin\theta}{\sin 2\theta + 2\theta\cos 2\theta}$

When $\theta = \dfrac{\pi}{2}$:

$\dfrac{dy}{dx} = -\dfrac{1}{2}$, $x = 0$ and $y = \dfrac{\pi^2}{4}$.

The gradient of the normal is 2.

Putting this into $y = mx + c$ gives:

$\dfrac{\pi^2}{4} = 2(0) + c \Rightarrow c = \dfrac{\pi^2}{4}$

So the equation of the normal is $y = 2x + \dfrac{\pi^2}{4}$.

Q6 **a)** $\dfrac{dy}{dx} = \dfrac{3 - 3t^2}{2t - 1}$

When $t = 2$:

$\dfrac{dy}{dx} = -3$, $x = 2$ and $y = -2$.

Putting this into $y = mx + c$ gives:

$-2 = -3(2) + c \Rightarrow c = 4$

So the equation of the tangent is $y = 4 - 3x$.

b) The gradient of the normal at $t = 2$ is $\dfrac{1}{3}$.

Putting this into $y = mx + c$ gives:

$-2 = \dfrac{1}{3}(2) + c \Rightarrow c = -\dfrac{8}{3}$

So the equation of the normal is $3y = x - 8$.

This crosses the x-axis at $y = 0$, so

$0 = x - 8 \Rightarrow x = 8$

and so the coordinates are $(8, 0)$.

Q7 **a)** $\dfrac{dy}{dx} = \dfrac{\theta\cos\theta + \sin\theta}{2\cos 2\theta - 2\sin\theta}$

b) When $\theta = \dfrac{\pi}{2}$: $\dfrac{dy}{dx} = -\dfrac{1}{4}$, $x = 0$ and $y = \dfrac{\pi}{2}$.

Putting this into $y = mx + c$ gives:

$\dfrac{\pi}{2} = -\dfrac{1}{4}(0) + c \Rightarrow c = \dfrac{\pi}{2}$

So the equation of the tangent is $y = \dfrac{\pi}{2} - \dfrac{1}{4}x$.

The gradient of the normal is 4. The normal also goes through the point $\left(0, \dfrac{\pi}{2}\right)$, so again $c = \dfrac{\pi}{2}$.

So the equation of the normal is $y = 4x + \dfrac{\pi}{2}$.

Q8 **a)** The path cuts the y-axis when $x = 0$, so $s^3 \ln s = 0$.

Since $\ln 0$ is undefined, $s = 0$ cannot be a solution, so the only solution is $s = 1$ (i.e. when $\ln s = 0$).

b) $\dfrac{dy}{dx} = \dfrac{3s^2 - s - 2s\ln s}{s^2 + 3s^2\ln s} = \dfrac{3s - 1 - 2\ln s}{s + 3s\ln s}$.

From a), when $x = 0$, $s = 1$.

When $s = 1$: $\dfrac{dy}{dx} = 2$, $x = 0$ and $y = 1$.

Putting this into $y = mx + c$ gives:

$1 = 2(0) + c \Rightarrow c = 1$.

So the equation of the tangent is $y = 2x + 1$.

Q9 **a)** $\dfrac{dy}{d\theta} = \dfrac{-\theta^3\sin\theta - 3\theta^2\cos\theta}{\theta^6} = \dfrac{-\theta\sin\theta - 3\cos\theta}{\theta^4}$

$\dfrac{dx}{d\theta} = \theta^2\cos\theta + 2\theta\sin\theta$

hence $\dfrac{dy}{dx} = \dfrac{-\theta\sin\theta - 3\cos\theta}{\theta^6\cos\theta + 2\theta^5\sin\theta}$

This looks a bit complicated but leave it as it is — you'll find the cos and sin terms usually disappear when you substitute.

When $\theta = \pi$, $\dfrac{dy}{dx} = \dfrac{-\pi(0) - 3(-1)}{\pi^6(-1) + 2\pi^5(0)} = -\dfrac{3}{\pi^6}$.

b) The gradient of the normal when $\theta = \pi$ is $\dfrac{\pi^6}{3}$, and $y = -\dfrac{1}{\pi^3}$, $x = 0$.

Putting this into $y = mx + c$ gives:

$-\dfrac{1}{\pi^3} = \dfrac{\pi^6}{3}(0) + c \Rightarrow c = -\dfrac{1}{\pi^3}$

So the equation of the normal is $y = \dfrac{\pi^6}{3}x - \dfrac{1}{\pi^3}$.

2. Implicit Differentiation
Exercise 2.1 — Implicit differentiation

Q1 **a)** $\dfrac{d}{dx}(y) + \dfrac{d}{dx}(y^3) = \dfrac{d}{dx}(x^2) + \dfrac{d}{dx}(4)$

$\dfrac{dy}{dx} + 3y^2\dfrac{dy}{dx} = 2x + 0$

$(1 + 3y^2)\dfrac{dy}{dx} = 2x$

$\dfrac{dy}{dx} = \dfrac{2x}{1 + 3y^2}$

b) $2x + 2y\dfrac{dy}{dx} = 2 + 2\dfrac{dy}{dx}$

$(2y - 2)\dfrac{dy}{dx} = 2 - 2x$

$\dfrac{dy}{dx} = \dfrac{2 - 2x}{2y - 2} = \dfrac{1 - x}{y - 1}$

c) $9x^2 - 4\dfrac{dy}{dx} = 2y\dfrac{dy}{dx} + 1$

$9x^2 - 1 = (2y + 4)\dfrac{dy}{dx}$

$\dfrac{dy}{dx} = \dfrac{9x^2 - 1}{2y + 4}$

d) $5 - 2y\dfrac{dy}{dx} = 5x^4 - 6\dfrac{dy}{dx}$

$5 - 5x^4 = (2y - 6)\dfrac{dy}{dx}$

$\dfrac{dy}{dx} = \dfrac{5 - 5x^4}{2y - 6}$

e) $-\sin x + \cos y \dfrac{dy}{dx} = 2x + 3y^2 \dfrac{dy}{dx}$

$(\cos y - 3y^2)\dfrac{dy}{dx} = 2x + \sin x$

$\dfrac{dy}{dx} = \dfrac{2x + \sin x}{\cos y - 3y^2}$

f) $3x^2y^2 + 2x^3y\dfrac{dy}{dx} - \sin x = 4y + 4x\dfrac{dy}{dx}$

$(2x^3y - 4x)\dfrac{dy}{dx} = 4y - 3x^2y^2 + \sin x$

$\dfrac{dy}{dx} = \dfrac{4y - 3x^2y^2 + \sin x}{2x^3y - 4x}$

g) $e^x + e^y\dfrac{dy}{dx} = 3x^2 - \dfrac{dy}{dx}$

$(e^y + 1)\dfrac{dy}{dx} = 3x^2 - e^x$

$\dfrac{dy}{dx} = \dfrac{3x^2 - e^x}{e^y + 1}$

h) $3y^2 + 6xy\dfrac{dy}{dx} + 4xy + 2x^2\dfrac{dy}{dx} = 3x^2 + 4$

$(6xy + 2x^2)\dfrac{dy}{dx} = 3x^2 + 4 - 3y^2 - 4xy$

$\dfrac{dy}{dx} = \dfrac{3x^2 + 4 - 3y^2 - 4xy}{6xy + 2x^2}$

Q2 a) $3x^2 + 2y + 2x\dfrac{dy}{dx} = 4y^3\dfrac{dy}{dx}$

$(4y^3 - 2x)\dfrac{dy}{dx} = 3x^2 + 2y$

$\dfrac{dy}{dx} = \dfrac{3x^2 + 2y}{4y^3 - 2x}$

b) $2xy + x^2\dfrac{dy}{dx} + 2y\dfrac{dy}{dx} = 3x^2$

$(x^2 + 2y)\dfrac{dy}{dx} = 3x^2 - 2xy$

$\dfrac{dy}{dx} = \dfrac{3x^2 - 2xy}{x^2 + 2y}$

c) $y^3 + 3xy^2\dfrac{dy}{dx} + \dfrac{dy}{dx} = \cos x$

$(3xy^2 + 1)\dfrac{dy}{dx} = \cos x - y^3$

$\dfrac{dy}{dx} = \dfrac{\cos x - y^3}{3xy^2 + 1}$

d) $-y\sin x + \cos x\dfrac{dy}{dx} + \sin y + x\cos y\dfrac{dy}{dx} = y + x\dfrac{dy}{dx}$

$(\cos x + x\cos y - x)\dfrac{dy}{dx} = y + y\sin x - \sin y$

$\dfrac{dy}{dx} = \dfrac{y + y\sin x - \sin y}{\cos x + x\cos y - x}$

e) $e^x + e^y\dfrac{dy}{dx} = y + x\dfrac{dy}{dx}$

$(e^y - x)\dfrac{dy}{dx} = y - e^x$

$\dfrac{dy}{dx} = \dfrac{y - e^x}{e^y - x}$

f) $\dfrac{1}{x} + 2x = 3y^2\dfrac{dy}{dx} + \dfrac{dy}{dx}$

$(3y^2 + 1)\dfrac{dy}{dx} = \dfrac{1}{x} + 2x$

$\dfrac{dy}{dx} = \dfrac{\frac{1}{x} + 2x}{3y^2 + 1} = \dfrac{1 + 2x^2}{3xy^2 + x}$

g) $2e^{2x} + 3e^{3y}\dfrac{dy}{dx} = 6xy^2 + 6x^2y\dfrac{dy}{dx}$

$(3e^{3y} - 6x^2y)\dfrac{dy}{dx} = 6xy^2 - 2e^{2x}$

$\dfrac{dy}{dx} = \dfrac{6xy^2 - 2e^{2x}}{3e^{3y} - 6x^2y}$

h) $\ln x + 1 + \dfrac{y}{x} + \ln x\dfrac{dy}{dx} = 5x^4 + 3y^2\dfrac{dy}{dx}$

$(\ln x - 3y^2)\dfrac{dy}{dx} = 5x^4 - \ln x - 1 - \dfrac{y}{x}$

$\dfrac{dy}{dx} = \dfrac{5x^4 - \ln x - 1 - \frac{y}{x}}{\ln x - 3y^2} = \dfrac{5x^5 - x\ln x - x - y}{x\ln x - 3xy^2}$

Q3 a) At $(0, 1)$: LHS: $e^0 + 2\ln 1 = 1$
RHS: $1^3 = 1$
So $(0, 1)$ is a point on the curve.

b) $e^x + \dfrac{2}{y}\dfrac{dy}{dx} = 3y^2\dfrac{dy}{dx}$

$\dfrac{dy}{dx} = \dfrac{e^x}{3y^2 - \frac{2}{y}} = \dfrac{ye^x}{3y^3 - 2}.$

At $(0, 1)$ the gradient is $\dfrac{1e^0}{3(1^3) - 2} = 1$

Q4 a) $3x^2 + 2y\dfrac{dy}{dx} - 2y - 2x\dfrac{dy}{dx} = 0$

$\dfrac{dy}{dx} = \dfrac{2y - 3x^2}{2y - 2x}$

b) Putting $x = -2$ into the equation gives:
$-8 + y^2 + 4y = 0$

Complete the square to solve...

$(y + 2)^2 - 4 - 8 = 0$

$y + 2 = \pm\sqrt{12} = \pm 2\sqrt{3}$

so $y = -2 \pm 2\sqrt{3}$

c) At $(-2, -2 + 2\sqrt{3})$:

$\dfrac{dy}{dx} = \dfrac{(-4 + 4\sqrt{3}) - 3(-2)^2}{(-4 + 4\sqrt{3}) - 2(-2)} = \dfrac{-16 + 4\sqrt{3}}{4\sqrt{3}}$

$= \dfrac{\sqrt{3} - 4}{\sqrt{3}}$

Rationalise the denominator: $= \dfrac{3 - 4\sqrt{3}}{3}$

$= 1 - \dfrac{4}{3}\sqrt{3}$

Q5 a) Putting $x = 1$ into the equation gives:
$1 - y = 2y^2 \Rightarrow 2y^2 + y - 1 = 0$
$\Rightarrow (2y - 1)(y + 1) = 0$
So $y = -1$ (given as the other point) and $y = \dfrac{1}{2}$.
So $a = \dfrac{1}{2}$.

b) $3x^2 - y - x\dfrac{dy}{dx} = 4y\dfrac{dy}{dx}$

$\dfrac{dy}{dx} = \dfrac{3x^2 - y}{4y + x}$

At $(1, -1)$, $\dfrac{dy}{dx} = \dfrac{3(1^2) - (-1)}{4(-1) + 1} = -\dfrac{4}{3}$

At $\left(1, \dfrac{1}{2}\right)$, $\dfrac{dy}{dx} = \dfrac{3(1^2) - \left(\frac{1}{2}\right)}{4\left(\frac{1}{2}\right) + 1} = \dfrac{5}{6}$

Q6 a) Putting $x = 1$ into the equation gives:
$y + y^2 - y - 4 = 0 \Rightarrow y^2 - 4 = 0$
so it cuts the curve at $y = 2$ and $y = -2$.

b) $2xy + x^2\dfrac{dy}{dx} + y^2 + 2xy\dfrac{dy}{dx} = y + x\dfrac{dy}{dx} + 0$

$(x^2 + 2xy - x)\dfrac{dy}{dx} = y - 2xy - y^2$

$\dfrac{dy}{dx} = \dfrac{y - 2xy - y^2}{x^2 + 2xy - x}$

At (1, 2), $\dfrac{dy}{dx} = \dfrac{2 - 2(1)(2) - 2^2}{1^2 + 2(1)(2) - 1} = -\dfrac{3}{2}$

At (1, –2), $\dfrac{dy}{dx} = \dfrac{(-2) - 2(1)(-2) - (-2)^2}{1^2 + 2(1)(-2) - 1} = \dfrac{1}{2}$

Exercise 2.2 — Applications of implicit differentiation

Q1 a) Differentiating:

$2x + 2 + 3\dfrac{dy}{dx} - 2y\dfrac{dy}{dx} = 0 \Rightarrow \dfrac{dy}{dx} = \dfrac{2x + 2}{2y - 3}$.

At the stationary points, $\dfrac{dy}{dx} = 0$, so:

$2x + 2 = 0 \Rightarrow x = -1$

When $x = -1$, $y^2 - 3y + 1 = 0 \Rightarrow y = \dfrac{3 \pm \sqrt{5}}{2}$

$= 2.62$ or 0.38 (to 2 d.p.)

So there are 2 stationary points with coordinates (–1, 2.62) and (–1, 0.38).

b) Putting $x = 0$ into the equation gives:

$3y - y^2 = 0 \Rightarrow y(3 - y) = 0$

$\Rightarrow y = 0$ and $y = 3$

At (0, 0), $\dfrac{dy}{dx} = \dfrac{2(0) + 2}{2(0) - 3} = -\dfrac{2}{3}$

The y-intercept is 0 (as it goes through (0, 0)).

So the equation of the tangent is $y = -\dfrac{2}{3}x$ or $3y = -2x$.

At (0, 3), $\dfrac{dy}{dx} = \dfrac{2(0) + 2}{2(3) - 3} = \dfrac{2}{3}$

The y-intercept is 3 (as it goes through (0, 3)).

Putting this into $y = mx + c$ gives: $y = \dfrac{2}{3}x + 3$.

So the equation of the tangent is $3y = 2x + 9$.

You could have left your answers in $y = mx + c$ form, but this looks neater.

Q2 a) Differentiating:

$3x^2 + 2x + \dfrac{dy}{dx} = 2y\dfrac{dy}{dx}$

$\Rightarrow \dfrac{dy}{dx} = \dfrac{3x^2 + 2x}{2y - 1}$.

At the stationary points, $\dfrac{dy}{dx} = 0$, so:

$3x^2 + 2x = 0$

$\Rightarrow x(3x + 2) = 0$

$\Rightarrow x = 0$ or $x = -\dfrac{2}{3}$

When $x = 0$, $y = y^2 \Rightarrow y(y - 1) = 0$

$\Rightarrow y = 0$ or $y = 1$.

When $x = -\dfrac{2}{3}$, $-\dfrac{8}{27} + \dfrac{4}{9} + y = y^2$

$\Rightarrow \dfrac{4}{27} + y = y^2 \Rightarrow 27y^2 - 27y - 4 = 0$

This has solutions $y = 1.13$ and -0.13, to 2 d.p.

So there are 4 stationary points with coordinates $(0, 0)$, $(0, 1)$, $\left(-\dfrac{2}{3}, 1.13\right)$ and $\left(-\dfrac{2}{3}, -0.13\right)$.

b) Putting $x = 2$ into the equation gives:

$8 + 4 + y = y^2 \Rightarrow y^2 - y - 12 = 0$

$\Rightarrow (y - 4)(y + 3) = 0$

$\Rightarrow y = 4$ and $y = -3$

At (2, 4), $\dfrac{dy}{dx} = \dfrac{3(2^2) + 2(2)}{2(4) - 1} = \dfrac{16}{7}$

Putting this into $y = mx + c$ gives:

$4 = \dfrac{16}{7}(2) + c \Rightarrow c = -\dfrac{4}{7}$

So the equation of the tangent is $7y = 16x - 4$.

At (2, –3), $\dfrac{dy}{dx} = \dfrac{3(2^2) + 2(2)}{2(-3) - 1} = -\dfrac{16}{7}$

Putting this into $y = mx + c$ gives:

$-3 = -\dfrac{16}{7}(2) + c \Rightarrow c = \dfrac{11}{7}$

So the equation of the tangent is $7y = 11 - 16x$.

Q3 a) Putting $y = 1$ into the equation gives:

$x^2 + 1 = x + 7 \Rightarrow x^2 - x - 6 = 0$

$(x - 3)(x + 2) = 0 \Rightarrow x = 3$ and $x = -2$.

Differentiating:

$2xy + x^2\dfrac{dy}{dx} + 3y^2\dfrac{dy}{dx} = 1$

$\dfrac{dy}{dx} = \dfrac{1 - 2xy}{x^2 + 3y^2}$

At (–2, 1), $\dfrac{dy}{dx} = \dfrac{1 - 2(-2)(1)}{(-2)^2 + 3(1^2)} = \dfrac{5}{7}$

so the gradient of the normal is $-\dfrac{7}{5}$.

Putting this into $y = mx + c$ gives:

$1 = -\dfrac{7}{5}(-2) + c \Rightarrow c = -\dfrac{9}{5}$

and so the equation of the normal is $5y = -7x - 9$.

At (3, 1), $\dfrac{dy}{dx} = \dfrac{1 - 2(3)(1)}{(3)^2 + 3(1^2)} = -\dfrac{5}{12}$

so the gradient of the normal is $\dfrac{12}{5}$.

Putting this into $y = mx + c$ gives:

$1 = \dfrac{12}{5}(3) + c \Rightarrow c = -\dfrac{31}{5}$

so the equation of the normal is $5y = 12x - 31$.

b) The normals intersect when:

$-7x - 9 = 12x - 31$

$22 = 19x \Rightarrow x = \dfrac{22}{19}$

And so $5y = \dfrac{264}{19} - 31 = -\dfrac{325}{19}$

$\Rightarrow y = -\dfrac{65}{19}$

So they intersect at $\left(\dfrac{22}{19}, -\dfrac{65}{19}\right)$.

Q4 a) Putting $x = 0$ into the equation gives:

$1 + y^2 = 5 - 3y \Rightarrow y^2 + 3y - 4 = 0$

$(y + 4)(y - 1) = 0 \Rightarrow y = -4$ or $y = 1$.

So $a = -4$ and $b = 1$ ($a < b$).

Differentiating:

$e^x + 2y\dfrac{dy}{dx} - y - x\dfrac{dy}{dx} = -3\dfrac{dy}{dx}$

$\dfrac{dy}{dx} = \dfrac{y - e^x}{2y - x + 3}$

At (0, 1), $\dfrac{dy}{dx} = \dfrac{1 - e^0}{2(1) - 0 + 3} = 0$

so this is a stationary point.

b) At $(0, -4)$, $\dfrac{dy}{dx} = \dfrac{(-4) - e^0}{2(-4) - 0 + 3} = 1$.

So the gradient of the tangent is 1 and the gradient of the normal is –1.

$-4 = 0 + c$ (so $c = -4$) for both, since $x = 0$, so the equation of the tangent is $y = x - 4$ and the equation of the normal is $y = -x - 4$.

Q5 a) When $x = 1$:

$0 + y^2 = y + 6 \Rightarrow y^2 - y - 6 = 0$

$(y - 3)(y + 2) = 0 \Rightarrow y = 3$ or $y = -2$.

So the curve passes through $(1, 3)$ and $(1, -2)$.

b) Differentiating:

$$\frac{1}{x} + 2y\frac{dy}{dx} = 2xy + x^2\frac{dy}{dx}$$

$$\frac{dy}{dx} = \frac{2xy - \frac{1}{x}}{2y - x^2} = \frac{2x^2y - 1}{2xy - x^3}$$

At $(1, 3)$, $\dfrac{dy}{dx} = \dfrac{2(1^2)(3) - 1}{2(1)(3) - (1)^3} = 1$

so the gradient of the normal is –1.
Putting this into $y = mx + c$ gives:
$3 = -1(1) + c \Rightarrow c = 4$
so the equation of the normal is $y = 4 - x$.

At $(1, -2)$, $\dfrac{dy}{dx} = \dfrac{2(1^2)(-2) - 1}{2(1)(-2) - (1)^3} = 1$,

so the gradient of the normal is also –1.
$-2 = -1(1) + c \Rightarrow c = -1$
so the equation of the normal is $y = -x - 1$.

Because the gradients are the same these lines are parallel and can never intersect.

Q6 When $y = 0$:

$1 + x^2 = 0 + 4x \Rightarrow x^2 - 4x + 1 = 0$

Complete the square to solve...

$(x - 2)^2 - 4 + 1 = 0 \Rightarrow x - 2 = \pm\sqrt{3} \Rightarrow x = 2 \pm \sqrt{3}$

So $a = 2 + \sqrt{3}$ and $b = 2 - \sqrt{3}$.

Differentiating:

$e^y\dfrac{dy}{dx} + 2x = 3y^2\dfrac{dy}{dx} + 4 \Rightarrow \dfrac{dy}{dx} = \dfrac{2x - 4}{3y^2 - e^y}$

At $(2 + \sqrt{3}, 0)$, $\dfrac{dy}{dx} = \dfrac{4 + 2\sqrt{3} - 4}{3(0) - e^0} = -2\sqrt{3}$

$0 = -2\sqrt{3}(2 + \sqrt{3}) + c \Rightarrow c = 4\sqrt{3} + 6$

So the tangent at this point is $y = 4\sqrt{3} + 6 - 2\sqrt{3}x$.

At $(2 - \sqrt{3}, 0)$, $\dfrac{dy}{dx} = \dfrac{4 - 2\sqrt{3} - 4}{3(0) - e^0} = 2\sqrt{3}$

$0 = 2\sqrt{3}(2 - \sqrt{3}) + c \Rightarrow c = 6 - 4\sqrt{3}$

So the tangent at this point is $y = 2\sqrt{3}x + 6 - 4\sqrt{3}$.

Q7 Differentiating:

$\ln x\dfrac{dy}{dx} + \dfrac{y}{x} + 2x = 2y\dfrac{dy}{dx} - \dfrac{dy}{dx}$

$\dfrac{dy}{dx} = \dfrac{\frac{y}{x} + 2x}{2y - \ln x - 1} = \dfrac{y + 2x^2}{2xy - x\ln x - x}$

$y + 2x^2 = 0 \Rightarrow \dfrac{dy}{dx} = \dfrac{y + 2x^2}{2xy - x\ln x - x} = 0$

So if a point on the curve satisfies $y + 2x^2 = 0$, then it's a stationary point.

Q8 a) Differentiating:

$2e^{2y}\dfrac{dy}{dx} + e^x = 2x\dfrac{dy}{dx} + 2y$

$\dfrac{dy}{dx} = \dfrac{2y - e^x}{2e^{2y} - 2x}$

When $y = 0$:

$1 + e^x - e^4 = 1$
$\Rightarrow e^x = e^4 \Rightarrow x = 4$

$\dfrac{dy}{dx} = \dfrac{2(0) - e^4}{2e^0 - 2(4)} = \dfrac{e^4}{6}$ (gradient of the tangent)

$0 = \dfrac{e^4}{6}(4) + c \Rightarrow c = -\dfrac{2e^4}{3}$.

So the equation of the tangent is $y = \dfrac{e^4}{6}(x - 4)$.

b) The gradient of the normal is $-6e^{-4}$.

$0 = -6e^{-4}(4) + c \Rightarrow c = 24e^{-4}$

So the normal is $y = 6e^{-4}(4 - x)$.

c) The lines intersect when

$\dfrac{e^4}{6}(x - 4) = 6e^{-4}(4 - x)$

$\Rightarrow e^8(x - 4) = 36(4 - x)$

$\Rightarrow e^8x + 36x = 4e^8 + 144$

$\Rightarrow x(e^8 + 36) = 4e^8 + 144$

$\Rightarrow x = \dfrac{4e^8 + 144}{e^8 + 36}$

Q9 When $x = 2$:

$2y^2 + 4y - 24 = 4 + 2$
$\Rightarrow 2y^2 + 4y - 30 = 0$
$\Rightarrow y^2 + 2y - 15 = 0$
$\Rightarrow (y + 5)(y - 3) = 0 \Rightarrow y = -5$ and $y = 3$.

Differentiating:

$y^2 + 2yx\dfrac{dy}{dx} + 2y + 2x\dfrac{dy}{dx} - 9x^2 = 2x$

$\dfrac{dy}{dx} = \dfrac{2x - y^2 - 2y + 9x^2}{2yx + 2x}$

At $(2, -5)$, $\dfrac{dy}{dx} = \dfrac{4 - 25 + 10 + 36}{-20 + 4} = -\dfrac{25}{16}$

This is the gradient of the tangent at $(2, -5)$, so:

$-5 = -\dfrac{25}{16}(2) + c \Rightarrow c = -\dfrac{15}{8}$

So the equation of the tangent at $(2, -5)$ is:

$y = -\dfrac{25}{16}x - \dfrac{15}{8}$ or $16y = -25x - 30$

At $(2, 3)$, $\dfrac{dy}{dx} = \dfrac{4 - 9 - 6 + 36}{12 + 4} = \dfrac{25}{16}$

This is the gradient of the tangent at $(2, 3)$, so:

$3 = \dfrac{25}{16}(2) + c \Rightarrow c = -\dfrac{1}{8}$

So the equation of the tangent at $(2, 3)$ is:

$y = \dfrac{25}{16}x - \dfrac{1}{8}$ or $16y = 25x - 2$

The two tangents intersect when:

$-25x - 30 = 25x - 2 \Rightarrow 50x = -28$

$\Rightarrow x = -\dfrac{14}{25}$

And $16y = 25\left(-\dfrac{14}{25}\right) - 2 \Rightarrow 16y = -16 \Rightarrow y = -1$.

So they intersect at $\left(-\dfrac{14}{25}, -1\right)$.

Q10 a) When $x = \dfrac{\pi}{2}$:

$\cos y \cos\dfrac{\pi}{2} + \cos y \sin\dfrac{\pi}{2} = \dfrac{1}{2}$,

$0 + \cos y = \dfrac{1}{2} \Rightarrow y = \dfrac{\pi}{3}$

This is the only solution for y in the given interval.

When $x = \pi$:

$\cos y \cos \pi + \cos y \sin \pi = \frac{1}{2}$,

$-\cos y + 0 = \frac{1}{2} \Rightarrow y = \frac{2\pi}{3}$

You can use the CAST diagram or the graph of cos x to find this solution.

b) Differentiating:

$-\cos y \sin x - \sin y \cos x \dfrac{dy}{dx} +$
$\qquad \cos y \cos x - \sin y \sin x \dfrac{dy}{dx} = 0$

$\dfrac{dy}{dx} = \dfrac{\cos y \cos x - \cos y \sin x}{\sin y \cos x + \sin y \sin x}$

At $\left(\frac{\pi}{2}, \frac{\pi}{3}\right)$, $\dfrac{dy}{dx} = \dfrac{\cos\frac{\pi}{3}\cos\frac{\pi}{2} - \cos\frac{\pi}{3}\sin\frac{\pi}{2}}{\sin\frac{\pi}{3}\cos\frac{\pi}{2} + \sin\frac{\pi}{3}\sin\frac{\pi}{2}}$

$\qquad = \dfrac{0 - \frac{1}{2}}{0 + \frac{\sqrt{3}}{2}} = -\dfrac{1}{\sqrt{3}}$

This is the gradient of the tangent, so:

$\frac{\pi}{3} = -\frac{1}{\sqrt{3}}\left(\frac{\pi}{2}\right) + c \Rightarrow c = \dfrac{(2 + \sqrt{3})\pi}{6}$

So the equation of the tangent at $\left(\frac{\pi}{2}, \frac{\pi}{3}\right)$ is

$y = -\frac{1}{\sqrt{3}}x + \dfrac{(2 + \sqrt{3})\pi}{6}$.

At $\left(\pi, \frac{2\pi}{3}\right)$, $\dfrac{dy}{dx} = \dfrac{\cos\frac{2\pi}{3}\cos\pi - \cos\frac{2\pi}{3}\sin\pi}{\sin\frac{2\pi}{3}\cos\pi + \sin\frac{2\pi}{3}\sin\pi}$

$\qquad = \dfrac{\frac{1}{2} - 0}{-\frac{\sqrt{3}}{2} + 0} = -\dfrac{1}{\sqrt{3}}$

This is the gradient of the tangent, so:

$\frac{2\pi}{3} = -\frac{1}{\sqrt{3}}(\pi) + c \Rightarrow c = \dfrac{(2 + \sqrt{3})\pi}{3}$

So the equation of the tangent at $\left(\pi, \frac{2\pi}{3}\right)$ is

$y = -\frac{1}{\sqrt{3}}x + \dfrac{(2 + \sqrt{3})\pi}{3}$.

3. Differentiation of a^x

Exercise 3.1 — Differentiating a^x

Q1 a) $\dfrac{dy}{dx} = 3^x \ln 3$

b) $\dfrac{dy}{dx} = 5^x \ln 5$

c) $\dfrac{dy}{dx} = 10^x \ln 10$

d) $\dfrac{dy}{dx} = p^x \ln p$

Q2 a) Let $u = 2x$ and $y = 3^u$, then

$\dfrac{du}{dx} = 2$ and $\dfrac{dy}{du} = 3^u \ln 3 = 3^{2x} \ln 3$, so

$\dfrac{dy}{dx} = \dfrac{du}{dx} \times \dfrac{dy}{du} = 2(3^{2x} \ln 3)$

b) $\dfrac{dy}{dx} = 3(6^{3x} \ln 6)$

c) $\dfrac{dy}{dx} = -(10^{-x} \ln 10)$

d) $\dfrac{dy}{dx} = q(p^{qx} \ln p)$

Q3 a) Let $u = 4x$, then $y = 2^u$ and
$\dfrac{dy}{dx} = \dfrac{d}{du}(2^u)\dfrac{d}{dx}(4x) = 4(2^{4x} \ln 2)$

b) When $x = 2$,
$\dfrac{dy}{dx} = 4(2^8 \ln 2) = 1024 \ln 2$
$y = 2^8 = 256$

Putting this into $y = mx + c$ gives:
$256 = 2048 \ln 2 + c \Rightarrow c = 256 - 2048 \ln 2$.

So the equation of the tangent is:
$y = (1024 \ln 2)x + 256 - 2048 \ln 2$
or $y = (1024 \ln 2)(x - 2) + 256$

Q4 a) $\dfrac{dy}{dx} = 3(3^{3x} \ln 3)$

b) When $x = -1$, $y = 3^{-3} = \frac{1}{3^3} = \frac{1}{27}$,
and $\dfrac{dy}{dx} = \dfrac{3}{27} \ln 3 = \frac{1}{9} \ln 3$

so the gradient of the normal is $-\dfrac{9}{\ln 3}$.

Putting this into $y = mx + c$ gives:
$\dfrac{1}{27} = \dfrac{9}{\ln 3} + c \Rightarrow c = \dfrac{1}{27} - \dfrac{9}{\ln 3}$.

So the equation of the normal is:
$y = \dfrac{1}{27} - \dfrac{9}{\ln 3} - \left(\dfrac{9}{\ln 3}\right)x$

Q5 a) When $x = 2$, $y = 5^4 = 625$.

b) $\dfrac{dy}{dx} = 2(5^{2x} \ln 5) = 1250 \ln 5$ at $x = 2$.

This is the gradient of the tangent at that point. Putting this into $y = mx + c$ gives:

$625 = 2500 \ln 5 + c \Rightarrow c = 625 - 2500 \ln 5$.

So the equation of the tangent at $(2, 625)$ is:
$y = (1250 \ln 5)x + 625 - 2500 \ln 5$.

Q6 a) When $x = 1$, $2^p = 32$, so $p = 5$.
You should just know this result, but if not you can take logs ($p \ln 2 = \ln 32$, so $p = \ln 32 \div \ln 2 = 5$).

b) $\dfrac{dy}{dx} = 5(2^{5x} \ln 2)$

When $x = 1$, $\dfrac{dy}{dx} = 5(32 \ln 2) = 160 \ln 2$

Q7 a) Let $u = x^2$, then $y = 7^u$, and so
$\dfrac{dy}{dx} = \dfrac{d}{du}(7^u)\dfrac{d}{dx}(x^2) = 2x(7^{x^2} \ln 7)$.

b) When $x = 3$,
$\dfrac{dy}{dx} = 6(7^9 \ln 7) = 4.71 \times 10^8$ (to 3 s.f.).

Q8 a) Let $u = x^3$, then $y = p^u$, and so
$\dfrac{dy}{dx} = \dfrac{d}{du}(p^u)\dfrac{d}{dx}(x^3) = 3x^2(p^{x^3} \ln p)$

b) When $x = 2$, $y = p^8 = 6561$.

So $p = \sqrt[8]{6561} = 3$.
You can also work this out by taking logs.
$8 \ln p = \ln 6561$, so $p = \exp\left(\dfrac{\ln 6561}{8}\right) = 3$.

c) The gradient at $x = 1$ is $3(3 \ln 3) = 9 \ln 3$.
Putting this into $y = mx + c$ gives:
$3 = 9 \ln 3 + c \Rightarrow c = 3 - 9 \ln 3$.
So the equation of the tangent is
$y = (9 \ln 3)x + (3 - 9 \ln 3)$

Q9 a) When $x = 25$, $y = 4^5 = 1024$, so a = 1024.

b) Let $u = x^{\frac{1}{2}}$ and $y = 4^u$, so

$$\frac{dy}{dx} = \frac{d}{du}(4^u)\frac{d}{dx}(x^{\frac{1}{2}}) = \frac{1}{2}x^{-\frac{1}{2}}(4^{\sqrt{x}}\ln 4).$$

c) The gradient of the tangent when $x = 25$ is $\frac{1}{10}(1024\ln 4) = 102.4\ln 4$.

Putting this into $y = mx + c$ gives:

$1024 = 2560\ln 4 + c \Rightarrow c = 1024 - 2560\ln 4$.

So the equation of the tangent is
$y = (102.4\ln 4)x + (1024 - 2560\ln 4)$
$\Rightarrow y = 142x - 2520$ to 3 s.f.

Q10 a) $\frac{dy}{dx} = -3(2^{-3x}\ln 2)$

b) When $x = 2$, $y = b = 2^{-6} = \frac{1}{64}$,

and $\frac{dy}{dx} = -\frac{3}{64}\ln 2$ (the gradient of the tangent).

Putting this into $y = mx + c$ gives:

$\frac{1}{64} = -\frac{6}{64}\ln 2 + c \Rightarrow c = \frac{1}{64} + \frac{6}{64}\ln 2$.

So the equation of the tangent is
$y = \frac{1 + 6\ln 2}{64} - \left(\frac{3\ln 2}{64}\right)x$
$\Rightarrow 64y = 1 + 6\ln 2 - (3\ln 2)x$.

Q11 a) When $x = 2$ and $y = 1$,

$1 = 2^2 a^2 \Rightarrow a^2 = \frac{1}{2^2} \Rightarrow a = \frac{1}{2}$

Take the positive root since a > 0.

b) $y = x^2\left(\frac{1}{2}\right)^x$

Using the product rule to differentiate:

$\frac{dy}{dx} = x^2\frac{d}{dx}\left(\frac{1}{2}\right)^x + \left(\frac{1}{2}\right)^x\frac{d}{dx}(x^2)$

$= x^2\left(\frac{1}{2}\right)^x\ln\left(\frac{1}{2}\right) + 2x\left(\frac{1}{2}\right)^x$

Using log laws,

$\ln\left(\frac{1}{2}\right) = \ln 1 - \ln 2 = 0 - \ln 2 = -\ln 2$, so...

$\frac{dy}{dx} = 2x\left(\frac{1}{2}\right)^x - x^2\left(\frac{1}{2}\right)^x\ln 2$

which can also be written as:

$\frac{dy}{dx} = \frac{2x - x^2\ln 2}{2^x}$.

c) At P, when $x = 2$, $\frac{dy}{dx} = \frac{4 - 4\ln 2}{4} = 1 - \ln 2$.
This is the gradient of the tangent.

Putting the values into $y = mx + c$ gives:

$1 = 2 - 2\ln 2 + c \Rightarrow c = 2\ln 2 - 1$

So the equation of the tangent is
$y = (1 - \ln 2)x + 2\ln 2 - 1$

4. Connected Rates of Change
Exercise 4.1 — Connected rates of change

Q1 $\frac{dx}{dt} = -0.1$ (negative as the cube is shrinking),

and $V = x^3$, so $\frac{dV}{dx} = 3x^2$

$\frac{dV}{dt} = \frac{dx}{dt} \times \frac{dV}{dx} = -0.3x^2$ cm³ min⁻¹

Q2 $V = 30x^3$ so $\frac{dV}{dx} = 90x^2$, and $\frac{dx}{d\theta} = 0.15$.

$\frac{dV}{d\theta} = \frac{dV}{dx} \times \frac{dx}{d\theta} = 13.5x^2$ cm³ °C⁻¹
You have to spot that 0.15 is dx/dθ.

When $x = 3$, $\frac{dV}{d\theta} = 121.5$ cm³ °C⁻¹

Q3 $A = 4\pi r^2$ so $\frac{dA}{dr} = 8\pi r$, and $\frac{dr}{dt} = -1.6$.

$\frac{dA}{dt} = \frac{dA}{dr} \times \frac{dr}{dt} = -12.8\pi r$ cm² h⁻¹
When $r = 5.5$ cm, $\frac{dA}{dt} = -221.17$ cm² h⁻¹ (2 d.p.)

Q4 $\frac{dr}{d\theta} = 2 \times 10^{-2}$ mm °C⁻¹ $= 2 \times 10^{-5}$ m °C⁻¹,

and $V = \frac{4}{3}\pi r^3$ m³, so $\frac{dV}{dr} = 4\pi r^2$ m³ m⁻¹.

$\frac{dV}{d\theta} = \frac{dr}{d\theta} \times \frac{dV}{dr} = 8 \times 10^{-5}\pi r^2$ m³ °C⁻¹
You could have converted to mm instead, and given your answer in mm³ °C⁻¹.

Q5 The surface area of the tank,
$A = 2(\pi r^2) + 3r(2\pi r) = 8\pi r^2$, so $\frac{dA}{dr} = 16\pi r$,

and $\frac{dH}{dA} = -2$ (negative as heat is lost).

$\frac{dH}{dr} = \frac{dH}{dA} \times \frac{dA}{dr} = -32\pi r$ J cm⁻¹
When $r = 12.3$, $\frac{dH}{dr} = -1236.53$ J cm⁻¹ (2 d.p.)

Q6 $\frac{dH}{dt} = -0.5$ mm h⁻¹ $= -0.05$ cm h⁻¹
(length is decreasing).

$V = \pi r^2 H$, so $\frac{dV}{dH} = \pi r^2$.

$\frac{dV}{dt} = \frac{dH}{dt} \times \frac{dV}{dH} = -0.05\pi r^2$ cm³ h⁻¹

Q7 a) Using Pythagoras, the height of the triangle is
$\sqrt{x^2 - \left(\frac{x}{2}\right)^2} = \frac{\sqrt{3}x}{2}$, so the area of the end is

$A = \frac{1}{2}\left(\frac{\sqrt{3}x}{2}\right)x = \frac{\sqrt{3}x^2}{4}$.

b) $V = A \times h = 5\sqrt{3}\ x^2$, so $\frac{dV}{dx} = 10\sqrt{3}\ x$.

$\frac{dx}{dt} = 0.6$.

$\frac{dV}{dt} = \frac{dV}{dx} \times \frac{dx}{dt} = 6\sqrt{3}\ x$ mm³ per day

c) $x = 0.5 \Rightarrow \frac{dV}{dt} = 3\sqrt{3} = 5.20$ mm³ per day (2 d.p.)

Q8 a) $n = kD$, so $\frac{dn}{dD} = k = 104$.

$D = 1 + 2^{\lambda t}$, so $\frac{dD}{dt} = \lambda 2^{\lambda t}\ln 2$.

Use the rule for differentiating a^x from earlier in the chapter.

So $\frac{dn}{dt} = \frac{dn}{dD} \times \frac{dD}{dt} = 104\lambda 2^{\lambda t}\ln 2$ per day.

b) If $t = 1$ day and $\lambda = 5$,
$\frac{dn}{dt} = 104 \times 5 \times 2^5 \times \ln 2 = 16640\ln 2$
$= 1.15 \times 10^4$ per day.

Q9 a) Volume of water $V = \pi r^2 h$, so $\frac{dV}{dh} = \pi r^2$.

$\frac{dV}{dt} = -0.3$.

It's negative because the volume of water remaining is decreasing with time.

$$\frac{dh}{dt} = \frac{dV}{dt} \times \frac{dh}{dV}$$
$$= \frac{dV}{dt} \times \frac{1}{\frac{dV}{dh}} = -0.3 \times \frac{1}{\pi r^2} = -\frac{3}{10\pi r^2} \text{ cm s}^{-1}$$

b) $r = 6$, so $\frac{dh}{dt} = -\frac{1}{120\pi}$ cm s^{-1}.

So the water level falls at a constant rate of $\frac{1}{120\pi}$ cm s^{-1} and $\frac{1}{2\pi} = 0.159$ cm min^{-1}.

You don't actually need to use h in the calculation.

Q10 a) $\frac{dV}{d\theta} = k$, $V = \frac{2}{3}\pi r^3$, so $\frac{dV}{dr} = 2\pi r^2$.

$$\frac{dr}{d\theta} = \frac{dV}{d\theta} \times \frac{dr}{dV}$$
$$= \frac{dV}{d\theta} \times \frac{1}{\frac{dV}{dr}} = k \times \frac{1}{2\pi r^2} = \frac{k}{2\pi r^2} \text{ cm °C}^{-1}$$

b) $V = 4$, so $r = \sqrt[3]{\frac{6}{\pi}} = 1.240...$, and $k = 1.5$.

So $\frac{dr}{d\theta} = \frac{1.5}{2\pi(1.240...)^2} = 0.155$ cm °C^{-1}.

Review Exercise — Chapter 4

Q1 a) $\frac{dx}{dt} = 2t$, $\frac{dy}{dt} = 9t^2 - 4$, so
$$\frac{dy}{dx} = \frac{dy}{dt} \div \frac{dx}{dt} = \frac{9t^2 - 4}{2t}$$

b) The stationary points are when $\frac{9t^2 - 4}{2t} = 0$
$$\Rightarrow 9t^2 = 4 \Rightarrow t = \pm\frac{2}{3}$$

When $t = \frac{2}{3}$: $x = \left(\frac{2}{3}\right)^2 = \frac{4}{9}$,
$$y = 3\left(\frac{2}{3}\right)^3 - 4\left(\frac{2}{3}\right) = \frac{8}{9} - \frac{8}{3} = -\frac{16}{9}$$

When $t = -\frac{2}{3}$: $x = \left(-\frac{2}{3}\right)^2 = \frac{4}{9}$,
$$y = 3\left(-\frac{2}{3}\right)^3 - 4\left(-\frac{2}{3}\right) = -\frac{8}{9} + \frac{8}{3} = \frac{16}{9}$$

So the stationary points are $\left(\frac{4}{9}, -\frac{16}{9}\right)$ and $\left(\frac{4}{9}, \frac{16}{9}\right)$.

Q2 a) $\frac{dx}{dt} = \ln t + 1$, $\frac{dy}{dt} = 6t^2 - 2t$,

so $\frac{dy}{dx} = \frac{6t^2 - 2t}{\ln t + 1}$

b) When $t = 1$, $\frac{dy}{dx} = \frac{6 - 2}{0 + 1} = 4$.

c) E.g. you can't evaluate $\frac{dy}{dx}$ at this point as the curve itself is not defined when $t = 0$ as the value of x cannot be evaluated.

Q3 a) $\frac{dy}{dx} = \frac{6t^2 - 12t - 18}{2t - 6} = \frac{6(t+1)(t-3)}{2(t-3)} = 3(t+1)$

b) At stationary points, $\frac{dy}{dx} = 0 \Rightarrow 3(t+1) = 0$, so $t = -1$.
$x = (-1)^2 - 6(-1) = 7$
and $y = 2(-1)^3 - 6(-1)^2 - 18(-1) = 10$
So the stationary point is $(7, 10)$.

Q4 a) $\frac{dy}{dx} = \frac{3t^2 + 6t - 9}{3t^2 - 2t}$.

At the turning point $\frac{dy}{dx} = 0$, so:
$3t^2 + 6t - 9 = 0$
$\Rightarrow 3(t^2 + 2t - 3) = 0$
$\Rightarrow 3(t-1)(t+3) = 0 \Rightarrow t = 1$ or $t = -3$
When $t = 1$, $x = 0$, $y = -5$.
When $t = -3$, $x = -36$, $y = 27$.
So the coordinates of the turning points are $(0, -5)$ and $(-36, 27)$.

b) C cuts the x-axis when $y = 0$,
$\Rightarrow t^3 + 3t^2 - 9t = 0 \Rightarrow t(t^2 + 3t - 9) = 0$
$$\Rightarrow t = 0 \text{ or } t = \frac{-3 \pm 3\sqrt{5}}{2}.$$
When $t = 0$, $x = 0$ and $y = 0$, so C passes through the origin.

Use the quadratic formula to find the other values of t.

c) When $t = 2$, $\frac{dy}{dx} = \frac{3(2)^2 + 6(2) - 9}{3(2)^2 - 2(2)} = \frac{15}{8}$,
$x = 2^3 - 2^2 = 4$, and $y = 2^3 + 3(2)^2 - 9(2) = 2$.

Putting this into $y = mx + c$ gives:
$2 = \frac{15}{8}(4) + c \Rightarrow c = -\frac{11}{2}$
The equation of the tangent is $y = \frac{15}{8}x - \frac{11}{2}$
or $8y = 15x - 44$.

Q5 a) $\frac{dy}{dx} = \frac{2e^{2s} + 2se^{2s} + e^{2s}}{3se^s + 3e^s}$
$$= \frac{e^{2s}(3 + 2s)}{3e^s(s + 1)} = \frac{e^s(3 + 2s)}{3(s + 1)}$$
When $s = 0$, $\frac{dy}{dx} = 1$, $x = 0$, $y = 1$,
so the equation of the tangent is $y = x + 1$.
When $s = 2$, $\frac{dy}{dx} = \frac{7e^2}{9}$, $y = 3e^4$, $x = 6e^2$.
Putting this into $y = mx + c$ gives:
$3e^4 = \left(\frac{7e^2}{9}\right)6e^2 + c \Rightarrow c = \frac{27e^4 - 42e^4}{9} = -\frac{15e^4}{9}$
so the equation of the tangent is $y = \left(\frac{7e^2}{9}\right)x - \frac{15e^4}{9}$
or $9y = 7e^2 x - 15e^4$.

b) The lines intersect when:
$9x + 9 = 7e^2x - 15e^4$
$(7e^2 - 9)x = 9 + 15e^4$
$x = \frac{9 + 15e^4}{7e^2 - 9}$, $y = \frac{9 + 15e^4}{7e^2 - 9} + 1$

Q6 a) Using the quotient rule, with $u = \sin\theta$ and $v = \theta^2$.
$$\frac{dx}{d\theta} = \frac{v\frac{du}{d\theta} - u\frac{dv}{d\theta}}{v^2} = \frac{\theta^2\cos\theta - 2\theta\sin\theta}{\theta^4}$$
$$= \frac{\theta\cos\theta - 2\sin\theta}{\theta^3}$$
and $\frac{dy}{d\theta} = \cos 2\theta - 2\theta\sin 2\theta$

so $\frac{dy}{dx} = \frac{\theta^3(\cos 2\theta - 2\theta\sin 2\theta)}{\theta\cos\theta - 2\sin\theta}$

Answers **199**

When $\theta = \frac{\pi}{2}$,

$$\frac{dy}{dx} = \frac{\frac{\pi^3}{8}(\cos\pi - \pi\sin\pi)}{\frac{\pi}{2}\cos\frac{\pi}{2} - 2\sin\frac{\pi}{2}} = \frac{\frac{\pi^3}{8}(-1-0)}{0-2} = \frac{\pi^3}{16}$$

b) When $\theta = \frac{\pi}{2}$, $x = \frac{4}{\pi^2}$ and $y = -\frac{\pi}{2}$.

Putting this into $y = mx + c$ gives:

$$-\frac{\pi}{2} = \frac{\pi^3}{16}\left(\frac{4}{\pi^2}\right) + c \Rightarrow c = -\frac{3\pi}{4}$$

So $y = \frac{\pi^3}{16}x - \frac{3\pi}{4}$, or $16y = \pi^3 x - 12\pi$

c) The curve cuts the x-axis where $y = 0$, so $\theta\cos 2\theta = 0$.

$\theta = 0$ is a solution to $\theta\cos 2\theta = 0$, but x is undefined at this point.

Other solutions are when $2\theta = \frac{\pi}{2}, \frac{3\pi}{2}, \frac{5\pi}{2}$ ... etc.

The solution with $0 \le \theta \le \frac{\pi}{2}$ is $\theta = \frac{\pi}{4}$.

When $\theta = \frac{\pi}{4}$, $x = \frac{\frac{1}{\sqrt{2}}}{\frac{\pi^2}{16}} = \frac{16}{\sqrt{2}\pi^2} = \frac{8\sqrt{2}}{\pi^2}$,

so the coordinates of the first point where the curve cuts the x-axis are $\left(\frac{8\sqrt{2}}{\pi^2}, 0\right)$.

Q7 a) The gradient $\frac{dy}{dx} = \frac{t-6}{3t^2 + 2t}$.

b) The turning point is when $t - 6 = 0$, so $t = 6$, because the denominator cannot be 0.
When $t = 6$, $x = 252$ and $y = -18$, so the coordinates of the turning point are (252, –18).

c) When $y = 0$:

$\frac{1}{2}t^2 - 6t = 0 \Rightarrow t^2 - 12t = 0 \Rightarrow t(t-12) = 0$

$\Rightarrow t = 0$ or $t = 12$

When $t = 0$, the gradient is undefined.

When $t = 12$, $\frac{dy}{dx} = \frac{1}{76}$ and $x = 1872$.

Putting this into $y = mx + c$ gives:

$0 = \frac{1}{76}(1872) + c \Rightarrow c = -\frac{468}{19}$

So the equation of the tangent is

$y = \frac{1}{76}x - \frac{468}{19}$

Q8 a) Differentiate each term separately with respect to x:

$\frac{d}{dx}4x^2 - \frac{d}{dx}2y^2 = \frac{d}{dx}7x^2y$

Differentiate $4x^2$ first:

$\Rightarrow 8x - \frac{d}{dx}2y^2 = \frac{d}{dx}7x^2y$

Differentiate $2y^2$ using chain rule:

$\Rightarrow 8x - \frac{d}{dy}2y^2\frac{dy}{dx} = \frac{d}{dx}7x^2y$

$\Rightarrow 8x - 4y\frac{dy}{dx} = \frac{d}{dx}7x^2y$

Differentiate $7x^2y$ using product rule:

$\Rightarrow 8x - 4y\frac{dy}{dx} = 7x^2\frac{d}{dx}y + y\frac{d}{dx}7x^2$

$\Rightarrow 8x - 4y\frac{dy}{dx} = 7x^2\frac{dy}{dx} + 14xy$

Rearrange to make $\frac{dy}{dx}$ the subject:

$\Rightarrow (4y + 7x^2)\frac{dy}{dx} = 8x - 14xy$

$\Rightarrow \frac{dy}{dx} = \frac{8x - 14xy}{4y + 7x^2}$

b) Differentiate each term separately with respect to x:

$\frac{d}{dx}3x^4 - \frac{d}{dx}2xy^2 = \frac{d}{dx}y$

$\Rightarrow 12x^3 - 2y^2 - 4xy\frac{dy}{dx} = \frac{dy}{dx}$

Rearrange to make $\frac{dy}{dx}$ the subject:

$\Rightarrow (1 + 4xy)\frac{dy}{dx} = 12x^3 - 2y^2$

$\Rightarrow \frac{dy}{dx} = \frac{12x^3 - 2y^2}{1 + 4xy}$

c) Differentiate each term separately with respect to x:

$\frac{d}{dx}\cos x \sin y = \frac{d}{dx}xy$

$\Rightarrow (\cos x \cos y)\frac{dy}{dx} - \sin y \sin x = x\frac{dy}{dx} + y$

Rearrange to make $\frac{dy}{dx}$ the subject:

$\Rightarrow (\cos x \cos y - x)\frac{dy}{dx} = y + \sin x \sin y$

$\Rightarrow \frac{dy}{dx} = \frac{\sin x \sin y + y}{\cos x \cos y - x}$

Q9 a) At (1, –4), $\frac{dy}{dx} = \frac{8x - 14xy}{4y + 7x^2}$

$= \frac{8(1) - 14(1)(-4)}{4(-4) + 7(1)^2} = \frac{8 + 56}{-16 + 7} = -\frac{64}{9}$

b) At (1, 1), $\frac{dy}{dx} = \frac{12x^3 - 2y^2}{1 + 4xy}$

$= \frac{12(1)^3 - 2(1)^2}{1 + 4(1)(1)} = \frac{12 - 2}{1 + 4} = \frac{10}{5} = 2$

So the gradient of the normal is $-\frac{1}{2}$.

Q10 a) $y + y^2 - 2 = 0$
$(y - 1)(y + 2) = 0$
So $y = 1$, $y = -2$ ((1, –2) is the other point given).
Hence $a = 1$.

b) $2xy + x^2\frac{dy}{dx} + 2y\frac{dy}{dx} = 2x$

$\Rightarrow (x^2 + 2y)\frac{dy}{dx} = 2x - 2xy$

$\Rightarrow \frac{dy}{dx} = \frac{2x - 2xy}{x^2 + 2y}$

At (1, –2), $\frac{dy}{dx} = \frac{2 - (-4)}{1 + (-4)} = \frac{6}{-3} = -2$

c) From part a), you know that $a = 1$. So if (1, 1) is a turning point, the gradient here will be 0.

$\frac{dy}{dx} = \frac{2x - 2xy}{x^2 + 2y} = \frac{2 - 2}{1 + 2} = 0$,

so (1, 1) is a turning point.

Q11 a) Substitute $x = 0$ and $y = 1$ into the equation.
$1\cos 0 - 1 = 0\sin 0$, that is, $1 - 1 = 0$, so this is a solution.

b) $-y\sin x + \cos x\frac{dy}{dx} - 2y\frac{dy}{dx} = x\cos x + \sin x$

$\Rightarrow \frac{dy}{dx}(\cos x - 2y) = x\cos x + \sin x + y\sin x$

$$\Rightarrow \frac{dy}{dx} = \frac{x\cos x + (1+y)\sin x}{\cos x - 2y}$$

At a turning point, $\frac{dy}{dx} = 0$, so if $(0, 1)$ is a turning point then $\frac{dy}{dx} = 0$ here.

Substitute in $x = 0$ and $y = 1$:

$$\frac{dy}{dx} = \frac{0\cos 0 + 2\sin 0}{\cos 0 - 2} = \frac{0}{-1} = 0$$

so $(0, 1)$ is a turning point.

Q12 a) $\cos x - x\sin x + y\cos x + \sin x \frac{dy}{dx} = 3y^2 \frac{dy}{dx}$

$$\frac{dy}{dx} = \frac{\cos x - x\sin x + y\cos x}{3y^2 - \sin x}$$

b) At the stationary points, $\frac{dy}{dx} = 0$, hence

$\cos x - x\sin x + y\cos x = 0$

$y\cos x = x\sin x - \cos x$,

so $y = \frac{x\sin x}{\cos x} - \frac{\cos x}{\cos x} = x\tan x - 1$, as required.

Use the identity $\tan x \equiv \sin x\ /\ \cos x$ for the last part.

c) When $x = \frac{\pi}{2}$, $\frac{\pi}{2}(0) + y = y^3$, hence $y^3 - y = 0$
$\Rightarrow y(y + 1)(y - 1) = 0$, giving $y = 0$, $y = 1$ and $y = -1$, so the three points on the curve have coordinates $(\frac{\pi}{2}, 0)$, $(\frac{\pi}{2}, 1)$ and $(\frac{\pi}{2}, -1)$.

d) $(\frac{\pi}{2}, 0)$: $\frac{dy}{dx} = \frac{0 - \frac{\pi}{2} + 0}{0 - 1} = \frac{\pi}{2}$
$0 = \frac{\pi^2}{4} + c$, so the equation of the tangent is
$y = \frac{\pi}{2}x - \frac{\pi^2}{4}$
$(\frac{\pi}{2}, 1)$: $\frac{dy}{dx} = \frac{0 - \frac{\pi}{2} + 0}{3 - 1} = -\frac{\pi}{4}$
$1 = -\frac{\pi^2}{8} + c$, so the equation of the tangent is
$y = (1 + \frac{\pi^2}{8}) - \frac{\pi}{4}x$
$(\frac{\pi}{2}, -1)$: $\frac{dy}{dx} = \frac{0 - \frac{\pi}{2} + 0}{3 - 1} = -\frac{\pi}{4}$
$-1 = -\frac{\pi^2}{8} + c$, so the equation of the tangent is
$y = (\frac{\pi^2}{8} - 1) - \frac{\pi}{4}x$
The last two tangents both have gradient $-\frac{\pi}{4}$, so they are parallel and will never intersect.

Q13 $4y + 4y^2 = 8 \Rightarrow y^2 + y - 2 = 0 \Rightarrow (y - 1)(y + 2) = 0$
$\Rightarrow y = 1$ or $y = -2$, so $a = 1$ and $b = -2$.

$4\frac{dy}{dx} + 2xy^2 + 2x^2y\frac{dy}{dx} = 4$, so

$$\frac{dy}{dx} = \frac{4 - 2xy^2}{4 + 2x^2y} = \frac{2 - xy^2}{2 + x^2y}$$

At $(2, 1)$, $\frac{dy}{dx} = 0$, so $(2, 1)$ is a stationary point and the equation of the tangent is $y = 1$.

At $(2, -2)$, $\frac{dy}{dx} = \frac{-6}{-6} = 1$, so $-2 = 2 + c \Rightarrow c = -4$ and the equation of the tangent is $y = x - 4$.

The tangents intersect where $1 = x - 4$, so $x = 5$, $y = 1$.

Q14 a) When $x = 1$, $y = y^2 - 6$, so $y^2 - y - 6 = 0$
$\Rightarrow (y - 3)(y + 2) = 0 \Rightarrow y = 3$, $y = -2$,
so $a = 3$, $b = -2$.

b) $\ln x + 1 + 2xy + x^2\frac{dy}{dx} = y^2 + 2yx\frac{dy}{dx} - 6$

$$\frac{dy}{dx} = \frac{\ln x + 2xy - y^2 + 7}{2xy - x^2}$$

At $(1, 3)$: $\frac{dy}{dx} = \frac{0 + 6 - 9 + 7}{6 - 1} = \frac{4}{5}$
Gradient of normal is $-\frac{5}{4}$
$3 = -\frac{5}{4} + c \Rightarrow c = \frac{17}{4}$
Hence the equation of the normal is $4y = 17 - 5x$
At $(1, -2)$: $\frac{dy}{dx} = \frac{0 - 4 - 4 + 7}{-4 - 1} = \frac{-1}{-5} = \frac{1}{5}$
Gradient of normal is -5
$-2 = -5 + c \Rightarrow c = 3$
Hence the equation of the normal is $y = 3 - 5x$

c) The normals intersect where $\frac{17}{4} - \frac{5}{4}x = 3 - 5x$
$\frac{15}{4}x = -\frac{5}{4} \Rightarrow x = -\frac{1}{3}$, so $y = 3 + \frac{5}{3} = \frac{14}{3}$,
so the point of intersection is at $(-\frac{1}{3}, \frac{14}{3})$.

Q15 Take the log of both sides of the equation:
$y = a^x \Rightarrow \ln y = \ln a^x \Rightarrow \ln y = x\ln a$ (using log laws)
Now use implicit differentiation to find $\frac{dy}{dx}$:
$\ln y = x\ln a \Rightarrow \frac{d}{dx}(\ln y) = \frac{d}{dx}(x\ln a)$
$\Rightarrow \frac{d}{dy}(\ln y)\frac{dy}{dx} = \ln a$
$\Rightarrow \frac{1}{y}\frac{dy}{dx} = \ln a$
$\Rightarrow \frac{dy}{dx} = y\ln a$
So as $y = a^x$, $\frac{dy}{dx} = a^x\ln a$

Q16 $A = 2(x)(2x) + 2(x)(3x) + 2(2x)(3x)$
$= 4x^2 + 6x^2 + 12x^2 = 22x^2$. So $\frac{dA}{dx} = 44x$.
$V = (x)(2x)(3x) = 6x^3$. So $\frac{dV}{dx} = 18x^2$.
By the chain rule:
$$\frac{dA}{dt} = \frac{dA}{dx} \times \frac{dx}{dt} = 44x \times \frac{dx}{dt}$$
To find $\frac{dx}{dt}$, use the chain rule again:
$$\frac{dx}{dt} = \frac{dx}{dV} \times \frac{dV}{dt} = \frac{1}{\left(\frac{dV}{dx}\right)} \times \frac{dV}{dt} = \frac{1}{18x^2} \times 3 = \frac{1}{6x^2}$$
So $\frac{dA}{dt} = 44x \times \frac{1}{6x^2} = \frac{22}{3x}$

Q17 a) Modelling as a sphere, $V = \frac{4}{3}\pi r^3$
So $\frac{dV}{dr} = 4\pi r^2$
From the information in the question,
$\frac{dr}{d\theta} = -2500$ km K^{-1}, so
$$\frac{dV}{d\theta} = \frac{dV}{dr} \times \frac{dr}{d\theta}$$
$= 4\pi r^2 \times (-2500) = -10\,000\,\pi r^2$ km³ K⁻¹

b) Density $\rho = \frac{m}{V} = \frac{m}{kD^3}$
So $\frac{d\rho}{dD} = -\frac{3m}{kD^4}$
From the question, $\frac{dD}{d\theta} = -215$ km K⁻¹, so
$$\frac{d\rho}{d\theta} = \frac{d\rho}{dD} \times \frac{dD}{d\theta}$$
$= -\frac{3m}{kD^4} \times -215 = \frac{645m}{kD^4}$ kg km⁻³ K⁻¹

Exam-Style Questions — Chapter 4

Q1 a) Start by differentiating x and y with respect to θ:

$$\frac{dy}{d\theta} = 2\cos\theta \quad \textit{[1 mark]}$$

$$\frac{dx}{d\theta} = 3 + 3\sin 3\theta \quad \textit{[1 mark]}$$

$$\frac{dy}{dx} = \frac{dy}{d\theta} \div \frac{dx}{d\theta} = \frac{2\cos\theta}{3 + 3\sin 3\theta} \quad \textit{[1 mark]}$$

b) (i) We need the value of θ at $(\pi + 1, \sqrt{3})$:

$y = 2\sin\theta = \sqrt{3}$, for $-\pi \le \theta \le \pi$

$$\Rightarrow \theta = \frac{\pi}{3} \text{ or } \frac{2\pi}{3} \quad \textit{[1 mark]}$$

If $\theta = \frac{\pi}{3}$, then

$x = 3\theta - \cos 3\theta = \pi - \cos\pi = \pi + 1$.

If $\theta = \frac{2\pi}{3}$, then

$x = 3\theta - \cos 3\theta = 2\pi - \cos 2\pi = 2\pi - 1$.

So at $(\pi + 1, \sqrt{3})$, $\theta = \frac{\pi}{3}$ $\textit{[1 mark]}$

$\theta = \frac{\pi}{3}$

$$\Rightarrow \frac{dy}{dx} = \frac{2\cos\frac{\pi}{3}}{3 + 3\sin\pi} = \frac{2\left(\frac{1}{2}\right)}{3 + 0} = \frac{1}{3} \quad \textit{[1 mark]}$$

(ii) $\theta = \frac{\pi}{6} \Rightarrow x = \frac{\pi}{2} - \cos\frac{\pi}{2} = \frac{\pi}{2} - 0 = \frac{\pi}{2}$

$\theta = \frac{\pi}{6} \Rightarrow y = 2\sin\frac{\pi}{6} = 2 \times \frac{1}{2} = 1$

So $\theta = \frac{\pi}{6}$ at the point $(\frac{\pi}{2}, 1)$ $\textit{[1 mark]}$

$$\theta = \frac{\pi}{6} \Rightarrow \frac{dy}{dx} = \frac{2\cos\frac{\pi}{6}}{3 + 3\sin\frac{\pi}{2}}$$

$$= \frac{2\left(\frac{\sqrt{3}}{2}\right)}{3 + 3(1)} = \frac{\sqrt{3}}{6} \quad \textit{[1 mark]}$$

Gradient of normal =

$$-\frac{1}{\left(\frac{dy}{dx}\right)} = -\frac{6}{\sqrt{3}} = -\frac{6\sqrt{3}}{3} = -2\sqrt{3} \quad \textit{[1 mark]}$$

So the normal is $y = -2\sqrt{3}\,x + c$ for some c.

$$\Rightarrow 1 = -2\sqrt{3} \times \frac{\pi}{2} + c = -\pi\sqrt{3} + c$$

$$\Rightarrow c = 1 + \pi\sqrt{3}$$

The equation of the normal is

$y = -2\sqrt{3}\,x + 1 + \pi\sqrt{3}$ $\textit{[1 mark]}$

Q2 a) c is the value of y when $x = 2$. If $x = 2$, then

$6x^2y - 7 = 5x - 4y^2 - x^2$

$\Rightarrow 6(2)^2y - 7 = 5(2) - 4y^2 - (2)^2$

$\Rightarrow 24y - 7 = 6 - 4y^2$

$\Rightarrow 4y^2 + 24y - 13 = 0$

$\Rightarrow (2y + 13)(2y - 1) = 0$

$\Rightarrow y = -6.5$ or $y = 0.5$ $\textit{[1 mark]}$

$c > 0$, so $c = 0.5$ $\textit{[1 mark]}$

b) (i) Q is another point on C where $y = 0.5$.

If $y = 0.5$, then $6x^2y - 7 = 5x - 4y^2 - x^2$

$\Rightarrow 6x^2(0.5) - 7 = 5x - 4(0.5)^2 - x^2$ $\textit{[1 mark]}$

$\Rightarrow 3x^2 - 7 = 5x - 1 - x^2$

$\Rightarrow 4x^2 - 5x - 6 = 0$

$\Rightarrow (x - 2)(4x + 3)$

$\Rightarrow x = 2$ or $x = -0.75$

$x \ne 2$, as $x = 2$ at the other point where T

crosses C. So the coordinates of Q are

$(-0.75, 0.5)$. $\textit{[1 mark]}$

(ii) To find the gradient of C, use implicit differentiation.

Differentiate each term separately with respect to x:

$$\frac{d}{dx}6x^2y - \frac{d}{dx}7 = \frac{d}{dx}5x - \frac{d}{dx}4y^2 - \frac{d}{dx}x^2$$

$\textit{[1 mark]}$

Differentiate x-terms and constant terms:

$$\Rightarrow \frac{d}{dx}6x^2y - 0 = 5 - \frac{d}{dx}4y^2 - 2x$$

$\textit{[1 mark]}$

Differentiate y-terms using chain rule:

$$\Rightarrow \frac{d}{dx}6x^2y = 5 - \frac{d}{dy}4y^2\frac{dy}{dx} - 2x$$

$$\Rightarrow \frac{d}{dx}6x^2y = 5 - 8y\frac{dy}{dx} - 2x \quad \textit{[1 mark]}$$

Differentiate xy-terms using product rule:

$$\Rightarrow 6x^2\frac{dy}{dx} + y\frac{d}{dx}6x^2 = 5 - 8y\frac{dy}{dx} - 2x$$

$$\Rightarrow 6x^2\frac{dy}{dx} + 12xy = 5 - 8y\frac{dy}{dx} - 2x$$

$\textit{[1 mark]}$

Rearrange to make $\frac{dy}{dx}$ the subject:

$$\Rightarrow 6x^2\frac{dy}{dx} + 8y\frac{dy}{dx} = 5 - 2x - 12xy$$

$$\Rightarrow \frac{dy}{dx} = \frac{5 - 2x - 12xy}{6x^2 + 8y} \quad \textit{[1 mark]}$$

So at $Q = (-0.75, 0.5)$,

$$\frac{dy}{dx} = \frac{5 - 2(-0.75) - 12(-0.75)(0.5)}{6(-0.75)^2 + 8(0.5)}$$

$$= \frac{11}{7.375} = 1.49 \text{ to 3 s.f.} \quad \textit{[1 mark]}$$

Q3 a) $y = 4^x \Rightarrow \frac{dy}{dx} = 4^x \ln 4$ $\textit{[1 mark]}$

So $\frac{dy}{dx} = \ln 4 \Rightarrow 4^x = 1 \Rightarrow x = 0 \Rightarrow y = 4^0 = 1$

$\frac{dy}{dx} = \ln 4$ at coordinates $(0, 1)$ $\textit{[1 mark]}$

b) Use the chain rule to find $\frac{dy}{dx}$:

Let $u = (x - 4)^3$.

Then $\frac{dy}{dx} = \frac{dy}{du} \times \frac{du}{dx} = \frac{d}{du}(4^u) \times \frac{d}{dx}(x - 4)^3$

$\textit{[1 mark]}$

$= (4^u \ln 4)(3(x - 4)^2 \times 1)$

(using chain rule again to find $\frac{du}{dx}$)

$= 4^{(x-4)^3} 3(x - 4)^2 \ln 4$ $\textit{[1 mark]}$

So when $x = 3$, $\frac{dy}{dx} = 4^{(3-4)^3} 3(3 - 4)^2 \ln 4$

$\textit{[1 mark]}$

$\frac{dy}{dx} = 4^{-1} 3 \ln 4 = \frac{3}{4} \ln 4 = 1.040$ (to 3 d.p.)

$\textit{[1 mark]}$

Q4 a) $x^2y + y^2x - 2y^2 - xy^3 = 0$

$$\Rightarrow \frac{d}{dx}x^2y + \frac{d}{dx}y^2x - \frac{d}{dx}2y^2 - \frac{d}{dx}xy^3 = 0$$

$$\Rightarrow \frac{d}{dx}x^2y + \frac{d}{dx}y^2x - \frac{d}{dx}2y^2 - \frac{d}{dx}xy^3 = 0$$

$$\Rightarrow 2xy + x^2\frac{dy}{dx} + y^2 + 2yx\frac{dy}{dx}$$

$$- 4y\frac{dy}{dx} - y^3 - 3xy^2\frac{dy}{dx} = 0 \quad \textit{[1 mark]}$$

$$\Rightarrow x^2\frac{dy}{dx} + 2yx\frac{dy}{dx} - 4y\frac{dy}{dx} - 3xy^2\frac{dy}{dx}$$
$$= y^3 - y^2 - 2xy \textbf{ [1 mark]}$$

$$\frac{dy}{dx} = \frac{2xy + y^2 - y^3}{3xy^2 - x^2 - 2xy + 4y} \textbf{ [1 mark]}$$

b) At stationary points, $\frac{dy}{dx} = 0$,

so $2xy + y^2 - y^3 = 0$ **[1 mark]**

$\Rightarrow 2xy = y^3 - y^2$

$\Rightarrow x = \frac{y^3 - y^2}{2y}$

and hence $x = \frac{y^2 - y}{2}$ as required. **[1 mark]**

c) When $x = 2$, $4y + 2y^2 - 2y^2 - 2y^3 = 0$ **[1 mark]**

$\Rightarrow 4y - 2y^3 = 0 \Rightarrow 2y(2 - y^2) = 0$,

giving $y = 0$, $y = \pm\sqrt{2}$ as required. **[1 mark]**

d) $\frac{dy}{dx} = \frac{4\sqrt{2} + 2 - 2\sqrt{2}}{12 - 4 - 4\sqrt{2} + 4\sqrt{2}}$

$$= \frac{2\sqrt{2} + 2}{8} = \frac{\sqrt{2} + 1}{4} \textbf{ [1 mark]}$$

The equation of the tangent is the equation of the curve **[1 mark]**

$\sqrt{2} = \frac{\sqrt{2}}{2} + \frac{1}{2} + c$, hence $c = \frac{\sqrt{2} - 1}{2}$ **[1 mark]**

and the equation of the tangent is:

$$y = \left(\frac{\sqrt{2} + 1}{4}\right)x + \frac{\sqrt{2} - 1}{2} \textbf{ [1 mark]}$$

Q5 a) (i) Using implicit differentiation:

$$3e^x + 6y = 2x^2y \Rightarrow \frac{d}{dx}3e^x + \frac{d}{dx}6y = \frac{d}{dx}2x^2y$$

$$\Rightarrow 3e^x + 6\frac{dy}{dx} = 2x^2\frac{dy}{dx} + y\frac{d}{dx}2x^2$$

$$\Rightarrow 3e^x + 6\frac{dy}{dx} = 2x^2\frac{dy}{dx} + 4xy \textbf{ [1 mark]}$$

$$\Rightarrow (2x^2 - 6)\frac{dy}{dx} = 3e^x - 4xy \textbf{ [1 mark]}$$

$$\Rightarrow \frac{dy}{dx} = \frac{3e^x - 4xy}{2x^2 - 6} \textbf{ [1 mark]}$$

(ii) At the stationary points of C, $\frac{dy}{dx} = 0$

$$\Rightarrow \frac{3e^x - 4xy}{2x^2 - 6} = 0 \textbf{ [1 mark]}$$

$$\Rightarrow 3e^x - 4xy = 0$$

$$\Rightarrow y = \frac{3e^x}{4x} \textbf{ [1 mark]}$$

b) Substitute $y = \frac{3e^x}{4x}$ into the original equation of curve C:

$$3e^x + 6y = 2x^2y \Rightarrow 3e^x + 6\frac{3e^x}{4x} = 2x^2\frac{3e^x}{4x} \textbf{ [1 mark]}$$

$\Rightarrow 3e^x(1 + \frac{3}{2x} - \frac{x}{2}) = 0$

$3e^x = 0$ has no solutions, so $(1 + \frac{3}{2x} - \frac{x}{2}) = 0$ **[1 mark]**

$\Rightarrow x^2 - 2x - 3 = 0$

$\Rightarrow (x + 1)(x - 3) = 0$

$\Rightarrow x = -1$ and $x = 3$

$x = -1 \Rightarrow y = \frac{3e^{-1}}{4(-1)} = -\frac{3}{4e}$

$x = 3 \Rightarrow y = \frac{3e^3}{4(3)} = \frac{1}{4}e^3$

So the stationary points of C are $(-1, -\frac{3}{4e})$ and $(3, \frac{1}{4}e^3)$

[2 marks — 1 mark for each correct pair of coordinates]

Don't forget — if the question asks you for an exact answer, that usually means leaving it in terms of something like π or ln or, in this case, e.

Q6 a) First find the value of t when $y = -6$:

$y = 2 - t^3 = -6 \Rightarrow t^3 = 8 \Rightarrow t = 2$ **[1 mark]**

$\Rightarrow x = 2^2 + 2(2) - 3 = 5$

Now find the gradient of the curve:

$$\frac{dy}{dt} = -3t^2, \quad \frac{dx}{dt} = 2t + 2$$

So $\frac{dy}{dx} = \frac{dy}{dt} \div \frac{dx}{dt} = \frac{-3t^2}{2t + 2}$ **[1 mark]**

So when $t = 2$, $\frac{dy}{dx} = \frac{-3(2)^2}{2(2) + 2} = \frac{-12}{6} = -2$ **[1 mark]**

So the tangent at $y = -6$ is

$y = -2x + c \Rightarrow -6 = -2(5) + c \Rightarrow c = 4$

The equation of L is $y = -2x + 4$ **[1 mark]**

b) (i) Substitute $y = 2 - t^3$ and $x = t^2 + 2t - 3$ into the equation of L:

$y = -2x + 4$

$\Rightarrow 2 - t^3 = -2(t^2 + 2t - 3) + 4$ **[1 mark]**

$\Rightarrow 2 - t^3 = -2t^2 - 4t + 10$

$\Rightarrow t^3 - 2t^2 - 4t + 8 = 0$

We know from part (a) that $t = 2$ is a root, so take out $(t - 2)$ as a factor:

$\Rightarrow (t - 2)(t^2 - 4) = 0$ **[1 mark]**

$\Rightarrow (t - 2)(t + 2)(t - 2) = 0$

$\Rightarrow t = 2$ or $t = -2$ **[1 mark]**

So t must be -2 at P.

$t = -2 \Rightarrow x = (-2)^2 + 2(-2) - 3 = -3$,

$y = 2 - (-2)^3 = 10$.

The coordinates of P are $(-3, 10)$ **[1 mark]**

(ii) At P, $t = -2$,

so $\frac{dy}{dx} = \frac{-3(-2)^2}{2(-2) + 2} = \frac{-12}{-2} = 6$ **[1 mark]**

So the gradient of the normal at P is

$-\frac{1}{\left(\frac{dy}{dx}\right)} = -\frac{1}{6}$ **[1 mark]**

The equation of the normal at P is

$y = -\frac{1}{6}x + c \Rightarrow 10 = -\frac{(-3)}{6} + c \Rightarrow c = \frac{19}{2}$

So the normal to the curve at point P is

$y = -\frac{1}{6}x + \frac{19}{2}$ **[1 mark]**

Q7 a) Start by finding the missing side length of the triangular faces. Call the missing length s:

$s = \sqrt{x^2 + \left(\frac{3}{4}x\right)^2}$

$= \sqrt{x^2 + \frac{9}{16}x^2}$

$= \sqrt{\frac{25}{16}x^2}$

$= \frac{5}{4}x$ **[1 mark]**

Now find A by adding up the area of each of the faces:

$A = 2(\frac{1}{2} \times \frac{3}{2}x \times x) + (\frac{3}{2}x \times 4x) + 2(\frac{5}{4}x \times 4x)$
[1 mark]

$= \frac{3}{2}x^2 + 6x^2 + 10x^2$

$= \frac{35}{2}x^2$ **[1 mark]**

b) $\frac{dA}{dt} = 0.07$

$A = \frac{35}{2}x^2 \Rightarrow \frac{dA}{dx} = 35x$ **[1 mark]**

Using chain rule, $\frac{dx}{dt} = \frac{dx}{dA} \times \frac{dA}{dt}$ **[1 mark]**

$= \frac{1}{\left(\frac{dA}{dx}\right)} \times \frac{dA}{dt} = \frac{1}{35x} \times 0.07$

$= \frac{0.07}{35 \times 0.5} = 0.004 \text{ m s}^{-1}$ **[1 mark]**

c) First you need to figure out what the question is asking for. 'Find the rate of change of V' means we're looking for $\frac{dV}{dt}$.

Start by finding an expression for V:
$V = (\frac{1}{2} \times \frac{3}{2}x \times x) \times 4x = 3x^3$ **[1 mark]**

So $\frac{dV}{dx} = 9x^2$ **[1 mark]**

Using chain rule, $\frac{dV}{dt} = \frac{dV}{dx} \times \frac{dx}{dt}$ **[1 mark]**

$= 9x^2 \times \frac{0.07}{35x} = \frac{9(1.2)^2 \times 0.07}{35 \times 1.2} = 0.0216 \text{ m}^3 \text{ s}^{-1}$

[1 mark]

Chapter 5: Integration 1

1. Integration of $(ax + b)^n$

Exercise 1.1
— Integrating $(ax + b)^n$, $n \neq -1$
Q1 a) $\int (2x + 9)^4 \, dx = \frac{1}{2 \times 5}(2x + 9)^5 + C$

$= \frac{1}{10}(2x + 9)^5 + C$

b) $\int (x + 10)^{10} \, dx = \frac{1}{1 \times 11}(x + 10)^{11} + C$

$= \frac{1}{11}(x + 10)^{11} + C$

c) $\int (4x + 3)^5 \, dx = \frac{1}{4 \times 6}(4x + 3)^6 + C$

$= \frac{1}{24}(4x + 3)^6 + C$

d) $\int (5x)^7 \, dx = \frac{1}{5 \times 8}(5x)^8 + C = \frac{1}{40}(5x)^8 + C$

$= \frac{1}{40}5^8 x^8 + C = \frac{5^8}{40}x^8 + C = \frac{78125x^8}{8} + C$

e) $\int (7x - 2)^{-8} \, dx = \frac{1}{7 \times -7}(7x - 2)^{-7} + C$

$= -\frac{1}{49}(7x - 2)^{-7} + C = -\frac{1}{49(7x - 2)^7} + C$

f) $\int (3 - 5x)^{-2} \, dx = \frac{1}{-5 \times -1}(3 - 5x)^{-1} + C$

$= \frac{1}{5}(3 - 5x)^{-1} + C = \frac{1}{5(3 - 5x)} + C$

g) $\int (10x - 3)^{\frac{11}{8}} \, dx = \frac{1}{10 \times \frac{19}{8}}(10x - 3)^{\frac{19}{8}} + C$

$= \frac{1}{\left(\frac{95}{4}\right)}(10x - 3)^{\frac{19}{8}} + C = \frac{4}{95}(10x - 3)^{\frac{19}{8}} + C$

h) $\int (3x - 4)^{-\frac{4}{3}} \, dx = \frac{1}{3 \times \left(-\frac{1}{3}\right)}(3x - 4)^{-\frac{1}{3}} + C$

$= \frac{1}{-1}(3x - 4)^{-\frac{1}{3}} + C = -(3x - 4)^{-\frac{1}{3}} + C$

$= \frac{-1}{\sqrt[3]{3x - 4}} + C$

Q2 a) Begin by taking the constant of 8 outside of the integration and then integrate $\int (2x - 4)^4 \, dx$ as usual.

$\int 8(2x - 4)^4 \, dx = 8 \int (2x - 4)^4 \, dx$

$= 8 \times \left(\frac{1}{2 \times 5}(2x - 4)^5 + c\right)$

$= \frac{8}{10}(2x - 4)^5 + C$

$= \frac{4}{5}(2x - 4)^5 + C$

$= \frac{4(2x - 4)^5}{5} + C$

b) *Use your answer to part a). The integral you found will be the same but without the constant of integration — it'll have limits instead.*

$\int_{\frac{3}{2}}^{\frac{5}{2}} 8(2x - 4)^4 \, dx = \frac{4}{5}[(2x - 4)^5]_{\frac{3}{2}}^{\frac{5}{2}}$

$= \frac{4}{5}\left(\left[\left(2\left(\frac{5}{2}\right) - 4\right)^5\right] - \left[\left(2\left(\frac{3}{2}\right) - 4\right)^5\right]\right)$

$= \frac{4}{5}([(1)^5] - [(-1)^5])$

$= \frac{4}{5}([1] - [-1]) = \frac{8}{5}$

Q3 $\int_0^1 (6x + 1)^{-3} \, dx = \left[\frac{1}{6 \times -2}(6x + 1)^{-2}\right]_0^1$

$= -\frac{1}{12}[(6x + 1)^{-2}]_0^1$

$= -\frac{1}{12}([(7)^{-2}] - [(1)^{-2}])$

$= -\frac{1}{12}\left(\frac{1}{49} - 1\right) = \frac{4}{49}$

Q4 You've been given that $f'(x) = (8 - 7x)^4$ and you need to find $f(x)$, so integrate with respect to x.

$f(x) = \int f'(x) \, dx = \int (8 - 7x)^4 \, dx$

$= \frac{1}{-7 \times 5}(8 - 7x)^5 + C = -\frac{1}{35}(8 - 7x)^5 + C$

Substitute in the values of x and y at the point given to find the value of C.

$\frac{3}{35} = -\frac{1}{35}(8 - (7 \times 1))^5 + C$

$\Rightarrow \frac{3}{35} = -\frac{1}{35}(1)^5 + C$

$\Rightarrow C = \frac{4}{35}$

So $f(x) = -\frac{1}{35}(8 - 7x)^5 + \frac{4}{35}$

Q5 To find the area between the curve $y = (-x - 1)^{12}$ and the x-axis for $-1 \leq x \leq 0$ you just need to integrate the curve between -1 and 0 with respect to x.

$$\int_{-1}^{0} (-x - 1)^{12}\, dx = \left[\frac{1}{-1 \times 13}(-x - 1)^{13}\right]_{-1}^{0}$$

$$= -\frac{1}{13}\left[(-x - 1)^{13}\right]_{-1}^{0}$$

$$= -\frac{1}{13}\left([(-1)^{13}] - [(0)^{13}]\right) = -\frac{1}{13}(-1 - 0) = \frac{1}{13}$$

Q6 *Watch out — this integration is with respect to y, not x.*

$$\int (9 - y)^{\frac{1}{6}} + (9 - y)^{-6}\, dy$$

$$= \int (9 - y)^{\frac{1}{6}}\, dy + \int (9 - y)^{-6}\, dy$$

$$= \frac{1}{-1 \times \frac{7}{6}}(9 - y)^{\frac{7}{6}} + \frac{1}{-1 \times -5}(9 - y)^{-5} + C$$

$$= -\frac{6}{7}(9 - y)^{\frac{7}{6}} + \frac{1}{5}(9 - y)^{-5} + C$$

Q7 You need an integral of the form $\int (ax + b)^n\, dx$ if you want to use the formula, so write $\frac{-6}{(12x + 5)^2}$ as $-6(12x + 5)^{-2}$:

$$\int \frac{-6}{(12x + 5)^2}\, dx = \int -6(12x + 5)^{-2}\, dx$$

$$= -6\int (12x + 5)^{-2}\, dx$$

$$= -6\left(\frac{1}{12 \times -1} \times (12x + 5)^{-1} + c\right)$$

$$= \frac{-6}{-12}(12x + 5)^{-1} + C$$

$$= \frac{1}{2}(12x + 5)^{-1} + C$$

$$= \frac{1}{2(12x + 5)} + C$$

$$= \frac{1}{24x + 10} + C$$

2. Integration of e^x and $\frac{1}{x}$

Exercise 2.1 — Integrating e^x and e^{ax+b}

Q1 a) $\int 2e^x\, dx = 2\int e^x\, dx = 2e^x + C$

b) $\int 4x + 7e^x\, dx = \int 4x\, dx + \int 7e^x\, dx$
$$= \int 4x\, dx + 7\int e^x\, dx = 2x^2 + 7e^x + C$$

c) $\int e^{10x}\, dx = \frac{1}{10}e^{10x} + C$

d) $\int e^{-3x} + x\, dx = \int e^{-3x}\, dx + \int x\, dx$
$$= -\frac{1}{3}e^{-3x} + \frac{1}{2}x^2 + C$$

e) $\int e^{\frac{7}{2}x}\, dx = \frac{1}{\left(\frac{7}{2}\right)}e^{\frac{7}{2}x} + C = \frac{2}{7}e^{\frac{7}{2}x} + C$

f) $\int e^{4x-2}\, dx = \frac{1}{4}e^{4x-2} + C$

g) $\int \frac{1}{2}e^{2 - \frac{3}{2}x}\, dx = \frac{1}{2}\int e^{2 - \frac{3}{2}x}\, dx$
$$= \frac{1}{2} \times \left(\frac{1}{(-\frac{3}{2})}e^{2 - \frac{3}{2}x} + c\right) = \left(\frac{1}{2} \times -\frac{2}{3}e^{2 - \frac{3}{2}x}\right) + C$$
$$= -\frac{1}{3}e^{2 - \frac{3}{2}x} + C$$

h) $\int e^{4(\frac{x}{3} + 1)}\, dx = \int e^{\frac{4}{3}x + 4}\, dx$
$$= \frac{1}{\left(\frac{4}{3}\right)}e^{\frac{4}{3}x + 4} + C = \frac{3}{4}e^{4(\frac{x}{3} + 1)} + C$$

Q2 You've been given the derivative of the curve, so integrate it to get the equation of the curve.

$$y = \int \frac{dy}{dx}\, dx = \int 10e^{-5x - 1}\, dx = 10\int e^{-5x - 1}\, dx$$

$$= 10 \times \left(\frac{1}{-5}e^{-5x - 1} + c\right) = -2e^{-5x - 1} + C$$

To find C, use the fact that the curve goes through the origin $(0, 0)$. The equation of the curve is $y = -2e^{-5x - 1} + C$ and substituting in $x = 0$ and $y = 0$ gives:

$$0 = -2e^{-(5 \times 0) - 1} + C = -2e^{-1} + C = -\frac{2}{e} + C \text{ so } C = \frac{2}{e}.$$

So the curve has equation $y = -2e^{-5x - 1} + \frac{2}{e}$.

Q3 $\int e^{8y + 5}\, dy = \frac{1}{8}e^{8y + 5} + C$

Q4 a) $\int_{2}^{3} e^{2x}\, dx = \frac{1}{2}[e^{2x}]_{2}^{3} = \frac{1}{2}([e^6] - [e^4])$
$$= \frac{1}{2}(e^6 - e^4)$$

b) $\int_{-1}^{0} 12e^{12x + 12}\, dx = \left[12 \times \frac{1}{12}e^{12x + 12}\right]_{-1}^{0}$
$$= [e^{12x + 12}]_{-1}^{0} = e^{12} - e^0 = e^{12} - 1$$

c) $\int_{-\frac{\pi}{2}}^{\frac{\pi}{2}} e^{\pi - 2x}\, dx = \left[\frac{1}{-2}e^{\pi - 2x}\right]_{-\frac{\pi}{2}}^{\frac{\pi}{2}}$
$$= -\frac{1}{2}[e^{\pi - 2x}]_{-\frac{\pi}{2}}^{\frac{\pi}{2}}$$
$$= -\frac{1}{2}([e^{\pi - \pi}] - [e^{\pi + \pi}])$$
$$= -\frac{1}{2}(e^0 - e^{2\pi}) = \frac{1}{2}(e^{2\pi} - 1)$$

d) $\int_{3}^{6} \sqrt[6]{e^x} + \frac{1}{\sqrt[3]{e^x}}\, dx = \int_{3}^{6} (e^x)^{\frac{1}{6}} + (e^x)^{-\frac{1}{3}}\, dx$
$$= \int_{3}^{6} e^{\frac{x}{6}} + e^{-\frac{x}{3}}\, dx = \left[\frac{1}{(\frac{1}{6})}e^{\frac{x}{6}} + \frac{1}{(-\frac{1}{3})}e^{-\frac{x}{3}}\right]_{3}^{6}$$
$$= [6e^{\frac{x}{6}} - 3e^{-\frac{x}{3}}]_{3}^{6}$$
$$= [6e^1 - 3e^{-2}] - [6e^{\frac{1}{2}} - 3e^{-1}]$$
$$= 6e - \frac{3}{e^2} - 6\sqrt{e} + \frac{3}{e}$$

Exercise 2.2 — Integrating $\frac{1}{x}$ and $\frac{1}{ax + b}$

Q1 a) $\int \frac{19}{x}\, dx = 19\int \frac{1}{x}\, dx = 19\ln|x| + C$

b) $\int \frac{1}{7x}\, dx = \frac{1}{7}\int \frac{1}{x}\, dx = \frac{1}{7}\ln|x| + C$

An equivalent answer to b) would be $\frac{1}{7}\ln|7x| + C$ if you used the general formula for integrating $\frac{1}{ax + b}$ instead.

c) There is no constant term to take out here, so use the general formula:
$$\int \frac{1}{7x + 2}\, dx = \frac{1}{7}\ln|7x + 2| + C$$

d) $\int \frac{4}{1 - 3x}\, dx = 4\left(\frac{1}{-3}\ln|1 - 3x| + c\right)$
$$= -\frac{4}{3}\ln|1 - 3x| + C$$

Q2 $\int \frac{1}{8x} - \frac{20}{x}\,dx = \frac{1}{8}\int \frac{1}{x}\,dx - 20\int \frac{1}{x}\,dx$

$= \frac{1}{8}\ln|x| - 20\ln|x| + C = -\frac{159}{8}\ln|x| + C$

You could also notice that $\frac{1}{8x} - \frac{20}{x} = \frac{1-160}{8x} = \frac{-159}{8x}$ and integrate $\frac{-159}{8x}$ using the method for $\frac{1}{x}$.

Q3 a) $\int \frac{6}{x} - \frac{3}{x}\,dx = \int \frac{3}{x}\,dx = 3\ln|x| + C$

$= \ln|x|^3 + C = \ln|x^3| + C$

b) $\int_4^5 \frac{6}{x} - \frac{3}{x}\,dx = [\ln|x^3|]_4^5$

$= [\ln 5^3] - [\ln 4^3] = 3\ln 5 - 3\ln 4$

$= 3(\ln 5 - \ln 4) = 3\ln\left(\frac{5}{4}\right)$

You could also have written your answer as $\ln\frac{125}{64}$.

Q4 $\int_b^a 15(5 + 3x)^{-1}\,dx = \int_b^a \frac{15}{(5 + 3x)}\,dx$

$= \left[15 \times \frac{1}{3}\ln|5 + 3x|\right]_b^a = 5[\ln|5 + 3x|]_b^a$

$= 5(\ln|5 + 3a| - \ln|5 + 3b|)$

$= 5\ln\left(\frac{|5 + 3a|}{|5 + 3b|}\right) = 5\ln\left|\frac{5 + 3a}{5 + 3b}\right|$

$= \ln\left|\frac{5 + 3a}{5 + 3b}\right|^5$

Q5 Integrate the derivative to find f(x).

$f(x) = \int f'(x)\,dx = \int \frac{4}{10 - 9x}\,dx$

$= 4 \times \frac{1}{-9}\ln|10 - 9x| + C = -\frac{4}{9}\ln|10 - 9x| + C$

Now the curve passes through the point (1, 2), so substitute these values to find C.

$2 = -\frac{4}{9}\ln|10 - (9 \times 1)| + C$

$2 = -\frac{4}{9}\ln|1| + C$

$2 = 0 + C$

So C = 2 and the equation of f(x) is

$f(x) = -\frac{4}{9}\ln|10 - 9x| + 2$.

Q6 a) The area required is the shaded area below:

This is found by integrating the curve with respect to x between the limits x = -3 and x = 0.

So the area is expressed by the integral

$\int_{-3}^0 \frac{-7}{16 - 2x}\,dx$.

b) $\int_{-3}^0 \frac{-7}{16 - 2x} = \left[-7 \times \frac{1}{-2}\ln|16 - 2x|\right]_{-3}^0$

$= \frac{7}{2}[\ln|16 - 2x|]_{-3}^0$

$= \frac{7}{2}(\ln 16 - \ln 22)$

$= \frac{7}{2}\ln\frac{16}{22} = \frac{7}{2}\ln\frac{8}{11} = \ln\left[\left(\frac{8}{11}\right)^{\frac{7}{2}}\right]$

Q7 Work out the integral and put in the limits to find A.

$\int_1^A \frac{4}{6x - 5}\,dx = 10$

$\left[4 \times \frac{1}{6}\ln|6x - 5|\right]_1^A = 10$

$\frac{2}{3}[\ln|6x - 5|]_1^A = 10$

$\frac{2}{3}(\ln|6A - 5| - \ln|1|) = 10$

$\frac{2}{3}(\ln|6A - 5| - 0) = 10$

$\frac{2}{3}\ln|6A - 5| = 10$

$\ln|6A - 5| = \frac{10}{\left(\frac{2}{3}\right)} = 15$

Take the exponential of both sides to get rid of the ln.

$|6A - 5| = e^{15}$

$A = \frac{e^{15} + 5}{6}$

Note that A must be greater than or equal to 1, since it is the upper integration limit and 1 is the lower integration limit — so 6A − 5 must be greater than 6 − 5 = 1, so the modulus can be removed as it'll always be positive.

3. Integrating Using Partial Fractions

Exercise 3.1 — Use of partial fractions

Q1 a) First write the function as partial fractions. Factorise the denominator and write as an identity:

$\frac{24(x - 1)}{9 - 4x^2} = \frac{24(x - 1)}{(3 - 2x)(3 + 2x)} \equiv \frac{A}{(3 - 2x)} + \frac{B}{(3 + 2x)}$

Add the fractions and cancel denominators:

$\frac{24(x - 1)}{(3 - 2x)(3 + 2x)} \equiv \frac{A(3 + 2x) + B(3 - 2x)}{(3 - 2x)(3 + 2x)}$

$\Rightarrow 24(x - 1) \equiv A(3 + 2x) + B(3 - 2x)$

Substituting $x = -\frac{3}{2}$ gives: $-60 = 6B \Rightarrow B = -10$.

Substituting $x = \frac{3}{2}$ gives: $12 = 6A \Rightarrow A = 2$.

So $\frac{24(x - 1)}{9 - 4x^2} \equiv \frac{2}{(3 - 2x)} - \frac{10}{(3 + 2x)}$.

So the integral can be expressed:

$\int \frac{24(x - 1)}{9 - 4x^2}\,dx = \int \frac{2}{(3 - 2x)} - \frac{10}{(3 + 2x)}\,dx$

$= \frac{2}{-2}\ln|3 - 2x| - \frac{10}{2}\ln|3 + 2x| + C$

$= -\ln|3 - 2x| - 5\ln|3 + 2x| + C$

b) $\frac{-4x^2 - 21x + 82}{(5x + 2)(x - 3)(x - 4)} = \frac{A}{5x + 2} + \frac{B}{x - 3} + \frac{C}{x - 4}$

$\frac{-4x^2 - 21x + 82}{(5x + 2)(x - 3)(x - 4)} \equiv$

$\frac{A(x - 3)(x - 4) + B(5x + 2)(x - 4) + C(5x + 2)(x - 3)}{(5x + 2)(x - 3)(x - 4)}$

$-4x^2 - 21x + 82 \equiv$

$A(x - 3)(x - 4) + B(5x + 2)(x - 4) + C(5x + 2)(x - 3)$

Substituting $x = 3$ gives: $-17 = -17B \Rightarrow B = 1$

Substituting $x = 4$ gives: $-66 = 22C \Rightarrow C = -3$

Equating coefficients of x^2 gives
$A + 5B + 5C = -4 \Rightarrow A + 5 + -15 = -4 \Rightarrow A = 6$

So $\dfrac{-4x^2 - 21x + 82}{(5x + 2)(x - 3)(x - 4)} \equiv \dfrac{6}{5x + 2} + \dfrac{1}{x - 3} - \dfrac{3}{x - 4}$

So the integral can be expressed as:

$\displaystyle\int \dfrac{-4x^2 - 21x + 82}{(5x + 2)(x - 3)(x - 4)}\,dx$

$= \displaystyle\int \dfrac{6}{5x + 2} + \dfrac{1}{x - 3} - \dfrac{3}{x - 4}\,dx$

$= \dfrac{6}{5}\ln|5x + 2| + \ln|x - 3| - 3\ln|x - 4| + C$

c) *In this case there is a repeated factor in the denominator so it'll need to feature in two of the denominators of the partial fractions (once on its own and once squared).*

$\dfrac{7x + 4}{(x + 2)^2(x - 3)} \equiv \dfrac{A}{(x + 2)^2} + \dfrac{B}{(x + 2)} + \dfrac{C}{(x - 3)}$

Add the fractions and cancel denominators:

$\dfrac{7x + 4}{(x + 2)^2(x - 3)}$

$= \dfrac{A(x - 3) + B(x + 2)(x - 3) + C(x + 2)^2}{(x + 2)^2(x - 3)}$

$7x + 4 \equiv A(x - 3) + B(x + 2)(x - 3) + C(x + 2)^2$

Substituting $x = 3$ gives: $25 = 25C \Rightarrow C = 1$

Substituting $x = -2$ gives: $-10 = -5A \Rightarrow A = 2$

No value can be substituted to get B on its own, so equate coefficients:

Equating coefficients of x^2 we get:
$B + C = 0 \Rightarrow B + 1 = 0 \Rightarrow B = -1$

So

$\dfrac{7x + 4}{(x + 2)^2(x - 3)} \equiv \dfrac{2}{(x + 2)^2} - \dfrac{1}{(x + 2)} + \dfrac{1}{(x - 3)}$

So the integral can be expressed:

$\displaystyle\int \dfrac{7x + 4}{(x + 2)^2(x - 3)}\,dx$

$= \displaystyle\int \dfrac{2}{(x + 2)^2} - \dfrac{1}{(x + 2)} + \dfrac{1}{(x - 3)}\,dx$

$= -\dfrac{2}{x + 2} - \ln|x + 2| + \ln|x - 3| + C$

$= \ln\left|\dfrac{x - 3}{x + 2}\right| - \dfrac{2}{x + 2} + C$

Q2 First write the function as partial fractions:

$\dfrac{x}{(x - 2)(x - 3)} \equiv \dfrac{A}{x - 2} + \dfrac{B}{x - 3}$

$\Rightarrow \dfrac{x}{(x - 2)(x - 3)} \equiv \dfrac{A(x - 3) + B(x - 2)}{(x - 2)(x - 3)}$

$\Rightarrow x \equiv A(x - 3) + B(x - 2)$

Substituting $x = 3$: $B = 3$

Substituting $x = 2$: $-A = 2 \Rightarrow A = -2$

So $\dfrac{x}{(x - 2)(x - 3)} \equiv \dfrac{-2}{x - 2} + \dfrac{3}{x - 3}$

$\equiv \dfrac{3}{x - 3} - \dfrac{2}{x - 2}$

$\Rightarrow \displaystyle\int_0^1 \dfrac{x}{(x - 2)(x - 3)}\,dx = \int_0^1 \dfrac{3}{x - 3} - \dfrac{2}{x - 2}\,dx$

$= [3\ln|x - 3| - 2\ln|x - 2|]_0^1$

$= [3\ln|1 - 3| - 2\ln|1 - 2|]$
$\quad - [3\ln|0 - 3| - 2\ln|0 - 2|]$

$= 3\ln 2 - 2\ln 1 - 3\ln 3 + 2\ln 2$

$= 0 + 5\ln 2 - 3\ln 3$

$= \ln 2^5 - \ln 3^3 = \ln\dfrac{32}{27}$

Note that the modulus is important in this question, for example $|1 - 2| = |-1| = 1$.

Q3 a) First factorise the denominator and then express as an identity.

$\dfrac{6}{2x^2 - 5x + 2} = \dfrac{6}{(2x - 1)(x - 2)}$

$\equiv \dfrac{A}{2x - 1} + \dfrac{B}{x - 2}$

$\Rightarrow 6 \equiv A(x - 2) + B(2x - 1)$

Substituting $x = 2$ gives $6 = 3B$ so $B = 2$.

Substituting $x = \frac{1}{2}$ gives $6 = -\dfrac{3}{2}A$ so $A = -4$.

So $\dfrac{6}{2x^2 - 5x + 2} \equiv -\dfrac{4}{2x - 1} + \dfrac{2}{x - 2}$

$= \dfrac{2}{x - 2} - \dfrac{4}{2x - 1}$

b) Using part a)

$\displaystyle\int \dfrac{6}{2x^2 - 5x + 2}\,dx = \int \dfrac{2}{x - 2} - \dfrac{4}{2x - 1}\,dx$

$= 2\ln|x - 2| - \dfrac{4}{2}\ln|2x - 1| + C$

$= 2\ln|x - 2| - 2\ln|2x - 1| + C$

$x > 2$ so $x - 2 > 0$ and $2x - 1 > 3$ so the modulus signs can be removed. So:

$\displaystyle\int \dfrac{6}{2x^2 - 5x + 2}\,dx$

$= 2\ln(x - 2) - 2\ln(2x - 1) + C$

$= 2\ln\left(\dfrac{x - 2}{2x - 1}\right) + C = \ln\left[\left(\dfrac{x - 2}{2x - 1}\right)^2\right] + C$

c) Using part b)

$\displaystyle\int_3^5 \dfrac{6}{2x^2 - 5x + 2}\,dx = \left[\ln\left[\left(\dfrac{x - 2}{2x - 1}\right)^2\right]\right]_3^5$

$= \ln\left[\left(\dfrac{5 - 2}{10 - 1}\right)^2\right] - \ln\left[\left(\dfrac{3 - 2}{6 - 1}\right)^2\right]$

$= \ln\dfrac{1}{9} - \ln\dfrac{1}{25} = \ln\dfrac{25}{9}$

Q4 First express the fraction as an identity:

$\dfrac{3y + 5}{y(y + 10)} \equiv \dfrac{A}{y} + \dfrac{B}{y + 10}$

$\Rightarrow 3y + 5 \equiv A(y + 10) + By$

Now use the equating coefficients method:

Equating constant terms: $10A = 5$ so $A = \dfrac{1}{2}$.

Equating y coefficients: $A + B = 3 \Rightarrow \dfrac{1}{2} + B = 3$

$\Rightarrow B = \dfrac{5}{2}$.

So $\dfrac{3y + 5}{y(y + 10)} \equiv \dfrac{1}{2y} + \dfrac{5}{2(y + 10)}$

Now the integration can be expressed:

$$\int_1^2 \frac{3y + 5}{y(y + 10)}\, dy = \int_1^2 \frac{1}{2y} + \frac{5}{2(y + 10)}\, dy$$

$$= \left[\tfrac{1}{2}\ln|y| + \tfrac{5}{2}\ln|y + 10|\right]_1^2$$

$$= \left[\tfrac{1}{2}\ln|2| + \tfrac{5}{2}\ln|2 + 10|\right] - \left[\tfrac{1}{2}\ln|1| + \tfrac{5}{2}\ln|1 + 10|\right]$$

$$= \left[\tfrac{1}{2}\ln 2 + \tfrac{5}{2}\ln 12\right] - \left[0 + \tfrac{5}{2}\ln 11\right]$$

$$= \tfrac{1}{2}\ln 2 + \tfrac{5}{2}\ln 12 - \tfrac{5}{2}\ln 11 = \tfrac{1}{2}\left(\ln 2 + 5\ln \tfrac{12}{11}\right)$$

$$= \tfrac{1}{2}\left(\ln 2 + \ln\left(\tfrac{12}{11}\right)^5\right) = 0.564 \ \ (\text{3 d.p.})$$

Q5 First express $\dfrac{f(x)}{g(x)} = \dfrac{3x^2 + 17x - 32}{(x - 4)(x - 1)(x + 3)}$ as partial fractions. Write it out as an identity:

$$\frac{3x^2 + 17x - 32}{(x - 4)(x - 1)(x + 3)} \equiv \frac{A}{(x - 4)} + \frac{B}{(x - 1)} + \frac{C}{(x + 3)}$$

$$3x^2 + 17x - 32 \equiv A(x - 1)(x + 3)$$
$$+ B(x - 4)(x + 3)$$
$$+ C(x - 4)(x - 1)$$

Substituting $x = 1$ gives: $-12 = -12B \Rightarrow B = 1$

Substituting $x = -3$ gives: $-56 = 28C \Rightarrow C = -2$

Substituting $x = 4$ gives: $84 = 21A \Rightarrow A = 4$

So

$$\frac{3x^2 + 17x - 32}{(x - 4)(x - 1)(x + 3)} \equiv \frac{4}{(x - 4)} + \frac{1}{(x - 1)} - \frac{2}{(x + 3)}$$

Now the integral can be expressed:

$$\int_b^a \frac{f(x)}{g(x)}\, dx = \int_b^a \frac{3x^2 + 17x - 32}{(x - 4)(x - 1)(x + 3)}\, dx$$

$$= \int_b^a \frac{4}{(x - 4)} + \frac{1}{(x - 1)} - \frac{2}{(x + 3)}\, dx$$

$$= [4\ln|x - 4| + \ln|x - 1| - 2\ln|x + 3|]_b^a$$

Notice that $x > 4$, so $x - 4 > 0$, $x - 1 > 3$ and $x + 3 > 7$ so the modulus signs can be removed. You have:

$$\int_b^a \frac{f(x)}{g(x)}\, dx = [4\ln(x - 4) + \ln(x - 1) - 2\ln(x + 3)]_b^a$$

$$= [\ln(x - 4)^4 + \ln(x - 1) - \ln(x + 3)^2]_b^a$$

$$= \left[\ln\left(\frac{(x - 4)^4(x - 1)}{(x + 3)^2}\right)\right]_b^a$$

$$= \ln\left(\frac{(a - 4)^4(a - 1)(b + 3)^2}{(b - 4)^4(b - 1)(a + 3)^2}\right)$$

Q6 Again, begin by writing the function as partial fractions.

$$\frac{-(t + 3)}{(3t + 2)(t + 1)} \equiv \frac{A}{(3t + 2)} + \frac{B}{(t + 1)}$$

$$\Rightarrow -(t + 3) \equiv A(t + 1) + B(3t + 2)$$

Substituting $t = -1$ gives: $-2 = -B$ so $B = 2$

Equating coefficients of t gives
$A + 3B = -1 \Rightarrow A + 6 = -1 \Rightarrow A = -7$

So $\dfrac{-(t + 3)}{(3t + 2)(t + 1)} \equiv \dfrac{2}{(t + 1)} - \dfrac{7}{(3t + 2)}$

The integral can be expressed:

$$\int_0^{\frac{2}{3}} \frac{-(t + 3)}{(3t + 2)(t + 1)}\, dx = \int_0^{\frac{2}{3}} \frac{2}{(t + 1)} - \frac{7}{(3t + 2)}\, dx$$

$$= \left[2\ln|t + 1| - \tfrac{7}{3}\ln|3t + 2|\right]_0^{\frac{2}{3}}$$

$$= \left[2\ln\left|\tfrac{5}{3}\right| - \tfrac{7}{3}\ln|4|\right] - \left[2\ln|1| - \tfrac{7}{3}\ln|2|\right]$$

$$= \left[2\ln\left(\tfrac{5}{3}\right) - \tfrac{7}{3}\ln(4)\right] - \left[0 - \tfrac{7}{3}\ln(2)\right]$$

$$= 2\ln\left(\tfrac{5}{3}\right) - \tfrac{7}{3}\ln(4) + \tfrac{7}{3}\ln(2)$$

$$= 2\ln\left(\tfrac{5}{3}\right) - \tfrac{7}{3}(\ln(4) - \ln(2))$$

$$= 2\ln\left(\tfrac{5}{3}\right) - \tfrac{7}{3}\ln\left(\tfrac{4}{2}\right) = 2\ln\left(\tfrac{5}{3}\right) - \tfrac{7}{3}\ln 2$$

Q7 a) $\dfrac{18x^2 + 3x - 8}{(2x + 1)(3x - 1)} \equiv \dfrac{18x^2 + 3x - 8}{6x^2 + x - 1}$

$$6x^2 + x - 1 \overline{\smash{\big)}\ 18x^2 + 3x - 8}$$
$$\underline{-(18x^2 + 3x - 3)}$$
$$- 5$$

So $\dfrac{18x^2 + 3x - 8}{(2x + 1)(3x - 1)} \equiv 3 - \dfrac{5}{6x^2 + x - 1}$

$$\equiv 3 - \frac{5}{(2x + 1)(3x - 1)}$$

So $A = 3$ and $\dfrac{-5}{(2x + 1)(3x - 1)} \equiv \dfrac{B}{2x + 1} + \dfrac{C}{3x - 1}$

Solve this as you would with normal partial fractions:

$$\Rightarrow -5 \equiv B(3x - 1) + C(2x + 1)$$

Equating coefficients:
$$-5 = -B + C$$
$$0 = 3B + 2C$$

Solving simultaneously: $C = -3$ and $B = 2$
Your other option with questions like this is to just multiply through by the denominator of the original fraction, then use the substitution and equating coefficients methods to find A, B and C from there.

b) From a) you have:

$$\frac{18x^2 + 3x - 8}{(2x + 1)(3x - 1)} \equiv 3 + \frac{2}{(2x + 1)} - \frac{3}{(3x - 1)}$$

So the integral can be expressed:

$$\int_2^5 \frac{18x^2 + 3x - 8}{(2x + 1)(3x - 1)}\, dx$$

$$= \int_2^5 3 + \frac{2}{(2x + 1)} - \frac{3}{(3x - 1)}\, dx$$

$$= [3x + \ln|2x + 1| - \ln|3x - 1|]_2^5$$

$$= [15 + \ln|11| - \ln|14|] - [6 + \ln|5| - \ln|5|]$$

$$= 15 + \ln 11 - \ln 14 - 6 = 9 + \ln\left(\tfrac{11}{14}\right)$$

So $p = 9$ and $q = \dfrac{11}{14}$.

4. Integration of Trigonometric Functions

Exercise 4.1 —
Integration of sin x and cos x

Q1 **a)** $\int \frac{1}{7}\cos x\,dx = \frac{1}{7}\int \cos x\,dx = \frac{1}{7}\sin x + C$

b) $\int -3\sin x\,dx = -3\int \sin x\,dx$

$$= -3(-\cos x) + C = 3\cos x + C$$

c) $\int -3\cos x - 3\sin x\,dx = -3\int \cos x + \sin x\,dx$

$$= -3(\sin x - \cos x + c)$$

$$= -3\sin x + 3\cos x + C$$

d) $\int \sin 5x\,dx = -\frac{1}{5}\cos 5x + C$

e) $\int \cos\left(\frac{x}{7}\right)dx = \frac{1}{\left(\frac{1}{7}\right)}\sin\left(\frac{x}{7}\right) + C = 7\sin\left(\frac{x}{7}\right) + C$

f) $\int 2\sin(-3x)\,dx = 2\int \sin(-3x)\,dx$

$$= 2\left(-\left(-\frac{1}{3}\right)\cos(-3x) + c\right)$$

$$= \frac{2}{3}\cos(-3x) + C$$

An alternative solution would be $\frac{2}{3}\cos(3x) + C$ since cos(x) = cos(−x).

g) $\int 5\cos\left(3x + \frac{\pi}{5}\right)dx = 5\left(\frac{1}{3}\sin\left(3x + \frac{\pi}{5}\right) + c\right)$

$$= \frac{5}{3}\sin\left(3x + \frac{\pi}{5}\right) + C$$

h) $\int -4\sin\left(4x - \frac{\pi}{3}\right)dx = -4\left(-\frac{1}{4}\cos\left(4x - \frac{\pi}{3}\right) + c\right)$

$$= \cos\left(4x - \frac{\pi}{3}\right) + C$$

i) $\int \cos(4x + 3) + \sin(3 - 4x)\,dx$

$$= \frac{1}{4}\sin(4x + 3) + \frac{1}{-4}(-\cos(3 - 4x)) + C$$

$$= \frac{1}{4}\sin(4x + 3) + \frac{1}{4}\cos(3 - 4x) + C$$

Q2 $\int \frac{1}{2}\cos 3\theta - \sin\theta\,d\theta = \frac{1}{2}\left(\frac{1}{3}\sin 3\theta\right) - (-\cos\theta) + C$

$$= \frac{1}{6}\sin 3\theta + \cos\theta + C$$

Q3 **a)** $\int_0^{\frac{\pi}{2}} \sin x\,dx = [-\cos x]_0^{\frac{\pi}{2}} = -\cos\frac{\pi}{2} + \cos 0$

$$= 0 + 1 = 1$$

b) $\int_{\frac{\pi}{6}}^{\frac{\pi}{3}} \sin 3x\,dx = -\frac{1}{3}[\cos 3x]_{\frac{\pi}{6}}^{\frac{\pi}{3}}$

$$= -\frac{1}{3}\left(\left[\cos\left(3 \times \frac{\pi}{3}\right)\right] - \left[\cos\left(3 \times \frac{\pi}{6}\right)\right]\right)$$

$$= -\frac{1}{3}\left(\cos\pi - \cos\frac{\pi}{2}\right) = -\frac{1}{3}(-1 - 0) = \frac{1}{3}$$

c) $\int_{-1}^2 3\sin(\pi x + \pi)\,dx = -\frac{3}{\pi}[\cos(\pi x + \pi)]_{-1}^2$

$$= -\frac{3}{\pi}(\cos 3\pi - \cos 0)$$

$$= -\frac{3}{\pi}(-1 - 1) = \frac{6}{\pi}$$

Q4 Integrate the function with respect to x within the limits 1 and 2:

$$\int_1^2 2\pi\cos\left(\frac{\pi x}{2}\right)dx = \frac{2\pi}{\left(\frac{\pi}{2}\right)}\left[\sin\left(\frac{\pi x}{2}\right)\right]_1^2 = 4\left[\sin\left(\frac{\pi x}{2}\right)\right]_1^2$$

$$= 4\left(\sin(\pi) - \sin\left(\frac{\pi}{2}\right)\right) = 4(0 - 1) = -4$$

So the area required is 4.

The integral gives a negative value for the area of the region — this means that most or all of the area is below the x-axis (if most or all of the area was above the x-axis, the integral would be positive).

If you sketch the original function, you'll see that the entire area is below the x-axis.

Q5 $\int_{\frac{\pi}{3}}^{\frac{\pi}{2}} \sin(-x) + \cos(-x)\,dx = \int_{\frac{\pi}{3}}^{\frac{\pi}{2}} -\sin x + \cos x\,dx$

$$= [-(-\cos x) + \sin x]_{\frac{\pi}{3}}^{\frac{\pi}{2}}$$

$$= [\cos x + \sin x]_{\frac{\pi}{3}}^{\frac{\pi}{2}}$$

$$= \left[\cos\left(\frac{\pi}{2}\right) + \sin\left(\frac{\pi}{2}\right)\right] - \left[\cos\left(\frac{\pi}{3}\right) + \sin\left(\frac{\pi}{3}\right)\right]$$

$$= [0 + 1] - \left[\frac{1}{2} + \frac{\sqrt{3}}{2}\right]$$

$$= 1 - \frac{1}{2} - \frac{\sqrt{3}}{2} = \frac{1}{2} - \frac{\sqrt{3}}{2} = \frac{1 - \sqrt{3}}{2}$$

sin(−x) = −sin x and cos(−x) = cos x are used in the first step of this solution.

Q6 Integrate the function between -2π and π:

$$\int_{-2\pi}^{\pi} 5\cos\frac{x}{6}\,dx = \left[\frac{5}{\left(\frac{1}{6}\right)}\sin\left(\frac{x}{6}\right)\right]_{-2\pi}^{\pi} = 30\left[\sin\left(\frac{x}{6}\right)\right]_{-2\pi}^{\pi}$$

$$= 30\left(\sin\left(\frac{\pi}{6}\right) - \sin\left(-\frac{\pi}{3}\right)\right)$$

$$= 30\left(\frac{1}{2} - \left(-\frac{\sqrt{3}}{2}\right)\right)$$

$$= 30\left(\frac{1 + \sqrt{3}}{2}\right) = 15(1 + \sqrt{3})$$

Exercise 4.2 — Integration of sec² x

Q1 **a)** $\int 2\sec^2 x + 1\,dx = 2\tan x + x + C$

b) $\int \sec^2 9x\,dx = \frac{1}{9}\tan 9x + C$

c) $\int 20\sec^2 3y\,dy = 20 \times \frac{1}{3}\tan 3y + C$

$$= \frac{20}{3}\tan 3y + C$$

d) $\int \sec^2\frac{x}{7}\,dx = \frac{1}{\left(\frac{1}{7}\right)}\tan\left(\frac{x}{7}\right) + C$

$$= 7\tan\left(\frac{x}{7}\right) + C$$

e) $\int_0^{\frac{\pi}{3}} -\frac{1}{\cos^2\theta}\,d\theta = \int_0^{\frac{\pi}{3}} -\sec^2\theta\,d\theta = [-\tan\theta]_0^{\frac{\pi}{3}}$

$$= -\sqrt{3} + 0 = -\sqrt{3}$$

f) $\int_0^{\frac{\pi}{4}} 3\sec^2(-3x)\,dx = \left[-\frac{3}{3}\tan(-3x)\right]_0^{\frac{\pi}{4}}$

$$= [-\tan(-3x)]_0^{\frac{\pi}{4}}$$

$$= \left[-\tan\left(-3 \times \frac{\pi}{4}\right)\right] - [-\tan(0)]$$

$$= -1 + 0 = -1$$

Q2 Integrate the function between the limits:

$$\int_{\frac{2}{3}\pi}^{\pi} \sec^2 x \, dx = [\tan x]_{\frac{2}{3}\pi}^{\pi} = \tan \pi - \tan \frac{2\pi}{3}$$

$$= 0 - (-\sqrt{3}) = \sqrt{3}$$

Q3 The constants α and β do not affect the integration. You only need to worry about the coefficients of x.

$$\int \sec^2(x + \alpha) + \sec^2(3x + \beta) \, dx$$

$$= \tan(x + \alpha) + \frac{1}{3}\tan(3x + \beta) + C$$

Q4 $\int_{\frac{\pi}{12}}^{\frac{\pi}{6}} 5A \sec^2\left(\frac{\pi}{3} - 2\theta\right) d\theta = \left[-\frac{5A}{2}\tan\left(\frac{\pi}{3} - 2\theta\right)\right]_{\frac{\pi}{12}}^{\frac{\pi}{6}}$

$$= -\frac{5A}{2}\left[\tan\left(\frac{\pi}{3} - 2\theta\right)\right]_{\frac{\pi}{12}}^{\frac{\pi}{6}}$$

$$= -\frac{5A}{2}\left(\left[\tan\left(\frac{\pi}{3} - \frac{\pi}{3}\right)\right] - \left[\tan\left(\frac{\pi}{3} - \frac{\pi}{6}\right)\right]\right)$$

$$= -\frac{5A}{2}\left(\tan(0) - \tan\left(\frac{\pi}{6}\right)\right)$$

$$= -\frac{5A}{2}\left(0 - \frac{\sqrt{3}}{3}\right)$$

$$= \frac{5\sqrt{3}A}{6}$$

Exercise 4.3 — Integration of other trigonometric functions

Q1 **a)** $\int \csc^2 11x \, dx = -\frac{1}{11}\cot 11x + C$

b) $\int 5 \sec 10\theta \tan 10\theta \, d\theta = 5 \times \frac{1}{10}\sec 10\theta + C$

$$= \frac{1}{2}\sec 10\theta + C$$

c) $\int -\csc(x + 17)\cot(x + 17) \, dx$
$$= -(-\csc(x + 17)) + C$$
$$= \csc(x + 17) + C$$

d) $\int -3 \csc 3x \cot 3x \, dx = -3\left(-\frac{1}{3}\csc 3x\right) + C$
$$= \csc 3x + C$$

e) $\int 13 \sec\left(\frac{\pi}{4} - x\right)\tan\left(\frac{\pi}{4} - x\right) dx$
$$= 13\left(\frac{1}{-1}\sec\left(\frac{\pi}{4} - x\right)\right) + C$$
$$= -13 \sec\left(\frac{\pi}{4} - x\right) + C$$

Q2 $\int 10 \csc^2\left(\alpha - \frac{x}{2}\right) - 60 \sec(\alpha - 6x)\tan(\alpha - 6x) \, dx$

$$= -\frac{10}{\left(-\frac{1}{2}\right)}\cot\left(\alpha - \frac{x}{2}\right) - \frac{60}{-6}\sec(\alpha - 6x) + C$$

$$= 20 \cot\left(\alpha - \frac{x}{2}\right) + 10 \sec(\alpha - 6x) + C$$

Q3 $\int_{\frac{\pi}{12}}^{\frac{\pi}{8}} 6 \sec 2x \tan 2x + 6 \csc 2x \cot 2x \, dx$

$$= \left[\frac{6}{2}\sec 2x - \frac{6}{2}\csc 2x\right]_{\frac{\pi}{12}}^{\frac{\pi}{8}}$$

$$= 3\left[\sec 2x - \csc 2x\right]_{\frac{\pi}{12}}^{\frac{\pi}{8}}$$

$$= 3\left(\left[\sec\frac{\pi}{4} - \csc\frac{\pi}{4}\right] - \left[\sec\frac{\pi}{6} - \csc\frac{\pi}{6}\right]\right)$$

$$= 3\left(\sqrt{2} - \sqrt{2} - \frac{2}{\sqrt{3}} + 2\right)$$

$$= 3\left(2 - \frac{2}{\sqrt{3}}\right) = 6 - 2\sqrt{3}$$

Q4 $\int_{\frac{\pi}{12}}^{\frac{\pi}{6}} \csc^2(3x) \, dx = \left[-\frac{1}{3}\cot(3x)\right]_{\frac{\pi}{12}}^{\frac{\pi}{6}}$

$$= -\frac{1}{3}\left(\cot\left(\frac{\pi}{2}\right) - \cot\left(\frac{\pi}{4}\right)\right) = -\frac{1}{3}(0 - 1) = \frac{1}{3}$$

The graph of y = cot x is covered in Chapter 2 — remember that it is 1 at x = $\frac{\pi}{4}$ and O at x = $\frac{\pi}{2}$. Or if you know your tan values of common angles, you can use these instead.

5. Integration of $\dfrac{f'(x)}{f(x)}$

Exercise 5.1 — Integrating $\dfrac{f'(x)}{f(x)}$

Q1 **a)** Differentiating the denominator:
$$\frac{d}{dx}(x^4 - 1) = 4x^3 = \text{numerator}$$
$$\int \frac{4x^3}{x^4 - 1} \, dx = \ln|x^4 - 1| + C$$

b) $\frac{d}{dx}(x^2 - x) = 2x - 1 = \text{numerator}$
$$\int \frac{2x - 1}{x^2 - x} \, dx = \ln|x^2 - x| + C$$

c) $\frac{d}{dx}(3x^5 + 6) = 15x^4$
$$\int \frac{x^4}{3x^5 + 6} \, dx = \frac{1}{15}\int \frac{15x^4}{3x^5 + 6} \, dx$$
$$= \frac{1}{15}\ln|3x^5 + 6| + C$$

d) $\frac{d}{dx}(x^4 + 2x^3 - x) = 4x^3 + 6x^2 - 1$
$$\int \frac{12x^3 + 18x^2 - 3}{x^4 + 2x^3 - x} \, dx = \int \frac{3(4x^3 + 6x^2 - 1)}{x^4 + 2x^3 - x} \, dx$$
$$= 3\int \frac{4x^3 + 6x^2 - 1}{x^4 + 2x^3 - x} \, dx = 3 \ln|x^4 + 2x^3 - x| + C$$

e) $\frac{d}{dx}(e^x + 6) = e^x$
$$\int \frac{e^x}{e^x + 6} \, dx = \ln|e^x + 6| + C$$

f) $\frac{d}{dx}(e^{2x} + 6e^x) = 2e^{2x} + 6e^x = 2(e^{2x} + 3e^x)$
$$\int \frac{2(e^{2x} + 3e^x)}{e^{2x} + 6e^x} \, dx = \ln|e^{2x} + 6e^x| + C$$

g) $\frac{d}{dx}(e^x + 3) = e^x$
$$\int \frac{e^x}{3(e^x + 3)} \, dx = \frac{1}{3}\int \frac{e^x}{(e^x + 3)} \, dx$$
$$= \frac{1}{3}\ln|e^x + 3| + C$$

h) $\frac{d}{dx}(1 + \sin 2x) = 2 \cos 2x$
$$\int \frac{2 \cos 2x}{1 + \sin 2x} \, dx = \ln|1 + \sin 2x| + C$$

i) $\frac{d}{dx}(\cos 3x - 1) = -3 \sin 3x$
$$\int \frac{\sin 3x}{\cos 3x - 1} \, dx = -\frac{1}{3}\int \frac{-3 \sin 3x}{\cos 3x - 1} \, dx$$
$$= -\frac{1}{3}\ln|\cos 3x - 1| + C$$

j) $\frac{d}{dx}(\text{cosec}\,x - x^2 + 4) = -\text{cosec}\,x\cot x - 2x$

$\int \frac{3\,\text{cosec}\,x\cot x + 6x}{\text{cosec}\,x - x^2 + 4}\,dx$

$= \int \frac{-3(-\text{cosec}\,x\cot x - 2x)}{\text{cosec}\,x - x^2 + 4}\,dx$

$= -3\int \frac{-\text{cosec}\,x\cot x - 2x}{\text{cosec}\,x - x^2 + 4}\,dx$

$= -3\ln|\text{cosec}\,x - x^2 + 4| + C$

k) $\frac{d}{dx}(\tan x) = \sec^2 x$

$\int \frac{\sec^2 x}{\tan x}\,dx = \ln|\tan x| + C$

l) $\frac{d}{dx}(\sec x + 5) = \sec x\tan x$

$\int \frac{\sec x\tan x}{\sec x + 5}\,dx = \ln|\sec x + 5| + C$

Q2 $\frac{d}{dx}(\sin(2x + 7)) = 2\cos(2x + 7)$

$\int \frac{4\cos(2x + 7)}{\sin(2x + 7)}\,dx = 2\int \frac{2\cos(2x + 7)}{\sin(2x + 7)}\,dx$
$= 2(\ln|\sin(2x + 7)| + c) = 2(\ln|\sin(2x + 7)| + \ln k)$
$= 2\ln|k\sin(2x + 7)|$

Q3 a) Using the hint, multiply the inside of the integral by a fraction which is the same on the top and bottom (it's equal to 1, so it'll make no difference).

$\int \sec x\,dx = \int \sec x\left(\frac{\sec x + \tan x}{\sec x + \tan x}\right)dx$

$= \int \frac{\sec^2 x + \sec x\tan x}{\sec x + \tan x}\,dx$

Now differentiating the denominator of this integral gives:

$\frac{d}{dx}(\sec x + \tan x) = \sec x\tan x + \sec^2 x$

So the numerator is the derivative of the denominator, so use the result:

$\int \sec x\,dx = \int \frac{\sec^2 x + \sec x\tan x}{\sec x + \tan x}\,dx$

$= \ln|\sec x + \tan x| + C$

b) Use the same method as part a), this time using $\frac{\text{cosec}\,x + \cot x}{\text{cosec}\,x + \cot x}$:

$\int \text{cosec}\,x\,dx = \int \text{cosec}\,x\left(\frac{\text{cosec}\,x + \cot x}{\text{cosec}\,x + \cot x}\right)dx$

$= \int \frac{\text{cosec}^2 x + \text{cosec}\,x\cot x}{\text{cosec}\,x + \cot x}\,dx$

Differentiating the denominator of this integral:

$\frac{d}{dx}(\text{cosec}\,x + \cot x) = -\text{cosec}\,x\cot x - \text{cosec}^2 x$

$= -(\text{cosec}\,x\cot x + \text{cosec}^2 x)$

So the numerator is minus the derivative of the denominator, so use the result:

$\int \text{cosec}\,x\,dx = \int \frac{\text{cosec}^2 x + \text{cosec}\,x\cot x}{\text{cosec}\,x + \cot x}\,dx$

$= -\int \frac{-\text{cosec}^2 x - \text{cosec}\,x\cot x}{\text{cosec}\,x + \cot x}\,dx$

$= -\ln|\text{cosec}\,x + \cot x| + C$

Q4 a) $\int 2\tan x\,dx = 2\int \frac{\sin x}{\cos x}\,dx = -2\int \frac{-\sin x}{\cos x}\,dx$
$= -2\ln|\cos x| + C$

b) $\int \tan 2x\,dx = \int \frac{\sin 2x}{\cos 2x}\,dx = -\frac{1}{2}\int \frac{-2\sin 2x}{\cos 2x}\,dx$
$= -\frac{1}{2}\ln|\cos 2x| + C$

c) $\int 4\,\text{cosec}\,x\,dx = 4\int \text{cosec}\,x\,dx$
$= -4\ln|\text{cosec}\,x + \cot x| + C$

d) $\int \cot 3x\,dx = \frac{1}{3}\ln|\sin 3x| + C$

e) $\int \frac{1}{2}\sec 2x\,dx = \frac{1}{2}\left(\frac{1}{2}\ln|\sec 2x + \tan 2x| + c\right)$
$= \frac{1}{4}\ln|\sec 2x + \tan 2x| + C$

f) $\int 3\,\text{cosec}\,6x\,dx = 3\left(-\frac{1}{6}\ln|\text{cosec}\,6x + \cot 6x| + c\right)$
$= -\frac{1}{2}\ln|\text{cosec}\,6x + \cot 6x| + C$

Q5 *This one looks really complicated, but if you split it into parts and use some standard results it's actually pretty simple.*

$\int \frac{\sec^2 x}{2\tan x} - 4\sec 2x\tan 2x + \frac{\text{cosec}\,2x\cot 2x - 1}{\text{cosec}\,2x + 2x}\,dx$

$= \int \frac{\sec^2 x}{2\tan x}\,dx - \int 4\sec 2x\tan 2x\,dx$
$\quad + \int \frac{\text{cosec}\,2x\cot 2x - 1}{\text{cosec}\,2x + 2x}\,dx$

$= \frac{1}{2}\int \frac{\sec^2 x}{\tan x}\,dx - \int 4\sec 2x\tan 2x\,dx$
$\quad - \frac{1}{2}\int \frac{-2\,\text{cosec}\,2x\cot 2x + 2}{\text{cosec}\,2x + 2x}\,dx$

$= \frac{1}{2}\ln|\tan x| - 2\sec 2x - \frac{1}{2}\ln|\text{cosec}\,2x + 2x| + C$

The first and third integrals were put in the form $\int \frac{f'(x)}{f(x)}\,dx$, and the second one you can tackle by reversing the formula $\frac{d}{dx}(\sec x) = \sec x\tan x$ from C3.

6. Integrating $\frac{du}{dx}\,f'(u)$

Exercise 6.1 — Integrating using the reverse of the chain rule

Q1 Let $u = x^2$ so $\frac{du}{dx} = 2x$ and $f'(u) = e^u$ so $f(u) = e^u$.
Using the formula:
$\int 2xe^{x^2}\,dx = e^{x^2} + C$

Q2 Let $u = 2x^3$ so $\frac{du}{dx} = 6x^2$ and $f'(u) = e^u$ so $f(u) = e^u$.
Using the formula:
$\int 6x^2 e^{2x^3}\,dx = e^{2x^3} + C$

Q3 Let $u = \sqrt{x}$ so $\frac{du}{dx} = \frac{1}{2\sqrt{x}}$, and $f'(u) = e^u$ so $f(u) = e^u$.
Using the formula:
$\int \frac{1}{2\sqrt{x}}e^{\sqrt{x}}\,dx = e^{\sqrt{x}} + C$

Q4 Let $u = x^4$ so $\dfrac{du}{dx} = 4x^3$, and $f'(u) = e^u$ so $f(u) = e^u$.

Use the formula:

$$\int 4x^3 e^{x^4}\,dx = e^{x^4} + c$$

So divide by 4 to get the original integral:

$$\int x^3 e^{x^4}\,dx = \frac{1}{4}\int 4x^3 e^{x^4}\,dx = \frac{1}{4}e^{x^4} + C$$

Q5 Let $u = x^2 - \dfrac{1}{2}x$ so $\dfrac{du}{dx} = 2x - \dfrac{1}{2} = \dfrac{1}{2}(4x - 1)$, and $f'(u) = e^u$ so $f(u) = e^u$.

Use the formula:

$$\int \left(2x - \frac{1}{2}\right)e^{\left(x^2 - \frac{1}{2}x\right)}\,dx = e^{\left(x^2 - \frac{1}{2}x\right)} + c$$

Multiply by 2 to get the original integral:

$$\int (4x - 1)e^{\left(x^2 - \frac{1}{2}x\right)}\,dx = \int 2\left(2x - \frac{1}{2}\right)e^{\left(x^2 - \frac{1}{2}x\right)}\,dx$$
$$= 2\int \left(2x - \frac{1}{2}\right)e^{\left(x^2 - \frac{1}{2}x\right)}\,dx$$
$$= 2e^{\left(x^2 - \frac{1}{2}x\right)} + C$$

Q6 Let $u = x^2 + 1$ so $\dfrac{du}{dx} = 2x$, and $f'(u) = \sin u$ so $f(u) = -\cos u$.

Use the formula:

$$\int 2x\sin(x^2 + 1)\,dx = -\cos(x^2 + 1) + C$$

Q7 Let $u = x^4$ then $\dfrac{du}{dx} = 4x^3$, and $f'(u) = \cos u$ so $f(u) = \sin u$.

Use the formula:

$$\int 4x^3 \cos(x^4)\,dx = \sin(x^4) + c$$

Now divide by 4 to get the original integral:

$$\int x^3 \cos(x^4)\,dx = \frac{1}{4}\int 4x^3 \cos(x^4)\,dx$$
$$= \frac{1}{4}\sin(x^4) + C$$

Q8 Let $u = x^2$ then $\dfrac{du}{dx} = 2x$, and $f'(u) = \sec^2 u$ so $f(u) = \tan u$.

Use the formula:

$$\int 2x\sec^2(x^2)\,dx = \tan(x^2) + c$$

Now divide by 2 to get the original integral:

$$\int x\sec^2(x^2)\,dx = \frac{1}{2}\int 2x\sec^2(x^2)\,dx$$
$$= \frac{1}{2}\tan(x^2) + C$$

Q9 *It's less obvious which function to choose as u in this one — keep looking out for a function and its derivative. Here we have cos x and sin x. Remember to make u the one which is within another function, i.e. cos x.*

Let $u = \cos x$ then $\dfrac{du}{dx} = -\sin x$, and $f'(u) = e^u$ so $f(u) = e^u$.

Use the formula:

$$\int -\sin x\, e^{\cos x}\,dx = e^{\cos x} + c$$

Multiply by −1 to get the original integral:

$$\int \sin x\, e^{\cos x}\,dx = -\int -\sin x\, e^{\cos x}\,dx = -e^{\cos x} + C$$

Q10 Let $u = \sin 2x$ then $\dfrac{du}{dx} = 2\cos 2x$, and $f'(u) = e^u$ so $f(u) = e^u$.

Use the formula:

$$\int 2\cos 2x\, e^{\sin 2x}\,dx = e^{\sin 2x} + c$$

Divide by 2 to get the original integral:

$$\int \cos 2x\, e^{\sin 2x}\,dx = \frac{1}{2}\int 2\cos 2x\, e^{\sin 2x}\,dx$$
$$= \frac{1}{2}e^{\sin 2x} + C$$

Q11 Let $u = \tan x$ then $\dfrac{du}{dx} = \sec^2 x$, and $f'(u) = e^u$ so $f(u) = e^u$.

Use the formula:

$$\int \sec^2 x\, e^{\tan x}\,dx = e^{\tan x} + C$$

Q12 Let $u = \sec x$ then $\dfrac{du}{dx} = \sec x \tan x$, and $f'(u) = e^u$ so $f(u) = e^u$.

Use the formula: $\displaystyle\int \sec x \tan x\, e^{\sec x}\,dx = e^{\sec x} + C$

Exercise 6.2 — Integrating f'(x) × [f(x)]^n

Q1 **a)** Let $f(x) = x^2 + 5$ so $f'(x) = 2x$. $n = 2$ so $n + 1 = 3$.

Using the formula:

$$\int 3 \times 2x(x^2 + 5)^2\,dx = (x^2 + 5)^3 + C$$

So $\displaystyle\int 6x(x^2 + 5)^2\,dx = (x^2 + 5)^3 + C$

b) Let $f(x) = x^2 + 7x$ so $f'(x) = 2x + 7$.

$n = 4$ so $n + 1 = 5$.

Using the formula:

$$\int 5(2x + 7)(x^2 + 7x)^4\,dx = (x^2 + 7x)^5 + c$$

Divide by 5 to get the original integral:

$$\int (2x + 7)(x^2 + 7x)^4\,dx = \frac{1}{5}(x^2 + 7x)^5 + C$$

c) Let $f(x) = x^4 + 4x^2$ so $f'(x) = 4x^3 + 8x$.

$n = 3$ so $n + 1 = 4$.

Using the formula:

$$\int 4(4x^3 + 8x)(x^4 + 4x^2)^3\,dx = (x^4 + 4x^2)^4 + c$$

Divide by 16 to get the original integral:

$$\int (x^3 + 2x)(x^4 + 4x^2)^3\,dx$$
$$= \frac{1}{16}\int 4(4x^3 + 8x)(x^4 + 4x^2)^3\,dx$$
$$= \frac{1}{16}(x^4 + 4x^2)^4 + C$$

d) Let $f(x) = x^2 - 1$, so $f'(x) = 2x$.

$n = -3$ so $n + 1 = -2$.

Using the formula:

$$\int -2(2x)(x^2 - 1)^{-3}\,dx = (x^2 - 1)^{-2} + C$$

Divide by −2 to get the original integral:

$$\int \frac{2x}{(x^2 - 1)^3}\,dx = \int (2x)(x^2 - 1)^{-3}\,dx$$
$$= -\frac{1}{2}(x^2 - 1)^{-2} + C$$
$$= -\frac{1}{2(x^2 - 1)^2} + C$$

e) Let $f(x) = e^{3x} - 5$, so $f'(x) = 3e^{3x}$.

$n = -2$ so $n + 1 = -1$.

Using the formula:

$\int -1(3e^{3x})(e^{3x} - 5)^{-2}\, dx = (e^{3x} - 5)^{-1} + C$

Multiply by -2 to get the original integral:

$\int \dfrac{6e^{3x}}{(e^{3x} - 5)^2}\, dx = \int 6e^{3x}(e^{3x} - 5)^{-2}\, dx$

$= -2\int -3e^{3x}(e^{3x} - 5)^{-2}\, dx$

$= -2(e^{3x} - 5)^{-1} + C$

f) $\sin x \cos^5 x = \sin x(\cos x)^5$

Let $f(x) = \cos x$ so $f'(x) = -\sin x$.

$n = 5$ so $n + 1 = 6$.

Using the formula:

$\int 6(-\sin x)(\cos x)^5\, dx = (\cos x)^6 + c = \cos^6 x + c$

Divide by -6 to get the original integral:

$\int \sin x \cos^5 x\, dx = \dfrac{1}{-6}\int 6(-\sin x)(\cos x)^5\, dx$

$= -\dfrac{1}{6}\cos^6 x + C$

g) *It's a bit more difficult to tell which is the derivative and which is the function here — both functions are to a power. Remember that the derivative of tan x is sec² x.*

$2\sec^2 x \tan^3 x = 2\sec^2 x(\tan x)^3$

Let $f(x) = \tan x$ so $f'(x) = \sec^2 x$. $n = 3$ so $n + 1 = 4$.

Using the formula:

$\int 4\sec^2 x(\tan x)^3\, dx = (\tan x)^4 + c = \tan^4 x + c$

Divide by 2 to get the original integral:

$\int 2\sec^2 x \tan^3 x\, dx = \dfrac{1}{2}\int 4\sec^2 x(\tan x)^3\, dx$

$= \dfrac{1}{2}\tan^4 x + C$

h) Let $f(x) = e^x + 4$ so $f'(x) = e^x$. $n = 2$ so $n + 1 = 3$.

Using the formula: $\int 3e^x(e^x + 4)^2\, dx = (e^x + 4)^3 + C$

i) Let $f(x) = e^{4x} - 3x^2$ so $f'(x) = 4e^{4x} - 6x$.

$n = 7$ so $n + 1 = 8$.

Using the formula:

$\int 8(4e^{4x} - 6x)(e^{4x} - 3x^2)^7\, dx = (e^{4x} - 3x^2)^8 + c$

So $\int 16(2e^{4x} - 3x)(e^{4x} - 3x^2)^7\, dx = (e^{4x} - 3x^2)^8 + c$

Multiply by 2 to get the original integral:

$\int 32(2e^{4x} - 3x)(e^{4x} - 3x^2)^7\, dx$

$= 2\int 16(2e^{4x} - 3x)(e^{4x} - 3x^2)^7\, dx$

$= 2(e^{4x} - 3x^2)^8 + C$

j) Let $f(x) = 2 + \sin x$, so $f'(x) = \cos x$.

$n = -4$, so $n + 1 = -3$.

Using the formula:

$\int -3(\cos x)(2 + \sin x)^{-4}\, dx = (2 + \sin x)^{-3} + C$

Divide by -3 to get the original integral:

$\int \dfrac{\cos x}{(2 + \sin x)^4}\, dx = \int \cos x(2 + \sin x)^{-4}\, dx$

$= -\dfrac{1}{3}(2 + \sin x)^{-3} + C = -\dfrac{1}{3(2 + \sin x)^3} + C$

k) *Using the hint, you know that the derivative of cosec x is $-\text{cosec } x \cot x$.*

Let $f(x) = \text{cosec } x$ so $f'(x) = -\text{cosec } x \cot x$.

$n = 4$ so $n + 1 = 5$.

Using the formula:

$\int 5(-\text{cosec } x \cot x)(\text{cosec } x)^4\, dx = (\text{cosec } x)^5 + c$

Multiply by -1:

$\int 5\,\text{cosec } x \cot x\, \text{cosec}^4 x\, dx = -\text{cosec}^5 x + C$

l) *Using the hint, cot x differentiates to $-\text{cosec}^2$ x.*

Let $f(x) = \cot x$ so $f'(x) = -\text{cosec}^2 x$.

$n = 3$ so $n + 1 = 4$.

Using the formula:

$\int 4(-\text{cosec}^2 x)\cot^3 x\, dx = \cot^4 x + c$

Divide by -2 to get the original integral:

$\int 2\,\text{cosec}^2 x \cot^3 x\, dx = \dfrac{1}{-2}\int -4\,\text{cosec}^2 x \cot^3 x\, dx$

$= -\dfrac{1}{2}\cot^4 x + C$

Q2 a) *sec x differentiates to sec x tan x, so try to write the function as a product of sec x tan x and sec x to a power.*

$6\tan x \sec^6 x = 6\tan x \sec x \sec^5 x$

Let $f(x) = \sec x$ so $f'(x) = \sec x \tan x$.

$n = 5$ so $n + 1 = 6$.

Using the formula:

$\int 6(\tan x \sec x)(\sec^5 x)\, dx = \sec^6 x + C$

So $\int 6\tan x \sec^6 x\, dx = \sec^6 x + C$

b) *cosec x differentiates to $-\cot x \,\text{cosec } x$ so do the same as you did in part a).*

$\cot x \,\text{cosec}^3 x = \cot x \,\text{cosec } x \,\text{cosec}^2 x$

Let $f(x) = \text{cosec } x$ so $f'(x) = -\cot x \,\text{cosec } x$.

$n = 2$ so $n + 1 = 3$.

Using the formula:

$\int 3(-\cot x \,\text{cosec } x)(\text{cosec}^2 x)\, dx = \text{cosec}^3 x + c$

So $\int -3\cot x \,\text{cosec}^3 x\, dx = \text{cosec}^3 x + c$

Divide by -3 to get the original integral.

$\int \cot x \,\text{cosec}^3 x\, dx = \dfrac{1}{-3}\int -3\cot x \,\text{cosec}^3 x\, dx$

$= -\dfrac{1}{3}\text{cosec}^3 x + C$

Q3 a) *This one looks really complicated, but if you differentiate the bracket ($e^{\sin x} - 5$) using the chain rule, you'll get the function at the front.*

Let $f(x) = e^{\sin x} - 5$ so $f'(x) = \cos x\, e^{\sin x}$.

$n = 3$ so $n + 1 = 4$.

Using the formula:

$\int 4(\cos x\, e^{\sin x})(e^{\sin x} - 5)^3\, dx = (e^{\sin x} - 5)^4 + C$

b) Let $f(x) = e^{\cos x} + 4x$ so $f'(x) = -\sin x\, e^{\cos x} + 4$.

$n = 6$ so $n + 1 = 7$.

Using the formula:

$\int 7(-\sin x\, e^{\cos x} + 4)(e^{\cos x} + 4x)^6\, dx$

$= (e^{\cos x} + 4x)^7 + c$

So divide by –7 to get the original integral:

$$\int (\sin x \, e^{\cos x} - 4)(e^{\cos x} + 4x)^6 \, dx$$

$$= -\frac{1}{7}\int 7(-\sin x \, e^{\cos x} + 4)(e^{\cos x} + 4x)^6 \, dx$$

$$= -\frac{1}{7}(e^{\cos x} + 4x)^7 + C$$

Q4 a) Start by writing the function as $\sec^2 x \tan^{-4} x$.

Let $f(x) = \tan x$ so $f'(x) = \sec^2 x$.

$n = -4$ so $n + 1 = -3$.

Using the formula:

$$\int -3 \sec^2 x \tan^{-4} x \, dx = \tan^{-3} x + c$$

Divide by –3 to get the original integral:

$$\int \frac{\sec^2 x}{\tan^4 x} \, dx = -\frac{1}{3}\tan^{-3} x + C = -\frac{1}{3\tan^3 x} + C$$

b) Start by writing the function as

$\cot x \operatorname{cosec} x (\operatorname{cosec} x)^{\frac{1}{2}}$.

Let $f(x) = \operatorname{cosec} x$ so $f'(x) = -\cot x \operatorname{cosec} x$.

$n = \frac{1}{2}$ so $n + 1 = \frac{3}{2}$.

Using the formula:

$$\int \frac{3}{2}(-\cot x \operatorname{cosec} x)(\operatorname{cosec} x)^{\frac{1}{2}} \, dx = (\operatorname{cosec} x)^{\frac{3}{2}} + c$$

Divide by $-\frac{3}{2}$ to get the original integral:

$$\int \cot x \operatorname{cosec} x \sqrt{\operatorname{cosec} x} \, dx = -\frac{2}{3}(\operatorname{cosec} x)^{\frac{3}{2}} + C$$

$$= -\frac{2}{3}(\sqrt{\operatorname{cosec} x})^3 + C$$

7. Using Trigonometric Identities in Integration

Exercise 7.1 — Integrating using the double angle formulas

Q1 a) Using the cos double angle formula:

$\cos^2 x = \frac{1}{2}(\cos 2x + 1)$

So the integral is:

$$\int \cos^2 x \, dx = \int \frac{1}{2}(\cos 2x + 1) \, dx$$

$$= \frac{1}{2}\left(\frac{1}{2}\sin 2x + x\right) + C$$

$$= \frac{1}{4}\sin 2x + \frac{1}{2}x + C$$

b) $6 \sin x \cos x = 3(2 \sin x \cos x) = 3 \sin 2x$

So the integral is:

$$\int 6 \sin x \cos x \, dx = \int 3 \sin 2x \, dx = -\frac{3}{2}\cos 2x + C$$

c) $\sin^2 6x = \frac{1}{2}(1 - \cos(2 \times 6x)) = \frac{1}{2}(1 - \cos 12x)$

So the integral is:

$$\int \sin^2 6x \, dx = \int \frac{1}{2}(1 - \cos 12x) \, dx$$

$$= \frac{1}{2}\left(x - \frac{1}{12}\sin 12x\right) + C$$

$$= \frac{1}{2}x - \frac{1}{24}\sin 12x + C$$

d) Using the tan double angle formula:

$$\frac{2 \tan 2x}{1 - \tan^2 2x} = \tan 4x$$

So the integral is:

$$\int \frac{2 \tan 2x}{1 - \tan^2 2x} \, dx = \int \tan 4x \, dx$$

$$= -\frac{1}{4}\ln|\cos 4x| + C$$

$$\left(\text{or} = \frac{1}{4}\ln|\sec 4x| + C\right)$$

e) $2 \sin 4x \cos 4x = \sin 8x$

So the integral is:

$$\int 2 \sin 4x \cos 4x \, dx = \int \sin 8x \, dx = -\frac{1}{8}\cos 8x + C$$

f) $2 \cos^2 4x = 2\left(\frac{1}{2}(\cos 8x + 1)\right) = \cos 8x + 1$

So the integral is:

$$\int 2 \cos^2 4x \, dx = \int \cos 8x + 1 \, dx$$

$$= \frac{1}{8}\sin 8x + x + C$$

g) $\cos x \sin x = \frac{1}{2}(2 \cos x \sin x) = \frac{1}{2}\sin 2x$

So the integral is:

$$\int \cos x \sin x \, dx = \int \frac{1}{2}\sin 2x \, dx$$

$$= \frac{1}{2}\left(-\frac{1}{2}\cos 2x\right) + C$$

$$= -\frac{1}{4}\cos 2x + C$$

h) $\sin 3x \cos 3x = \frac{1}{2}(2 \sin 3x \cos 3x) = \frac{1}{2}\sin 6x$

So the integral is:

$$\int \sin 3x \cos 3x \, dx = \int \frac{1}{2}\sin 6x \, dx$$

$$= \frac{1}{2}\left(-\frac{1}{6}\cos 6x\right) + C$$

$$= -\frac{1}{12}\cos 6x + C$$

i) $\dfrac{6 \tan 3x}{1 - \tan^2 3x} = 3\left(\dfrac{2 \tan 3x}{1 - \tan^2 3x}\right) = 3 \tan 6x$

So the integral is:

$$\int \frac{6 \tan 3x}{1 - \tan^2 3x} \, dx = \int 3 \tan 6x \, dx$$

$$= 3\left(-\frac{1}{6}\ln|\cos 6x|\right) + C$$

$$= -\frac{1}{2}\ln|\cos 6x| + C$$

$$\left(\text{or} = \frac{1}{2}\ln|\sec 6x| + C\right)$$

j) $5 \sin 2x \cos 2x = \frac{5}{2}(2 \sin 2x \cos 2x) = \frac{5}{2}\sin 4x$

So the integral is:

$$\int 5 \sin 2x \cos 2x \, dx = \int \frac{5}{2}\sin 4x \, dx$$

$$= \frac{5}{2}\left(-\frac{1}{4}\cos 4x\right) + C$$

$$= -\frac{5}{8}\cos 4x + C$$

k) $(\sin x + \cos x)^2$

$\qquad = \sin^2 x + 2\sin x\cos x + \cos^2 x$

$\qquad = \sin^2 x + \cos^2 x + 2\sin x\cos x$

$\qquad = 1 + 2\sin x\cos x$

$\qquad = 1 + \sin 2x$

$\quad$ *$\sin^2 x + \cos^2 x \equiv 1$ has been used to simplify here.*

So the integral is:

$\displaystyle \int (\sin x + \cos x)^2 \, dx = \int 1 + \sin 2x \, dx$

$\qquad\qquad\qquad\qquad\quad = x - \tfrac{1}{2}\cos 2x + C$

l) $4\sin x\cos x\cos 2x = 2(2\sin x\cos x)\cos 2x$

$\qquad\qquad\qquad\quad = 2\sin 2x\cos 2x$

$\qquad\qquad\qquad\quad = \sin 4x$

So the integral is:

$\displaystyle \int 4\sin x\cos x\cos 2x \, dx = \int \sin 4x \, dx$

$\qquad\qquad\qquad\qquad\qquad = -\tfrac{1}{4}\cos 4x + C$

m) $(\cos x + \sin x)(\cos x - \sin x)$

$\qquad = \cos^2 x - \cos x\sin x + \sin x\cos x - \sin^2 x$

$\qquad = \cos^2 - \sin^2 x$

$\qquad = \cos 2x$

So the integral is:

$\displaystyle \int (\cos x + \sin x)(\cos x - \sin x) \, dx = \int \cos 2x \, dx$

$\qquad\qquad\qquad\qquad\qquad\qquad\qquad = \tfrac{1}{2}\sin 2x + C$

n) $\sin^2 x\cot x = \sin^2 x\dfrac{1}{\tan x} = \sin^2 x\dfrac{\cos x}{\sin x}$

$\qquad\qquad\quad = \sin x\cos x = \tfrac{1}{2}\sin 2x$

So the integral is:

$\displaystyle \int \sin^2 x\cot x \, dx = \int \tfrac{1}{2}\sin 2x \, dx$

$\qquad\qquad\qquad\qquad = \tfrac{1}{2}\left(-\tfrac{1}{2}\cos 2x\right) + C$

$\qquad\qquad\qquad\qquad = -\tfrac{1}{4}\cos 2x + C$

Q2 a) $\sin^2 x = \tfrac{1}{2}(1 - \cos 2x)$

So the integral is:

$\displaystyle \int_0^{\frac{\pi}{4}} \sin^2 x \, dx = \int_0^{\frac{\pi}{4}} \tfrac{1}{2}(1 - \cos 2x) \, dx$

$\qquad\qquad\quad = \tfrac{1}{2}\Big[\big(x - \tfrac{1}{2}\sin 2x\big)\Big]_0^{\frac{\pi}{4}}$

$\qquad\qquad\quad = \tfrac{1}{2}\Big(\big(\tfrac{\pi}{4} - \tfrac{1}{2}\sin\tfrac{\pi}{2}\big) - \big(-\tfrac{1}{2}\sin 0\big)\Big)$

$\qquad\qquad\quad = \tfrac{1}{2}\Big(\big(\tfrac{\pi}{4} - \big(\tfrac{1}{2}\times 1\big)\big) - \big(-\tfrac{1}{2}\times 0\big)\Big)$

$\qquad\qquad\quad = \tfrac{1}{2}\big(\tfrac{\pi}{4} - \tfrac{1}{2}\big) = \tfrac{\pi}{8} - \tfrac{1}{4}$

b) $\cos^2 2x = \tfrac{1}{2}(\cos 4x + 1)$

So the integral is:

$\displaystyle \int_0^{\pi} \tfrac{1}{2}(\cos 4x + 1) \, dx = \Big[\tfrac{1}{2}\big(\tfrac{1}{4}\sin 4x + x\big)\Big]_0^{\pi}$

$\qquad = \Big[\big(\tfrac{1}{8}\sin 4x + \tfrac{x}{2}\big)\Big]_0^{\pi}$

$\qquad = \big(\tfrac{1}{8}\sin 4\pi + \tfrac{\pi}{2}\big) - \big(\tfrac{1}{8}\sin 0 + \tfrac{0}{2}\big)$

$\qquad = \big(\tfrac{1}{8}\times 0 + \tfrac{\pi}{2}\big) - (0 + 0) = \tfrac{\pi}{2}$

c) $\sin\tfrac{x}{2}\cos\tfrac{x}{2} = \tfrac{1}{2}\big(2\sin\tfrac{x}{2}\cos\tfrac{x}{2}\big) = \tfrac{1}{2}\sin x$

So the integral is:

$\displaystyle \int_0^{\pi} \sin\tfrac{x}{2}\cos\tfrac{x}{2} \, dx = \int_0^{\pi} \tfrac{1}{2}\sin x \, dx$

$\qquad\qquad\qquad\qquad = -\tfrac{1}{2}[\cos x]_0^{\pi}$

$\qquad\qquad\qquad\qquad = -\tfrac{1}{2}(\cos\pi - \cos 0)$

$\qquad\qquad\qquad\qquad = -\tfrac{1}{2}(-1 - 1) = 1$

d) $\sin^2 2x = \tfrac{1}{2}(1 - \cos 4x)$

So the integral is:

$\displaystyle \int_{\frac{\pi}{4}}^{\frac{\pi}{2}} \sin^2 2x \, dx = \int_{\frac{\pi}{4}}^{\frac{\pi}{2}} \tfrac{1}{2}(1 - \cos 4x) \, dx$

$\qquad\qquad = \tfrac{1}{2}\Big[x - \tfrac{1}{4}\sin 4x\Big]_{\frac{\pi}{4}}^{\frac{\pi}{2}}$

$\qquad\qquad = \tfrac{1}{2}\Big(\big[\tfrac{\pi}{2} - \tfrac{1}{4}\sin 2\pi\big] - \big[\tfrac{\pi}{4} - \tfrac{1}{4}\sin\pi\big]\Big)$

$\qquad\qquad = \tfrac{1}{2}\Big(\big[\tfrac{\pi}{2} - 0\big] - \big[\tfrac{\pi}{4} - 0\big]\Big) = \tfrac{\pi}{8}$

e) $\cos 2x\sin 2x = \tfrac{1}{2}(2\sin 2x\cos 2x) = \tfrac{1}{2}\sin 4x$

So the integral is:

$\displaystyle \int_0^{\frac{\pi}{4}} \cos 2x\sin 2x \, dx = \int_0^{\frac{\pi}{4}} \tfrac{1}{2}\sin 4x \, dx$

$\qquad\qquad\qquad\quad = \tfrac{1}{2}\Big[\big(-\tfrac{1}{4}\cos 4x\big)\Big]_0^{\frac{\pi}{4}}$

$\qquad\qquad\qquad\quad = -\tfrac{1}{8}[\cos 4x]_0^{\frac{\pi}{4}}$

$\qquad\qquad\qquad\quad = -\tfrac{1}{8}(\cos\pi - \cos 0)$

$\qquad\qquad\qquad\quad = -\tfrac{1}{8}(-1 - 1) = \tfrac{1}{4}$

f) $\sin^2 x - \cos^2 x = -(\cos^2 x - \sin^2 x)$

$\qquad\qquad\qquad\quad = -\cos 2x$

So the integral is:

$\displaystyle \int_{\frac{\pi}{4}}^{\frac{\pi}{2}} \sin^2 x - \cos^2 x \, dx = \int_{\frac{\pi}{4}}^{\frac{\pi}{2}} -\cos 2x \, dx$

$\qquad\qquad\qquad\quad = -\tfrac{1}{2}[\sin 2x]_{\frac{\pi}{4}}^{\frac{\pi}{2}}$

$\qquad\qquad\qquad\quad = -\tfrac{1}{2}\big(\sin\pi - \sin\tfrac{\pi}{2}\big)$

$\qquad\qquad\qquad\quad = -\tfrac{1}{2}(0 - 1) = \tfrac{1}{2}$

Exercise 7.2 — Integration using other trigonometric identities

Q1 a) $\cot^2 x - 4 = (\text{cosec}^2 x - 1) - 4$

$\qquad\qquad\quad = \text{cosec}^2 x - 5$

So the integral is:

$\displaystyle \int \cot^2 x - 4 \, dx = \int \text{cosec}^2 x - 5 \, dx$

$\qquad\qquad\qquad\quad = -\cot x - 5x + C$

b) $\tan^2 x = \sec^2 x - 1$

So the integral is:

$$\int \tan^2 x \, dx = \int \sec^2 x - 1 \, dx$$
$$= \tan x - x + C$$

c) $3\cot^2 x = 3(\cosec^2 x - 1) = 3\cosec^2 x - 3$

So the integral is:

$$\int 3\cot^2 x \, dx = \int 3\cosec^2 x - 3 \, dx$$
$$= -3\cot x - 3x + C$$

d) $\tan^2 4x = \sec^2 4x - 1$

So the integral is:

$$\int \tan^2 4x \, dx = \int \sec^2 4x - 1 \, dx$$
$$= \frac{1}{4}\tan 4x - x + C$$

Q2 $\tan^2 x + \cos^2 x - \sin^2 x = (\sec^2 x - 1) + \cos 2x$

So the integral is:

$$\int_0^{\frac{\pi}{4}} \tan^2 x + \cos^2 x - \sin^2 x \, dx$$
$$= \int_0^{\frac{\pi}{4}} \sec^2 x - 1 + \cos 2x \, dx$$
$$= \left[\tan x - x + \frac{1}{2}\sin 2x\right]_0^{\frac{\pi}{4}}$$
$$= \left[\tan\frac{\pi}{4} - \frac{\pi}{4} + \frac{1}{2}\sin\frac{2\pi}{4}\right] - \left[\tan 0 - 0 + \frac{1}{2}\sin 0\right]$$
$$= \left[1 - \frac{\pi}{4} + \frac{1}{2}\right] - [0 - 0 + 0]$$
$$= \frac{3}{2} - \frac{\pi}{4}$$

Q3 **a)** $\tan^3 x + \tan^5 x = \tan^3 x(1 + \tan^2 x)$
$$= \tan^3 x \sec^2 x$$
$$= \sec^2 x \tan^3 x$$

This is a product containing tan x to a power, and its derivative $\sec^2 x$.

Using the formula with $f(x) = \tan x$, $f'(x) = \sec^2 x$, $n = 3$ and $n + 1 = 4$ gives:

$$\int 4\sec^2 x \tan^3 x \, dx = \tan^4 x + C$$

So the integral is:

$$\int \tan^3 x + \tan^5 x \, dx = \int \sec^2 x \tan^3 x \, dx$$
$$= \frac{1}{4}\int 4\sec^2 x \tan^3 x \, dx$$
$$= \frac{1}{4}\tan^4 x + C$$

b) $\cot^5 x + \cot^3 x = \cot^3 x(\cot^2 x + 1) = \cot^3 x \cosec^2 x$

Again, this is a product of a function to a power and its derivative so use the formula with $f(x) = \cot x$, $f'(x) = -\cosec^2 x$, $n = 3$ and $n + 1 = 4$.

$$\int -4\cosec^2 x \cot^3 x \, dx = \cot^4 x + C$$

So the integral is:

$$\int \cot^5 x + \cot^3 x \, dx = \int \cosec^2 x \cot^3 x \, dx$$
$$= -\frac{1}{4}\int -4\cosec^2 x \cot^3 x \, dx$$
$$= -\frac{1}{4}\cot^4 x + C$$

c) $\sin^3 x = \sin x \sin^2 x$
$$= \sin x(1 - \cos^2 x)$$
$$= \sin x - \sin x \cos^2 x$$

The second term of this function is a product of a function to a power and its derivative. Using the result with $f(x) = \cos x$, $f'(x) = -\sin x$, $n = 2$ and $n + 1 = 3$ gives:

$$\int -3\sin x \cos^2 x \, dx = \cos^3 x + c$$

So the integral is:

$$\int \sin^3 x \, dx = \int \sin x - \sin x \cos^2 x \, dx$$
$$= \int \sin x \, dx + \int -\sin x \cos^2 x \, dx$$
$$= -\cos x + \frac{1}{3}\cos^3 x + C$$

Q4 $(\sec x + \tan x)^2 = \sec^2 x + 2\tan x \sec x + \tan^2 x$
$$= \sec^2 x + 2\tan x \sec x + (\sec^2 x - 1)$$
$$= 2\sec^2 x + 2\tan x \sec x - 1$$

Remember that the derivative of sec x is sec x tan x.

So the integral is:

$$\int (\sec x + \tan x)^2 \, dx = \int 2\sec^2 x + 2\tan x \sec x - 1 \, dx$$
$$= 2\tan x + 2\sec x - x + C$$

Q5 $(\cot x + \cosec x)^2 = \cot^2 x + 2\cot x \cosec x + \cosec^2 x$
$$= (\cosec^2 x - 1) + 2\cot x \cosec x + \cosec^2 x$$
$$= 2\cosec^2 x + 2\cot x \cosec x - 1$$

Just keep using the identities that you know until you get to something that you know how to integrate.

So the integral is:

$$\int (\cot x + \cosec x)^2 \, dx$$
$$= \int 2\cosec^2 x + 2\cot x \cosec x - 1 \, dx$$
$$= -2\cot x - 2\cosec x - x + C$$

Q6 $4 + \cot^2 3x = 4 + (\cosec^2 3x - 1) = 3 + \cosec^2 3x$

So the integral is:

$$\int 4 + \cot^2 3x \, dx = \int 3 + \cosec^2 3x \, dx$$
$$= 3x - \frac{1}{3}\cot 3x + C$$

Q7 $\cos^2 4x + \cot^2 4x = \frac{1}{2}(\cos 8x + 1) + (\cosec^2 4x - 1)$
$$= \frac{1}{2}\cos 8x + \cosec^2 4x - \frac{1}{2}$$

So the integral is:

$$\int \cos^2 4x + \cot^2 4x \, dx = \int \frac{1}{2}\cos 8x + \cosec^2 4x - \frac{1}{2} \, dx$$
$$= \frac{1}{2}\left(\frac{1}{8}\sin 8x\right) - \frac{1}{4}\cot 4x - \frac{1}{2}x + C$$
$$= \frac{1}{16}\sin 8x - \frac{1}{4}\cot 4x - \frac{1}{2}x + C$$

Q8 **a)** Let $A = 5x$ and $B = 3x$, then

$$\sin 5x + \sin 3x \equiv 2\sin\left(\frac{5x + 3x}{2}\right)\cos\left(\frac{5x - 3x}{2}\right)$$
$$\equiv 2\sin 4x \cos x$$

b) $$\int 2\sin 4x \cos x \, dx = \int \sin 5x + \sin 3x \, dx$$
$$= -\frac{1}{5}\cos 5x - \frac{1}{3}\cos 3x + C$$

Review Exercise — Chapter 5

Q1 a) $\int \dfrac{1}{\sqrt[3]{(2-11x)}}\,dx = \int (2-11x)^{-\frac{1}{3}}\,dx$

$\qquad = \dfrac{1}{-11\times\left(\frac{2}{3}\right)}(2-11x)^{\frac{2}{3}} + C$

$\qquad = -\dfrac{3}{22}(2-11x)^{\frac{2}{3}} + C$

b) Integrate the curve between the two limits:

$\int_{-\frac{123}{11}}^{-\frac{62}{11}} \dfrac{1}{\sqrt[3]{(2-11x)}}\,dx = -\dfrac{3}{22}\left[(\sqrt[3]{2-11x})^2\right]_{-\frac{123}{11}}^{-\frac{62}{11}}$

$\qquad = -\dfrac{3}{22}\left([(\sqrt[3]{2+62})^2] - [(\sqrt[3]{2+123})^2]\right)$

$\qquad = -\dfrac{3}{22}\left((\sqrt[3]{64})^2 - (\sqrt[3]{125})^2\right)$

$\qquad = -\dfrac{3}{22}(16-25) = \dfrac{27}{22}$

Q2 To find y from $\dfrac{dy}{dx}$, integrate:

$y = \int \dfrac{dy}{dx}\,dx = \int (1-7x)^{\frac{1}{2}}\,dx$

$\qquad = \dfrac{1}{-7\times\frac{3}{2}}(1-7x)^{\frac{3}{2}} + C$

$\qquad = -\dfrac{2}{21}(1-7x)^{\frac{3}{2}} + C$

Given that the equation goes through the point $(0, 1)$, you can substitute in these values for x and y to get C.

$y = -\dfrac{2}{21}(1-7x)^{\frac{3}{2}} + C$

$1 = -\dfrac{2}{21}(1-0)^{\frac{3}{2}} + C$

$\Rightarrow C = \dfrac{23}{21}$

So the equation of the curve is:

$y = -\dfrac{2}{21}(1-7x)^{\frac{3}{2}} + \dfrac{23}{21}$

Q3 a) $\int 4e^{2x}\,dx = 4\left(\tfrac{1}{2}e^{2x}\right) + C = 2e^{2x} + C$

b) $\int e^{3x-5}\,dx = \tfrac{1}{3}e^{3x-5} + C$

c) $\int \dfrac{2}{3x}\,dx = \int \tfrac{2}{3}\times\tfrac{1}{x}\,dx = \tfrac{2}{3}\ln|x| + C$

d) $\int \dfrac{2}{2x+1}\,dx = 2\left(\tfrac{1}{2}\ln|2x+1|\right) + C$

$\qquad = \ln|2x+1| + C$

You could have written this down straight away if you'd noticed that the numerator is the derivative of the denominator.

Q4 $\int \dfrac{8}{2-x} - \dfrac{8}{x}\,dx = 8\left(\tfrac{1}{-1}\ln|2-x|\right) - 8\ln|x| + C$

$\qquad = -8\ln|2-x| - 8\ln|x| + C$

$\qquad = -8(\ln|2-x| + \ln|x|) + C$

$\qquad = -8(\ln|x(2-x)|) + C$

$\qquad = \ln|(2x-x^2)^{-8}| + C$

So $P = (2x-x^2)^{-8}$.

You can get rid of the modulus signs as anything raised to the power 8 will be positive.

Q5 $\dfrac{3x+10}{(2x+3)(x-4)} \equiv \dfrac{A}{2x+3} + \dfrac{B}{x-4}$

$\Rightarrow 3x+10 \equiv A(x-4) + B(2x+3)$

Use the substitution method to get A and B.

Substituting $x = 4$ gives: $\quad 22 = 11B \qquad \Rightarrow B = 2$.

Substituting $x = -\dfrac{3}{2}$ gives: $\quad \dfrac{11}{2} = -\dfrac{11}{2}A \quad \Rightarrow A = -1$.

So writing the function as partial fractions:

$\dfrac{3x+10}{(2x+3)(x-4)} \equiv -\dfrac{1}{2x+3} + \dfrac{2}{x-4}$

So the integral can be expressed:

$\int \dfrac{3x+10}{(2x+3)(x-4)}\,dx$

$= \int -\dfrac{1}{2x+3} + \dfrac{2}{x-4}\,dx$

$= -\dfrac{1}{2}\ln|2x+3| + 2\ln|x-4| + C$

Q6 Writing f(x) as partial fractions:

$\dfrac{-2x^2+12x+31}{(x-3)^2(2x+1)} \equiv \dfrac{A}{(x-3)^2} + \dfrac{B}{(x-3)} + \dfrac{C}{(2x+1)}$

$\Rightarrow \dfrac{-2x^2+12x+31}{(x-3)^2(2x+1)}$

$\qquad = \dfrac{A(2x+1) + B(x-3)(2x+1) + C(x-3)^2}{(x-3)^2(2x+1)}$

$\Rightarrow -2x^2+12x+31$

$\qquad = A(2x+1) + B(x-3)(2x+1) + C(x-3)^2$

Use the substitution method to work out some of the constants:

Substituting $x = 3$ gives: $\quad 49 = 7A \qquad \Rightarrow A = 7$.

Substituting $x = -\dfrac{1}{2}$ gives: $\quad \dfrac{49}{2} = \dfrac{49}{4}C \qquad \Rightarrow C = 2$.

Now equating coefficients of x^2 gives: $2B + C = -2$

$\Rightarrow 2B + 2 = -2 \Rightarrow 2B = -4 \Rightarrow B = -2$.

So writing f(x) as partial fractions:

$\dfrac{-2x^2+12x+31}{(x-3)^2(2x+1)} = \dfrac{7}{(x-3)^2} - \dfrac{2}{(x-3)} + \dfrac{2}{(2x+1)}$

So the integral can be expressed:

$\int_{-4}^{9} f(x)\,dx$

$= \int_{-4}^{9} \dfrac{-2x^2+12x+31}{(x-3)^2(2x+1)}\,dx$

$= \int_{-4}^{9} \dfrac{7}{(x-3)^2} - \dfrac{2}{(x-3)} + \dfrac{2}{(2x+1)}\,dx$

$= \int_{-4}^{9} 7(x-3)^{-2} - \dfrac{2}{(x-3)} + \dfrac{2}{(2x+1)}\,dx$

$= \left[\dfrac{1}{-1}(7(x-3)^{-1}) - 2\ln|x-3| + \ln|2x+1|\right]_{-4}^{9}$

$= \left[-\dfrac{7}{(x-3)} - 2\ln|x-3| + \ln|2x+1|\right]_{-4}^{9}$

$= \left[-\dfrac{7}{6} - 2\ln|6| + \ln|19|\right] - \left[-\dfrac{7}{1} - 2\ln|1| + \ln|9|\right]$

$= -\dfrac{7}{6} - 2\ln|6| + \ln|19| + 7 + 0 - \ln|9| \quad (\text{as } \ln 1 = 0)$

$= -\dfrac{7}{6} - \ln 36 + \ln 19 + 7 - \ln 9$

$= \dfrac{35}{6} + \ln\left(\dfrac{19}{36\times 9}\right) = \dfrac{35}{6} + \ln\left(\dfrac{19}{324}\right)$

Q7 a) $\int \cos(x + A)\,dx = \sin(x + A) + C$

b) $\int \sin(A - x)\,dx = \dfrac{1}{-1}(-\cos(A - x)) + C$

$= \cos(A - x) + C$

c) $\int \cosec^2((A + B)t + A + B)\,dt$

$= \dfrac{1}{A + B}(-\cot((A + B)t + A + B)) + C$

$= -\dfrac{1}{A + B}\cot((A + B)t + A + B) + C$

Q8 a) $\int \cos 4x - \sec^2 7x\,dx = \dfrac{1}{4}\sin 4x - \dfrac{1}{7}\tan 7x + C$

b) $\int 6\sec 3x\tan 3x - \cosec^2\dfrac{x}{5}\,dx$

$= 6\left(\dfrac{1}{3}\sec 3x\right) - \dfrac{1}{\left(\frac{1}{5}\right)}\left(-\cot\dfrac{x}{5}\right) + C$

$= 2\sec 3x + 5\cot\dfrac{x}{5} + C$

Q9 a) *The numerator is the derivative of the denominator so use the result* $\int \dfrac{f'(x)}{f(x)}\,dx = \ln|f(x)| + C$ *with* $f(x) = \sin x$.

$\int \dfrac{\cos x}{\sin x}\,dx = \ln|\sin x| + C$

b) Differentiating the denominator gives $5x^4 + 3x^2 - 3$. So the numerator is 4 times the derivative of the denominator.

$\int \dfrac{20x^4 + 12x^2 - 12}{x^5 + x^3 - 3x}\,dx = \int \dfrac{4(5x^4 + 3x^2 - 3)}{x^5 + x^3 - 3x}\,dx$

$= 4\ln|x^5 + x^3 - 3x| + C$

Q10 a) Let $u = x^3$ then $\dfrac{du}{dx} = 3x^2$, and $f'(u) = e^u$, so $f(u) = e^u$. Using the reverse chain rule formula:

$\int 3x^2 e^{x^3}\,dx = e^{x^3} + C$

b) Let $u = \sin(x^2)$ then $\dfrac{du}{dx} = 2x\cos(x^2)$ and $f'(u) = e^u$, so $f(u) = e^u$. Using the formula:

$\int 2x\cos(x^2)e^{\sin(x^2)}\,dx = e^{\sin(x^2)} + C$

c) Let $u = \sec(4x)$ then $\dfrac{du}{dx} = 4\sec(4x)\tan(4x)$, and $f'(u) = e^u$, so $f(u) = e^u$. Using the formula:

$\int 4\sec 4x\tan 4x\,e^{\sec 4x}\,dx = e^{\sec 4x} + c$

$\Rightarrow \int \sec 4x\tan 4x\,e^{\sec 4x}\,dx = \dfrac{1}{4}e^{\sec 4x} + C$

Q11 $\dfrac{2\tan 3x}{1 - \tan^2 3x} = \tan(2(3x)) = \tan 6x$

So $\int \dfrac{2\tan 3x}{1 - \tan^2 3x}\,dx = \int \tan 6x\,dx$

$= \dfrac{1}{6}(-\ln|\cos 6x|) + C$

$= -\dfrac{1}{6}\ln|\cos 6x| + C$

$\left(\text{or} = \dfrac{1}{6}\ln|\sec 6x| + C\right)$

Exam-Style Questions — Chapter 5

Q1 a) $\int 3e^{(5 - 6x)}\,dx = \dfrac{3}{-6}e^{(5 - 6x)} + C$

$= -\dfrac{1}{2}e^{(5 - 6x)} + C$

[1 mark for answer in the form $ke^{(5 - 6x)}$, 1 mark for the correct value of k]

b) $\int \dfrac{\cosec^2 x - 2}{\cot x + 2x}\,dx = \int \dfrac{-(-\cosec^2 x + 2)}{\cot x + 2x}\,dx$

$= -\ln|\cot x + 2x| + C$

[1 mark for answer in the form $k\ln|f(x)|$, 1 mark for correct value of k and 1 mark for correct function f(x). Lose 1 mark if C is missed off both answers a) and b)]

Q2 Use the identity $\cosec^2 x \equiv 1 + \cot^2 x$ to write $2\cot^2 x$ as $2\cosec^2 x - 2$ *[1 mark]*. The integral becomes:

$\int 2\cosec^2 x - 2\,dx = -2\cot x - 2x + C$

[1 mark for −2cot x, 1 mark for −2x + C]

Q3 Use the identity $\sec^2 x \equiv 1 + \tan^2 x$ to write $2\tan^2 3x + 2$ as $2\sec^2 3x$ *[1 mark]*. The integral becomes:

$\int 2\tan^2 3x + 2\,dx = \int 2\sec^2 3x\,dx = \dfrac{2}{3}\tan 3x + C$

[1 mark for 2/3, 1 mark for tan 3x]

Q4 a) $\dfrac{-8x^2 + x - 8}{(4x + 1)(1 - x)(x + 2)}$

$\equiv \dfrac{A}{(4x + 1)} + \dfrac{B}{(1 - x)} + \dfrac{C}{(x + 2)}$

$-8x^2 + x - 8$

$\equiv A(1 - x)(x + 2)$

$+ B(4x + 1)(x + 2)$

$+ C(4x + 1)(1 - x)$ *[1 mark]*

Use substitution to find A, B and C.

Substituting $x = 1$ gives: $-15 = 15B \Rightarrow B = -1$ *[1 mark]*

Substituting $x = -2$ gives: $-42 = -21C \Rightarrow C = 2$ *[1 mark]*

Substituting $x = -\dfrac{1}{4}$ gives: $-\dfrac{35}{4} = \dfrac{35}{16}A \Rightarrow A = -4$ *[1 mark]*

b) (i) From a), f(x) can be written as partial fractions:

$f(x) = \dfrac{-8x^2 + x - 8}{(4x + 1)(1 - x)(x + 2)}$

$= -\dfrac{4}{(4x + 1)} - \dfrac{1}{(1 - x)} + \dfrac{2}{(x + 2)}$

$\int f(x)\,dx$

$= \int -\dfrac{4}{(4x + 1)} - \dfrac{1}{(1 - x)} + \dfrac{2}{(x + 2)}\,dx$ *[1 mark]*

$= -\ln|4x + 1| + \ln|1 - x|$

$+ 2\ln|x + 2| + C$

[1 mark for each of the first three terms, lose 1 mark if +C is missing]

(ii) Put the limits into the integration from part (i):

$$\int_{-1}^{2} f(x)\,dx$$

$$= [-\ln|4x+1| + \ln|1-x| + 2\ln|x+2|]_{-1}^{2}$$

$$= [-\ln|9| + \ln|-1| + 2\ln|4|]$$

$$\quad - [-\ln|-3| + \ln|2| + 2\ln|1|]$$ *[1 mark]*

$$= [-\ln 9 + \ln 1 + 2\ln 4]$$

$$\quad - [-\ln 3 + \ln 2 + 2\ln 1]$$ *[1 mark]*

$$= -\ln 9 + 2\ln 4 + \ln 3 - \ln 2$$

$$= -\ln 9 + \ln 16 + \ln 3 - \ln 2$$

$$= \ln\left(\frac{16 \times 3}{9 \times 2}\right) = \ln\frac{48}{18} = \ln\frac{8}{3}$$ *[1 mark]*

Q5 Integrate the curve $y = \dfrac{2}{3(\sqrt[3]{5x-2})}$ with respect to x between 2 and 5.8 to find the shaded region:

$$\int_{2}^{5.8} \frac{2}{3(\sqrt[3]{5x-2})}\,dx = \int_{2}^{5.8} \frac{2}{3}(5x-2)^{-\frac{1}{3}}\,dx$$ *[1 mark]*

$$= \left[\frac{1}{5} \cdot \frac{2}{3} \cdot \frac{3}{2}(5x-2)^{\frac{2}{3}}\right]_{2}^{5.8}$$

$$= \left[\frac{1}{5}(\sqrt[3]{5x-2})^2\right]_{2}^{5.8}$$

$$= \frac{1}{5}(\sqrt[3]{27})^2 - \frac{1}{5}(\sqrt[3]{8})^2$$ *[1 mark]*

$$= \frac{3^2}{5} - \frac{2^2}{5} = \frac{5}{5} = 1$$ *[1 mark]*

Q6 a) Begin by factorising the denominator of f(x):

$$f(x) = \frac{11x^2 + 42x + 36}{3x^3 + 16x^2 + 28x + 16}$$

$$\equiv \frac{11x^2 + 42x + 36}{(x+2)^2(3x+4)}$$

Now express it as partial fractions:

$$\frac{11x^2 + 42x + 36}{(x+2)^2(3x+4)} = \frac{A}{(x+2)^2} + \frac{B}{x+2} + \frac{C}{3x+4}$$

$$\Rightarrow 11x^2 + 42x + 36$$

$$\equiv A(3x+4) + B(x+2)(3x+4) + C(x+2)^2$$ *[1 mark]*

Use the substitution method to find A and C:

Substituting $x = -2$ gives: $-4 = -2A \Rightarrow A = 2$.

Substituting $x = -\frac{4}{3}$ gives: $-\frac{4}{9} = \frac{4}{9}C \Rightarrow C = -1$.

[1 mark for finding A and C]

Use the equating coefficients method to find B:

Equating coefficients of x^2 gives: $3B + C = 11$

$\Rightarrow 3B - 1 = 11 \Rightarrow 3B = 12 \Rightarrow B = 4$ *[1 mark]*.

So $f(x) = \dfrac{2}{(x+2)^2} + \dfrac{4}{x+2} - \dfrac{1}{3x+4}$ *[1 mark]*.

b) $\int f(x)\,dx$

$$= \int \frac{2}{(x+2)^2} + \frac{4}{x+2} - \frac{1}{3x+4}\,dx$$

$$= \int 2(x+2)^{-2} + \frac{4}{x+2} - \frac{1}{3x+4}\,dx$$

$$= -2(x+2)^{-1} + 4\ln|x+2| - \frac{1}{3}\ln|3x+4| + C$$

$$= -\frac{2}{x+2} + 4\ln|x+2| - \frac{1}{3}\ln|3x+4| + C$$

[1 mark for each of the first three terms, lose 1 mark if +C is missing]

Chapter 6: Integration 2

1. Integration by Substitution
Exercise 1.1 — Integration by substitution

Q1 a) $u = x + 3 \Rightarrow \dfrac{du}{dx} = 1 \Rightarrow dx = du$

So $\int 12(x+3)^5\,dx = \int 12u^5\,du$

$$= 2u^6 + C$$

$$= 2(x+3)^6 + C$$

You could also have solved this by using the rule given on p63, it's of the form (ax + b)ⁿ.

b) $u = 11 - x \Rightarrow \dfrac{du}{dx} = -1 \Rightarrow dx = -du$

So $\int (11-x)^4\,dx = -\int u^4\,du$

$$= -\frac{1}{5}u^5 + C$$

$$= -\frac{1}{5}(11-x)^5 + C$$

c) $u = x^2 + 4 \Rightarrow \dfrac{du}{dx} = 2x \Rightarrow dx = \dfrac{1}{2x}du$

So $\int 24x(x^2+4)^3\,dx = \int 24x \times u^3 \times \dfrac{1}{2x}\,du$

$$= \int 12u^3\,du$$

$$= 3u^4 + C$$

$$= 3(x^2+4)^4 + C$$

d) $u = \sin x \Rightarrow \dfrac{du}{dx} = \cos x \Rightarrow dx = \dfrac{1}{\cos x}du$

So $\int \sin^5 x \cos x\,dx = \int u^5 \cos x \times \dfrac{1}{\cos x}\,du$

$$= \int u^5\,du$$

$$= \frac{1}{6}u^6 + C$$

$$= \frac{1}{6}\sin^6 x + C$$

e) $u = x - 1 \Rightarrow \dfrac{du}{dx} = 1 \Rightarrow dx = du$

and $u = x - 1 \Rightarrow x = u + 1$

So $\int x(x-1)^5\,dx = \int (u+1)u^5\,du = \int u^6 + u^5\,du$

$$= \frac{1}{7}u^7 + \frac{1}{6}u^6 + C$$

$$= \frac{1}{7}(x-1)^7 + \frac{1}{6}(x-1)^6 + C$$

f) $u = \sqrt{x+1} \Rightarrow \dfrac{du}{dx} = \dfrac{1}{2\sqrt{x+1}} = \dfrac{1}{2u} \Rightarrow dx = 2u$

$u = \sqrt{x+1} \Rightarrow x = u^2 - 1$

So $\int 6x\sqrt{x+1}\,dx = \int 6(u^2-1) \times u \times 2u\,du$

$$= \int 12u^4 - 12u^2\,du$$

$$= \frac{12}{5}u^5 - 4u^3 + C$$

$$= \frac{12}{5}(\sqrt{x+1})^5 - 4(\sqrt{x+1})^3 + C$$

g) $u = \sqrt{4-x} \Rightarrow \dfrac{du}{dx} = -\dfrac{1}{2\sqrt{4-x}} = -\dfrac{1}{2u}$

$\Rightarrow dx = -2u\,du$

$u = \sqrt{4-x} \Rightarrow x = 4 - u^2$

So $\int \frac{x}{\sqrt{4-x}}\,dx = \int \frac{4-u^2}{u} \times -2u\,du$

$= \int -2(4-u^2)\,du$

$= \int 2u^2 - 8\,du$

$= \frac{2}{3}u^3 - 8u + C$

$= \frac{2}{3}(\sqrt{4-x})^3 - 8(\sqrt{4-x}) + C$

h) $u = \ln x \Rightarrow \frac{du}{dx} = \frac{1}{x} \Rightarrow dx = x\,du$

So $\int \frac{15(\ln x)^4}{x}\,dx = \int \frac{15u^4}{x} \times x\,du = \int 15u^4\,du$

$= 3u^5 + C$

$= 3(\ln x)^5 + C$

Q2 a) Let $u = x + 2 \Rightarrow \frac{du}{dx} = 1 \Rightarrow dx = du$

So $\int 21(x+2)^6\,dx = \int 21u^6\,du$

$= 3u^7 + C$

$= 3(x+2)^7 + C$

b) Let $u = 5x + 4 \Rightarrow \frac{du}{dx} = 5 \Rightarrow dx = \frac{1}{5}du$

So $\int (5x+4)^3\,dx = \int \frac{1}{5}u^3\,du$

$= \frac{u^4}{20} + C$

$= \frac{(5x+4)^4}{20} + C$

c) Let $u = 2x + 3 \Rightarrow \frac{du}{dx} = 2 \Rightarrow dx = \frac{1}{2}du$

and $u = 2x + 3 \Rightarrow x = \frac{u-3}{2}$

So $\int x(2x+3)^3\,dx = \int \frac{u-3}{2} \times u^3 \times \frac{1}{2}\,du$

$= \frac{1}{4}\int u^4 - 3u^3\,du$

$= \frac{1}{4}\left(\frac{1}{5}u^5 - \frac{3}{4}u^4\right) + C$

$= \frac{1}{20}u^5 - \frac{3}{16}u^4 + C$

$= \frac{1}{20}(2x+3)^5 - \frac{3}{16}(2x+3)^4 + C$

d) Let $u = x^2 - 5 \Rightarrow \frac{du}{dx} = 2x \Rightarrow dx = \frac{1}{2x}du$

So $\int 24x(x^2-5)^7\,dx = \int 24x \times u^7 \times \frac{1}{2x}\,du$

$= \int 12u^7\,du$

$= \frac{3}{2}u^8 + C$

$= \frac{3}{2}(x^2-5)^8 + C$

Q3 $u = \sqrt{2x-1} \Rightarrow \frac{du}{dx} = \frac{1}{\sqrt{2x-1}} = \frac{1}{u} \Rightarrow dx = u\,du$

and $u = \sqrt{2x-1} \Rightarrow x = \frac{u^2+1}{2}$

So $\int \frac{4x}{\sqrt{(2x-1)}}\,dx = \int 4\left(\frac{u^2+1}{2}\right) \times \frac{1}{u} \times u\,du$

$= \int 2u^2 + 2\,du$

$= \frac{2}{3}u^3 + 2u + C$

$= \frac{2}{3}(\sqrt{2x-1})^3 + 2(\sqrt{2x-1}) + C$

Q4 $u = 4 - \sqrt{x} \Rightarrow \frac{du}{dx} = -\frac{1}{2\sqrt{x}} \Rightarrow -2\sqrt{x}\,du = dx$

and $u = 4 - \sqrt{x} \Rightarrow x = (4-u)^2 \Rightarrow dx$ can be written $-2(4-u)\,du = (2u-8)du$

So $\int \frac{1}{4-\sqrt{x}}\,dx = \int \frac{1}{u}(2u-8)\,du$

$= \int 2 - \frac{8}{u}\,du$

$= 2u - 8\ln|u| + c$

$= 2(4-\sqrt{x}) - 8\ln|4 - \sqrt{x}| + c$

$= -2\sqrt{x} - 8\ln|4 - \sqrt{x}| + C$

Don't forget that you can leave out any constant terms that appear after you integrate (like the 8 you get out of the term $2(4 - \sqrt{x})$ here) — they just get absorbed into the constant of integration, C.

Q5 $u = 1 + e^x \Rightarrow \frac{du}{dx} = e^x \Rightarrow dx = \frac{1}{e^x}\,du$

and $u = 1 + e^x \Rightarrow e^x = u - 1$

So $\int \frac{e^{2x}}{1+e^x}\,dx = \int \frac{e^{2x}}{u} \times \frac{1}{e^x}\,du$

$= \int \frac{e^x}{u}\,du$

$= \int \frac{u-1}{u}\,du$

$= \int 1 - \frac{1}{u}\,du$

$= u - \ln|u| + c$

$= 1 + e^x - \ln|1 + e^x| + c$

$= e^x - \ln(1 + e^x) + C$

You can remove the modulus because e^x is always positive, so $1 + e^x > 1$.

Exercise 1.2 — Definite integrals

Q1 a) $u = 3x - 2 \Rightarrow \frac{du}{dx} = 3 \Rightarrow dx = \frac{1}{3}du$

$x = \frac{2}{3} \Rightarrow u = 2 - 2 = 0$

$x = 1 \Rightarrow u = 3 - 2 = 1$

So $\int_{\frac{2}{3}}^{1} (3x-2)^4\,dx = \int_0^1 \frac{1}{3}u^4\,du$

$= \left[\frac{1}{15}u^5\right]_0^1 = \frac{1}{15}$

b) $u = x + 3 \Rightarrow \frac{du}{dx} = 1 \Rightarrow dx = 1\,du$

$u = x + 3 \Rightarrow x = u - 3$

$x = -2 \Rightarrow u = -2 + 3 = 1$

$x = 1 \Rightarrow u = 1 + 3 = 4$

So $\int_{-2}^{1} 2x(x+3)^4\,dx = \int_1^4 2(u-3) \times u^4 \times 1\,dx$

$= \int_1^4 (2u-6)u^4\,dx$

$= \int_1^4 (2u^5 - 6u^4)\,dx$

$= \left[\frac{u^6}{3} - \frac{6u^5}{5}\right]_1^4$

$= \left(\frac{4^6}{3} - \frac{6(4)^5}{5}\right) - \left(\frac{1^6}{3} - \frac{6(1)^5}{5}\right)$

$= \frac{687}{5} = 137.4$

c) $u = \sin x \Rightarrow \frac{du}{dx} = \cos x \Rightarrow dx = \frac{1}{\cos x}du$

$x = 0 \Rightarrow u = \sin(0) = 0$

$x = \frac{\pi}{6} \Rightarrow u = \sin\frac{\pi}{6} = \frac{1}{2}$

So $\int_0^{\frac{\pi}{6}} 8\sin^3 x \cos x \, dx = \int_0^{\frac{1}{2}} 8u^3 \cos x \times \frac{1}{\cos x} \, du$

$= \int_0^{\frac{1}{2}} 8u^3 \, du$

$= [2u^4]_0^{\frac{1}{2}}$

$= 2\left(\frac{1}{2}\right)^4 - 0 = \frac{1}{8}$

d) $u = \sqrt{x+1} \Rightarrow \dfrac{du}{dx} = \dfrac{1}{2\sqrt{x+1}} = \dfrac{1}{2u} \Rightarrow dx = 2u \, du$

$u = \sqrt{x+1} \Rightarrow x = u^2 - 1$

$x = 0 \Rightarrow u = \sqrt{x+1} = \sqrt{1} = 1$
$x = 3 \Rightarrow u = \sqrt{4} = 2$

So $\int_0^3 x\sqrt{x+1} \, dx = \int_1^2 (u^2 - 1) \times u \times 2u \, du$

$= \int_1^2 2u^4 - 2u^2 \, du$

$= \left[\frac{2}{5}u^5 - \frac{2}{3}u^3\right]_1^2$

$= \left[\left(\frac{64}{5} - \frac{16}{3}\right) - \left(\frac{2}{5} - \frac{2}{3}\right)\right]$

$= \frac{116}{15} = 7.73$ (2 d.p.)

Q2 a) Let $u = x^2 - 3 \Rightarrow \dfrac{du}{dx} = 2x \Rightarrow dx = \dfrac{1}{2x}du$

$x = 2 \Rightarrow u = 4 - 3 = 1$
$x = \sqrt{5} \Rightarrow u = 5 - 3 = 2$

So $\int_2^{\sqrt{5}} x(x^2 - 3)^4 \, dx = \int_1^2 x \times u^4 \times \dfrac{1}{2x} \, du$

$= \int_1^2 \frac{1}{2}u^4 \, du$

$= \left[\frac{1}{10}u^5\right]_1^2$

$= \frac{32}{10} - \frac{1}{10} = \frac{31}{10} = 3.1$

b) Let $u = 3x - 4 \Rightarrow \dfrac{du}{dx} = 3 \Rightarrow dx = \dfrac{1}{3}du$

and $u = 3x - 4 \Rightarrow x = \dfrac{u+4}{3}$

$x = 1 \Rightarrow u = 3 - 4 = -1$
$x = 2 \Rightarrow u = 6 - 4 = 2$

So $\int_1^2 x(3x-4)^3 \, dx = \int_{-1}^2 \frac{u+4}{3} \times u^3 \times \frac{1}{3} \, du$

$= \frac{1}{9}\int_{-1}^2 u^4 + 4u^3 \, du$

$= \frac{1}{9}\left[\frac{u^5}{5} + u^4\right]_{-1}^2$

$= \frac{1}{9}\left[\left(\frac{32}{5} + 16\right) - \left(\frac{-1}{5} + 1\right)\right]$

$= \frac{1}{9}\left[\frac{108}{5}\right] = \frac{12}{5} = 2.4$

c) Let $u = \sqrt{x-1} \Rightarrow \dfrac{du}{dx} = \dfrac{1}{2\sqrt{x-1}} = \dfrac{1}{2u}$
$\Rightarrow dx = 2u \, du$

and $u = \sqrt{x-1} \Rightarrow x = u^2 + 1$

Using $u = \sqrt{x-1}, x = 2 \Rightarrow u = \sqrt{1} = 1$
and $x = 10 \Rightarrow u = \sqrt{9} = 3$

So $\int_2^{10} \frac{x}{\sqrt{x-1}} \, dx = \int_1^3 \frac{u^2+1}{u} \times 2u \, du$

$= \int_1^3 2u^2 + 2 \, du$

$= \left[\frac{2}{3}u^3 + 2u\right]_1^3$

$= \left[(18+6) - \left(\frac{2}{3}+2\right)\right] = \frac{64}{3}$

Q3 $u = 3 - \sqrt{x} \Rightarrow \dfrac{du}{dx} = -\dfrac{1}{2\sqrt{x}} \Rightarrow dx = -2\sqrt{x} \, du$

$u = 3 - \sqrt{x} \Rightarrow x = (3-u)^2 \Rightarrow dx = (2u - 6) \, du$

So $x = 1 \Rightarrow u = 3 - 1 = 2$
and $x = 4 \Rightarrow u = 3 - 2 = 1$

So $\int_1^4 \frac{1}{3-\sqrt{x}} \, dx = \int_2^1 \frac{1}{u} \times (2u - 6) \, du$

$= \int_2^1 2 - \frac{6}{u} \, du$

$= [2u - 6\ln|u|]_2^1$

$= (2 - 6\ln 1) - (4 - 6\ln 2)$

$= 2 - 0 - 4 + 6\ln 2$

$= -2 + 6\ln 2$

You could have put 2 as the upper limit and 1 as the lower limit in the integral with respect to u, and put a minus sign in front. Both methods give the right answer, but whichever you use, be careful not to lose any minus signs.

Q4 $u = 1 + e^x \Rightarrow \dfrac{du}{dx} = e^x \Rightarrow dx = \dfrac{1}{e^x} \, du$

$x = 0 \Rightarrow u = 1 + e^0 = 2$
$x = 1 \Rightarrow u = 1 + e$

So $\int_0^1 2e^x(1+e^x)^3 \, dx = \int_2^{1+e} 2e^x u^3 \frac{1}{e^x} \, du$

$= \int_2^{1+e} 2u^3 \, du$

$= \left[\frac{u^4}{2}\right]_2^{1+e}$

$= \frac{(1+e)^4}{2} - 8 = 87.6$ to 1 d.p.

Q5 $u = \sqrt{3x+1} \Rightarrow \dfrac{du}{dx} = \dfrac{3}{2\sqrt{3x+1}} = \dfrac{3}{2u}$
$\Rightarrow dx = \dfrac{2}{3}u \, du$

and $u = \sqrt{3x+1} \Rightarrow x = \dfrac{u^2-1}{3}$

Using $u = \sqrt{3x+1}, x = 1 \Rightarrow u = \sqrt{4} = 2$
and $x = 5 \Rightarrow u = \sqrt{16} = 4$

So $\int_1^5 \frac{x}{\sqrt{3x+1}} \, dx = \int_2^4 \frac{u^2-1}{3u} \times \frac{2}{3}u \, du$

$= \frac{2}{9}\int_2^4 u^2 - 1 \, du$

$= \frac{2}{9}\left[\frac{1}{3}u^3 - u\right]_2^4$

$= \frac{2}{9}\left[\left(\frac{64}{3} - 4\right) - \left(\frac{8}{3} - 2\right)\right]$

$= \frac{2}{9}\left[\frac{50}{3}\right] = \frac{100}{27}$

Q6 $u = \sqrt{x} \Rightarrow \dfrac{du}{dx} = \dfrac{1}{2}x^{-\frac{1}{2}} = \dfrac{1}{2\sqrt{x}} \Rightarrow dx = 2\sqrt{x} \, du = 2u \, du$

and $u = \sqrt{x} \Rightarrow x = u^2$.

Using $u = \sqrt{x}, x = 9 \Rightarrow u = \sqrt{9} = 3$
and $x = 16 \Rightarrow u = \sqrt{16} = 4$

So

$\int_9^{16} \frac{4}{\sqrt{x}(9x-4)} \, dx = \int_3^4 \frac{4}{u(9u^2-4)} 2u \, dx$

$= \int_3^4 \frac{8}{(9u^2-4)} \, dx$

This function still needs some work before it can be integrated. The next step is to write it as partial fractions.

$\dfrac{8}{(9u^2-4)} \equiv \dfrac{8}{(3u+2)(3u-2)} \equiv \dfrac{A}{(3u+2)} + \dfrac{B}{(3u-2)}$

So $8 = A(3u - 2) + B(3u + 2)$

Using substitution:

$u = \frac{2}{3} \Rightarrow 8 = 4B \Rightarrow 2 = B$

$u = -\frac{2}{3} \Rightarrow 8 = -4A \Rightarrow -2 = A$

So $\frac{8}{(9u^2 - 4)} \equiv \frac{-2}{(3u + 2)} + \frac{2}{(3u - 2)}$

So the integral can be expressed:

$\int_3^4 \frac{8}{(9u^2 - 4)} \, dx = \int_3^4 \frac{-2}{(3u + 2)} + \frac{2}{(3u - 2)} \, dx$

$= \left[\frac{2}{3} \ln|3u - 2| - \frac{2}{3} \ln|3u + 2| \right]_3^4$

$= \left[\frac{2}{3} \ln\left| \frac{3u - 2}{3u + 2} \right| \right]_3^4$

$= \frac{2}{3} \ln\frac{10}{14} - \frac{2}{3} \ln\frac{7}{11} = \frac{2}{3} \ln\frac{55}{49}$

Exercise 1.3 — Trig identities

Q1 $x = \tan \theta \Rightarrow \frac{dx}{d\theta} = \sec^2 \theta \Rightarrow dx = \sec^2 \theta \, d\theta$

$x = 0 \Rightarrow \tan \theta = 0 \Rightarrow \theta = 0$

$x = 1 \Rightarrow \tan \theta = 1 \Rightarrow \theta = \frac{\pi}{4}$

So using the identity $\sec^2 \theta \equiv 1 + \tan^2 \theta$

$\int_0^1 \frac{1}{1 + x^2} \, dx = \int_0^{\frac{\pi}{4}} \frac{1}{1 + \tan^2\theta} \times \sec^2\theta \, d\theta$

$= \int_0^{\frac{\pi}{4}} \frac{\sec^2\theta}{\sec^2\theta} \, d\theta$

$= \int_0^{\frac{\pi}{4}} 1 \, d\theta = [\theta]_0^{\frac{\pi}{4}} = \frac{\pi}{4}$

Q2 $u = \sin x \Rightarrow \frac{du}{dx} = \cos x \Rightarrow dx = \frac{1}{\cos x} du$

$x = 0 \Rightarrow u = \sin 0 = 0$

$x = \frac{\pi}{6} \Rightarrow u = \sin \frac{\pi}{6} = \frac{1}{2}$

So using the identity $\sin 2x \equiv 2\sin x \cos x$

$\int_0^{\frac{\pi}{6}} 3 \sin x \sin 2x \, dx \equiv \int_0^{\frac{\pi}{6}} 6 \sin^2 x \cos x \, dx$

$= \int_0^{\frac{1}{2}} 6u^2 \cos x \times \frac{1}{\cos x} du$

$= \int_0^{\frac{1}{2}} 6u^2 \, du$

$= [2u^3]_0^{\frac{1}{2}}$

$= \frac{1}{4}$

Q3 $x = 2\sin \theta \Rightarrow \frac{dx}{d\theta} = 2\cos \theta \Rightarrow dx = 2\cos \theta \, d\theta$

$x = 1 \Rightarrow \sin \theta = \frac{1}{2} \Rightarrow \theta = \frac{\pi}{6}$

$x = \sqrt{3} \Rightarrow \sin \theta = \frac{\sqrt{3}}{2} \Rightarrow \theta = \frac{\pi}{3}$

So using the identity $\sin^2 \theta + \cos^2 \theta \equiv 1$

$\int_1^{\sqrt{3}} \frac{1}{(4 - x^2)^{\frac{3}{2}}} \, dx = \int_{\frac{\pi}{6}}^{\frac{\pi}{3}} \frac{1}{(4 - 4\sin^2\theta)^{\frac{3}{2}}} \times 2\cos \theta \, d\theta$

$= \int_{\frac{\pi}{6}}^{\frac{\pi}{3}} \frac{2\cos \theta}{(4 - 4 + 4\cos^2\theta)^{\frac{3}{2}}} \, d\theta$

$= \int_{\frac{\pi}{6}}^{\frac{\pi}{3}} \frac{2\cos\theta}{8\cos^3\theta} \, d\theta$

$= \int_{\frac{\pi}{6}}^{\frac{\pi}{3}} \frac{1}{4} \sec^2\theta \, d\theta = \frac{1}{4}[\tan \theta]_{\frac{\pi}{6}}^{\frac{\pi}{3}}$

$= \frac{1}{4}\left(\sqrt{3} - \frac{1}{\sqrt{3}} \right) = \frac{\sqrt{3}}{6}$

Q4 $x = \cos \theta \Rightarrow \frac{dx}{d\theta} = -\sin \theta \Rightarrow dx = -\sin \theta \, d\theta$

$x = \frac{1}{2} \Rightarrow \cos \theta = \frac{1}{2} \Rightarrow \theta = \frac{\pi}{3}$

$x = 1 \Rightarrow \cos \theta = 1 \Rightarrow \theta = 0$

So using the identity $\sin^2 \theta + \cos^2 \theta \equiv 1$

$\int_{\frac{1}{2}}^1 \frac{1}{x^2\sqrt{1 - x^2}} \, dx = \int_{\frac{\pi}{3}}^0 \frac{1}{\cos^2\theta\sqrt{1 - \cos^2\theta}} \times -\sin \theta \, d\theta$

$= \int_{\frac{\pi}{3}}^0 -\frac{\sin \theta}{\cos^2\theta \sin \theta} \, d\theta$

$= \int_0^{\frac{\pi}{3}} \frac{\sin \theta}{\cos^2\theta \sin \theta} \, d\theta$

$= \int_0^{\frac{\pi}{3}} \frac{1}{\cos^2\theta} \, d\theta$

$= \int_0^{\frac{\pi}{3}} \sec^2\theta \, d\theta$

$= [\tan \theta]_0^{\frac{\pi}{3}}$

$= \sqrt{3} - 0 = \sqrt{3}$

Q5 $u = \sec^2 x \Rightarrow \frac{du}{dx} = 2\sec^2 x \tan x$

$\Rightarrow dx = \frac{1}{2\sec^2 x \tan x} du = \frac{1}{2u \tan x} du$

And using the identity

$\sec^2 x \equiv 1 + \tan^2 x \Rightarrow \tan^2 x \equiv \sec^2 x - 1 = u - 1$

$\int 2 \tan^3 x \, dx = \int 2 \tan x(u - 1) \times \frac{1}{2u \tan x} du$

$= \int \frac{u - 1}{u} du = \int 1 - \frac{1}{u} du$

$= u - \ln |u| + C$

$= \sec^2 x - \ln(\sec^2 x) + C$

2. Integration by Parts

Exercise 2.1 — Integration by parts

Q1 **a)** Let $u = x$ and $\frac{dv}{dx} = e^x$.

Then $\frac{du}{dx} = 1$ and $v = e^x$.

So $\int xe^x \, dx = xe^x - \int e^x \, dx$

$= xe^x - e^x + C$

b) Let $u = x$ and $\frac{dv}{dx} = e^{-x}$.

Then $\frac{du}{dx} = 1$ and $v = -e^{-x}$.

So $\int xe^{-x} \, dx = -xe^{-x} - \int -e^{-x} \, dx$

$= -xe^{-x} - e^{-x} + C$

c) Let $u = x$ and $\frac{dv}{dx} = e^{-\frac{x}{3}}$.

Then $\frac{du}{dx} = 1$ and $v = -3e^{-\frac{x}{3}}$.

So $\int xe^{-\frac{x}{3}} \, dx = -3xe^{-\frac{x}{3}} - \int -3e^{-\frac{x}{3}} \, dx$

$= -3xe^{-\frac{x}{3}} - 9e^{-\frac{x}{3}} + C$

d) Let $u = x$ and $\frac{dv}{dx} = e^x + 1$.

Then $\frac{du}{dx} = 1$ and $v = e^x + x$.

So $\int x(e^x + 1) \, dx = x(e^x + x) - \int e^x + x \, dx$

$= xe^x + x^2 - e^x - \frac{1}{2}x^2 + C$

$= xe^x - e^x + \frac{1}{2}x^2 + C$

You might have spotted a pattern here — all the parts of this question had $u = x$ and $\frac{dv}{dx}$ as a function involving e. Your answers might look a bit different if you factorised them

Q2 **a)** Let $u = x$ and $\frac{dv}{dx} = \sin x$.

Then $\frac{du}{dx} = 1$ and $v = -\cos x$.

So $\int_0^\pi x \sin x\, dx = [-x\cos x]_0^\pi - \int_0^\pi -\cos x\, dx$

$= [-x\cos x]_0^\pi + [\sin x]_0^\pi$

$= (\pi - 0) + (0 - 0)$

$= \pi$

b) Let $u = 2x$ and $\frac{dv}{dx} = \cos x$.

Then $\frac{du}{dx} = 2$ and $v = \sin x$.

So $\int 2x \cos x\, dx = 2x \sin x - \int 2\sin x\, dx$

$= 2x \sin x + 2\cos x + C$

c) Let $u = 3x$ and $\frac{dv}{dx} = \cos \frac{1}{2}x$.

Then $\frac{du}{dx} = 3$ and $v = 2\sin \frac{1}{2}x$.

So $\int 3x \cos \frac{1}{2}x\, dx = 6x \sin \frac{1}{2}x - \int 6 \sin \frac{1}{2}x\, dx$

$= 6x \sin \frac{1}{2}x + 12\cos \frac{1}{2}x + C$

d) Let $u = 2x$ and $\frac{dv}{dx} = 1 - \sin x$.

Then $\frac{du}{dx} = 2$ and $v = x + \cos x$.

So $\int_{-\frac{\pi}{2}}^{\frac{\pi}{2}} 2x(1 - \sin x)\, dx$

$= [2x(x + \cos x)]_{-\frac{\pi}{2}}^{\frac{\pi}{2}} - \int_{-\frac{\pi}{2}}^{\frac{\pi}{2}} 2(x + \cos x)\, dx$

$= [2x(x + \cos x)]_{-\frac{\pi}{2}}^{\frac{\pi}{2}} - [x^2 + 2\sin x]_{-\frac{\pi}{2}}^{\frac{\pi}{2}}$

$= [\pi(\frac{\pi}{2} + 0) - -\pi(-\frac{\pi}{2} + 0)] - [(\frac{\pi^2}{4} + 2) - (\frac{\pi^2}{4} - 2)]$

$= -4$

Q3 **a)** Let $u = \ln x$ and $\frac{dv}{dx} = 2$.

Then $\frac{du}{dx} = \frac{1}{x}$ and $v = 2x$.

So $\int 2 \ln x\, dx = 2x \ln x - \int 2\, dx$

$= 2x \ln x - 2x + C$

b) Let $u = \ln x$ and $\frac{dv}{dx} = x^4$.

Then $\frac{du}{dx} = \frac{1}{x}$ and $v = \frac{1}{5}x^5$.

So $\int x^4 \ln x\, dx = \frac{1}{5}x^5 \ln x - \int \frac{1}{5}x^4\, dx$

$= \frac{1}{5}x^5 \ln x - \frac{1}{25}x^5 + C$

c) Let $u = \ln 4x$ and $\frac{dv}{dx} = 1$.

Then $\frac{du}{dx} = \frac{1}{x}$ and $v = x$.

So $\int \ln 4x\, dx = x \ln 4x - \int 1\, dx$

$= x \ln 4x - x + C$

d) Let $u = \ln x^3$ and $\frac{dv}{dx} = 1$.

Then $\frac{du}{dx} = \frac{3}{x}$ and $v = x$.

So $\int \ln x^3\, dx = x \ln x^3 - \int 3\, dx$

$= x \ln x^3 - 3x + C$

For parts a), c) and d), if the question hadn't told you to use integration by parts, you could have just used the result for integrating $\ln x$ shown on p.102 (you'd need to rewrite the logs in parts c) and d) as $\ln 4 + \ln x$ and $3\ln x$).

Q4 **a)** Let $u = 20x$ and $\frac{dv}{dx} = (x + 1)^3$.

Then $\frac{du}{dx} = 20$ and $v = \frac{1}{4}(x + 1)^4$.

So $\int_{-1}^1 20x(x + 1)^3\, dx$

$= [5x(x + 1)^4]_{-1}^1 - \int_{-1}^1 5(x + 1)^4\, dx$

$= [5x(x + 1)^4]_{-1}^1 - [(x + 1)^5]_{-1}^1$

$= [5(2^4) - 0] - [(2^5) - 0]$

$= 80 - 32 = 48$

b) Let $u = 30x$ and $\frac{dv}{dx} = (2x + 1)^{\frac{1}{2}}$.

Then $\frac{du}{dx} = 30$ and $v = \frac{1}{3}(2x + 1)^{\frac{3}{2}}$.

So $\int_0^{1.5} 30x \sqrt{(2x + 1)}\, dx$

$= [10x(2x + 1)^{\frac{3}{2}}]_0^{1.5} - \int_0^{1.5} 10(2x + 1)^{\frac{3}{2}}\, dx$

$= [10x(2x + 1)^{\frac{3}{2}}]_0^{1.5} - [2(2x + 1)^{\frac{5}{2}}]_0^{1.5}$

$= [15(4)^{\frac{3}{2}} - 0] - [2(4)^{\frac{5}{2}} - 2(1)^{\frac{5}{2}}]$

$= 120 - 62 = 58$

Q5 **a)** Let $u = x$ and $\frac{dv}{dx} = 12e^{2x}$.

Then $\frac{du}{dx} = 1$ and $v = 6e^{2x}$.

So $\int_0^1 12xe^{2x}\, dx = [6xe^{2x}]_0^1 - \int_0^1 6e^{2x}\, dx$

$= 6e^2 - [3e^{2x}]_0^1$

$= 6e^2 - (3e^2 - 3e^0)$

$= 3e^2 + 3$

b) Let $u = x$ and $\frac{dv}{dx} = 18\sin 3x$.

Then $\frac{du}{dx} = 1$ and $v = -6\cos 3x$.

So $\int_0^{\frac{\pi}{3}} 18x \sin 3x\, dx$

$= [-6x\cos 3x]_0^{\frac{\pi}{3}} - \int_0^{\frac{\pi}{3}} -6 \cos 3x\, dx$

$= -2\pi\cos \pi + [2 \sin 3x]_0^{\frac{\pi}{3}}$

$= 2\pi + [2\sin \pi - 2\sin 0]$

$= 2\pi$

c) Let $u = \ln x$ and $\frac{dv}{dx} = \frac{1}{x^2}$.

Then $\frac{du}{dx} = \frac{1}{x}$ and $v = -\frac{1}{x}$.

So $\int_1^2 \frac{1}{x^2} \ln x\, dx = [-\frac{1}{x} \ln x]_1^2 - \int_1^2 -\frac{1}{x^2}\, dx$

$= -\frac{1}{2}\ln 2 + \ln 1 - [\frac{1}{x}]_1^2$

$= -\frac{1}{2}\ln 2 - \frac{1}{2} + 1$

$= \frac{1}{2} - \frac{1}{2}\ln 2$

Q6 Let $u = x$ and $\frac{dv}{dx} = e^{-2x}$.

Then $\frac{du}{dx} = 1$ and $v = -\frac{1}{2}e^{-2x}$.

So $\int \dfrac{x}{e^{2x}}\,dx = -\dfrac{x}{2}e^{-2x} - \int -\dfrac{1}{2}e^{-2x}\,dx$

$= -\dfrac{x}{2e^{2x}} - \dfrac{1}{4e^{2x}} + C$

Q7 Let $u = x + 1$ and $\dfrac{dv}{dx} = (x+2)^{\frac{1}{2}}$.

Then $\dfrac{du}{dx} = 1$ and $v = \dfrac{2}{3}(x+2)^{\frac{3}{2}}$.

So $\int (x+1)\sqrt{(x+2)}\,dx$

$\quad = \dfrac{2}{3}(x+1)(x+2)^{\frac{3}{2}} - \int \dfrac{2}{3}(x+2)^{\frac{3}{2}}\,dx$

$\quad = \dfrac{2}{3}(x+1)(x+2)^{\frac{3}{2}} - \dfrac{4}{15}(x+2)^{\frac{5}{2}} + C$

Q8 Let $u = \ln(x+1)$ and $\dfrac{dv}{dx} = 1$.

Then $\dfrac{du}{dx} = \dfrac{1}{x+1}$ and $v = x$.

So $\int \ln(x+1)\,dx = x\ln(x+1) - \int \dfrac{x}{x+1}\,dx$

$\quad = x\ln(x+1) - \int \dfrac{x+1-1}{x+1}\,dx$

$\quad = x\ln(x+1) - \int 1 - \dfrac{1}{x+1}\,dx$

$\quad = x\ln|x+1| - x + \ln|x+1| + C$

$\quad = (x+1)\ln|x+1| - x + C$

Exercise 2.2 — Repeated use of integration by parts

Q1 **a)** Let $u = x^2$ and $\dfrac{dv}{dx} = e^x$.

Then $\dfrac{du}{dx} = 2x$ and $v = e^x$.

So $\int x^2 e^x\,dx = x^2 e^x - \int 2x e^x\,dx$

Integrate by parts again to find $\int 2x e^x\,dx$:

Let $u = 2x$ and $\dfrac{dv}{dx} = e^x$.

Then $\dfrac{du}{dx} = 2$ and $v = e^x$.

So $\int 2x e^x\,dx = 2x e^x - \int 2e^x\,dx$

$\quad = 2x e^x - 2e^x + c$

So $\int x^2 e^x\,dx = x^2 e^x - \int 2x e^x\,dx$

$\quad = x^2 e^x - (2x e^x - 2e^x + c)$

$\quad = x^2 e^x - 2x e^x + 2e^x + C$

b) Let $u = x^2$ and $\dfrac{dv}{dx} = \cos x$.

Then $\dfrac{du}{dx} = 2x$ and $v = \sin x$.

So $\int x^2 \cos x\,dx = x^2 \sin x - \int 2x \sin x\,dx$

Integrate by parts again to find $\int 2x \sin x\,dx$:

Let $u = 2x$ and $\dfrac{dv}{dx} = \sin x$.

Then $\dfrac{du}{dx} = 2$ and $v = -\cos x$.

So $\int 2x \sin x\,dx = -2x\cos x - \int -2\cos x\,dx$

$\quad = -2x\cos x + 2\sin x + c$

So $\int x^2 \cos x\,dx = x^2 \sin x - \int 2x \sin x\,dx$

$\quad = x^2 \sin x - (-2x\cos x + 2\sin x + c)$

$\quad = x^2 \sin x + 2x\cos x - 2\sin x + C$

c) Let $u = x^2$ and $\dfrac{dv}{dx} = 4\sin 2x$.

Then $\dfrac{du}{dx} = 2x$ and $v = -2\cos 2x$.

So $\int 4x^2 \sin 2x\,dx = -2x^2\cos 2x + \int 4x\cos 2x\,dx$

Integrate by parts again to find $\int 4x\cos 2x\,dx$:

Let $u = x$ and $\dfrac{dv}{dx} = 4\cos 2x$.

Then $\dfrac{du}{dx} = 1$ and $v = 2\sin 2x$.

So $\int 4x\cos 2x\,dx = 2x\sin 2x - \int 2\sin 2x\,dx$

$\quad = 2x\sin 2x + \cos 2x + C$

So $\int 4x^2 \sin 2x\,dx = -2x^2\cos 2x + \int 4x\cos 2x\,dx$

$\quad = -2x^2\cos 2x + (2x\sin 2x + \cos 2x + C)$

$\quad = -2x^2\cos 2x + 2x\sin 2x + \cos 2x + C$

d) Let $u = 40x^2$ and $\dfrac{dv}{dx} = (2x-1)^4$.

Then $\dfrac{du}{dx} = 80x$ and $v = \dfrac{1}{10}(2x-1)^5$.

So $\int 40x^2 (2x-1)^4\,dx$

$\quad = 4x^2(2x-1)^5 - \int 8x(2x-1)^5\,dx$

Integrate by parts again to find $\int 8x(2x-1)^5\,dx$:

Let $u = 8x$ and $\dfrac{dv}{dx} = (2x-1)^5$.

Then $\dfrac{du}{dx} = 8$ and $v = \dfrac{1}{12}(2x-1)^6$.

So $\int 8x(2x-1)^5\,dx$

$\quad = \dfrac{2x}{3}(2x-1)^6 - \int \dfrac{2}{3}(2x-1)^6\,dx$

$\quad = \dfrac{2x}{3}(2x-1)^6 - \dfrac{1}{21}(2x-1)^7 + C$

So $\int 40x^2 (2x-1)^4\,dx$

$\quad = 4x^2(2x-1)^5 - \dfrac{2x}{3}(2x-1)^6 + \dfrac{1}{21}(2x-1)^7 + C$

Q2 Let $u = x^2$ and $\dfrac{dv}{dx} = (x+1)^4$

Then $\dfrac{du}{dx} = 2x$ and $v = \dfrac{1}{5}(x+1)^5$.

So $\int_{-1}^{0} x^2(x+1)^4\,dx = \left[\dfrac{x^2}{5}(x+1)^5\right]_{-1}^{0} - \int_{-1}^{0} \dfrac{2}{5}x(x+1)^5\,dx$

$\quad = 0 - \int_{-1}^{0} \dfrac{2}{5}x(x+1)^5\,dx$

Integrate by parts again to find $\int_{-1}^{0} \dfrac{2}{5}x(x+1)^5\,dx$:

Let $u = x$ and $\dfrac{dv}{dx} = \dfrac{2}{5}(x+1)^5$.

Then $\dfrac{du}{dx} = 1$ and $v = \dfrac{1}{15}(x+1)^6$.

So $\int_{-1}^{0} \dfrac{2}{5}x(x+1)^5\,dx = \left[\dfrac{x}{15}(x+1)^6\right]_{-1}^{0} - \int_{-1}^{0} \dfrac{1}{15}(x+1)^6\,dx$

$\quad = 0 - \left[\dfrac{1}{105}(x+1)^7\right]_{-1}^{0}$

$\quad = -\dfrac{1}{105}$

So $\int_{-1}^{0} x^2(x+1)^4\,dx = 0 - \int_{-1}^{0} \dfrac{2}{5}x(x+1)^5\,dx$

$\quad = -\left(-\dfrac{1}{105}\right) = \dfrac{1}{105}$

Q3 Let $u = x^2$ and $\dfrac{dv}{dx} = e^{-2x}$.

Then $\dfrac{du}{dx} = 2x$ and $v = -\dfrac{1}{2}e^{-2x}$.

So area $= \int_{0}^{1} x^2 e^{-2x}\,dx = \left[-\dfrac{x^2}{2}e^{-2x}\right]_{0}^{1} + \int_{0}^{1} x e^{-2x}\,dx$

Integrate by parts again to find $\int_0^1 xe^{-2x}\,dx$:

Let $u = x$ and $\dfrac{dv}{dx} = e^{-2x}$.

Then $\dfrac{du}{dx} = 1$ and $v = -\dfrac{1}{2}e^{-2x}$.

So $\int_0^1 xe^{-2x}\,dx = \left[-\dfrac{x}{2}e^{-2x}\right]_0^1 + \int_0^1 \dfrac{1}{2}e^{-2x}\,dx$

$= \left[-\dfrac{x}{2}e^{-2x}\right]_0^1 + \left[-\dfrac{1}{4}e^{-2x}\right]_0^1$

So area $= \left[-\dfrac{x^2}{2}e^{-2x}\right]_0^1 + \left[-\dfrac{x}{2}e^{-2x}\right]_0^1 + \left[-\dfrac{1}{4}e^{-2x}\right]_0^1$

$= -\dfrac{1}{2}e^{-2} - \dfrac{1}{2}e^{-2} - \dfrac{1}{4}e^{-2} + \dfrac{1}{4}$

$= \dfrac{1}{4} - \dfrac{5}{4}e^{-2}$

3. Volumes of Revolution

Exercise 3.1 — Volumes of revolution

Q1 a) $y^2 = 16x^2$

So $V = \pi \int_1^2 16x^2\,dx = \pi\left[\dfrac{16}{3}x^3\right]_1^2$

$= \pi\left[\dfrac{128}{3} - \dfrac{16}{3}\right] = \dfrac{112}{3}\pi$

b) $y^2 = x + 2$

So $V = \pi \int_0^2 x + 2\,dx = \pi\left[\dfrac{1}{2}x^2 + 2x\right]_0^2$

$= \pi\left[\left(\dfrac{1}{2}2^2 + 4\right) - 0\right] = 6\pi$

c) $y^2 = 4 - x^2$

So $V = \pi \int_0^2 4 - x^2\,dx = \pi\left[4x - \dfrac{1}{3}x^3\right]_0^2$

$= \pi\left[\left(8 - \dfrac{8}{3}\right) - 0\right] = \dfrac{16}{3}\pi$

Q2 a) $y^2 = \dfrac{4}{x^2}$

So $V = \pi \int_2^8 4x^{-2}\,dx = \pi\left[-\dfrac{4}{x}\right]_2^8$

$= \pi\left[-\dfrac{1}{2} - (-2)\right] = \dfrac{3}{2}\pi$

b) $y^2 = e^{2x}$

So $V = \pi \int_0^2 e^{2x}\,dx = \pi\left[\dfrac{1}{2}e^{2x}\right]_0^2$

$= \pi\left[\dfrac{1}{2}e^4 - \dfrac{1}{2}e^0\right] = \dfrac{\pi}{2}(e^4 - 1)$

c) $y^2 = \dfrac{9}{x}$

So $V = \pi \int_1^2 \dfrac{9}{x}\,dx = \pi[9\ln|x|]_1^2 = 9\pi\ln 2$

d) $y^2 = (1 + \sqrt{x})^2 = 1 + 2\sqrt{x} + x$

So $V = \pi \int_0^1 1 + 2x^{\frac{1}{2}} + x\,dx$

$= \pi\left[x + \dfrac{4}{3}x^{\frac{3}{2}} + \dfrac{1}{2}x^2\right]_0^1$

$= \pi\left[\left(1 + \dfrac{4}{3} + \dfrac{1}{2}\right) - 0\right] = \dfrac{17}{6}\pi$

Q3 a) $y^2 = \sin 2x$

So $V = \pi \int_0^{\frac{\pi}{6}} \sin 2x\,dx = \pi\left[-\dfrac{1}{2}\cos 2x\right]_0^{\frac{\pi}{6}}$

$= \pi\left[\left(-\dfrac{1}{2} \times \dfrac{1}{2}\right) - \left(-\dfrac{1}{2}\right)\right] = \dfrac{\pi}{4}$

b) $y^2 = \cos^2 x = \dfrac{1}{2}(1 + \cos 2x)$

So $V = \dfrac{\pi}{2}\int_0^{\frac{\pi}{2}} 1 + \cos 2x\,dx = \dfrac{\pi}{2}\left[x + \dfrac{1}{2}\sin 2x\right]_0^{\frac{\pi}{2}}$

$= \dfrac{\pi}{2}\left[\left(\dfrac{\pi}{2} + 0\right) - 0\right] = \dfrac{\pi^2}{4}$

c) $y^2 = \dfrac{4}{1 + 2x}$

So $V = \pi \int_0^3 \dfrac{4}{1 + 2x}\,dx = \pi[2\ln|1 + 2x|]_0^3$

$= 2\pi\ln 7$

d) $y^2 = \dfrac{1}{(1 + 3x)^2}$

So $V = \pi \int_0^1 \dfrac{1}{(1 + 3x)^2}\,dx = \pi\left[-\dfrac{1}{3(1 + 3x)}\right]_0^1$

$= \pi\left[-\dfrac{1}{12} + \dfrac{1}{3}\right] = \dfrac{\pi}{4}$

e) $y^2 = 4x^2e^{2x}$

So $V = \pi \int_0^1 4x^2e^{2x}\,dx$

Use integration by parts:

Let $u = 4x^2$ and $\dfrac{dv}{dx} = e^{2x}$.

Then $\dfrac{du}{dx} = 8x$ and $v = \dfrac{1}{2}e^{2x}$.

So $V = \pi \int_0^1 4x^2e^{2x}\,dx = \pi\left([2x^2e^{2x}]_0^1 - \int_0^1 4xe^{2x}\,dx\right)$

Integrate by parts again to find $\int_0^1 4xe^{2x}\,dx$:

Let $u = 4x$ and $\dfrac{dv}{dx} = e^{2x}$.

Then $\dfrac{du}{dx} = 4$ and $v = \dfrac{1}{2}e^{2x}$.

So $\int_0^1 4xe^{2x}\,dx = [2xe^{2x}]_0^1 - \int_0^1 2e^{2x}\,dx$

$= [2xe^{2x}]_0^1 - [e^{2x}]_0^1$

So $V = \pi([2x^2e^{2x}]_0^1 - [2xe^{2x}]_0^1 + [e^{2x}]_0^1)$

$= \pi(2e^2 - 2e^2 + e^2 - e^0) = \pi(e^2 - 1)$

f) $y^2 = x^2\sin x$

So $V = \pi \int_0^{\frac{\pi}{4}} x^2\sin x\,dx$

So using integration by parts:

$V = \pi[-x^2\cos x + 2x\sin x + 2\cos x]_0^{\frac{\pi}{4}}$

$= \pi\left[-\dfrac{\pi^2}{16\sqrt{2}} + \dfrac{\pi}{2\sqrt{2}} + \dfrac{2}{\sqrt{2}} - 2\right]$

$= -\dfrac{\pi^3\sqrt{2}}{32} + \dfrac{\pi^2\sqrt{2}}{4} + \pi(\sqrt{2} - 2)$

The full working for the integration of $x^2\sin x$ is shown in Example 1 on p103.

Exercise 3.2 — Finding volumes of revolution using parametric equations

Q1 a) First, convert the limits from x to t:

$x = 0 \Rightarrow 5t - t^2 = t(5 - t) = 0 \Rightarrow t = 0$ or $t = 5$,
so as $t \geq 3$, $t_1 = 5$

$x = 4 \Rightarrow 5t - t^2 = 4 \Rightarrow t^2 - 5t + 4 = (t - 1)(t - 4)$
$= 0 \Rightarrow t = 1$ or $t = 4$, so as $t \geq 3$, $t_2 = 4$

Differentiate x with respect to t so you can convert the integral to dt:

$\dfrac{dx}{dt} = 5 - 2t$

So $A = \int_5^4 y\dfrac{dx}{dt}\,dt = \int_5^4 \sqrt{t - 3}(5 - 2t)\,dt$

Using the substitution $u = t - 3$:

$\dfrac{du}{dt} = 1 \Rightarrow du = dt$, $t = 5 \Rightarrow u = 2$, $t = 4 \Rightarrow u = 1$

$A = \int_2^1 u^{\frac{1}{2}}(-1 - 2u)\,du = -\int_1^2 u^{\frac{1}{2}}(-1 - 2u)\,du$

$$= \int_2^1 u^{\frac{1}{2}} + 2u^{\frac{3}{2}}\, du = \left[\frac{2}{3}u^{\frac{3}{2}} + \frac{4}{5}u^{\frac{5}{2}}\right]_1^2$$

$$= \left(\frac{4\sqrt{2}}{3} + \frac{16\sqrt{2}}{5}\right) - \left(\frac{2}{3} + \frac{4}{5}\right)$$

$$= \frac{68\sqrt{2}}{15} - \frac{22}{15} = 4.94 \text{ to 2 d.p.}$$

b) $V = \pi \int_{t_1}^{t_2} y^2 \frac{dx}{dt}\, dt = \pi \int_0^1 (t^2)^2 \times 1\, dt = \pi \int_0^1 t^4\, dt$

$$= \pi\left[\frac{1}{5}t^5\right]_0^1 = \pi\left[\frac{1}{5}(1)^5 - \frac{1}{5}(0)^5\right] = \frac{\pi}{5}$$

Q2 a) Convert the limits:

$x = 0 \Rightarrow t^2 = 0 \Rightarrow t_1 = 0$

$x = 1 \Rightarrow t^2 = 1 \Rightarrow t = \pm 1$, so as $t \geq 0$, $t_2 = 1$

Differentiate x with respect to t:

$\dfrac{dx}{dt} = 2t$

So $A = \int_0^1 y\, dx = \int_{t_1}^{t_2} y\frac{dx}{dt}\, dt = \int_0^1 2te^t\, dt$

Use integration by parts:

Let $u = 2t$ and $\dfrac{dv}{dt} = e^t$.

Then $\dfrac{du}{dt} = 2$ and $v = e^t$.

So $\int_0^1 2te^t\, dt = [2te^t]_0^1 - \int_0^1 2e^t\, dt$

$$= [2te^t]_0^1 - [2e^t]_0^1$$

$$= 2e^1 - (2e^1 - 2e^0)$$

$$= 2e^0 = 2$$

b) $V = \pi \int_{t_1}^{t_2} y^2 \frac{dx}{dt}\, dt = \pi \int_0^1 2te^{2t}\, dt$

Use integration by parts:

Let $u = 2t$ and $\dfrac{dv}{dt} = e^{2t}$.

Then $\dfrac{du}{dt} = 2$ and $v = \dfrac{1}{2}e^{2t}$.

So $\pi \int_0^1 2te^{2t}\, dt = \pi[te^{2t}]_0^1 - \pi \int_0^1 e^{2t}\, dt$

$$= \pi\left([te^{2t}]_0^1 - \left[\frac{1}{2}e^{2t}\right]_0^1\right)$$

$$= \pi\left(e^2 - \left[\frac{1}{2}e^2 - \frac{1}{2}e^0\right]\right) = \frac{\pi}{2}(e^2 + 1)$$

Q3 Convert the limits:

$x = 1 \Rightarrow \sec\theta = 1 \Rightarrow \cos\theta = 1 \Rightarrow \theta_1 = 0$

$x = 2 \Rightarrow \sec\theta = 2 \Rightarrow \cos\theta = \dfrac{1}{2} \Rightarrow \theta_2 = \dfrac{\pi}{3}$

Differentiate x with respect to θ:

$\dfrac{dx}{d\theta} = \sec\theta\tan\theta$

So $A = \int_1^2 y\, dx = \int_0^{\frac{\pi}{3}} (1 + \cos\theta)\sec\theta\tan\theta\, d\theta$

$$= \int_0^{\frac{\pi}{3}} \sec\theta\tan\theta + \tan\theta\, d\theta$$

$$= [\sec\theta - \ln|\cos\theta|]_0^{\frac{\pi}{3}}$$

The formula sheet gives $\ln|\sec\theta|$ as the integral of $\tan\theta$, but this is just the same as $-\ln|(\sec\theta)^{-1}| = -\ln|\cos\theta|$.

$$= \left(2 - \ln\frac{1}{2}\right) - (1 - \ln 1)$$

$$= 1 - \ln\frac{1}{2}$$

$$= 1 + \ln 2$$

$V = \pi \int_{\theta_1}^{\theta_2} y^2 \frac{dx}{d\theta}\, d\theta = \pi \int_0^{\frac{\pi}{3}} (1 + \cos\theta)^2 \sec\theta\tan\theta\, d\theta$

$$= \pi \int_0^{\frac{\pi}{3}} (1 + 2\cos\theta + \cos^2\theta)\sec\theta\tan\theta\, d\theta$$

$$= \pi \int_0^{\frac{\pi}{3}} \sec\theta\tan\theta + 2\tan\theta + \sin\theta\, d\theta$$

$$= \pi[\sec\theta - 2\ln|\cos\theta| - \cos\theta]_0^{\frac{\pi}{3}}$$

$$= \pi\left[\left(2 - 2\ln\frac{1}{2} - \frac{1}{2}\right) - (1 - 2\ln 1 - 1)\right]$$

$$= \pi\left(\frac{3}{2} - 2\ln\frac{1}{2}\right)$$

$$= \pi\left(\frac{3}{2} + \ln 4\right)$$

You'll need to know your log laws to simplify ones like this.

Q4 a) Convert the limits:

$x = 0 \Rightarrow \sin\theta = 0 \Rightarrow \theta_1 = 0$

$x = \dfrac{1}{\sqrt{2}} \Rightarrow \sin\theta = \dfrac{1}{\sqrt{2}} \Rightarrow \theta_2 = \dfrac{\pi}{4}$

Differentiate x with respect to θ:

$\dfrac{dx}{d\theta} = \cos\theta$

So $A = \int_0^{\frac{1}{\sqrt{2}}} y\, dx = \int_{\theta_1}^{\theta_2} y\frac{dx}{d\theta}\, d\theta$

$$= \int_0^{\frac{\pi}{4}} (2 + \tan\theta)\cos\theta\, d\theta$$

$$= \int_0^{\frac{\pi}{4}} 2\cos\theta + \sin\theta\, d\theta$$

$$= [2\sin\theta - \cos\theta]_0^{\frac{\pi}{4}}$$

$$= \left(\frac{2}{\sqrt{2}} - \frac{1}{\sqrt{2}}\right) - (0 - 1)$$

$$= \frac{2 + \sqrt{2}}{2} = 1.71 \text{ to 2 d.p.}$$

b) $V = \pi \int_{\theta_1}^{\theta_2} y^2 \frac{dx}{d\theta}\, d\theta = \pi \int_0^{\frac{\pi}{4}} (2 + \tan\theta)^2 \cos\theta\, d\theta$

$$= \pi \int_0^{\frac{\pi}{4}} (4 + 4\tan\theta + \tan^2\theta)\cos\theta\, d\theta$$

$$= \pi \int_0^{\frac{\pi}{4}} 4\cos\theta + 4\sin\theta + (\sec^2\theta - 1)\cos\theta\, d\theta$$

$$= \pi \int_0^{\frac{\pi}{4}} 3\cos\theta + 4\sin\theta + \sec\theta\, d\theta$$

$$= \pi[3\sin\theta - 4\cos\theta + \ln|\sec\theta + \tan\theta|]_0^{\frac{\pi}{4}}$$

$$= \pi\left[\left(\frac{3}{\sqrt{2}} - \frac{4}{\sqrt{2}} + \ln(1 + \sqrt{2})\right) - (0 - 4 + 0)\right]$$

$$= \pi\left[-\frac{1}{\sqrt{2}} + 4 + \ln(1 + \sqrt{2})\right]$$

$$= 13.11 \text{ to 2 d.p.}$$

Q5 a) Convert the limits:

$x = \ln 3 \Rightarrow t^2 - 1 = 3 \Rightarrow t^2 = 4 \Rightarrow t = \pm 2$

so as $t \geq 1$, $t_1 = 2$

$x = \ln 8 \Rightarrow t^2 - 1 = 8 \Rightarrow t^2 = 9 \Rightarrow t = \pm 3$

so as $t \geq 1$, $t_2 = 3$

Differentiate x with respect to t:

$\dfrac{dx}{dt} = \dfrac{2t}{t^2 - 1}$

So $A = \int_{\ln 3}^{\ln 8} y\, dx = \int_2^3 \dfrac{1}{2t} \times \dfrac{2t}{t^2 - 1}\, dt$

$$= \int_2^3 \frac{1}{t^2 - 1}\, dt$$

$$= \int_2^3 \frac{1}{(t + 1)(t - 1)}\, dt$$

Using partial fractions, this can be rewritten as:

$$A = \frac{1}{2}\int_2^3 \frac{1}{t - 1} - \frac{1}{t + 1}\, dt$$

$$= \frac{1}{2}[\ln|t - 1| - \ln|t + 1|]_2^3$$

$$= \frac{1}{2}\big[\ln\big|\tfrac{t-1}{t+1}\big|\big]_2^3$$

$$= \frac{1}{2}\big[\ln\big(\tfrac{1}{2}\big) - \ln\big(\tfrac{1}{3}\big)\big]$$

$$= \frac{1}{2}\ln\big(\tfrac{3}{2}\big) = 0.203 \text{ to 3 s.f.}$$

b) $V = \pi\displaystyle\int_{t_1}^{t_2} y^2 \frac{dx}{dt}\, dt = \pi\displaystyle\int_2^3 \big(\tfrac{1}{2t}\big)^2 \frac{2t}{t^2-1}\, dt$

$$= \pi\int_2^3 \frac{1}{2t(t+1)(t-1)}\, dt$$

Using partial fractions, this can be rewritten as:

$$V = \pi\int_2^3 -\frac{1}{2t} + \frac{1}{4(t+1)} + \frac{1}{4(t-1)}\, dt$$

$$= \pi\Big[-\frac{1}{2}\ln|t| + \frac{1}{4}\ln|t+1| + \frac{1}{4}\ln|t-1|\Big]_2^3$$

$$= \frac{\pi}{4}\Big[\ln\frac{|t+1||t-1|}{t^2}\Big]_2^3$$

$$= \frac{\pi}{4}\Big[\ln\frac{8}{9} - \ln\frac{3}{4}\Big]$$

$$= \frac{\pi}{4}\ln\frac{32}{27}$$

$$= 0.133 \text{ to 3 s.f.}$$

4. Numerical Integration

Exercise 4.1 — The trapezium rule

Q1 a) $h = (2 - 0) \div 2 = 1$, so the x-values are 0, 1, 2.

$\displaystyle\int_0^2 \sqrt{x+2}\, dx \approx \frac{h}{2}[y_0 + 2y_1 + y_2]$

$$= \frac{1}{2}[\sqrt{2} + 2\sqrt{3} + \sqrt{4}]$$

$$= \frac{1}{2}[1.4142 + 3.4641 + 2]$$

$$= 3.44 \text{ to 3 s.f.}$$

b) $h = (3 - 1) \div 4 = 0.5$,
so the x-values are 1, 1.5, 2, 2.5, 3.

$\displaystyle\int_1^3 2(\ln x)^2\, dx \approx \frac{h}{2}[y_0 + 2(y_1 + y_2 + y_3) + y_4]$

$$= \frac{1}{4}[2(\ln 1)^2 + 2(2(\ln 1.5)^2 + 2(\ln 2)^2 + 2(\ln 2.5)^2) + 2(\ln 3)^2]$$

$$= \frac{1}{4}[0 + 2(0.3288 + 0.9609 + 1.6792) + 2.4139]$$

$$= 2.09 \text{ to 3 s.f.}$$

c) $h = (0.4 - 0) \div 2 = 0.2$,
so the x-values are 0, 0.2, 0.4.

$\displaystyle\int_0^{0.4} e^{x^2}\, dx \approx \frac{h}{2}[y_0 + 2y_1 + y_2]$

$$= \frac{0.2}{2}[e^0 + 2e^{0.04} + e^{0.16}]$$

$$= 0.1[1 + 2.0816 + 1.1735]$$

$$= 0.426 \text{ to 3 s.f.}$$

d) $h = \frac{\pi}{2} \div 3 = \frac{\pi}{6}$, so the x-values are $0, \frac{\pi}{6}, \frac{\pi}{3}, \frac{\pi}{2}$.

$\displaystyle\int_0^{\frac{\pi}{2}} \sqrt{\sin x}\, dx \approx \frac{h}{2}[y_0 + 2(y_1 + y_2) + y_3]$

$$= \frac{\pi}{12}\big[\sqrt{\sin 0} + 2\big(\sqrt{\sin\tfrac{\pi}{6}} + \sqrt{\sin\tfrac{\pi}{3}}\big) + \sqrt{\sin\tfrac{\pi}{2}}\big]$$

$$= \frac{\pi}{12}[0 + 2(0.7071 + 0.9306) + 1]$$

$$= 1.12 \text{ to 3 s.f.}$$

e) $h = \big(\frac{\pi}{4} - -\frac{\pi}{4}\big) \div 4 = \frac{\pi}{8}$,
so the x-values are $-\frac{\pi}{4}, -\frac{\pi}{8}, 0, \frac{\pi}{8}, \frac{\pi}{4}$.

$\displaystyle\int_{-\frac{\pi}{4}}^{\frac{\pi}{4}} 4x \tan x\, dx \approx \frac{h}{2}[y_0 + 2(y_1 + y_2 + y_3) + y_4]$

$$= \frac{\pi}{16}\Big[-\pi\tan\big(-\tfrac{\pi}{4}\big) + 2\big(-\tfrac{\pi}{2}\tan\big(-\tfrac{\pi}{8}\big) + 0 + \tfrac{\pi}{2}\tan\big(\tfrac{\pi}{8}\big)\big) + \pi\tan\big(\tfrac{\pi}{4}\big)\Big]$$

$$= \frac{\pi}{16}[\pi + 2(0.6506 + 0.6506) + \pi]$$

$$= 1.74 \text{ to 3 s.f.}$$

f) $h = (0.3 - 0) \div 6 = 0.05$,
so the x-values are 0, 0.05, 0.1, 0.15, 0.2, 0.25, 0.3.

$\displaystyle\int_0^{0.3} \sqrt{e^x + 1}\, dx \approx \frac{h}{2}[y_0 + 2(y_1 + y_2 + y_3 + y_4 + y_5) + y_6]$

$$= \frac{0.05}{2}[\sqrt{e^0 + 1} + 2(\sqrt{e^{0.05} + 1} + \sqrt{e^{0.1} + 1} + \sqrt{e^{0.15} + 1} + \sqrt{e^{0.2} + 1} + \sqrt{e^{0.25} + 1}) + \sqrt{e^{0.3} + 1}]$$

$$= 0.025[\sqrt{2} + 2(\sqrt{2.0513} + \sqrt{2.1052} + \sqrt{2.1618} + \sqrt{2.2214} + \sqrt{2.2840}) + \sqrt{2.3499}]$$

$$= 0.025[1.4142 + 2(1.4322 + 1.4509 + 1.4703 + 1.4904 + 1.5113) + 1.5329]$$

$$= 0.441 \text{ to 3 s.f.}$$

g) $h = (4 - 1) \div 3 = 1$, so the x-values are 1, 2, 3, 4.

$\displaystyle\int_1^4 (1 + \ln x)^4\, dx \approx \frac{h}{2}[y_0 + 2(y_1 + y_2) + y_3]$

$$= \frac{1}{2}[(1 + \ln 1)^4 + 2((1 + \ln 2)^4 + (1 + \ln 3)^4) + (1 + \ln 4)^4]$$

$$= \frac{1}{2}[1 + 2(8.2182 + 19.3967) + 32.4262]$$

$$= 44.3 \text{ to 3 s.f.}$$

h) $h = \frac{\pi}{6}$, so the x-values are $0, \frac{\pi}{6}, \frac{\pi}{3}, \frac{\pi}{2}, \frac{2\pi}{3}, \frac{5\pi}{6}, \pi$.

$\displaystyle\int_0^{\pi} \ln(2 + \sin x)\, dx \approx \frac{h}{2}[y_0 + 2(y_1 + y_2 + y_3 + y_4 + y_5) + y_6]$

$$= \frac{\pi}{12}\Big[\ln(2 + \sin 0) + 2\big(\ln(2 + \sin\tfrac{\pi}{6}) + \ln(2 + \sin\tfrac{\pi}{3}) + \ln(2 + \sin\tfrac{\pi}{2}) + \ln(2 + \sin\tfrac{2\pi}{3}) + \ln(2 + \sin\tfrac{5\pi}{6})\big) + \ln(2 + \sin\pi)\Big]$$

$$= \frac{\pi}{12}[0.6931 + 2(0.9163 + 1.0529 + 1.0986 + 1.0529 + 0.9163) + 0.6931]$$

$$= 3.00 \text{ to 3 s.f.}$$

Q2 $h = \frac{\pi}{2} \div 3 = \frac{\pi}{6}$, so the x-values are $0, \frac{\pi}{6}, \frac{\pi}{3}, \frac{\pi}{2}$.

$\displaystyle\int_0^{\frac{\pi}{2}} \sin^3\theta\, d\theta \approx \frac{h}{2}[y_0 + 2(y_1 + y_2) + y_3]$

$$= \frac{\pi}{12}\Big[\sin^3 0 + 2\big(\sin^3\tfrac{\pi}{6} + \sin^3\tfrac{\pi}{3}\big) + \sin^3\tfrac{\pi}{2}\Big]$$

$$= \frac{\pi}{12}[0 + 2(0.125 + 0.6495) + 1]$$

$$= 0.667 \text{ to 3 d.p.}$$

Q3 $h = (7 - 2) \div 5 = 1$, so the x-values are 2, 3, 4, 5, 6, 7.

$\displaystyle\int_2^7 \sqrt{\ln x}\, dx \approx \frac{h}{2}[y_0 + 2(y_1 + y_2 + y_3 + y_4) + y_5]$

$$= \frac{1}{2}[\sqrt{\ln 2} + 2(\sqrt{\ln 3} + \sqrt{\ln 4} + \sqrt{\ln 5} + \sqrt{\ln 6}) + \sqrt{\ln 7}]$$

$$= \frac{1}{2}[0.8326 + 2(1.0481 + 1.1774 + 1.2686 + 1.3386) + 1.3950]$$

$$= 5.947 \text{ to 3 d.p.}$$

Q4 a)

x	0	$\frac{\pi}{8}$	$\frac{\pi}{4}$	$\frac{3\pi}{8}$	$\frac{\pi}{2}$
y	2.718	2.028	1.000	**0.493**	**0.368**

b) $\int_0^{\frac{\pi}{2}} e^{\cos 2x}\, dx \approx \frac{h}{2}[y_0 + 2(y_1 + y_2 + y_3) + y_4]$

$= \frac{\pi}{16}[2.718 + 2(2.028 + 1 + 0.493) + 0.368]$

$= 1.99$ to 2 d.p.

Q5 a)

x	0	$\frac{\pi}{8}$	$\frac{\pi}{4}$	$\frac{3\pi}{8}$	$\frac{\pi}{2}$
y	1	1.466	**2.028**	**2.519**	2.718

b) (i) $\int_0^{\frac{\pi}{2}} e^{\sin x}\, dx \approx \frac{\pi}{8}[1 + 2(2.028) + 2.718]$

$= 3.05$ to 2 d.p.

(ii) $\int_0^{\frac{\pi}{2}} e^{\sin x}\, dx$

$\approx \frac{\pi}{16}[1 + 2(1.466 + 2.028 + 2.519) + 2.718]$

$= 3.09$ to 2 d.p.

c) 3.09 is the better estimate as more intervals have been used in the calculation.

Q6 a) $h = (4 - 2) \div 4 = 0.5$,
so the x-values are 2, 2.5, 3, 3.5, 4.

$\int_2^4 \frac{3}{\ln x}\, dx \approx \frac{1}{4}\left[\frac{3}{\ln 2} + 2\left(\frac{3}{\ln 2.5} + \frac{3}{\ln 3} + \frac{3}{\ln 3.5}\right) + \frac{3}{\ln 4}\right]$

$= 0.25[4.3281 + 2(3.2741 + 2.7307 + 2.3947) + 2.1640]$

$= 5.82$ to 2 d.p.

b) It is an over-estimate as the top of each trapezium lies above the curve.

Exercise 4.2 — Calculating error

Q1 a) $h = (6 - 0) \div 3 = 2$, so the x-values are 0, 2, 4, 6.

$\int_0^6 \sqrt{x^2 + 1}\, dx \approx \frac{h}{2}[y_0 + 2(y_1 + y_2) + y_3]$

$= \frac{2}{2}[\sqrt{1} + 2(\sqrt{5} + \sqrt{17}) + \sqrt{37}]$

$= [1 + 2(2.2361 + 4.1231) + 6.0828]$

$= 19.801$ to 3 d.p.

b) Error $= \left|\frac{19.494 - 19.801}{19.494}\right| \times 100 = 1.57\%$

Q2 a) $h = (5 - 1) \div 4 = 1$, so the x-values are 1, 2, 3, 4, 5.

$\int_1^5 \ln x\, dx \approx \frac{h}{2}[y_0 + 2(y_1 + y_2 + y_3) + y_4]$

$= \frac{1}{2}[0 + 2(\ln 2 + \ln 3 + \ln 4) + \ln 5]$

$= 3.983$ to 3 d.p.

b) $\int_1^5 \ln x\, dx = [x\ln x - x]_1^5$

$= [(5\ln 5 - 5) - (0 - 1)]$

$= 5\ln 5 - 4$

c) Error $= \left|\frac{(5\ln 5 - 4) - 3.983}{(5\ln 5 - 4)}\right| \times 100 = 1.59\%$

d) The shape of the graph means that the tops of the trapeziums lie underneath the curve so the area of the trapeziums will be less than the area under the curve.

Q3 a) $h = \frac{\pi}{2} \div 4 = \frac{\pi}{8}$, so the x-values are 0, $\frac{\pi}{8}, \frac{\pi}{4}, \frac{3\pi}{8}, \frac{\pi}{2}$.

$\int_0^{\frac{\pi}{2}} x\sin x\, dx \approx \frac{h}{2}[y_0 + 2(y_1 + y_2 + y_3) + y_4]$

$= \frac{\pi}{16}\left[0 + 2\left(\frac{\pi}{8}\sin\frac{\pi}{8} + \frac{\pi}{4}\sin\frac{\pi}{4} + \frac{3\pi}{8}\sin\frac{3\pi}{8}\right) + \frac{\pi}{2}\sin\frac{\pi}{2}\right]$

$= \frac{\pi}{16}[0 + 2(0.1503 + 0.5554 + 1.0884) + 1.5708]$

$= 1.013$ to 3 d.p.

b) $\int_0^{\frac{\pi}{2}} x\sin x\, dx = [-x\cos x + \sin x]_0^{\frac{\pi}{2}}$

$= \left(-\frac{\pi}{2}\cos\frac{\pi}{2} + \sin\frac{\pi}{2}\right) - \sin 0 = 1$

Error $= \left|\frac{1 - 1.013}{1}\right| \times 100 = 1.3\%$

Q4 a) $h = 2 \div 4 = 0.5$, so the x-values are 0, 0.5, 1, 1.5, 2.

$\int_0^2 \frac{2x}{x^2 + 1}\, dx \approx \frac{h}{2}[y_0 + 2(y_1 + y_2 + y_3) + y_4]$

$= \frac{1}{4}\left[0 + 2\left(\frac{1}{1.25} + \frac{2}{2} + \frac{3}{3.25}\right) + \frac{4}{5}\right]$

$= 1.562$ to 3 d.p.

b) This integral is of the form $\frac{f'(x)}{f(x)}$:

$\int_0^2 \frac{2x}{x^2 + 1}\, dx = [\ln|x^2 + 1|]_0^2 = \ln 5$

So error $= \left|\frac{\ln 5 - 1.562}{\ln 5}\right| \times 100 = 2.95\%$

5. Differential Equations
Exercise 5.1 — Differential equations

Q1 The rate of change of N with respect to t is $\frac{dN}{dt}$.

So $\frac{dN}{dt} \propto N \Rightarrow \frac{dN}{dt} = kN$, for some $k > 0$.

Q2 The rate of change of x with respect to t is $\frac{dx}{dt}$.

So $\frac{dx}{dt} \propto \frac{1}{x^2} \Rightarrow \frac{dx}{dt} = \frac{k}{x^2}$, for some $k > 0$.

Q3 Let the variable t represent time.

Then the rate of change of A with respect to t is $\frac{dA}{dt}$.

So $\frac{dA}{dt} \propto \sqrt{A} \Rightarrow \frac{dA}{dt} = -k\sqrt{A}$, for some $k > 0$.

Don't forget to include a minus sign when the situation involves a rate of decrease.

Q4 Let the variable t represent time.

Then the rate of change of y with respect to t is $\frac{dy}{dt}$.

So $\frac{dy}{dt} \propto (y - \lambda) \Rightarrow \frac{dy}{dt} = -k(y - \lambda)$, for some $k > 0$.

Q5 Let the variable t represent time.
V is the volume in the container and it is equal to $V_{in} - V_{out}$. Then the rate of change of V with respect to t is $\frac{dV}{dt} = \frac{dV_{in}}{dt} - \frac{dV_{out}}{dt}$.

$\frac{dV_{in}}{dt}$ is directly proportional to V so $\frac{dV_{in}}{dt} = kV$ for some constant k, $k > 0$ and $\frac{dV_{out}}{dt} = 20$.

So the overall rate of change of V is $\frac{dV}{dt} = kV - 20$, for some $k > 0$.

Exercise 5.2 — Solving differential equations

Q1 a) $\dfrac{dy}{dx} = 8x^3 \quad \Rightarrow \quad dy = 8x^3\,dx$

$\Rightarrow \displaystyle\int 1\,dy = \int 8x^3\,dx$

$\Rightarrow y = 2x^4 + C$

b) $\dfrac{dy}{dx} = 5y \quad \Rightarrow \quad \dfrac{1}{y}dy = 5\,dx$

$\Rightarrow \displaystyle\int \dfrac{1}{y}\,dy = \int 5\,dx$

$\Rightarrow \ln|y| = 5x + \ln k$

$\Rightarrow y = e^{5x + \ln k} = ke^{5x}$

c) $\dfrac{dy}{dx} = 6x^2 y \quad \Rightarrow \quad \dfrac{1}{y}dy = 6x^2 dx$

$\Rightarrow \displaystyle\int \dfrac{1}{y}\,dy = \int 6x^2\,dx$

$\Rightarrow \ln|y| = 2x^3 + \ln k$

$\Rightarrow y = e^{2x^3 + \ln k} = ke^{2x^3}$

d) $\dfrac{dy}{dx} = \dfrac{y}{x} \quad \Rightarrow \quad \dfrac{1}{y}dy = \dfrac{1}{x}dx$

$\Rightarrow \displaystyle\int \dfrac{1}{y}\,dy = \int \dfrac{1}{x}\,dx$

$\Rightarrow \ln|y| = \ln|x| + \ln k = \ln|kx|$

$\Rightarrow y = kx$

e) $\dfrac{dy}{dx} = (y + 1)\cos x \quad \Rightarrow \quad \dfrac{1}{y + 1}dy = \cos x\,dx$

$\Rightarrow \displaystyle\int \dfrac{1}{y + 1}\,dy = \int \cos x\,dx$

$\Rightarrow \ln|y + 1| = \sin x + \ln k$

$\Rightarrow y + 1 = e^{\sin x + \ln k}$

$\Rightarrow y = ke^{\sin x} - 1$

f) $\dfrac{dy}{dx} = \dfrac{(3x - 6)y}{(x - 4)(2x - 5)}$

$\Rightarrow \dfrac{1}{y}dy = \dfrac{(3x - 6)}{(x - 4)(2x - 5)}\,dx$

$\Rightarrow \displaystyle\int \dfrac{1}{y}\,dy = \int \dfrac{(3x - 6)}{(x - 4)(2x - 5)}\,dx$

The integration on the right hand side needs to be split into partial fractions before you can integrate.

$\dfrac{(3x - 6)}{(x - 4)(2x - 5)} \equiv \dfrac{A}{(x - 4)} + \dfrac{B}{(2x - 5)}$

$\Rightarrow (3x - 6) \equiv A(2x - 5) + B(x - 4)$

Substitution:

$x = 4: \quad 6 = 3A \quad \Rightarrow \quad A = 2$

$x = \dfrac{5}{2}: \quad \dfrac{3}{2} = -\dfrac{3}{2}B \quad \Rightarrow \quad B = -1$

So

$\displaystyle\int \dfrac{(3x - 6)}{(x - 4)(2x - 5)}\,dx \equiv \int \dfrac{2}{(x - 4)} - \dfrac{1}{(2x - 5)}\,dx$

So $\displaystyle\int \dfrac{1}{y}dy = \int \dfrac{2}{(x - 4)} - \dfrac{1}{(2x - 5)}\,dx$

$\Rightarrow \ln|y| = 2\ln|x - 4| - \dfrac{1}{2}\ln|2x - 5| + \ln k$

$\Rightarrow \ln|y| = \ln|(x - 4)^2| - \ln|\sqrt{2x - 5}| + \ln k$

$\Rightarrow \ln|y| = \ln\left|\dfrac{k(x - 4)^2}{\sqrt{2x - 5}}\right|$

$\Rightarrow y = \dfrac{k(x - 4)^2}{\sqrt{2x - 5}}$

Q2 a) $\dfrac{dy}{dx} = -\dfrac{x}{y} \quad \Rightarrow \quad y\,dy = -x\,dx$

$\Rightarrow \displaystyle\int y\,dy = \int -x\,dx$

$\Rightarrow \dfrac{1}{2}y^2 = -\dfrac{1}{2}x^2 + c$

$\Rightarrow y^2 = -x^2 + C$

So when $x = 0$ and $y = 2$, $C = 4 \quad \Rightarrow \quad y^2 + x^2 = 4$

b) $\dfrac{dx}{dt} = \dfrac{2}{\sqrt{x}} \quad \Rightarrow \quad \sqrt{x}\,dx = 2\,dt$

$\Rightarrow \displaystyle\int x^{\frac{1}{2}}\,dx = \int 2\,dt$

$\Rightarrow \dfrac{2}{3}x^{\frac{3}{2}} = 2t + C$

So when $t = 5$ and $x = 9$,

$\dfrac{2}{3}(27) = 10 + C \quad \Rightarrow \quad 18 = 10 + C \quad \Rightarrow \quad C = 8$

$\Rightarrow \dfrac{2}{3}x^{\frac{3}{2}} = 2t + 8$

$\Rightarrow x^{\frac{3}{2}} = 3t + 12$

$\Rightarrow x^3 = (3t + 12)^2$

You could have left out the last couple of steps here, as the question didn't specify the form of the answer.

c) $\dfrac{dV}{dt} = 3(V - 1) \quad \Rightarrow \quad \dfrac{1}{V - 1}dV = 3\,dt$

$\Rightarrow \displaystyle\int \dfrac{1}{V - 1}\,dV = \int 3\,dt$

$\Rightarrow \ln|V - 1| = 3t + \ln k$

$\Rightarrow V = ke^{3t} + 1$

So when $t = 0$ and $V = 5$,

$5 = k + 1 \quad \Rightarrow \quad k = 4$

$\Rightarrow V = 4e^{3t} + 1$

d) $\dfrac{dy}{dx} = \dfrac{\tan y}{x} \quad \Rightarrow \quad \dfrac{1}{\tan y}dy = \dfrac{1}{x}dx$

$\Rightarrow \displaystyle\int \cot y\,dy = \int \dfrac{1}{x}\,dx$

$\Rightarrow \ln|\sin y| = \ln|x| + \ln k$

$\Rightarrow \sin y = kx$

So when $x = 2$ and $y = \dfrac{\pi}{2}$,

$1 = 2k \quad \Rightarrow \quad k = \dfrac{1}{2} \quad \Rightarrow \quad \sin y = \dfrac{x}{2}$

e) $\dfrac{dx}{dt} = 10x(x + 1) \quad \Rightarrow \quad \dfrac{1}{x(x + 1)}dx = 10\,dt$

Using partial fractions, $\dfrac{1}{x(x + 1)} \equiv \dfrac{1}{x} - \dfrac{1}{x + 1}$,

so $\displaystyle\int \dfrac{1}{x} - \dfrac{1}{x + 1}\,dx = \int 10\,dt$

$\Rightarrow \ln|x| - \ln|x + 1| = 10t + \ln k$

$\Rightarrow \ln\left|\dfrac{x}{x + 1}\right| = 10t + \ln k$

$\Rightarrow \dfrac{x}{x + 1} = ke^{10t}$

So when $t = 0$ and $x = 1$, $\dfrac{1}{2} = k$

$\Rightarrow \dfrac{x}{x + 1} = \dfrac{1}{2}e^{10t}$

Q3 a) $\dfrac{dV}{dt} = a - bV \quad \Rightarrow \quad \dfrac{1}{a - bV}dV = dt$

$\Rightarrow \displaystyle\int \dfrac{1}{a - bV}\,dV = \int 1\,dt$

$\Rightarrow -\dfrac{1}{b}\ln|a - bV| = t + C$

$\Rightarrow \ln|a - bV| = -bt - bC$

b and C are both constants, so let $-bC = \ln k$:

$$\Rightarrow \ln|a - bV| = -bt + \ln k$$
$$\Rightarrow a - bV = ke^{-bt}$$
$$\Rightarrow bV = a - ke^{-bt}$$
$$\Rightarrow V = \frac{a}{b} - Ae^{-bt} \text{ (letting } A = k \div b)$$

b) When $t = 0$ and $V = \frac{a}{4b}$,

$$\frac{a}{4b} = \frac{a}{b} - A \quad \Rightarrow A = \frac{a}{b} - \frac{a}{4b} = \frac{4a - a}{4b} = \frac{3a}{4b}$$

c) As t gets very large, e^{-bt} gets very close to zero, so V approaches $\frac{a}{b}$.

Q4 a) $\frac{dx}{dt} = (x + 2)(2x + 3)\tan t$

$$\Rightarrow \frac{1}{(x + 2)(2x + 3)}dx = \tan t \, dt$$

Using partial fractions,

$$\frac{1}{(x + 2)(2x + 3)} \equiv \frac{2}{2x + 3} - \frac{1}{x + 2},$$

so $\int \frac{2}{2x + 3} - \frac{1}{x + 2} \, dx = \int \tan t \, dt$

$$\Rightarrow \ln(2x + 3) - \ln(x + 2) = \ln(\sec t) + \ln k$$

$$\Rightarrow \ln\frac{2x + 3}{x + 2} = \ln(k \sec t)$$

$$\Rightarrow \frac{2x + 3}{x + 2} = k \sec t = \frac{k}{\cos t}$$

So when $t = 0$ and $x = 0$, $\frac{3}{2} = k$

$$\Rightarrow \frac{2x + 3}{x + 2} = \frac{3}{2 \cos t}$$

b) $t = \frac{\pi}{3} \Rightarrow \frac{2x + 3}{x + 2} = \frac{3}{2 \cos \frac{\pi}{3}} = 3$

$$\Rightarrow 2x + 3 = 3x + 6 \Rightarrow x = -3$$

Exercise 5.3 — Applying differential equations to real-life problems

Q1 a) $\frac{dN}{dt} = kN \Rightarrow \frac{1}{N}dN = k\,dt$

$$\Rightarrow \int\frac{1}{N}dN = \int k \, dt$$
$$\Rightarrow \ln N = kt + \ln A$$
$$\Rightarrow N = e^{kt + \ln A} = Ae^{kt}$$

Note that you don't need to put modulus signs in ln N here, as N can't be negative — you can't have a negative number of germs in your body. The same principle will apply to a lot of real-life differential equations questions.

b) $t = 0, N = 200 \Rightarrow 200 = Ae^0 = A$
$$\Rightarrow N = 200e^{kt}$$
$t = 8, N = 400 \Rightarrow 400 = 200e^{8k}$
$$\Rightarrow \ln 2 = 8k$$
$$\Rightarrow k = \frac{1}{8}\ln 2$$
$$\Rightarrow N = 200e^{\frac{t}{8}\ln 2}$$
So $t = 24 \Rightarrow N = 200e^{3\ln 2} = 1600$

Q2 a) $\frac{dV}{dt} \propto V \Rightarrow \frac{dV}{dt} = -kV$, for some $k > 0$

$$\Rightarrow \frac{1}{V}dV = -k\,dt$$
$$\Rightarrow \int\frac{1}{V}dV = \int -k \, dt$$
$$\Rightarrow \ln V = -kt + \ln A$$
$$\Rightarrow V = Ae^{-kt}$$

$t = 0, V = V_0 \Rightarrow V_0 = Ae^0 = A$
$$\Rightarrow V = V_0e^{-kt}$$

b) $t = 1, V = \frac{1}{2}V_0 \Rightarrow \frac{1}{2}V_0 = V_0e^{-k}$

$$\Rightarrow \frac{1}{2} = e^{-k}$$
$$\Rightarrow \ln\frac{1}{2} = -k$$
$$\Rightarrow k = \ln 2$$
$$\Rightarrow V = V_0e^{-t\ln 2}$$

So $V = 0.05V_0 \Rightarrow 0.05V_0 = V_0e^{-t\ln 2}$
$$\Rightarrow 0.05 = e^{-t\ln 2}$$
$$\Rightarrow \ln 0.05 = -t\ln 2$$
$$\Rightarrow t = \ln 0.05 \div -\ln 2 = 4.322 \text{ years}$$
$$\Rightarrow t = 4 \text{ years, 4 months}$$
$$\text{(or 52 months)}$$

You could have used months as the units of time instead, and started with t = 12. You'd get the same answer.

Q3 a) $\frac{dN}{dt} \propto N \quad \Rightarrow \frac{dN}{dt} = kN$

b) $\frac{dN}{dt} = kN \quad \Rightarrow \int\frac{1}{N}dN = \int k \, dt$

$$\Rightarrow \ln N = kt + \ln A$$
$$\Rightarrow N = e^{kt + \ln A} = Ae^{kt}$$

$N = 20$ at $t = 0 \Rightarrow 20 = Ae^0 = A \quad \Rightarrow N = 20e^{kt}$
$N = 30$ at $t = 4 \Rightarrow 30 = 20e^{4k}$
$$\Rightarrow k = 0.25 \ln 1.5$$
$$\Rightarrow N = 20e^{0.25t\ln 1.5}$$
So $N = 1000 \quad \Rightarrow 1000 = 20e^{0.25t\ln 1.5}$
$$\Rightarrow \ln 50 = 0.25t\ln 1.5$$
$$\Rightarrow t = 4\ln 50 \div \ln 1.5 = 38.59$$
So the field will be over-run in 39 weeks.

c) $\frac{dN}{dt} \propto \sqrt{N} \Rightarrow \frac{dN}{dt} = k\sqrt{N}$

$$\Rightarrow \int\frac{1}{\sqrt{N}}dN = \int k \, dt$$
$$\Rightarrow 2\sqrt{N} = kt + C$$

$N = 20$ at $t = 0 \Rightarrow 2\sqrt{20} = 4\sqrt{5} = C$
$$\Rightarrow 2\sqrt{N} = kt + 4\sqrt{5}$$
$N = 30$ at $t = 4 \Rightarrow 2\sqrt{30} = 4k + 4\sqrt{5}$
$$\Rightarrow k = \frac{\sqrt{30} - 2\sqrt{5}}{2}$$
$$\Rightarrow 2\sqrt{N} = \frac{\sqrt{30} - 2\sqrt{5}}{2}t + 4\sqrt{5}$$
So $N = 1000 \quad \Rightarrow 2\sqrt{1000} = \frac{\sqrt{30} - 2\sqrt{5}}{2}t + 4\sqrt{5}$

$$\Rightarrow t = \frac{4\sqrt{1000} - 8\sqrt{5}}{\sqrt{30} - 2\sqrt{5}} = 108.05$$

So the field will be over-run in 108 weeks.
Be careful with all these square roots knocking about — it's easy to make a mistake.

Q4 a) $\frac{dx}{dt} = \frac{1}{x^2(t + 1)}$

$V = x^3 \Rightarrow \frac{dV}{dx} = 3x^2$

So $\frac{dV}{dt} = \frac{dV}{dx} \times \frac{dx}{dt} = \frac{3x^2}{x^2(t + 1)} = \frac{3}{t + 1}$

b) $\frac{dV}{dt} = \frac{3}{t + 1} \quad \Rightarrow \int 1 \, dV = \int\frac{3}{t + 1}dt$

$$\Rightarrow V = 3\ln(t + 1) + C$$
$V = 15$ at $t = 0 \Rightarrow 15 = 3\ln(1) + C \Rightarrow C = 15$
$$\Rightarrow V = 3\ln(t + 1) + 15$$

So $V = 19$ $\Rightarrow$ $19 = 3\ln(t + 1) + 15$

$\quad\quad\quad\quad \Rightarrow \dfrac{4}{3} = \ln(t + 1)$

$\quad\quad\quad\quad \Rightarrow t = e^{\frac{4}{3}} - 1 = 2.79$ seconds (3 s.f.)

Q5 a) $\dfrac{dy}{dt} = k(p - y)$ $\Rightarrow$ $\displaystyle\int \dfrac{1}{p - y}\,dy = \int k\,dt$

$\quad\quad\quad \Rightarrow -\ln(p - y) = kt + \ln a$

$\quad\quad\quad \Rightarrow \ln(p - y) = -kt - \ln a$

$\quad\quad\quad \Rightarrow p - y = e^{-kt - \ln a} = e^{-kt}e^{-\ln a}$

$\quad\quad\quad\quad e^{-kt}e^{\ln\frac{1}{a}} = \dfrac{1}{a}e^{-kt} = Ae^{-kt}$

$\quad\quad\quad \Rightarrow y = p - Ae^{-kt}$

b) If $p = 30\,000$ and $y = 10\,000$ at $t = 0$, then

$10\,000 = 30\,000 - Ae^0 = 30\,000 - A$

$\quad\quad\quad\quad \Rightarrow A = 20\,000$

$\quad\quad\quad\quad \Rightarrow y = 30\,000 - 20\,000e^{-kt}$

$t = 5, y = 12\,000$

$\quad\quad\quad \Rightarrow 12\,000 = 30\,000 - 20\,000e^{-5k}$

$\quad\quad\quad \Rightarrow e^{-5k} = 18\,000 \div 20\,000 = 0.9$

$\quad\quad\quad \Rightarrow -5k = \ln 0.9$

$\quad\quad\quad \Rightarrow k = -0.2\ln 0.9$

$\quad\quad\quad \Rightarrow y = 30\,000 - 20\,000e^{0.2t\ln 0.9}$

So $y = 25\,000$ $\Rightarrow$ $20\,000e^{0.2t\ln 0.9} = 5000$

$\quad\quad\quad\quad \Rightarrow e^{0.2t\ln 0.9} = 0.25$

$\quad\quad\quad\quad \Rightarrow 0.2t\ln 0.9 = \ln 0.25$

$\quad\quad\quad\quad \Rightarrow t = 5\ln 0.25 \div \ln 0.9$

$\quad\quad\quad\quad\quad = 65.79 = 66$ days

c)

$y = 30\,000 - 20\,000e^{0.2\ln 0.9t}$

Remember that 0.2ln0.9t is negative when sketching the graph.

d) $t = 92$ $\Rightarrow$ $y = 30\,000 - 20\,000e^{18.4\ln 0.9}$

$\quad\quad\quad\quad = 30\,000 - 20\,000e^{-1.939}$

$\quad\quad\quad\quad = 30\,000 - 20\,000(0.1439)$

$\quad\quad\quad\quad = 27122$ members

So no, the target will not be achieved.

Don't forget, you'll often need to relate your answer back to the question when you've finished calculating.

Review Exercise — Chapter 6

Q1 a) $u = 5 - x^2$ $\Rightarrow$ $\dfrac{du}{dx} = -2x$ $\Rightarrow$ $-\dfrac{1}{2x}du = dx$

Substituting this into the integral gives:

$\displaystyle\int 16x \times u^5 \times -\dfrac{1}{2x}du = \int -8u^5\,du$

$\quad\quad\quad\quad\quad\quad = -\dfrac{4}{3}u^6 + C$

$\quad\quad\quad\quad\quad\quad = -\dfrac{4}{3}(5 - x^2)^6 + C$

Make sure you reverse the substitution at the end to get your final answer in terms of x.

b) $u = \cos\theta$ $\Rightarrow$ $\dfrac{du}{d\theta} = -\sin\theta$ $\Rightarrow$ $-\dfrac{1}{\sin\theta}du = d\theta$

Substituting this into the integral gives:

$\displaystyle\int 3\sin\theta \times u^4 \times -\dfrac{1}{\sin\theta}du = \int -3u^4\,du$

$\quad\quad\quad\quad\quad\quad\quad = -\dfrac{3}{5}u^5 + C$

$\quad\quad\quad\quad\quad\quad\quad = -\dfrac{3}{5}\cos^5\theta + C$

c) $u = e^x - 1$ $\Rightarrow$ $\dfrac{du}{dx} = e^x$ $\Rightarrow$ $\dfrac{1}{e^x}du = dx$

and $e^x + 1 = u + 2$

Substituting this into the integral gives:

$\displaystyle\int e^x(u + 2)u^2\dfrac{du}{e^x} = \int (u + 2)u^2\,du$

$\quad\quad\quad\quad\quad\quad = \int u^3 + 2u^2\,du$

$\quad\quad\quad\quad\quad\quad = \dfrac{1}{4}u^4 + \dfrac{2}{3}u^3 + C$

$\quad\quad\quad\quad\quad\quad = \dfrac{1}{4}(e^x - 1)^4 + \dfrac{2}{3}(e^x - 1)^3 + C$

Q2 a) $u = x^2 - 4$ $\Rightarrow$ $\dfrac{du}{dx} = 2x$ $\Rightarrow$ $\dfrac{du}{2x} = dx$

Change the limits:

$x = 2$ $\Rightarrow$ $u = 2^2 - 4 = 0$, $x = 4$ $\Rightarrow$ $u = 4^2 - 4 = 12$

Substituting into the integral gives:

$\displaystyle\int_0^{12} x\,u^3\dfrac{du}{2x} = \int_0^{12} \dfrac{1}{2}u^3\,du$

$\quad\quad\quad\quad\quad = \left[\dfrac{1}{8}u^4\right]_0^{12}$

$\quad\quad\quad\quad\quad = \dfrac{12^4}{8} = 2592$

b) $u = \sec x$ $\Rightarrow$ $\dfrac{du}{dx} = \sec x \tan x$ $\Rightarrow$ $\dfrac{du}{\sec x \tan x} = dx$

Change the limits: $x = \dfrac{\pi}{4}$ $\Rightarrow$ $u = \sec\dfrac{\pi}{4} = \sqrt{2}$,

$\quad\quad\quad\quad\quad\quad x = \dfrac{\pi}{3}$ $\Rightarrow$ $u = \sec\dfrac{\pi}{3} = 2$

Substituting into the integral gives:

$\displaystyle\int_{\sqrt{2}}^2 \sec x \tan x\,u^3\dfrac{du}{\sec x \tan x} = \int_{\sqrt{2}}^2 u^3\,du$

$\quad\quad\quad\quad\quad\quad\quad = \left[\dfrac{1}{4}u^4\right]_{\sqrt{2}}^2$

$\quad\quad\quad\quad\quad\quad\quad = \dfrac{16}{4} - \dfrac{4}{4} = 4 - 1 = 3$

c) $u = \sqrt{3x - 8}$ $\Rightarrow$ $\dfrac{du}{dx} = \dfrac{3}{2\sqrt{3x - 8}} = \dfrac{3}{2u}$

$\quad\quad \Rightarrow \dfrac{2}{3}u\,du = dx$ and $x = \dfrac{8 + u^2}{3}$

Change the limits:

$x = 3$ $\Rightarrow$ $u = \sqrt{9 - 8} = 1$,

$x = 11$ $\Rightarrow$ $u = \sqrt{33 - 8} = 5$

Substituting into the integral gives:

$\displaystyle\int_1^5 2\left(\dfrac{8 + u^2}{3}\right) \times \dfrac{1}{u} \times \dfrac{2}{3}u\,du = \int_1^5 \dfrac{4}{9}(8 + u^2)\,du$

$\quad\quad\quad\quad\quad\quad\quad = \dfrac{4}{9}\left[8u + \dfrac{1}{3}u^3\right]_1^5$

$\quad\quad\quad\quad\quad\quad\quad = \dfrac{4}{9}\left[\left(40 + \dfrac{125}{3}\right) - \left(8 + \dfrac{1}{3}\right)\right] = \dfrac{880}{27}$

Q3 a) $u = \cos x$ $\Rightarrow$ $\dfrac{du}{dx} = -\sin x$ $\Rightarrow$ $-\dfrac{du}{\sin x} = dx$

$\sin 2x \equiv 2\sin x \cos x$

Change the limits:

$x = 0$ $\Rightarrow$ $u = \cos 0 = 1$

$x = \dfrac{\pi}{2}$ $\Rightarrow$ $u = \cos\dfrac{\pi}{2} = 0$

Substituting into the integral gives:

$$\int_0^{\frac{\pi}{2}} \frac{1}{4}\cos x \times 2\sin x \cos x \, dx = \int_0^{\frac{\pi}{2}} \frac{1}{2}\cos^2 x \sin x \, dx$$

$$= \int_1^0 \frac{1}{2}\sin x \times u^2 \times -\frac{1}{\sin x}\, du$$

$$= \int_1^0 -\frac{1}{2}u^2 \, du = \int_0^1 \frac{1}{2}u^2 \, du$$

$$= \left[\frac{1}{6}u^3\right]_0^1 = \frac{1}{6} - 0 = \frac{1}{6}$$

b) $x = \cot\theta \Rightarrow \dfrac{dx}{d\theta} = -\text{cosec}^2\theta \Rightarrow dx = -\text{cosec}^2\theta\, d\theta$

Change the limits:

$x = 1 \Rightarrow \theta = \frac{\pi}{4},\ x = \sqrt{3} \Rightarrow \theta = \frac{\pi}{6}$

Substituting into the integral and using the identity $\text{cosec}^2\theta \equiv 1 + \cot^2\theta$ gives:

$$\int_{\frac{\pi}{4}}^{\frac{\pi}{6}} \frac{4\cot\theta}{\sqrt{1+\cot^2\theta}} \times -\text{cosec}^2\theta\, d\theta$$

$$= \int_{\frac{\pi}{4}}^{\frac{\pi}{6}} -\frac{4\cot\theta\,\text{cosec}^2\theta}{\sqrt{\text{cosec}^2\theta}}\, d\theta$$

$$= \int_{\frac{\pi}{6}}^{\frac{\pi}{4}} \frac{4\cot\theta\,\text{cosec}^2\theta}{\sqrt{\text{cosec}^2\theta}}\, d\theta$$

$$= \int_{\frac{\pi}{6}}^{\frac{\pi}{4}} 4\cot\theta\,\text{cosec}\,\theta\, d\theta$$

$$= \left[-4\,\text{cosec}\,\theta\right]_{\frac{\pi}{6}}^{\frac{\pi}{4}}$$

$$= -4(\sqrt{2}) - (-4(2)) = 8 - 4\sqrt{2}$$

Q4 a) Let $u = \ln x$ and let $\dfrac{dv}{dx} = 3x^2$.

So $\dfrac{du}{dx} = \dfrac{1}{x}$ and $v = x^3$.

Putting these into the formula gives:

$$\int 3x^2 \ln x\, dx = x^3 \ln x - \int \frac{x^3}{x}\, dx$$

$$= x^3 \ln x - \int x^2 dx$$

$$= x^3 \ln x - \frac{1}{3}x^3 + C$$

$$= x^3(\ln x - \frac{1}{3}) + C$$

b) Let $u = 4x$, and let $\dfrac{dv}{dx} = \cos 4x$.

So $\dfrac{du}{dx} = 4$ and $v = \dfrac{1}{4}\sin 4x$.

Putting these into the formula gives:

$$\int 4x\cos 4x\, dx = 4x\left(\frac{1}{4}\sin 4x\right) - \int 4\left(\frac{1}{4}\sin 4x\right)dx$$

$$= x\sin 4x - \int \sin 4x\, dx$$

$$= x\sin 4x + \frac{1}{4}\cos 4x + C$$

c) Let $u = x^2$, and let $\dfrac{dv}{dx} = e^{\frac{x}{2}}$.

So $\dfrac{du}{dx} = 2x$ and $v = 2e^{\frac{x}{2}}$.

Putting these into the formula gives:

$$\int_0^4 x^2 e^{\frac{x}{2}}\, dx = \left[2x^2 e^{\frac{x}{2}}\right]_0^4 - \int_0^4 4xe^{\frac{x}{2}}\, dx$$

Now use integration by parts again on $\int_0^4 4xe^{\frac{x}{2}}\, dx$:

Let $u = 4x$, and let $\dfrac{dv}{dx} = e^{\frac{x}{2}}$.

So $\dfrac{du}{dx} = 4$ and $v = 2e^{\frac{x}{2}}$.

Putting these into the formula gives:

$$\int_0^4 4xe^{\frac{x}{2}}\, dx = \left[8xe^{\frac{x}{2}}\right]_0^4 - \int_0^4 8e^{\frac{x}{2}}\, dx$$

$$= \left[8xe^{\frac{x}{2}}\right]_0^4 - \left[16e^{\frac{x}{2}}\right]_0^4$$

So the original integral is given by:

$$\int_0^4 x^2 e^{\frac{x}{2}}\, dx = \left[2x^2 e^{\frac{x}{2}}\right]_0^4 - \left[8xe^{\frac{x}{2}}\right]_0^4 + \left[16e^{\frac{x}{2}}\right]_0^4$$

$$= 32e^2 - 32e^2 + 16e^2 - 16$$

$$= 16e^2 - 16$$

Q5 $y^2 = (2x-1)^2 = 4x^2 - 4x + 1$

So $V = \pi \displaystyle\int_1^3 4x^2 - 4x + 1\, dx$

$$= \pi\left[\frac{4}{3}x^3 - 2x^2 + x\right]_1^3$$

$$= \pi\left[(36 - 18 + 3) - \left(\frac{4}{3} - 2 + 1\right)\right] = \frac{62}{3}\pi$$

Q6 If $y = \dfrac{1}{x}$ then $y^2 = \dfrac{1}{x^2}$.

Putting this into the integral gives:

$$V = \pi\int_2^4 \frac{1}{x^2}\, dx = \pi\left[-\frac{1}{x}\right]_2^4 = \pi\left[\left(-\frac{1}{4}\right) - \left(-\frac{1}{2}\right)\right] = \frac{\pi}{4}$$

Q7 $y^2 = 16\ln x$

So $V = \pi\displaystyle\int_1^2 16\ln x\, dx$

$$= 16\pi[x\ln x - x]_1^2$$

$$= 16\pi(2\ln 2 - 1)$$

Remember, $\int \ln x\, dx$ was covered on p.102.

Q8 a) Convert the limits:

$x = 4 \Rightarrow t^2 - 3t - 4 = 0 \Rightarrow (t+1)(t-4) = 0$
$\qquad\Rightarrow t = -1$ or $t = 4 \Rightarrow t_1 = 4$ as $t > 2$
$x = 54 \Rightarrow t^2 - 3t - 54 = 0 \Rightarrow (t+6)(t-9) = 0$
$\qquad\Rightarrow t = -6$ or $t = 9 \Rightarrow t_2 = 9$ as $t > 2$

Differentiate x with respect to t:

$\dfrac{dx}{dt} = 2t - 3$

So $A = \displaystyle\int_4^{54} y\, dx = \int_4^9 \frac{1}{\sqrt{t^3}} \times (2t - 3)\, dt$

$$= \int_4^9 \frac{2t}{t^{\frac{3}{2}}} - \frac{3}{t^{\frac{3}{2}}}\, dt$$

$$= \int_4^9 2t^{-\frac{1}{2}} - 3t^{-\frac{3}{2}}\, dt$$

$$= \left[4t^{\frac{1}{2}} + 6t^{-\frac{1}{2}}\right]_4^9$$

$$= \left(4\sqrt{9} + \frac{6}{\sqrt{9}}\right) - \left(4\sqrt{4} + \frac{6}{\sqrt{4}}\right)$$

$$= (12 + 2) - (8 + 3) = 3$$

b) $V = \pi\displaystyle\int_{t_1}^{t_2} y^2 \frac{dx}{dt}\, dt = \pi\int_4^9 \frac{2t-3}{t^3}\, dt$

$$= \pi\int_4^9 2t^{-2} - 3t^{-3}\, dt$$

$$= \pi\left[-2t^{-1} + \frac{3}{2}t^{-2}\right]_4^9$$

$$= \pi\left[\left(-\frac{2}{9} + \frac{1}{54}\right) - \left(-\frac{1}{2} + \frac{3}{32}\right)\right]$$

$$= \frac{175}{864}\pi = 0.636 \text{ to 3 d.p.}$$

Q9 a) Differentiate x with respect to θ:

$\dfrac{dx}{d\theta} = -\sin\theta + 1$

So $A = \displaystyle\int_{x_1}^{x_2} y\, dx = \int_{\theta_1}^{\theta_2} y\frac{dx}{d\theta}\, d\theta$

$$= \int_{\frac{\pi}{6}}^{\frac{\pi}{2}} \cot\theta(-\sin\theta + 1)\, d\theta$$

$$= \int_{\frac{\pi}{6}}^{\frac{\pi}{2}} -\cos\theta + \cot\theta\, d\theta$$

$$= \left[-\sin\theta + \ln|\sin\theta|\right]_{\frac{\pi}{6}}^{\frac{\pi}{2}}$$

$$= (-1 + \ln 1) - \left(-\frac{1}{2} + \ln\frac{1}{2}\right)$$

$$= \ln 2 - \frac{1}{2} = 0.193 \text{ to 3 s.f.}$$

The limits here were already given in terms of θ, so you didn't need to convert them.

b) $V = \pi \int_{\theta_1}^{\theta_2} y^2 \frac{dx}{d\theta} d\theta = \pi \int_{\frac{\pi}{6}}^{\frac{\pi}{2}} \cot^2\theta(1 - \sin\theta) d\theta$

So using $\cot^2\theta \equiv \frac{\cos^2\theta}{\sin^2\theta}$:

$$V = \pi \int_{\frac{\pi}{6}}^{\frac{\pi}{2}} \cot^2\theta - \frac{\cos^2\theta}{\sin\theta} d\theta$$

Now using $\cot^2\theta \equiv \csc^2\theta - 1$
and $\cos^2\theta \equiv 1 - \sin^2\theta$:

$$V = \pi \int_{\frac{\pi}{6}}^{\frac{\pi}{2}} \csc^2\theta - 1 - \frac{1 - \sin^2\theta}{\sin\theta} d\theta$$

$$= \pi \int_{\frac{\pi}{6}}^{\frac{\pi}{2}} \csc^2\theta - 1 - \csc\theta + \sin\theta \, d\theta$$

c) $V = \pi[-\cot\theta - \theta + \ln|\csc\theta + \cot\theta| - \cos\theta]_{\frac{\pi}{6}}^{\frac{\pi}{2}}$

$$= \pi\left[\left(0 - \frac{\pi}{2} + \ln 1 - 0\right)\right.$$
$$\left. - \left(-\sqrt{3} - \frac{\pi}{6} + \ln(2 + \sqrt{3}) - \frac{\sqrt{3}}{2}\right)\right]$$

$$= \pi\left[-\frac{\pi}{3} + \frac{3\sqrt{3}}{2} - \ln(2 + \sqrt{3})\right]$$

$$= 0.735 \text{ to 3 s.f.}$$

Q10 a) $h = (7 - 1) \div 3 = 2$, so the x-values are 1, 3, 5, 7.

$$\int_1^7 \frac{5}{x} dx \approx \frac{h}{2}[y_0 + 2(y_1 + y_2) + y_3]$$

$$= \frac{2}{2}\left[\frac{5}{1} + 2\left(\frac{5}{3} + \frac{5}{5}\right) + \frac{5}{7}\right]$$

$$= 5 + \frac{16}{3} + \frac{5}{7}$$

$$= 11.0 \text{ to 3 s.f.}$$

b) $\int_1^7 \frac{5}{x} dx = [5\ln x]_1^7 = 5\ln 7$

So error $= \left|\frac{5\ln 7 - 11.0}{5\ln 7}\right| \times 100 = 13.1\%$

Q11 a)

x	1	1.1	1.2	1.3	1.4	1.5
y	1.609	1.674	1.745	**1.824**	1.909	**1.998**

b) $\int_1^{1.5} \ln(x^3 + 4) dx \approx \frac{h}{2}[y_0 + 2(y_1 + y_2 + y_3 + y_4) + y_5]$

$$= 0.05[1.609 + 2(1.674 + 1.745$$
$$+ 1.824 + 1.909) + 1.998]$$

$$= 0.90 \text{ to 2 d.p.}$$

Q12 For the trapezium rule using 4 strips, $h = 1.5$ and you need to work out the values of y at $x = 0, 1.5, 3, 4.5, 6$:
$x_0 = 0, y_0 = -108, x_1 = 1.5, y_1 = -1.6875, x_2 = 3, y_2 = 0$,
$x_3 = 4.5, y_3 = 413.4375, x_4 = 6, y_4 = 5400$.
Putting these values into the formula gives:
$A \approx 0.75[-108 + 2(-1.6875 + 0 + 413.4375) + 5400]$
$= 4586.625$

Using 6 strips, $h = 1$ and you need the y-values for
$x = 0, 1, 2, 3, 4, 5, 6$.
You already know the values for $x = 0, 3, 6$.
$(x_0 = 0, y_0 = -108), x_1 = 1, y_1 = 0, x_2 = 2, y_2 = 0$,
$(x_3 = 3, y_3 = 0), x_4 = 4, y_4 = 108, x_5 = 5, y_5 = 1152$,
$(x_6 = 6, y_6 = 5400)$.

Putting these values into the formula gives:
$A \approx \frac{1}{2}[-108 + 2(0 + 0 + 0 + 108 + 1152) + 5400]$
$= 3906$

To calculate the percentage error, first work out the exact value of the integral.
Using the formula
$\int (n + 1)f'(x)[f(x)]^n dx = [f(x)]^{n+1} + C$:

$$\int_0^6 (6x - 12)(x^2 - 4x + 3)^2 dx = [(x^2 - 4x + 3)^3]_0^6$$

$$= (6^2 - 4(6) + 3)^3 - (0 - 0 + 3)^3$$

$$= 3375 - 27$$

$$= 3348$$

So for 4 strips the error is:

$$\frac{4586.625 - 3348}{3348} \times 100 = 37.00\% \text{ (4 s.f.)}$$

and for 6 strips:

$$\frac{3906 - 3348}{3348} \times 100 = 16.67\% \text{ (4 s.f.)}$$

Neither of these estimates was particularly accurate — but the one with more strips had a lower % error (as you would expect).

Q13 a) $\frac{dx}{dy} \propto x^2 \Rightarrow \frac{dx}{dy} = kx^2$, for some $k > 0$

b) $\frac{dV}{dt} \propto \frac{1}{\sqrt{V}} \Rightarrow \frac{dV}{dt} = -\frac{k}{\sqrt{V}}$, for some $k > 0$

c) $\frac{ds}{dt} \propto (s_0 - s) \Rightarrow \frac{ds}{dt} = -k(s_0 - s)$, for some $k > 0$

Q14 $\frac{dy}{dx} = \frac{1}{y}\cos x \Rightarrow y \, dy = \cos x \, dx$

so $\int y \, dy = \int \cos x \, dx \Rightarrow \frac{y^2}{2} = \sin x + C_0$

$\Rightarrow y^2 = 2\sin x + C_1$ (where $C_1 = 2C_0$)

Q15 $\frac{dx}{dt} = kte^t \Rightarrow dx = kte^t \, dt$

$\Rightarrow \int 1 \, dx = \int kte^t \, dt$

$\Rightarrow x = k(te^t - e^t) + C$
(using integration by parts)

$x = 0, t = 1 \Rightarrow 0 = k(e - e) + C \Rightarrow C = 0$

$x = -3, t = 0 \Rightarrow -3 = k(0 - e^0) = -k \Rightarrow k = 3$

So $x = 3(te^t - e^t) = 3e^t(t - 1)$

Q16 a) $\frac{dx}{d\theta} = \cos^2 x \cot\theta \Rightarrow \int \sec^2 x \, dx = \int \cot\theta \, d\theta$

$\Rightarrow \tan x = \ln|\sin\theta| + C$

b) $x = \frac{\pi}{4}, \theta = \frac{\pi}{2} \Rightarrow \tan\frac{\pi}{4} = \ln\left|\sin\frac{\pi}{2}\right| + C$

$\Rightarrow 1 = \ln 1 + C$

$\Rightarrow C = 1$

$\Rightarrow \tan x = \ln|\sin\theta| + 1$

c) $\theta = \frac{\pi}{6} \Rightarrow \tan x = \ln\left|\sin\frac{\pi}{6}\right| + 1$

$= \ln\frac{1}{2} + 1 = 0.306...$

$\Rightarrow x = 0.298$ to 3 d.p.

Q17 a) $\frac{dS}{dt} = kS$

b) $\frac{dS}{dt} = kS \Rightarrow \int \frac{1}{S} dS = \int k \, dt$

$\Rightarrow \ln|S| = kt + \ln A$

$\Rightarrow S = Ae^{kt}$

At $t = 0$, $S = 30 \Rightarrow 30 = Ae^0$
$$\Rightarrow A = 30$$
$$\Rightarrow S = 30e^{kt}$$

When $t = 0$, $\frac{dS}{dt} = 6$ and $S = 30$
$$\Rightarrow \frac{dS}{dt} = kS \Rightarrow 6 = k \times 30 \Rightarrow k = \frac{6}{30} = 0.2$$
So $S = 30e^{0.2t}$.

So $S = 150 \Rightarrow 150 = 30e^{0.2t}$
$$\Rightarrow \ln 5 = 0.2t$$
$$\Rightarrow t = 5 \ln 5 = 8.047$$

It will take the squirrels 8 weeks to take over the forest.

Q18 a) $\frac{dT}{dt} = -k(T - 21) \Rightarrow \int \frac{1}{T - 21} dT = \int -k \, dt$
$$\Rightarrow \ln(T - 21) = -kt + \ln A$$
$$\Rightarrow T = Ae^{-kt} + 21$$

$T = 90$ at $t = 0$ $\quad \Rightarrow 90 = Ae^0 + 21$
$$\Rightarrow A = 90 - 21 = 69$$
$$\Rightarrow T = 69e^{-kt} + 21$$

So $T = 80$ at $t = 5$ $\quad \Rightarrow 80 = 69e^{-5k} + 21$
$$\Rightarrow e^{-5k} = \frac{59}{69}$$
$$\Rightarrow k = -\frac{1}{5}\ln\frac{59}{69} = 0.0313$$
$$\Rightarrow T = 69e^{-0.0313t} + 21$$

b) (i) $t = 15 \Rightarrow T = 69e^{-0.470} + 21 = 64.1 \, °C$

(ii) $T = 40 \Rightarrow 40 = 69e^{-0.0313t} + 21$
$$\Rightarrow e^{-0.0313t} = \frac{19}{69}$$
$$\Rightarrow t = 41.2 \text{ mins}$$

c)

If you struggled sketching this graph look back at your C3 notes for sketching exponential graphs.

Exam-Style Questions — Chapter 6

Q1 $V = \pi \int_{\frac{\pi}{4}}^{\frac{\pi}{3}} y^2 \, dx = \pi \int_{\frac{\pi}{4}}^{\frac{\pi}{3}} \text{cosec}^2 x \, dx = \pi[-\cot x]_{\frac{\pi}{4}}^{\frac{\pi}{3}}$
$$= \pi\left[\left(-\cot\frac{\pi}{3}\right) - \left(-\cot\frac{\pi}{4}\right)\right]$$
$$= \pi\left[-\frac{1}{\sqrt{3}} + 1\right] = 1.328 \text{ (3 d.p.)}.$$

[3 marks available — 1 mark for correct function for y^2, 1 mark for integrating, 1 mark for substituting in values of x to obtain correct answer]
Don't forget π here.

Q2 a) When $x = \frac{\pi}{2}$, $y = \frac{\pi}{2}\sin\frac{\pi}{2} = \frac{\pi}{2} = 1.5708$ *[1 mark]*,

and when $x = \frac{3\pi}{4}$, $y = \frac{3\pi}{4}\sin\frac{3\pi}{4} = 1.6661$

[1 mark]

b) The width of each strip (h) is $\frac{\pi}{4}$, so the trapezium rule is:
$$A = \frac{1}{2} \times \frac{\pi}{4}[0 + 2(0.5554 + 1.5708 + 1.6661) + 0]$$
$$= \frac{\pi}{8}[2(3.7923)] = 2.978 \text{ (3 d.p.)}$$

[4 marks available — 1 mark for correct value of h, 2 marks for correct use of formula, 1 mark for correct answer]
You're given the trapezium rule on the formula sheet (it's hidden away in the C2 section), but it's a good idea to learn it anyway.

c) Let $u = x$, so $\frac{du}{dx} = 1$. Let $\frac{dv}{dx} = \sin x$, so $v = -\cos x$

[1 mark for both parts correct]

Using integration by parts,
$$\int_0^\pi x \sin x \, dx = [-x\cos x]_0^\pi - \int_0^\pi -\cos x \, dx \quad \text{[1 mark]}$$
$$= [-x\cos x]_0^\pi + [\sin x]_0^\pi \quad \text{[1 mark]}$$
$$= (\pi - 0) + (0) = \pi \quad \text{[1 mark]}$$

If you'd tried to use $u = \sin x$, you'd have ended up with a more complicated function to integrate ($x^2 \cos x$).

d) To find the percentage error, divide the difference between the approximate answer and the exact answer by the exact answer and multiply by 100:
$$\left|\frac{\pi - 2.978}{\pi}\right| \times 100 = 5.2\% \text{ (2 s.f.)}$$
[2 marks available — 1 mark for appropriate method and 1 mark for correct answer]

Q3 If $u = \ln x$, then $\frac{du}{dx} = \frac{1}{x}$, so $x \, du = dx$.
Changing the limits: when $x = 1$, $u = \ln 1 = 0$
when $x = 2$, $u = \ln 2$

Substituting all this into the integral gives:
$$\int_1^2 \frac{8}{x}(\ln x + 2)^3 \, dx = \int_0^{\ln 2} \frac{8}{x}(u + 2)^3 x \, du = \int_0^{\ln 2} 8(u + 2)^3 \, du$$
$$= [2(u + 2)^4]_0^{\ln 2}$$
$$= [2(\ln 2 + 2)^4] - [2(0 + 2)^4]$$
$$= 105.21 - 32 = 73.21 \text{ (4 s.f.)}$$
[6 marks available — 1 mark for finding substitution for dx, 1 mark for finding correct limits, 1 mark for correct integral in terms of u, 2 marks for integration (1 mark for an answer in the form $k(u + 2)^n$, 1 mark for correct values of k and n), 1 mark for final answer (to 4 s.f.)]

Q4 a) $\frac{1}{x(2x - 3)} \equiv \frac{A}{x} + \frac{B}{2x - 3} \Rightarrow 1 \equiv A(2x - 3) + Bx$

Substituting $x = 0$ gives $A = -\frac{1}{3}$ *[1 mark]*
Substituting $x = \frac{3}{2}$ gives $B = \frac{2}{3}$ *[1 mark]*

$$\Rightarrow \frac{1}{x(2x - 3)} \equiv \frac{2}{3(2x - 3)} - \frac{1}{3x}$$

So $\int \frac{1}{x(2x - 3)} \, dx = \int \frac{2}{3(2x - 3)} - \frac{1}{3x} \, dx$
$$= \int \frac{2}{3}(2x - 3)^{-1} - \frac{1}{3}x^{-1} \, dx$$
$$= \frac{1}{3}\ln|2x - 3| - \frac{1}{3}\ln|x| + C$$
$$= \frac{1}{3}\ln\left|\frac{2x - 3}{x}\right| + C$$

[1 mark for each ln term — deduct 1 mark if + C is missing]

b) Let $u = \ln x$, so $\frac{du}{dx} = \frac{1}{x}$.

Let $\frac{dv}{dx} = \frac{2}{(2x-3)^2} = 2(2x-3)^{-2}$, so $v = -(2x-3)^{-1}$

[1 mark for both parts correct]

Using integration by parts,

$$\int_1^4 \frac{2\ln x}{(2x-3)^2}\,dx = \left[-\frac{\ln x}{2x-3}\right]_1^4 - \int_1^4 -\frac{1}{x(2x-3)}\,dx$$

[1 mark]

$$= \left[-\frac{\ln x}{2x-3}\right]_1^4 + \left[\frac{1}{3}\ln\left|\frac{2x-3}{x}\right|\right]_1^4 \quad \text{[1 mark]}$$

$$= \left[-\frac{\ln 4}{5} - -\frac{\ln 1}{-1}\right] + \left[\frac{1}{3}\ln\frac{5}{4} - \frac{1}{3}\ln|-1|\right] \quad \text{[1 mark]}$$

$$= -\frac{1}{5}\ln 4 + \frac{1}{3}\ln\frac{5}{4} \quad \text{[1 mark]}$$

Q5 a) The question tells you that $\frac{dV}{dt} = 4.2$. *[1 mark]*
The volume of the prism is
$$V = \frac{1}{2}b \times h \times l = \frac{1}{2}x \times \frac{\sqrt{3}}{2}x \times 4x = \sqrt{3}x^3$$
So $\frac{dV}{dx} = 3\sqrt{3}x^2$. *[1 mark]*
By the chain rule: $\frac{dx}{dt} = \frac{dV}{dt} \div \frac{dV}{dx} = \frac{4.2}{3\sqrt{3}x^2}$
$$= \frac{1.4}{\sqrt{3}x^2} \quad \text{[1 mark]}$$
So when $x = 6$, $\frac{dx}{dt} = 0.0225$ mm s^{-1} *[1 mark]*

b) The cross sectional area of the prism is
$$A = \frac{1}{2}b \times h = \frac{1}{2}x \times \frac{\sqrt{3}}{2}x = \frac{\sqrt{3}}{4}x^2$$
So $\frac{dA}{dx} = \frac{\sqrt{3}}{2}x$ *[1 mark]*. From a), $\frac{dx}{dt} = \frac{1.4}{\sqrt{3}x^2}$.
By the chain rule,
$$\frac{dA}{dt} = \frac{dA}{dx} \times \frac{dx}{dt} = \frac{\sqrt{3}}{2}x \times \frac{1.4}{\sqrt{3}x^2} = \frac{0.7}{x} \quad \text{[1 mark]}$$
So when $x = 3$, $\frac{dA}{dt} = 0.233$ *[1 mark]*

Q6 a) (i) $\frac{dr}{dt} = -krt$, $k > 0$

[1 mark for RHS, 1 mark for LHS]

(ii) S = area of curved surface
$$\qquad\qquad + \text{area of circular surface}$$
$$= \frac{1}{2}(4\pi r^2) + \pi r^2$$
$$= 3\pi r^2 \quad \text{[1 mark]}$$
So $\frac{dS}{dr} = 6\pi r$ *[1 mark]*
$$\frac{dS}{dt} = \frac{dS}{dr} \times \frac{dr}{dt} \quad \text{[1 mark]}$$
$$= 6\pi r \times -krt$$
$$= -6\pi kr^2 t$$
$$= -2kt(3\pi r^2)$$
$$= -2ktS \quad \text{[1 mark]}$$

b) (i) $\frac{dS}{dt} = -2ktS \Rightarrow \frac{dS}{S} = -2kt\,dt$
$$\Rightarrow \int \frac{1}{S}\,dS = \int -2kt\,dt \quad \text{[1 mark]}$$
$$\Rightarrow \ln S = -kt^2 + \ln A$$

[1 mark for correct integration of both sides, plus a constant term]

$$\Rightarrow S = e^{-kt^2 + \ln A} = Ae^{-kt^2} \quad \text{[1 mark]}$$
$S = 200$ at $t = 10$ $\Rightarrow 200 = Ae^{-100k}$
$S = 50$ at $t = 30$ $\Rightarrow 50 = Ae^{-900k}$
$$\Rightarrow Ae^{-100k} = 4Ae^{-900k}$$
[1 mark]

$$\Rightarrow e^{-100k} = 4e^{-900k}$$
$$\Rightarrow -100k = \ln 4 - 900k$$
$$\Rightarrow 800k = \ln 4$$
$$\Rightarrow k = 0.00173 \quad \text{[1 mark]}$$
So $200 = Ae^{-100k} = Ae^{-0.173} = 0.841A$
$$\Rightarrow A = 237.8 \quad \text{[1 mark]}$$
So $S = 237.8e^{-0.00173t^2}$

(ii) The initial surface area is given when $t = 0$
$$\Rightarrow S = 237.8e^0 = 237.8 \quad \text{[1 mark]}$$

Q7 Convert the limits from x to t:
$x = 27 \Rightarrow t^2 - 6t - 27 = 0$
$$\Rightarrow (t+3)(t-9) = 0$$
$$\Rightarrow t = -3 \text{ or } t = 9 \Rightarrow t_1 = 9, \text{ as } t > 6$$
$x = 72 \Rightarrow t^2 - 6t - 72 = 0$
$$\Rightarrow (t+6)(t-12) = 0$$
$$\Rightarrow t = -6 \text{ or } t = 12 \Rightarrow t_2 = 12, \text{ as } t > 6$$
[1 mark for both limits correct]
$$\frac{dx}{dt} = 2t - 6 \quad \text{[1 mark]}$$
$$V = \pi\int_{t_1}^{t_2} y^2 \frac{dx}{dt}\,dt = \pi\int_9^{12} 3t(2t-6)\,dt \quad \text{[1 mark]}$$
$$= \pi\int_9^{12} 6t^2 - 18t\,dt$$
$$= \pi[2t^3 - 9t^2]_9^{12} \quad \text{[1 mark]}$$
$$= \pi[(2(12)^3 - 9(12)^2) - (2(9)^3 - 9(9)^2)]$$
$$= \pi[2160 - 729] = 1431\pi \quad \text{[1 mark]}$$

Q8 a) $\frac{dy}{dx} = \frac{\cos x \cos^2 y}{\sin x} \Rightarrow \frac{1}{\cos^2 y}\,dy = \frac{\cos x}{\sin x}\,dx$
$$\Rightarrow \int \sec^2 y\,dy = \int \frac{\cos x}{\sin x}\,dx$$
$$\Rightarrow \tan y = \ln|\sin x| + C$$
[4 marks available — 1 mark for separating the variables into functions of x and y, 1 mark for correct integration of RHS, 1 mark for correct integration of LHS, 1 mark for general solution]

b) If $y = \pi$ when $x = \frac{\pi}{6}$, that means that
$$\tan \pi = \ln\left|\sin\frac{\pi}{6}\right| + C \Rightarrow 0 = \ln\left|\frac{1}{2}\right| + C \quad \text{[1 mark]}$$
So $C = -\ln\frac{1}{2} = \ln 2$
So $\tan y = \ln|\sin x| + \ln 2$
or $\tan y = \ln|2\sin x|$ *[1 mark]*
This is the particular solution — you found the general solution in part a).

Q9 a) Let $u = x$, so $\frac{du}{dx} = 1$.
Let $\frac{dv}{dx} = \sin 4x$, so $v = -\frac{1}{4}\cos 4x$

[1 mark for both parts correct]

Using integration by parts,
$$\int x\sin 4x\,dx = -\frac{1}{4}x\cos 4x - \int -\frac{1}{4}\cos 4x\,dx$$
[1 mark]
$$= -\frac{1}{4}x\cos 4x + \frac{1}{16}\sin 4x + C \quad \text{[1 mark]}$$

b) Let $u = x^2$, so $\frac{du}{dx} = 2x$.
Let $\frac{dv}{dx} = \cos 4x$, so $v = \frac{1}{4}\sin 4x$

[1 mark for both parts correct]

Using integration by parts,

$$\int x^2 \cos 4x \, dx = \frac{1}{4}x^2 \sin 4x - \int \frac{1}{2}x \sin 4x \, dx$$
[1 mark]

$$= \frac{1}{4}x^2 \sin 4x - \frac{1}{2}(-\frac{1}{4}x\cos 4x + \frac{1}{16}\sin 4x) + C$$
[1 mark]

$$= \frac{1}{4}x^2 \sin 4x + \frac{1}{8}x\cos 4x - \frac{1}{32}\sin 4x + C \quad \textit{[1 mark]}$$

Q10 a)

x	0	0.25	0.5	0.75	1
y	0	1.0645	**2.5681**	**5.2652**	10.8731

[2 marks available — 1 mark for each correct value]

b) The width of each strip (h) is 0.25, so the trapezium rule is:

$$A = \frac{0.25}{2}[0 + 2(1.0645 + 2.5681 + 5.2652) + 10.8731]$$

$$= \frac{1}{8}[28.6687] = 3.584 \text{ (4 s.f.)}$$

[4 marks available — 1 mark for correct value of h, 2 marks for correct use of formula, 1 mark for correct answer]

c) If $u = x^2$, then $\frac{du}{dx} = 2x$, so $\frac{1}{2x}du = dx$. *[1 mark]*
Changing the limits: when $x = 0$, $u = 0$
              when $x = 1$, $u = 1$
[1 mark for both limits correct]

Substituting all this into the integral gives:

$$\int_0^1 4xe^{x^2} dx = \int_0^1 4xe^u \frac{1}{2x} du$$

$$= \int_0^1 2e^u \, du \quad \textit{[1 mark]}$$

$$= [2e^u]_0^1 = 2e - 2 \quad \textit{[1 mark]}$$

d) $\left|\frac{(2e-2) - 3.584}{2e-2}\right| \times 100 = 4.3\%$

[2 marks available — 1 mark for method and 1 mark for correct answer]

Q11 a) First solve the differential equation to find S:

$$\frac{dS}{dt} = k\sqrt{S} \Rightarrow \frac{1}{\sqrt{S}} dS = k \, dt$$

$$\Rightarrow \int S^{-\frac{1}{2}} dS = \int k \, dt \quad \textit{[1 mark]}$$

$$\Rightarrow 2S^{\frac{1}{2}} = kt + C$$

$$\Rightarrow S = \left(\frac{1}{2}(kt + C)\right)^2 = \frac{1}{4}(kt + C)^2 \quad \textit{[1 mark]}$$

At the start of the campaign, $t = 0$.
Putting $t = 0$ and $S = 81$ into the equation gives:
$81 = \frac{1}{4}(0 + C)^2 \Rightarrow 324 = C^2 \Rightarrow C = 18$
(C must be positive, otherwise the sales would be decreasing). *[1 mark]*.
This gives the equation $S = \frac{1}{4}(kt + 18)^2$ *[1 mark]*.

b) When $t = 0$, $S = 81$ and $\frac{dS}{dt} = 18$.
Substituting this into $\frac{dS}{dt} = k\sqrt{S}$ gives $k = 2$.
Using $S = \frac{1}{4}(kt + 18)^2$ with $t = 5$ and $k = 2$ gives
$\frac{1}{4}((5 \times 2) + 18)^2 = 196$ kg sold.
[3 marks available — 1 mark for finding the value of k, 1 mark for substituting correct values of t and k and 1 mark for answer]

c) To find the value of t when $S = 225$, solve the equation $225 = \frac{1}{4}(2t + 18)^2$ *[1 mark]*:

$225 = \frac{1}{4}(2t + 18)^2 \Rightarrow 900 = (2t + 18)^2$

$\Rightarrow 30 = 2t + 18 \Rightarrow 12 = 2t \Rightarrow 6 = t$

So it will be 6 days *[1 mark]* before 225 kg of cheese is sold.

Chapter 7: Vectors

1. Vectors
Exercise 1.1 — Introducing vectors
Q1 a) vector   **b)** scalar   **c)** vector

Q2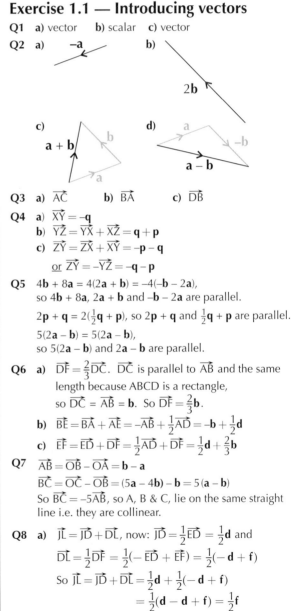

Q3 a) $\overrightarrow{AC}$ **b)** $\overrightarrow{BA}$ **c)** $\overrightarrow{DB}$

Q4 a) $\overrightarrow{XY} = -\mathbf{q}$
  b) $\overrightarrow{YZ} = \overrightarrow{YX} + \overrightarrow{XZ} = \mathbf{q} + \mathbf{p}$
  c) $\overrightarrow{ZY} = \overrightarrow{ZX} + \overrightarrow{XY} = -\mathbf{p} - \mathbf{q}$
    or $\overrightarrow{ZY} = -\overrightarrow{YZ} = -\mathbf{q} - \mathbf{p}$

Q5 $4\mathbf{b} + 8\mathbf{a} = 4(2\mathbf{a} + \mathbf{b}) = -4(-\mathbf{b} - 2\mathbf{a})$,
so $4\mathbf{b} + 8\mathbf{a}$, $2\mathbf{a} + \mathbf{b}$ and $-\mathbf{b} - 2\mathbf{a}$ are parallel.
$2\mathbf{p} + \mathbf{q} = 2(\frac{1}{2}\mathbf{q} + \mathbf{p})$, so $2\mathbf{p} + \mathbf{q}$ and $\frac{1}{2}\mathbf{q} + \mathbf{p}$ are parallel.
$5(2\mathbf{a} - \mathbf{b}) = 5(2\mathbf{a} - \mathbf{b})$,
so $5(2\mathbf{a} - \mathbf{b})$ and $2\mathbf{a} - \mathbf{b}$ are parallel.

Q6 a) $\overrightarrow{DF} = \frac{2}{3}\overrightarrow{DC}$. $\overrightarrow{DC}$ is parallel to $\overrightarrow{AB}$ and the same length because ABCD is a rectangle, so $\overrightarrow{DC} = \overrightarrow{AB} = \mathbf{b}$. So $\overrightarrow{DF} = \frac{2}{3}\mathbf{b}$.
  b) $\overrightarrow{BE} = \overrightarrow{BA} + \overrightarrow{AE} = -\overrightarrow{AB} + \frac{1}{2}\overrightarrow{AD} = -\mathbf{b} + \frac{1}{2}\mathbf{d}$
  c) $\overrightarrow{EF} = \overrightarrow{ED} + \overrightarrow{DF} = \frac{1}{2}\overrightarrow{AD} + \overrightarrow{DF} = \frac{1}{2}\mathbf{d} + \frac{2}{3}\mathbf{b}$

Q7 $\overrightarrow{AB} = \overrightarrow{OB} - \overrightarrow{OA} = \mathbf{b} - \mathbf{a}$
$\overrightarrow{BC} = \overrightarrow{OC} - \overrightarrow{OB} = (5\mathbf{a} - 4\mathbf{b}) - \mathbf{b} = 5(\mathbf{a} - \mathbf{b})$
So $\overrightarrow{BC} = -5\overrightarrow{AB}$, so A, B & C, lie on the same straight line i.e. they are collinear.

Q8 a) $\overrightarrow{JL} = \overrightarrow{JD} + \overrightarrow{DL}$, now: $\overrightarrow{JD} = \frac{1}{2}\overrightarrow{ED} = \frac{1}{2}\mathbf{d}$ and
    $\overrightarrow{DL} = \frac{1}{2}\overrightarrow{DF} = \frac{1}{2}(-\overrightarrow{ED} + \overrightarrow{EF}) = \frac{1}{2}(-\mathbf{d} + \mathbf{f})$
    So $\overrightarrow{JL} = \overrightarrow{JD} + \overrightarrow{DL} = \frac{1}{2}\mathbf{d} + \frac{1}{2}(-\mathbf{d} + \mathbf{f})$
                    $= \frac{1}{2}(\mathbf{d} - \mathbf{d} + \mathbf{f}) = \frac{1}{2}\mathbf{f}$
  b) JL is parallel to EF and has half the length of EF.

Exercise 1.2 — Position vectors and Three-dimensional vectors

Q1 $\overrightarrow{OA} = \begin{pmatrix} 2 \\ 3 \end{pmatrix}$ $\overrightarrow{OB} = \begin{pmatrix} 4 \\ -5 \end{pmatrix}$

Q2 $\overrightarrow{OR} = 4\mathbf{i} - 5\mathbf{j} + \mathbf{k}$ $\overrightarrow{OS} = -3\mathbf{i} - \mathbf{k}$

There's no $\mathbf{j}$ component written for $\overrightarrow{OS}$ because its $\mathbf{j}$ component is zero (you don't write $-3\mathbf{i} + 0\mathbf{j} - \mathbf{k}$).

Q3 a) C (–1, 2), D (4, –3)

   b) $\overrightarrow{CD} = \overrightarrow{OD} - \overrightarrow{OC} = (4\mathbf{i} - 3\mathbf{j}) - (-\mathbf{i} + 2\mathbf{j}) = 5\mathbf{i} - 5\mathbf{j}$
   $\overrightarrow{DC} = -\overrightarrow{CD} = -(5\mathbf{i} - 5\mathbf{j}) = -5\mathbf{i} + 5\mathbf{j}$

Q4 $\overrightarrow{GH} = \overrightarrow{OH} - \overrightarrow{OG} = \begin{pmatrix} -1 \\ 4 \\ 9 \end{pmatrix} - \begin{pmatrix} 2 \\ -3 \\ 4 \end{pmatrix} = \begin{pmatrix} -3 \\ 7 \\ 5 \end{pmatrix}$

$\overrightarrow{HG} = -\overrightarrow{GH} = -\begin{pmatrix} -3 \\ 7 \\ 5 \end{pmatrix} = \begin{pmatrix} 3 \\ -7 \\ -5 \end{pmatrix}$

Q5 $\overrightarrow{PM} = \overrightarrow{MQ}$ because M is the midpoint of PQ.
This is because the lines are the same length and point in the same direction.

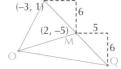

$\overrightarrow{MQ} = \overrightarrow{PM} = \overrightarrow{OM} - \overrightarrow{OP} = 2\mathbf{i} - 5\mathbf{j} - (-3\mathbf{i} + \mathbf{j}) = 5\mathbf{i} - 6\mathbf{j}$
So $\overrightarrow{OQ} = \overrightarrow{OM} + \overrightarrow{MQ} = 2\mathbf{i} - 5\mathbf{j} + (5\mathbf{i} - 6\mathbf{j}) = 7\mathbf{i} - 11\mathbf{j}$

Q6 $\overrightarrow{OA} = \begin{pmatrix} 2 \\ 4 \end{pmatrix}$, $\overrightarrow{OB} = \begin{pmatrix} 0 \\ 1 \end{pmatrix}$, $\overrightarrow{OC} = \begin{pmatrix} -1 \\ 3 \end{pmatrix}$

You could use unit form instead of column vectors to answer this question if you prefer.

$\overrightarrow{AB} = \overrightarrow{OB} - \overrightarrow{OA} = \begin{pmatrix} 0 \\ 1 \end{pmatrix} - \begin{pmatrix} 2 \\ 4 \end{pmatrix} = \begin{pmatrix} -2 \\ -3 \end{pmatrix}$

$\overrightarrow{BC} = \overrightarrow{OC} - \overrightarrow{OB} = \begin{pmatrix} -1 \\ 3 \end{pmatrix} - \begin{pmatrix} 0 \\ 1 \end{pmatrix} = \begin{pmatrix} -1 \\ 2 \end{pmatrix}$

$\overrightarrow{CA} = \overrightarrow{OA} - \overrightarrow{OC} = \begin{pmatrix} 2 \\ 4 \end{pmatrix} - \begin{pmatrix} -1 \\ 3 \end{pmatrix} = \begin{pmatrix} 3 \\ 1 \end{pmatrix}$

Q7 a) $\overrightarrow{DE} = 4\mathbf{i} + \mathbf{j}$, $\overrightarrow{EF} = 2\mathbf{i} + 6\mathbf{j}$,
   $\overrightarrow{FG} = -2\mathbf{i} + 5\mathbf{j}$, $\overrightarrow{GD} = -4\mathbf{i} - 12\mathbf{j}$
   Column vectors would also be fine for this question.

   b) DEFG is a trapezium. $\overrightarrow{GD} = -2\overrightarrow{EF}$ so GD is parallel to EF – but DE is not parallel to FG

You can use unit form or column vectors for Q8.

Q8 $\overrightarrow{JK} = \overrightarrow{OK} - \overrightarrow{OJ} = -\mathbf{i} + 3\mathbf{j} - (4\mathbf{i} - 3\mathbf{k}) = -5\mathbf{i} + 3\mathbf{j} + 3\mathbf{k}$

$\overrightarrow{KL} = \overrightarrow{OL} - \overrightarrow{OK} = 2\mathbf{i} + 2\mathbf{j} + 7\mathbf{k} - (-\mathbf{i} + 3\mathbf{j}) = 3\mathbf{i} - \mathbf{j} + 7\mathbf{k}$

$\overrightarrow{LJ} = \overrightarrow{OJ} - \overrightarrow{OL} = 4\mathbf{i} - 3\mathbf{k} - (2\mathbf{i} + 2\mathbf{j} + 7\mathbf{k}) = 2\mathbf{i} - 2\mathbf{j} - 10\mathbf{k}$
Don't get put off by the three dimensional coordinates of this triangle's vertices — the triangle is in three dimensions but you work out the answers in exactly the same way you would with a two-dimensional triangle.

2. Magnitude of Vectors
Exercise 2.1 — Magnitude of two-dimensional vectors

Q1 a) $\sqrt{6^2 + 8^2} = \sqrt{36 + 64} = \sqrt{100} = 10$

   b) $\sqrt{12^2 + (-5)^2} = 13$

   c) $\sqrt{2^2 + 4^2} = \sqrt{20} = 2\sqrt{5}$

   d) $\sqrt{(-3)^2 + (-1)^2} = \sqrt{10}$

   e) $\sqrt{(24)^2 + (-7)^2} = 25$

   f) $\sqrt{(-\sqrt{13})^2 + 6^2} = \sqrt{13 + 36} = \sqrt{49} = 7$

   g) $\sqrt{3^2 + (\sqrt{7})^2} = 4$

   h) $\sqrt{0^2 + (-7)^2} = 7$

Q2 $|\overrightarrow{OS}| = \sqrt{10^2 + 5^2} = \sqrt{100 + 25} = \sqrt{125} = 5\sqrt{5}$

Q3 a) $\mathbf{a} + \mathbf{b} = (2\mathbf{i} + \mathbf{j}) + (2\mathbf{i} - 4\mathbf{j}) = 4\mathbf{i} - 3\mathbf{j}$
   The magnitude of the resultant is $\sqrt{4^2 + (-3)^2} = 5$

   b) $\mathbf{u} + \mathbf{v} = 4\mathbf{i} - 4\mathbf{j}$, $|4\mathbf{i} - 4\mathbf{j}| = \sqrt{4^2 + 4^2} = \sqrt{32} = 4\sqrt{2}$

   c) $\mathbf{f} + \mathbf{g} = \begin{pmatrix} 24 \\ -10 \end{pmatrix}$, $\left| \begin{pmatrix} 24 \\ -10 \end{pmatrix} \right| = \sqrt{24^2 + (-10)^2} = 26$

   d) $\mathbf{d} + \mathbf{e} = \begin{pmatrix} 3 \\ -6 \end{pmatrix}$, $\left| \begin{pmatrix} 3 \\ -6 \end{pmatrix} \right| = \sqrt{3^2 + (-6)^2} = \sqrt{45} = 3\sqrt{5}$

Q4 $\overrightarrow{AC} = 4\mathbf{i} + 3\mathbf{j}$, $|\overrightarrow{AC}| = \sqrt{4^2 + 3^2} = 5$

Q5 $|\mathbf{b} - \mathbf{a}| = |9\mathbf{i} - 12\mathbf{j}| = \sqrt{9^2 + (-12)^2} = 15$

Q6 $\overrightarrow{MN} = -11\mathbf{i} + 60\mathbf{j}$, $|\overrightarrow{MN}| = \sqrt{(-11)^2 + 60^2} = 61$

Q7 $\left| \begin{pmatrix} 16 \\ -12 \end{pmatrix} \right| = \sqrt{16^2 + (-12)^2} = 20$
The unit vector is $\frac{1}{20} \begin{pmatrix} 16 \\ -12 \end{pmatrix} = \begin{pmatrix} \frac{16}{20} \\ -\frac{12}{20} \end{pmatrix} = \begin{pmatrix} 0.8 \\ -0.6 \end{pmatrix}$

Q8 $\overrightarrow{TU} = -8\mathbf{i} + 6\mathbf{j}$, $|\overrightarrow{TU}| = \sqrt{(-8)^2 + 6^2} = 10$
The unit vector is $\frac{1}{10}(-8\mathbf{i} + 6\mathbf{j}) = -0.8\mathbf{i} + 0.6\mathbf{j}$

Q9 $\overrightarrow{FG} = \overrightarrow{OG} - \overrightarrow{OF} = \begin{pmatrix} a \\ -5 \end{pmatrix} - \begin{pmatrix} 4 \\ 7 \end{pmatrix} = \begin{pmatrix} a - 4 \\ -12 \end{pmatrix}$

$|\overrightarrow{FG}| = \sqrt{(a-4)^2 + (-12)^2} = \sqrt{a^2 - 8a + 160}$
$|\overrightarrow{FG}| = 13$, so: $a^2 - 8a + 160 = 13^2 = 169$
$$a^2 - 8a - 9 = 0$$
$$(a + 1)(a - 9) = 0$$
So $a = -1$ or $a = 9$

Exercise 2.2 — Magnitude of three-dimensional vectors

Q1 a) $\sqrt{1^2 + 4^2 + 8^2} = \sqrt{1 + 16 + 64} = \sqrt{81} = 9$

   b) $\sqrt{4^2 + 2^2 + 4^2} = \sqrt{36} = 6$

   c) $\sqrt{(-4)^2 + (-5)^2 + 20^2} = \sqrt{441} = 21$

   d) $\sqrt{7^2 + 1^2 + (-7)^2} = \sqrt{99} = 3\sqrt{11}$

   e) $\sqrt{(-2)^2 + 4^2 + (-6)^2} = \sqrt{56} = \sqrt{4}\sqrt{14} = 2\sqrt{14}$

Q2 a) The resultant is:
   $(\mathbf{i} + \mathbf{j} + 2\mathbf{k}) + (\mathbf{i} + 2\mathbf{j} + 4\mathbf{k}) = 2\mathbf{i} + 3\mathbf{j} + 6\mathbf{k}$
   Its magnitude is: $\sqrt{2^2 + 3^2 + 6^2} = \sqrt{49} = 7$

   b) resultant: $2\mathbf{i} + 14\mathbf{j} + 23\mathbf{k}$
   magnitude: $\sqrt{2^2 + 14^2 + 23^2} = \sqrt{729} = 27$

   c) resultant: $\begin{pmatrix} 2 \\ 6 \\ 9 \end{pmatrix}$, magnitude: $\sqrt{2^2 + 6^2 + 9^2} = 11$

d) resultant: $\begin{pmatrix} 2 \\ 5 \\ 14 \end{pmatrix}$, magnitude: $\sqrt{2^2 + 5^2 + 14^2} = 15$

e) resultant: $\begin{pmatrix} 10 \\ 2 \\ 14 \end{pmatrix}$

magnitude: $\sqrt{10^2 + 2^2 + 14^2} = 10\sqrt{3}$

Q3 a) $\sqrt{(5-3)^2 + (6-4)^2 + (6-5)^2}$
$= \sqrt{2^2 + 2^2 + 1^2} = \sqrt{4+4+1} = \sqrt{9} = 3$

b) $\sqrt{(-11-7)^2 + (1-2)^2 + (15-9)^2}$
$= \sqrt{324 + 1 + 36} = \sqrt{361} = 19$

c) $\sqrt{(6-10)^2 + (10-(-2))^2 + (-4-(-1))^2}$
$= \sqrt{16 + 144 + 9} = \sqrt{169} = 13$

d) $\sqrt{(7-0)^2 + (0-(-4))^2 + (14-10)^2}$
$= \sqrt{49 + 16 + 16} = \sqrt{81} = 9$

e) $\sqrt{(2-(-4))^2 + (4-7)^2 + (-12-10)^2}$
$= \sqrt{36 + 9 + 484} = \sqrt{529} = 23$

f) $\sqrt{(30-7)^2 + (9-(-1))^2 + (-6-4)^2}$
$= \sqrt{529 + 100 + 100} = \sqrt{729} = 27$

Q4 $|2\mathbf{m} - \mathbf{n}| = |-6\mathbf{i} - 5\mathbf{j} + 10\mathbf{k}|$
$= \sqrt{(-6)^2 + (-5)^2 + 10^2} = 12.68857... = 12.69$ to 4 s.f.

Q5 $|\overrightarrow{AO}| = |\overrightarrow{OA}| = \sqrt{1^2 + (-4)^2 + 3^2} = \sqrt{26}$
$|\overrightarrow{BO}| = |\overrightarrow{OB}| = \sqrt{(-1)^2 + (-3)^2 + 5^2} = \sqrt{35}$
It's pretty clear that the magnitude of $\overrightarrow{AO}$ is going to be the same as $\overrightarrow{OA}$ so there's no need to find $\overrightarrow{AO}$.

$\overrightarrow{BA} = \overrightarrow{OA} - \overrightarrow{OB} = (\mathbf{i} - 4\mathbf{j} + 3\mathbf{k}) - (-\mathbf{i} - 3\mathbf{j} + 5\mathbf{k})$
$= 2\mathbf{i} - \mathbf{j} - 2\mathbf{k}$
$|\overrightarrow{BA}| = \sqrt{2^2 + (-1)^2 + (-2)^2} = 3$
Triangle AOB is right-angled because:
$|\overrightarrow{AO}|^2 + |\overrightarrow{BA}|^2 = (\sqrt{26})^2 + 3^2 = 26 + 9$
$= 35 = (\sqrt{35})^2 = |\overrightarrow{BO}|^2$

Q6 $|\mathbf{v}| = \sqrt{4^2 + (-4)^2 + (-7)^2} = 9$
so the unit vector is $\frac{1}{9}\mathbf{v} = \frac{4}{9}\mathbf{i} - \frac{4}{9}\mathbf{j} - \frac{7}{9}\mathbf{k}$

Q7 $|\overrightarrow{PQ}| = \sqrt{(q-4)^2 + 6^2 + (2q-3)^2}$
So: $\sqrt{(q-4)^2 + 6^2 + (2q-3)^2} = 11$
$q^2 - 8q + 16 + 36 + 4q^2 - 12q + 9 = 121$
$5q^2 - 20q - 60 = 0$
$q^2 - 4q - 12 = 0$
$(q-6)(q+2) = 0$
Either $q = 6$, then Q is (4, 5, 13),
or $q = -2$, then Q is (-4, 5, -3).

3. Vector Equations of Lines
Exercise 3.1 —
Vector equations of lines in 2D

Q1 a) The gradient is $\frac{3}{1} = 3$
The y-intercept has position vector $\begin{pmatrix} 0 \\ 2 \end{pmatrix}$,
which gives it coordinates (0, 2).

b) $m = \frac{2}{1} = 2$
The y-intercept has coordinates (0, –5).

c) $m = \frac{15}{3} = 5$
The y-intercept has coordinates (0, 0).

For questions where you're asked to find the vector equation of a line there will always be alternative answers because the equation isn't unique. The answers given are the ones you'll get most easily from the information in the question.

Q2 a) E.g.
From the Cartesian equation $m = 1 = \frac{1}{1}$ and $c = 2$
So $\begin{pmatrix} 1 \\ 1 \end{pmatrix}$ is a vector in the direction of the line and
$\begin{pmatrix} 0 \\ 2 \end{pmatrix}$ is a point on the line.
That gives the equation: $\mathbf{r} = \begin{pmatrix} 0 \\ 2 \end{pmatrix} + t\begin{pmatrix} 1 \\ 1 \end{pmatrix}$

b) From the Cartesian equation y is constant, so the line is horizontal, so the direction vector must be horizontal (have a zero $\mathbf{j}$ component) e.g. $\begin{pmatrix} 1 \\ 0 \end{pmatrix}$.
$c = 7$, so $\begin{pmatrix} 0 \\ 7 \end{pmatrix}$ is a point on the line.
So an equation is e.g. $\mathbf{r} = \begin{pmatrix} 0 \\ 7 \end{pmatrix} + t\begin{pmatrix} 1 \\ 0 \end{pmatrix}$

c) $m = -4 = \frac{-4}{1}$ and $c = 0$
So $\begin{pmatrix} 1 \\ -4 \end{pmatrix}$ is a vector in the direction of the line and $\begin{pmatrix} 0 \\ 0 \end{pmatrix}$ is a point on the line.
That gives the equation, e.g. $\mathbf{r} = \begin{pmatrix} 0 \\ 0 \end{pmatrix} + t\begin{pmatrix} 1 \\ -4 \end{pmatrix}$

d) $m = -3 = \frac{-3}{1}$ and $c = 5$
So $\begin{pmatrix} 1 \\ -3 \end{pmatrix}$ is a vector in the direction of the line and $\begin{pmatrix} 0 \\ 5 \end{pmatrix}$ is a point on the line.
That gives the equation, e.g. $\mathbf{r} = \begin{pmatrix} 0 \\ 5 \end{pmatrix} + t\begin{pmatrix} 1 \\ -3 \end{pmatrix}$

Q3 a) E.g. $m = -3 = \frac{-3}{1}$, so $\begin{pmatrix} 1 \\ -3 \end{pmatrix}$ is a vector in the direction of the line and $\begin{pmatrix} 2 \\ 6 \end{pmatrix}$ lies on the line.
This gives the vector equation $\mathbf{r} = \begin{pmatrix} 2 \\ 6 \end{pmatrix} + t\begin{pmatrix} 1 \\ -3 \end{pmatrix}$

b) E.g. $m = \frac{1}{2}$, so $\begin{pmatrix} 2 \\ 1 \end{pmatrix}$ is in the direction of the line and $\begin{pmatrix} 2 \\ 2 \end{pmatrix}$ lies on the line, this gives $\mathbf{r} = \begin{pmatrix} 2 \\ 2 \end{pmatrix} + t\begin{pmatrix} 2 \\ 1 \end{pmatrix}$.

c) $m = 0$ so the Cartesian form of the line equation is $y = c$, i.e. the vertical coordinate stays constant along the line and the line is horizontal. So the direction vector must be horizontal (that is have a zero $\mathbf{j}$ component) e.g. $\begin{pmatrix} 1 \\ 0 \end{pmatrix}$, this gives equation e.g. $\mathbf{r} = \begin{pmatrix} 1 \\ -5 \end{pmatrix} + t\begin{pmatrix} 1 \\ 0 \end{pmatrix}$

Q4 a) $\begin{pmatrix} 0 \\ 0 \end{pmatrix}$ lies on the line, so the y-intercept is $c = 0$.
The direction of the line is $\begin{pmatrix} 1 \\ 1 \end{pmatrix}$, so the gradient is $\frac{1}{1} = 1 = m$.
This gives the equation $y = x$.

b) $\begin{pmatrix} 0 \\ -4 \end{pmatrix}$ lies on the line so $c = -4$.

The direction of the line is $\begin{pmatrix} -1 \\ 2 \end{pmatrix}$, so $m = \frac{2}{-1} = -2$.

This gives the equation $y = -2x - 4$

c) The gradient m is $\frac{1}{2}$, so $y = \frac{1}{2}x + c$
We want to find c. We know $\begin{pmatrix} 6 \\ 0 \end{pmatrix}$ is a point on
the line, so when $x = 6$, $y = 0$. Putting this into
the equation $y = \frac{1}{2}x + c$ gives that $c = -3$.
So the answer is $y = \frac{1}{2}x - 3$

d) The direction vector $\begin{pmatrix} 3 \\ 0 \end{pmatrix}$ tells us that as you
move along the line there is a vertical
displacement of zero for every horizontal
displacement of 3, so the line is horizontal which
means that y is constant.
We know $\begin{pmatrix} 1 \\ 2 \end{pmatrix}$ is a point on the line,
so when $x = 1$, $y = 2$. But y is constant so it's
always 2, so the answer is $y = 2$

e) The gradient m is $\frac{5}{2}$, so $y = \frac{5}{2}x + c$
We want to find c. We know $\begin{pmatrix} -2 \\ 3 \end{pmatrix}$ is a point on
the line, so when $x = -2$, $y = 3$. Putting this into
the equation $y = \frac{5}{2}x + c$ gives that $c = 8$.
So the answer is $y = \frac{5}{2}x + 8$.

f) The direction vector $\begin{pmatrix} 0 \\ 1 \end{pmatrix}$ tells us that as you
move along the line there is a horizontal
displacement of zero for every vertical
displacement of 1, so the line is vertical which
means that x is constant.
We know $\begin{pmatrix} 5 \\ 0 \end{pmatrix}$ is a point on the line,
so when $y = 0$, $x = 5$. But x is constant so it's
always 5, so the answer is $x = 5$.

Q5 a) The position vector of point A on the line is $\begin{pmatrix} 2 \\ 5 \end{pmatrix}$.
$\mathbf{b} = \begin{pmatrix} -1 \\ 2 \end{pmatrix}$ is a vector with the same direction
as the line, so a vector equation of the line is
e.g. $\mathbf{r} = \begin{pmatrix} 2 \\ 5 \end{pmatrix} + t\begin{pmatrix} -1 \\ 2 \end{pmatrix}$ so $\mathbf{r} = 2\mathbf{i} + 5\mathbf{j} + t(2\mathbf{j} - \mathbf{i})$.
You can always rearrange your answers so that they're
in the form r = ai + bj. Here r = i(2 − t) + j(5 + 2t).

b) The position vector of point A on the line is $\begin{pmatrix} -1 \\ 0 \end{pmatrix}$.
$\mathbf{b} = \begin{pmatrix} 3 \\ 4 \end{pmatrix}$ is a vector with the same direction
as the line so an equation is e.g. $\mathbf{r} = \begin{pmatrix} -1 \\ 0 \end{pmatrix} + t\begin{pmatrix} 3 \\ 4 \end{pmatrix}$
so $\mathbf{r} = -\mathbf{i} + t(3\mathbf{i} + 4\mathbf{j})$.

c) The position vector of point A on the line is $\begin{pmatrix} -3 \\ -1 \end{pmatrix}$.
$\mathbf{b} = \begin{pmatrix} 6 \\ -1 \end{pmatrix}$ is a vector with the same direction
as the line so an equation is e.g. $\mathbf{r} = \begin{pmatrix} -3 \\ -1 \end{pmatrix} + t\begin{pmatrix} 6 \\ -1 \end{pmatrix}$
so $\mathbf{r} = -3\mathbf{i} - \mathbf{j} + t(6\mathbf{i} - \mathbf{j})$.

d) The position vector of point A on the line is $\begin{pmatrix} 0 \\ 4 \end{pmatrix}$.
$\mathbf{b} = \begin{pmatrix} -3 \\ -5 \end{pmatrix} \left(\text{or} \begin{pmatrix} 3 \\ 5 \end{pmatrix} \right)$ is a vector with the same
direction as the line so an equation is e.g.

$\mathbf{r} = \begin{pmatrix} 0 \\ 4 \end{pmatrix} + t\begin{pmatrix} -3 \\ -5 \end{pmatrix}$ or $\begin{pmatrix} 0 \\ 4 \end{pmatrix} + t\begin{pmatrix} 3 \\ 5 \end{pmatrix}$
so $\mathbf{r} = 4\mathbf{j} + t(-3\mathbf{i} - 5\mathbf{j})$ or $4\mathbf{j} + t(3\mathbf{i} + 5\mathbf{j})$.

Q6 a) Plugging the vectors $\mathbf{p} = \mathbf{i} = \begin{pmatrix} 1 \\ 0 \end{pmatrix}$ and
$\mathbf{q} = 2\mathbf{i} + \mathbf{j} = \begin{pmatrix} 2 \\ 1 \end{pmatrix}$ into the formula $\mathbf{r} = \mathbf{c} + t(\mathbf{d} - \mathbf{c})$
gives the equation: $\mathbf{r} = \mathbf{p} + t(\mathbf{q} - \mathbf{p}) = \begin{pmatrix} 1 \\ 0 \end{pmatrix} + t\begin{pmatrix} 1 \\ 1 \end{pmatrix}$
so $\mathbf{r} = \mathbf{i} + t(\mathbf{i} + \mathbf{j})$.

There are three other combinations you could have to
give you a different equation, e.g. r = q + t(p − q).

Parts b) and c) are answered in the same way as a)

b) E.g. $\mathbf{r} = \mathbf{f} + t(\mathbf{g} - \mathbf{f}) = \begin{pmatrix} 3 \\ -4 \end{pmatrix} + t\begin{pmatrix} -1 \\ 9 \end{pmatrix}$
so $\mathbf{r} = 3\mathbf{i} - 4\mathbf{j} + t(9\mathbf{j} - \mathbf{i})$.

c) E.g. $\mathbf{r} = \mathbf{n} + t(\mathbf{m} - \mathbf{n}) = \begin{pmatrix} -1 \\ 3 \end{pmatrix} + t\begin{pmatrix} -4 \\ \frac{9}{-\frac{9}{2}} \end{pmatrix}$
$= \begin{pmatrix} -1 \\ 3 \end{pmatrix} + t\begin{pmatrix} 8 \\ 9 \end{pmatrix}$ so $\mathbf{r} = -\mathbf{i} + 3\mathbf{j} + t(8\mathbf{i} + 9\mathbf{j})$.

You can multiply the direction vector by −2 to get
(positive) whole numbers because any parallel vector will
do, but the question doesn't ask you to do this so you
don't have to.

Exercise 3.2 —
Vector equations of lines in 3D

For questions where you're asked to find the vector equation of a
line there will always be alternative answers because the equation
isn't unique. The answers given are the ones you'll get most easily
from the information in the question.

Q1 a) $\overrightarrow{OX} = \mathbf{a} + \mathbf{b} = \begin{pmatrix} 4 \\ -3 \\ -2 \end{pmatrix} + \begin{pmatrix} 1 \\ 2 \\ 3 \end{pmatrix} = \begin{pmatrix} 4+1 \\ -3+2 \\ -2+3 \end{pmatrix} = \begin{pmatrix} 5 \\ -1 \\ 1 \end{pmatrix}$

$\overrightarrow{OY} = \mathbf{a} + 2\mathbf{b} = \begin{pmatrix} 4 \\ -3 \\ -2 \end{pmatrix} + 2\begin{pmatrix} 1 \\ 2 \\ 3 \end{pmatrix} = \begin{pmatrix} 6 \\ 1 \\ 4 \end{pmatrix}$

$\overrightarrow{OZ} = \begin{pmatrix} 7 \\ 3 \\ 7 \end{pmatrix}$, $\overrightarrow{OQ} = \begin{pmatrix} 3 \\ -5 \\ -5 \end{pmatrix}$

b) E.g. $\mathbf{r} = \begin{pmatrix} 4 \\ -3 \\ -2 \end{pmatrix} + \lambda\begin{pmatrix} 1 \\ 2 \\ 3 \end{pmatrix}$

Q2 Point C corresponds to $\lambda = 0$, so it has position vector
$\mathbf{r} = \begin{pmatrix} 2 \\ 1 \\ 3 \end{pmatrix} + 0 \times \begin{pmatrix} 1 \\ -1 \\ 4 \end{pmatrix} = \begin{pmatrix} 2 \\ 1 \\ 3 \end{pmatrix}$ and coordinates (2, 1, 3).

D has position vector $\mathbf{r} = \begin{pmatrix} 2 \\ 1 \\ 3 \end{pmatrix} + 1 \times \begin{pmatrix} 1 \\ -1 \\ 4 \end{pmatrix} = \begin{pmatrix} 3 \\ 0 \\ 7 \end{pmatrix}$ and
coordinates (3, 0, 7).

E has position vector $\mathbf{r} = \begin{pmatrix} 2 \\ 1 \\ 3 \end{pmatrix} + 4 \times \begin{pmatrix} 1 \\ -1 \\ 4 \end{pmatrix} = \begin{pmatrix} 6 \\ -3 \\ 19 \end{pmatrix}$ and
coordinates (6, −3, 19).

F has position vector $\mathbf{r} = \begin{pmatrix} 2 \\ 1 \\ 3 \end{pmatrix} + (-2) \times \begin{pmatrix} 1 \\ -1 \\ 4 \end{pmatrix} = \begin{pmatrix} 0 \\ 3 \\ -5 \end{pmatrix}$
and coordinates (0, 3, −5).

Q3 By choosing $t = 1$ you get the position vector
$\mathbf{r} = 3\mathbf{j} - 4\mathbf{k} + (-\mathbf{i} + 2\mathbf{j}) = -\mathbf{i} + 5\mathbf{j} - 4\mathbf{k}$. The coordinates of the point with this position vector are $(-1, 5, -4)$. Other points are $(0, 3, -4)$ and $(-2, 7, -4)$.
These are just example points, you can have any points found by choosing a value for t in the equation.

Q4 a) You know two points on the line:
S and the origin O.
S has coordinates $(-1, 4, 5)$, so position vector
$\mathbf{s} = \begin{pmatrix} -1 \\ 4 \\ 5 \end{pmatrix}$. O has position vector $\mathbf{o} = \begin{pmatrix} 0 \\ 0 \\ 0 \end{pmatrix}$.

Plugging these into the formula $\mathbf{r} = \mathbf{c} + \lambda(\mathbf{d} - \mathbf{c})$ gives, e.g.
$$\mathbf{r} = \lambda \begin{pmatrix} -1 \\ 4 \\ 5 \end{pmatrix} \text{ or } \mathbf{r} = \begin{pmatrix} -1 \\ 4 \\ 5 \end{pmatrix} + \lambda \begin{pmatrix} 1 \\ -4 \\ -5 \end{pmatrix}$$

b) The coordinates of 2 more points can be found by substituting 2 values in for the parameter λ.
E.g. When $\lambda = 2$, $\mathbf{r} = 2\begin{pmatrix} -1 \\ 4 \\ 5 \end{pmatrix} = \begin{pmatrix} -2 \\ 8 \\ 10 \end{pmatrix}$
which gives the point $(-2, 8, 10)$ and
when $\lambda = -1$, $\mathbf{r} = -1\begin{pmatrix} -1 \\ 4 \\ 5 \end{pmatrix} = \begin{pmatrix} 1 \\ -4 \\ -5 \end{pmatrix}$ which gives the point $(1, -4, -5)$.

Q5 a) (i) Using the formula $\mathbf{r} = \mathbf{a} + t\mathbf{b}$ for the vector equation of a line through the point with position vector $\mathbf{a}$ and parallel to $\mathbf{b}$ gives:
$$\mathbf{r} = \begin{pmatrix} 4 \\ 2 \\ -1 \end{pmatrix} + t \begin{pmatrix} -2 \\ 0 \\ 3 \end{pmatrix}$$
Parts (ii) and (iii) are answered in the same way
(ii) E.g. $\mathbf{r} = \begin{pmatrix} 0 \\ 0 \\ 1 \end{pmatrix} + t \begin{pmatrix} 1 \\ -1 \\ 0 \end{pmatrix}$
(iii) E.g. $\mathbf{r} = (2\mathbf{i} + \mathbf{j}) + t(5\mathbf{i} - \mathbf{k})$

b) First check if P lies on line **(i)**. If P lies on **(i)** there's some t that solves
$$\begin{pmatrix} -2 \\ 2 \\ 1 \end{pmatrix} = \begin{pmatrix} 4 \\ 2 \\ -1 \end{pmatrix} + t \begin{pmatrix} -2 \\ 0 \\ 3 \end{pmatrix} \Rightarrow \begin{pmatrix} -2 \\ 2 \\ 1 \end{pmatrix} = \begin{pmatrix} 4 - 2t \\ 2 \\ -1 + 3t \end{pmatrix}$$
$\Rightarrow -2 = 4 - 2t$ and $1 = -1 + 3t \Rightarrow t = 3$ and $t = \frac{2}{3}$
So P doesn't lie on **(i)**, now check if it lies on **(ii)**:
$$\begin{pmatrix} -2 \\ 2 \\ 1 \end{pmatrix} = \begin{pmatrix} 0 \\ 0 \\ 1 \end{pmatrix} + t \begin{pmatrix} 1 \\ -1 \\ 0 \end{pmatrix} \Rightarrow \begin{pmatrix} -2 \\ 2 \\ 1 \end{pmatrix} = \begin{pmatrix} t \\ -t \\ 1 \end{pmatrix}$$
$\Rightarrow -2 = t$ and $2 = -t \Rightarrow t = -2$
So P lies on **(ii)** and corresponds to $t = -2$
You find which line the remaining points lie on in the same way.
Now check if Q lies on line **(i)**. If Q lies on **(i)** there's some t that solves
$$\begin{pmatrix} 2 \\ 2 \\ 2 \end{pmatrix} = \begin{pmatrix} 4 \\ 2 \\ -1 \end{pmatrix} + t \begin{pmatrix} -2 \\ 0 \\ 3 \end{pmatrix} \Rightarrow \begin{pmatrix} 2 \\ 2 \\ 2 \end{pmatrix} = \begin{pmatrix} 4 - 2t \\ 2 \\ -1 + 3t \end{pmatrix}$$

$\Rightarrow 2 = 4 - 2t$ and $2 = -1 + 3t \Rightarrow t = 1$ and $t = 1$
Both equations are solved by the same value of t, so Q lies on line **(i)** and corresponds to $t = 1$.
R must lie on line **(iii)**, so solve:
$$\begin{pmatrix} -3 \\ 1 \\ 1 \end{pmatrix} = \begin{pmatrix} 2 \\ 1 \\ 0 \end{pmatrix} + t \begin{pmatrix} 5 \\ 0 \\ -1 \end{pmatrix} \Rightarrow \begin{pmatrix} -3 \\ 1 \\ 1 \end{pmatrix} = \begin{pmatrix} 2 + 5t \\ 1 \\ -t \end{pmatrix}$$
$\Rightarrow -3 = 2 + 5t$ and $1 = -t \Rightarrow t = -1$ and $t = -1$
R lies on **(iii)** and corresponds to $t = -1$.

Q6 Line L has equation $\mathbf{r} = -6\mathbf{i} - \mathbf{j} + \mathbf{k} + t(\mathbf{i} - 3\mathbf{k})$, so the vector it's parallel to is $(\mathbf{i} - 3\mathbf{k})$. The line that's parallel to L is also parallel to $(\mathbf{i} - 3\mathbf{k})$, so the direction vector of this new line is $(\mathbf{i} - 3\mathbf{k})$. The line passes through the point with position vector $(5\mathbf{i} - \mathbf{j} + 3\mathbf{k})$, so the equation is: $\mathbf{r} = (5\mathbf{i} - \mathbf{j} + 3\mathbf{k}) + t(\mathbf{i} - 3\mathbf{k})$.

Q7 For P, $\begin{pmatrix} -4 \\ a \\ 10 \end{pmatrix} = \begin{pmatrix} -2 \\ 5 \\ 4 \end{pmatrix} + s \begin{pmatrix} 1 \\ 2 \\ -3 \end{pmatrix} = \begin{pmatrix} -2 + s \\ 5 + 2s \\ 4 - 3s \end{pmatrix}$, so:
$-4 = -2 + s \Rightarrow s = -2$, then $5 + 2s = a$, so $a = 1$
b and c are found using the same method.
For Q, $\begin{pmatrix} b \\ c \\ -11 \end{pmatrix} = \begin{pmatrix} -2 \\ 5 \\ 4 \end{pmatrix} + s \begin{pmatrix} 1 \\ 2 \\ -3 \end{pmatrix} = \begin{pmatrix} -2 + s \\ 5 + 2s \\ 4 - 3s \end{pmatrix}$
$4 - 3s = -11 \Rightarrow s = 5$, then $-2 + s = b$, so $b = 3$,
also $5 + 2s = c$, so $c = 15$.

Q8 a) Any vector parallel to $\begin{pmatrix} 3 \\ 2 \\ -1 \end{pmatrix}$ will do,
so any scalar multiple, e.g. $\mathbf{r} = \begin{pmatrix} -4 \\ 0 \\ 1 \end{pmatrix} + s \begin{pmatrix} 6 \\ 4 \\ -2 \end{pmatrix}$.

b) Any other point on the line will do, so find a point by choosing a value for s in the original equation,
e.g. $s = 1$ gives: $\mathbf{r} = \begin{pmatrix} -4 \\ 0 \\ 1 \end{pmatrix} + \begin{pmatrix} 3 \\ 2 \\ -1 \end{pmatrix} = \begin{pmatrix} -1 \\ 2 \\ 0 \end{pmatrix}$ as the
position vector of a new point on the line.
So the new equation is $\mathbf{r} = \begin{pmatrix} -1 \\ 2 \\ 0 \end{pmatrix} + s \begin{pmatrix} 3 \\ 2 \\ -1 \end{pmatrix}$.

Q9 a) We have position vectors $\mathbf{c} = \begin{pmatrix} 7 \\ 0 \\ -3 \end{pmatrix}$ and $\mathbf{d} = \begin{pmatrix} -1 \\ 1 \\ -3 \end{pmatrix}$,
put these into $\mathbf{r} = \mathbf{c} + t(\mathbf{d} - \mathbf{c})$:
$$\mathbf{r} = \begin{pmatrix} 7 \\ 0 \\ -3 \end{pmatrix} + t \begin{pmatrix} -8 \\ 1 \\ 0 \end{pmatrix}$$

b) We have position vectors $\mathbf{c} = \begin{pmatrix} -1 \\ 1 \\ 4 \end{pmatrix}$ and $\mathbf{d} = \begin{pmatrix} -4 \\ 1 \\ 0 \end{pmatrix}$,
put these into $\mathbf{r} = \mathbf{c} + t(\mathbf{d} - \mathbf{c})$:
$$\mathbf{r} = \begin{pmatrix} -1 \\ 1 \\ 4 \end{pmatrix} + t \begin{pmatrix} -3 \\ 0 \\ -4 \end{pmatrix}$$

c) We have position vectors $\mathbf{c} = \begin{pmatrix} 2 \\ 5 \\ 0 \end{pmatrix}$ and $\mathbf{d} = \begin{pmatrix} -2 \\ -1 \\ 2 \end{pmatrix}$,
put these into $\mathbf{r} = \mathbf{c} + t(\mathbf{d} - \mathbf{c})$:
$$\mathbf{r} = \begin{pmatrix} 2 \\ 5 \\ 0 \end{pmatrix} + t \begin{pmatrix} -4 \\ -6 \\ 2 \end{pmatrix}$$

Exercise 3.3 —
Intersecting, parallel and skew lines

For questions where you're asked to find the vector equation of a line there will always be alternative answers because the equation isn't unique. The answers given are the ones you'll get most easily from the information in the question.

Q1 a) $\begin{pmatrix} 0 \\ 7 \\ 0 \end{pmatrix} = -\frac{7}{2}\begin{pmatrix} 0 \\ -2 \\ 0 \end{pmatrix}$ which means the direction vectors

of the lines are parallel, so the lines are parallel.

b) Not parallel as the direction vectors ($\mathbf{j} + \mathbf{k}$) and ($2\mathbf{i} + 2\mathbf{k}$) aren't parallel (the first vector has a zero $\mathbf{i}$ component and the second doesn't so they can't be parallel).

Q2 a) $\begin{pmatrix} a \\ 0 \\ -1 \end{pmatrix}$ and $\begin{pmatrix} 10 \\ b \\ -5 \end{pmatrix}$ are parallel, so $\begin{pmatrix} a \\ 0 \\ -1 \end{pmatrix} = \lambda\begin{pmatrix} 10 \\ b \\ -5 \end{pmatrix}$

for some λ,

$-1 = -5\lambda$ so $\lambda = \frac{1}{5}$

$\Rightarrow a = \frac{1}{5} \times 10 = 2$ and $0 = \frac{1}{5}b \Rightarrow b = 0$

b) $\begin{pmatrix} 2 \\ c \\ -4 \end{pmatrix}$ and $\begin{pmatrix} d \\ 3 \\ 2 \end{pmatrix}$ are parallel, so $\begin{pmatrix} 2 \\ c \\ -4 \end{pmatrix} = s\begin{pmatrix} d \\ 3 \\ 2 \end{pmatrix}$

for some s,

$-4 = 2s$ so $s = -2$

and $c = (-2) \times 3 \Rightarrow c = -6$ and

$2 = -2d \Rightarrow d = -1$

$c = -6, d = -1$

Q3 a) Lines intersect when $\begin{pmatrix} 2 \\ 1 \\ 0 \end{pmatrix} + \lambda\begin{pmatrix} 1 \\ -2 \\ 1 \end{pmatrix} = \begin{pmatrix} -3 \\ 0 \\ -1 \end{pmatrix} + \mu\begin{pmatrix} 4 \\ 3 \\ 0 \end{pmatrix}$

This gives us the equations:

$2 + \lambda = -3 + 4\mu$
$1 - 2\lambda = 3\mu$
$\lambda = -1$

Plug $\lambda = -1$ from the third row into the other rows: $\quad 2 - 1 = -3 + 4\mu \Rightarrow 4\mu = 4 \Rightarrow \mu = 1$

$1 + 2 = 3\mu \Rightarrow 3 = 3\mu \Rightarrow \mu = 1$

There is a consistent solution so the lines intersect at the point with position vector:

$\begin{pmatrix} 2 \\ 1 \\ 0 \end{pmatrix} - \begin{pmatrix} 1 \\ -2 \\ 1 \end{pmatrix} = \begin{pmatrix} -3 \\ 0 \\ -1 \end{pmatrix} + \begin{pmatrix} 4 \\ 3 \\ 0 \end{pmatrix} = \begin{pmatrix} 1 \\ 3 \\ -1 \end{pmatrix}$

So the coordinates are (1, 3, –1)
Don't forget to give your answer as coordinates instead of leaving it as a vector.

b) Lines intersect when $\begin{pmatrix} -1 \\ 7 \\ 1 \end{pmatrix} + \lambda\begin{pmatrix} 2 \\ -2 \\ 1 \end{pmatrix} = \begin{pmatrix} 1 \\ 3 \\ 2 \end{pmatrix} + \mu\begin{pmatrix} 2 \\ -1 \\ 1 \end{pmatrix}$

This gives us the equations:

$-1 + 2\lambda = 1 + 2\mu$
$7 - 2\lambda = 3 - \mu$
$1 + \lambda = 2 + \mu$

Solve simultaneously:

(eqn 2) + (eqn 3): $\quad 8 - \lambda = 5 \Rightarrow \lambda = 3$

Plugging this back into (eqn 2) gives:

$7 - (2 \times 3) = 3 - \mu \Rightarrow \mu = 2$

Plug this into the first equation to check the solution is consistent:

$-1 + 2\lambda = 1 + 2\mu \Rightarrow -1 + (2 \times 3) = 1 + (2 \times 2)$
$\Rightarrow 5 = 5$

This is true so there's a consistent solution and the lines intersect at the point with position vector:

$\begin{pmatrix} -1 \\ 7 \\ 1 \end{pmatrix} + 3\begin{pmatrix} 2 \\ -2 \\ 1 \end{pmatrix} = \begin{pmatrix} 1 \\ 3 \\ 2 \end{pmatrix} + 2\begin{pmatrix} 2 \\ -1 \\ 1 \end{pmatrix} = \begin{pmatrix} 5 \\ 1 \\ 4 \end{pmatrix}$

So the coordinates are (5, 1, 4)

c) Lines intersect when

$\begin{pmatrix} 5 \\ 7 \\ -3 \end{pmatrix} + s\begin{pmatrix} 1 \\ 3 \\ -2 \end{pmatrix} = \begin{pmatrix} -4 \\ 15 \\ -10 \end{pmatrix} + t\begin{pmatrix} 1 \\ -4 \\ 3 \end{pmatrix}$

This gives us the equations:

$5 + s = -4 + t$
$7 + 3s = 15 + -4t$
$-3 + -2s = -10 + 3t$

Solve simultaneously:

(eqn 2) – 3(eqn 1): $-8 = 27 - 7t \Rightarrow t = 5$

Putting this back into (eqn 1) gives:

$5 + s = -4 + 5 \Rightarrow s = -4$

Plug this into the third equation to check the solution is consistent: $\quad -3 + -2s = -10 + 3t$

$\Rightarrow -3 + (-2 \times (-4)) = -10 + (3 \times 5) \Rightarrow 5 = 5$

This is true so there's a consistent solution and the lines intersect at the point with position vector:

$\begin{pmatrix} 5 \\ 7 \\ -3 \end{pmatrix} + -4\begin{pmatrix} 1 \\ 3 \\ -2 \end{pmatrix} = \begin{pmatrix} -4 \\ 15 \\ -10 \end{pmatrix} + 5\begin{pmatrix} 1 \\ -4 \\ 3 \end{pmatrix} = \begin{pmatrix} 1 \\ -5 \\ 5 \end{pmatrix}$

So the coordinates are (1, –5, 5)

Q4 $\begin{pmatrix} 1 \\ 0 \\ a \end{pmatrix} + \lambda\begin{pmatrix} -1 \\ b \\ 2 \end{pmatrix} = \begin{pmatrix} 2 \\ -3 \\ 2 \end{pmatrix} = \begin{pmatrix} 0 \\ c \\ 3 \end{pmatrix} + \mu\begin{pmatrix} 2 \\ 1 \\ d \end{pmatrix}$

Solving along the top row:

$1 - \lambda = 2 \Rightarrow \lambda = -1, 2 = 2\mu \Rightarrow \mu = 1$

Now plug the values for λ and μ back into each line equation and solve each separately:

$\begin{pmatrix} 1 \\ 0 \\ a \end{pmatrix} - \begin{pmatrix} -1 \\ b \\ 2 \end{pmatrix} = \begin{pmatrix} 2 \\ -b \\ a-2 \end{pmatrix} = \begin{pmatrix} 2 \\ -3 \\ 2 \end{pmatrix} \Rightarrow b = 3, a = 4$

$\begin{pmatrix} 0 \\ c \\ 3 \end{pmatrix} + \begin{pmatrix} 2 \\ 1 \\ d \end{pmatrix} = \begin{pmatrix} 2 \\ c+1 \\ 3+d \end{pmatrix} = \begin{pmatrix} 2 \\ -3 \\ 2 \end{pmatrix} \Rightarrow c = -4, d = -1$

Q5 a) If the lines are intersecting there will be a solution

to: $\begin{pmatrix} 4 \\ 0 \\ 1 \end{pmatrix} + \lambda\begin{pmatrix} 1 \\ 2 \\ 1 \end{pmatrix} = \begin{pmatrix} -1 \\ 3 \\ 2 \end{pmatrix} + \mu\begin{pmatrix} -1 \\ 1 \\ 0 \end{pmatrix}$

This gives equations: $\quad 4 + \lambda = -1 - \mu$
$2\lambda = 3 + \mu$
$1 + \lambda = 2$

The third row gives that $\lambda = 1$, plugging this into the other rows gives: $\quad 4 + 1 = -1 - \mu \Rightarrow \mu = -6$
$2 = 3 + \mu \Rightarrow \mu = -1$

There's no consistent solution so the lines don't intersect. Their direction vectors are also not scalar multiples of one another as one has a zero coefficient and the other doesn't.

This means the lines are not parallel.
Therefore the lines are neither parallel nor intersecting, so they must be skew.

b) If the lines are intersecting there will be a solution

to: $\begin{pmatrix} 1 \\ 1 \\ -1 \end{pmatrix} + \lambda \begin{pmatrix} -1 \\ 2 \\ 3 \end{pmatrix} = \begin{pmatrix} -2 \\ 4 \\ 1 \end{pmatrix} + \mu \begin{pmatrix} 1 \\ -1 \\ 3 \end{pmatrix}$

This gives equations: $\quad 1 - \lambda = -2 + \mu$
$\qquad\qquad\qquad\qquad 1 + 2\lambda = 4 - \mu$
$\qquad\qquad\qquad\qquad -1 + 3\lambda = 1 + 3\mu$

Solving simultaneously:
(eqn 1) + (eqn 2): $\quad 2 + \lambda = 2 \implies \lambda = 0$
Plugging this back into equation 1 gives:
$\quad 1 - 0 = -2 + \mu \implies \mu = 3$
Plugging these values into equation 3 gives:
$\quad -1 + 3\lambda = 1 + 3\mu \implies -1 + 0 = 1 + 9$
$\qquad\qquad\qquad\qquad \implies -1 = 10$
This isn't true which means there's no consistent solution so the lines don't intersect.
Their direction vectors are also not scalar multiples of one another, otherwise $\dfrac{-1}{1} = \dfrac{2}{-1} = \dfrac{3}{3}$ would hold.
This means the lines are not parallel.
Therefore the lines are neither parallel nor intersecting, so they must be skew.

c) If the lines are intersecting there will be a solution

to: $\begin{pmatrix} 3 \\ 1 \\ 1 \end{pmatrix} + s \begin{pmatrix} -1 \\ 2 \\ 1 \end{pmatrix} = \begin{pmatrix} 2 \\ -2 \\ 0 \end{pmatrix} + t \begin{pmatrix} 1 \\ 1 \\ -3 \end{pmatrix}$

This gives equations: $\quad 3 - s = 2 + t$
$\qquad\qquad\qquad\qquad 1 + 2s = -2 + t$
$\qquad\qquad\qquad\qquad 1 + s = -3t$

Solving simultaneously:
(eqn 1) − (eqn 2): $2 - 3s = 4 \implies 3s = -2 \implies s = -\dfrac{2}{3}$
Plugging this back into equation 1 gives:
$\dfrac{11}{3} = 2 + t \implies t = \dfrac{5}{3}$
Plugging these values into equation 3 gives:
$1 + s = -3t \implies \dfrac{1}{3} = -3 \times \dfrac{5}{3} \implies \dfrac{1}{3} = -5$
This isn't true which means there's no consistent solution so the lines don't intersect.
Their direction vectors are also not scalar multiples of one another, since if they were you'd have $\dfrac{-1}{1} = \dfrac{2}{1} = \dfrac{1}{-3}$, which doesn't hold.
This means the lines are not parallel.
Therefore the lines are neither parallel nor intersecting, so they must be skew.

Q6 If the lines are the same then all of their points are the same so there will be solutions to:
$\begin{pmatrix} 3 - \lambda \\ 4 + \lambda \\ -\lambda \end{pmatrix} = \begin{pmatrix} -6 - \mu \\ -8 + \mu \\ -\mu \end{pmatrix}$
Solving each line gives: $\lambda = \mu + 9$, $\lambda = \mu - 12$, $\lambda = \mu$.
There's no consistent solution so the lines aren't the same, they're just parallel.

Q7 a) If the lines are intersecting there will be a solution

to: $\begin{pmatrix} 4 \\ -5 \\ 1 \end{pmatrix} + p \begin{pmatrix} 2 \\ 4 \\ 3 \end{pmatrix} = \begin{pmatrix} 2 \\ -1 \\ 0 \end{pmatrix} + q \begin{pmatrix} 1 \\ 3 \\ 2 \end{pmatrix}$

This gives equations: $\quad 4 + 2p = 2 + q \qquad$ (eqn 1)
$\qquad\qquad\qquad\qquad -5 + 4p = -1 + 3q \quad$ (eqn 2)
$\qquad\qquad\qquad\qquad 1 + 3p = 2q \qquad$ (eqn 3)
Taking 2 × (eqn 1) − (eqn 3) gives:
$\qquad\qquad\qquad\qquad 7 + p = 4 \implies p = -3$
Plugging this back into (eqn 1) gives: $q = -4$
Check this in (eqn 2): $\quad -5 + 4(-3) = -1 + 3(-4)$
$\qquad\qquad\qquad\qquad\qquad -17 = -13$
This doesn't hold so the lines don't intersect, so they must be skew.

b) If the lines are intersecting there will be a solution

to: $\begin{pmatrix} 1 \\ -1 \\ 4 \end{pmatrix} + \lambda \begin{pmatrix} 1 \\ -1 \\ 1 \end{pmatrix} = \begin{pmatrix} 2 \\ 4 \\ 7 \end{pmatrix} + \mu \begin{pmatrix} 2 \\ 1 \\ 3 \end{pmatrix}$

This gives equations: $\quad 1 + \lambda = 2 + 2\mu \qquad$ (eqn 1)
$\qquad\qquad\qquad\qquad -1 - \lambda = 4 + \mu \qquad$ (eqn 2)
$\qquad\qquad\qquad\qquad 4 + \lambda = 7 + 3\mu \qquad$ (eqn 3)
(eqn 1) + (eqn 2) gives: $0 = 6 + 3\mu \implies \mu = -2$
Plugging this back into (eqn 2) gives:
$-1 - \lambda = 4 + \mu \implies -1 - \lambda = 2 \implies \lambda = -3$
Check this in (eqn 3): $\qquad 4 + \lambda = 7 + 3\mu$
$\qquad\qquad\qquad \implies \qquad 4 - 3 = 7 + 3(-2)$
$\qquad\qquad\qquad \implies \qquad\qquad 1 = 1$
This is true so $\lambda = -3$ and $\mu = -2$ solve all of the equations and the lines intersect. Plugging either of these values back into the appropriate equation gives the intersection position vector as: $\begin{pmatrix} -2 \\ 2 \\ 1 \end{pmatrix}$

Q8 a) $\vec{AC} = \vec{OC} - \vec{OA} = \begin{pmatrix} 1 \\ 4 \\ 2 \end{pmatrix} - \begin{pmatrix} 2 \\ 1 \\ 1 \end{pmatrix} = \begin{pmatrix} -1 \\ 3 \\ 1 \end{pmatrix}$

This is a direction vector for the line containing AC.

A, with position vector $\begin{pmatrix} 2 \\ 1 \\ 1 \end{pmatrix}$ lies on the line containing AC.
So an equation for the line containing AC is:

$$\mathbf{r} = \begin{pmatrix} 2 \\ 1 \\ 1 \end{pmatrix} + s \begin{pmatrix} -1 \\ 3 \\ 1 \end{pmatrix}$$

$\vec{BD} = \vec{OD} - \vec{OB} = \begin{pmatrix} -1 \\ 3 \\ -3 \end{pmatrix} - \begin{pmatrix} 3 \\ -1 \\ 1 \end{pmatrix} = \begin{pmatrix} -4 \\ 4 \\ -4 \end{pmatrix}$

This is a direction vector for the line containing BD.

B, with position vector $\begin{pmatrix} 3 \\ -1 \\ 1 \end{pmatrix}$ lies on the line containing BD.
So an equation for the line containing BD is:

$$\mathbf{r} = \begin{pmatrix} 3 \\ -1 \\ 1 \end{pmatrix} + t \begin{pmatrix} -4 \\ 4 \\ -4 \end{pmatrix} = \begin{pmatrix} 3 \\ -1 \\ 1 \end{pmatrix} + t \begin{pmatrix} -1 \\ 1 \\ -1 \end{pmatrix}$$

You could have used point C rather than A or point D rather than B. You can, and probably should, simplify the direction vector like has been done above by cancelling the scalar multiple of 4.

b) The lines containing the diagonals intersect when
$$\begin{pmatrix} 2 \\ 1 \\ 1 \end{pmatrix} + s \begin{pmatrix} -1 \\ 3 \\ 1 \end{pmatrix} = \begin{pmatrix} 3 \\ -1 \\ 1 \end{pmatrix} + t \begin{pmatrix} -1 \\ 1 \\ -1 \end{pmatrix}$$

This gives equations:
$$2 - s = 3 - t \quad \text{(eqn 1)}$$
$$1 + 3s = -1 + t \quad \text{(eqn 2)}$$
$$1 + s = 1 - t \quad \text{(eqn 3)}$$

(eqn 1) + (eqn 2) gives: $3 + 2s = 2 \Rightarrow s = -\frac{1}{2}$

Plugging this back into (eqn 1) gives:

$2 - s = 3 - t \Rightarrow 2 + \frac{1}{2} = 3 - t \Rightarrow t = \frac{1}{2}$

Check this in (eqn 3): $\qquad 1 + s = 1 - t$

$$\Rightarrow \quad 1 - \frac{1}{2} = 1 - \frac{1}{2}$$

$$\Rightarrow \qquad \frac{1}{2} = \frac{1}{2}$$

This is true so $s = -\frac{1}{2}$ and $t = \frac{1}{2}$ solve all of the equations and the lines intersect. Plugging either of these values back into the appropriate equation gives the coordinates of the point of intersection as $\left(\frac{5}{2}, -\frac{1}{2}, \frac{1}{2}\right)$.

So the coordinates of E are $\left(\frac{5}{2}, -\frac{1}{2}, \frac{1}{2}\right)$

4. Scalar Product
Exercise 4.1 — The scalar product

Q1 a) We use the formula $\mathbf{a.b} = |\mathbf{a}||\mathbf{b}|\cos\theta$.
We have $|\mathbf{a}| = 4$, $|\mathbf{b}| = 6$ and $\theta = 60°$, so:
$\mathbf{a.b} = 4 \times 6 \times \cos(60°) = 4 \times 6 \times 0.5 = 12$

b) If you draw both vectors away from the same point, then the angle between them is 30°.

$|\mathbf{a}| = 5$, $|\mathbf{b}| = 10$, $\theta = 30°$, $\mathbf{a.b} = 5 \times 10 \times \frac{\sqrt{3}}{2}$
$= 25\sqrt{3}$

c) $\mathbf{a.b} = 0$, as the vectors are perpendicular.

d) $|\mathbf{a}| = 8$, $|\mathbf{b}| = 11$, $\theta = 180° - 60° = 120°$ as both vectors must be pointing away from θ,
$\mathbf{a.b} = 8 \times 11 \times \left(-\frac{1}{2}\right) = -44$

Q2 a) $\mathbf{i.3j} = 0$, because $\mathbf{i}$ and $\mathbf{j}$ are perpendicular

b) $2\mathbf{j}.-\mathbf{j} = -|2| \times |1| = -2$, because the vectors are parallel but in opposite directions.

c) $4\mathbf{k}.-\mathbf{i} = 0$, because $\mathbf{i}$ and $\mathbf{k}$ are perpendicular.

d) $\mathbf{k}.6\mathbf{k} = |1| \times |6| = 6$, because $\mathbf{k}$ and $6\mathbf{k}$ are parallel.

Q3 a) We use the formula $\mathbf{a.b} = |\mathbf{a}||\mathbf{b}|\cos\theta$.
We have $|\mathbf{a}| = 2$, $|\mathbf{b}| = 5$ and $\mathbf{a.b} = 3$, so:
$3 = 2 \times 5 \times \cos\theta = 10\cos\theta$
$$\Rightarrow \cos\theta = \frac{3}{10} \Rightarrow \theta = 72.54...°$$
So θ is 73° to the nearest degree.

b) $|\mathbf{a}| = 1.2$, $|\mathbf{b}| = 5.6$ and $\mathbf{a.b} = 3$,
call the angle between the two vectors ϕ, so:
$3 = 1.2 \times 5.6 \times \cos\phi = 6.72\cos\phi$
$$\Rightarrow \cos\phi = \frac{3}{6.72} \Rightarrow \phi = 63.48...°$$
$\theta = 180° - \phi$, so $\theta = 180° - 63.48...° = 117°$
to the nearest degree

Exercise 4.2 —
Scalar product from vector components

Q1 a) $\mathbf{a} = \begin{pmatrix} 1 \\ 4 \end{pmatrix}$, $\mathbf{b} = \begin{pmatrix} -2 \\ 1 \end{pmatrix}$,
$\mathbf{a.b} = a_1b_1 + a_2b_2 = (1 \times (-2)) + (4 \times 1) = 2$

b) $\mathbf{a.b} = (2 \times 1) + ((-1) \times 3) = 2 - 3 = -1$

c) $\mathbf{a.b} = ((-2) \times (-1)) + ((-6) \times 2) + (1 \times 9)$
$= 2 - 12 + 9 = -1$

d) $\mathbf{a.b} = (3 \times 2) + (1 \times 3) + ((-4) \times 1) = 6 + 3 - 4 = 5$

e) $\mathbf{a.b} = (0 \times 6) + (5 \times 0) + ((-6) \times 5) = 0 + 0 - 30 = -30$

Q2 a) $8 = \begin{pmatrix} 4 \\ e \end{pmatrix} \cdot \begin{pmatrix} -2 \\ 4 \end{pmatrix} = -8 + 4e \Rightarrow 4e = 16 \Rightarrow e = 4$

b) $8 = -14 - f + 15 \Rightarrow f = -7$

c) $8 = -2g - 10 + 12 \Rightarrow g = -3$

Q3 a) Scalar product $= 40 + 40 = 80$
Perpendicular vectors have a scalar product of 0, so the vectors are not perpendicular.

b) Scalar product $= 0 + 0 + 0 = 0$, perpendicular.

c) Scalar product $= -6 + 24 - 10 = 8$, not perpendicular.

d) Scalar product $= -2 - 2 + 4 = 0$, perpendicular.

e) Scalar product $= 0 + 50 + 0 = 50$, not perpendicular.

Q4 a) $4\mathbf{i} + a\mathbf{j}$ and $5\mathbf{i} - 10\mathbf{j}$ are perpendicular, so their scalar product is 0.
$0 = (4\mathbf{i} + a\mathbf{j}).(5\mathbf{i} - 10\mathbf{j}) = 20 - 10a \Rightarrow 10a = 20$
$$\Rightarrow a = 2$$

b) $0 = 10b + 6 - 36 \Rightarrow b = 3$

c) $0 = -2 + 3 + c \Rightarrow c = -1$

d) $0 = -3d + 27 - 48 \Rightarrow d = -7$

Q5 Let $\mathbf{a} = \begin{pmatrix} 4 \\ -1 \\ 3 \end{pmatrix}$ and $\mathbf{b} = \begin{pmatrix} -12 \\ 3 \\ -9 \end{pmatrix}$.

$\mathbf{a.b} = -48 - 3 - 27 = -78$
$|\mathbf{a}| = \sqrt{4^2 + (-1)^2 + 3^2} = \sqrt{26}$
$|\mathbf{b}| = \sqrt{(-12)^2 + 3^2 + (-9)^2} = \sqrt{234}$
$|\mathbf{a}||\mathbf{b}| = \sqrt{26}\sqrt{234} = \sqrt{26}\sqrt{3}\sqrt{78} = \sqrt{78}\sqrt{78} = 78$
$|\mathbf{a}||\mathbf{b}| = -\mathbf{a.b}$ so $\mathbf{a}$ and $\mathbf{b}$ are parallel.

Q6 We need to find vectors $(\alpha\mathbf{i} + \beta\mathbf{j} + \gamma\mathbf{k})$ so that:
$(3\mathbf{i} - \mathbf{j} - 2\mathbf{k}).(\alpha\mathbf{i} + \beta\mathbf{j} + \gamma\mathbf{k}) = 3\alpha - \beta - 2\gamma = 0$
So pick any α, β and γ so that this holds, e.g.
fix $\alpha = 1$ and $\beta = 1 \Rightarrow 3 - 1 - 2\gamma = 0 \Rightarrow \gamma = 1$
So $\mathbf{i} + \mathbf{j} + \mathbf{k}$ is perpendicular to $3\mathbf{i} - \mathbf{j} - 2\mathbf{k}$
You can find other perpendicular vectors by fixing any two of the coefficients as other values.
To make sure they're not parallel to the first vector you find, you could keep $\alpha = 1$ and just vary β.

Exercise 4.3 —
Finding angles between vectors

Q1 a) $|\mathbf{p}| = \sqrt{4^2 + 3^2} = 5$, $|\mathbf{q}| = \sqrt{12^2 + 5^2} = 13$
$\mathbf{p.q} = (4 \times 12) + (3 \times 5) = 63$

Using the formula $\cos\theta = \frac{\mathbf{p.q}}{|\mathbf{p}||\mathbf{q}|}$,

we get $\cos\theta = \frac{63}{5 \times 13} \Rightarrow \theta = 14.3°$ to 1 d.p.

b) $|\mathbf{r}| = \sqrt{2^2 + (-1)^2} = \sqrt{5}$, $|\mathbf{s}| = \sqrt{(-6)^2 + 3^2} = \sqrt{45}$

  $\mathbf{r.s} = -12 - 3 = -15$

  $\cos\theta = \dfrac{-15}{\sqrt{5}\sqrt{45}} \Rightarrow \theta = 180.0°$ to 1 d.p.

c) $|\mathbf{a}| = \sqrt{(-2)^2 + (-4)^2} = 2\sqrt{5}$,

  $|\mathbf{b}| = \sqrt{3^2 + (-1)^2} = \sqrt{10}$

  $\mathbf{a.b} = -6 + 4 = -2$

  $\cos\theta = \dfrac{-2}{2\sqrt{5}\sqrt{10}} \Rightarrow \theta = 98.1°$ to 1 d.p.

Q2 a) $|\mathbf{a}| = 3$, $|\mathbf{b}| = 7$, $\mathbf{a.b} = 8$,

  so $\cos\theta = \dfrac{8}{3 \times 7} \Rightarrow \theta = 67.6°$ to 1 d.p.

b) $\cos\theta = \dfrac{38}{9 \times 11} \Rightarrow \theta = 67.4°$ to 1 d.p.

c) $\cos\theta = \dfrac{49}{11 \times 9} \Rightarrow \theta = 60.3°$ to 1 d.p.

d) $\cos\theta = \dfrac{-5}{19\sqrt{51}} \Rightarrow \theta = 92.1°$ to 1 d.p.

e) $\cos\theta = \dfrac{126}{27 \times 6} \Rightarrow \theta = 38.9°$ to 1 d.p.

Q3 a) $\vec{AB} = \vec{OB} - \vec{OA} = \begin{pmatrix} -1 \\ 3 \end{pmatrix} - \begin{pmatrix} -4 \\ -1 \end{pmatrix} = \begin{pmatrix} 3 \\ 4 \end{pmatrix}$

  $\vec{AC} = \vec{OC} - \vec{OA} = \begin{pmatrix} 4 \\ 5 \end{pmatrix} - \begin{pmatrix} -4 \\ -1 \end{pmatrix} = \begin{pmatrix} 8 \\ 6 \end{pmatrix}$

b) $|\vec{AB}| = \sqrt{3^2 + 4^2} = 5$, $|\vec{AC}| = \sqrt{8^2 + 6^2} = 10$

c) $(\vec{AB}).(\vec{AC}) = 24 + 24 = 48$

d) $\cos\theta = \dfrac{48}{5 \times 10} \Rightarrow \theta = 16.260...°$,

  so angle BAC is 16° to the nearest degree.

Q4 a) $\vec{PQ} = \mathbf{q} - \mathbf{p} = 2\mathbf{i} + 9\mathbf{j} + 14\mathbf{k}$

  $\vec{PR} = \mathbf{r} - \mathbf{p} = 2\mathbf{i} + 6\mathbf{j} - 2\mathbf{k}$

b) $|\vec{PQ}| = \sqrt{281}$, $|\vec{PR}| = \sqrt{44}$

c) $(\vec{PQ}).(\vec{PR}) = 4 + 54 - 28 = 30$

d) $\cos(QPR) = \dfrac{30}{\sqrt{281} \times \sqrt{44}}$

  $\Rightarrow$ Angle QPR = 74.3° to 3 significant figures.

Q5 a) $\vec{TS} = -\mathbf{t} + \mathbf{s} = \begin{pmatrix} -2 \\ -2 \\ 3 \end{pmatrix}$ and $\vec{RS} = -\mathbf{r} + \mathbf{s} = \begin{pmatrix} 4 \\ -1 \\ 2 \end{pmatrix}$

  $(\vec{TS}).(\vec{RS}) = \begin{pmatrix} -2 \\ -2 \\ 3 \end{pmatrix}.\begin{pmatrix} 4 \\ -1 \\ 2 \end{pmatrix} = -8 + 2 + 6 = 0$

b) TS is perpendicular to RS because their scalar product is zero. So TS is a line of symmetry of triangle TRU since TRU is isosceles with TR = TU. So S is the midpoint of RU.

c) $\vec{OU} = \vec{OS} + \vec{SU}$ and S is the midpoint of RU, therefore $\vec{SU} = \vec{RS}$.

  So $\vec{OU} = \vec{OS} + \vec{RS} = \begin{pmatrix} 1 \\ -1 \\ 3 \end{pmatrix} + \begin{pmatrix} 4 \\ -1 \\ 2 \end{pmatrix} = \begin{pmatrix} 5 \\ -2 \\ 5 \end{pmatrix}$

Q6 a) $\vec{OD} = \vec{OA} + \vec{AD} = \vec{OA} + \vec{BC}$ since ABCD is a parallelogram, so AD and BC are parallel and the same length.

  $\vec{OD} = \vec{OA} + \vec{BC} = \vec{OA} + \vec{OC} - \vec{OB}$

   $= \mathbf{i}(-4 + 6 - 0) + \mathbf{j}(5 + 13 - 4) + \mathbf{k}(-6 + 0 - 2)$

   $= 2\mathbf{i} + 14\mathbf{j} - 8\mathbf{k}$

b) $\vec{AB} = \mathbf{b} - \mathbf{a} = \mathbf{i}(0 - -4) + \mathbf{j}(4 - 5) + \mathbf{k}(2 - -6)$

   $= 4\mathbf{i} - \mathbf{j} + 8\mathbf{k}$,

$\vec{AD} = \mathbf{d} - \mathbf{a} = \mathbf{i}(2 - -4) + \mathbf{j}(14 - 5) + \mathbf{k}(-8 - -6)$

   $= 6\mathbf{i} + 9\mathbf{j} - 2\mathbf{k}$

c) $|\vec{AB}| = 9$, $|\vec{AD}| = 11$

d) $\vec{AB} \cdot \vec{AD} = (4 \times 6) + (-1 \times 9) + (8 \times -2) = -1$

  $\cos(\angle BAD) = \dfrac{-1}{9 \times 11} \Rightarrow \angle BAD = 90.58°$ (to 4 s.f.)

Q7 a) O is the midpoint of AB, so $\vec{AO} = \vec{OB} = \mathbf{p}$, then:
  $\vec{AC} = \vec{AO} + \vec{OC} = \mathbf{p} + \mathbf{q}$, $\vec{CB} = \vec{OB} - \vec{OC} = \mathbf{p} - \mathbf{q}$

b) Apply the commutative and distributive laws:
  *Remember that the commutative law says that it doesn't matter which way round you multiply the vectors **p.q** or **q.p** and the distributive law says that you can multiply out the brackets.*

  $(\vec{AC}).(\vec{CB}) = (\mathbf{p} + \mathbf{q}).(\mathbf{p} - \mathbf{q}) = \mathbf{p}.(\mathbf{p} - \mathbf{q}) + \mathbf{q}.(\mathbf{p} - \mathbf{q})$

   $= \mathbf{p.p} + \mathbf{p}.(-\mathbf{q}) + \mathbf{q.p} + \mathbf{q}.(-\mathbf{q})$

   $= \mathbf{p.p} - \mathbf{p.q} + \mathbf{q.p} - \mathbf{q.q}$

   $= \mathbf{p.p} - \mathbf{q.p} + \mathbf{q.p} - \mathbf{q.q} = \mathbf{p.p} - \mathbf{q.q}$

c) $\mathbf{p.p} = |\mathbf{p}||\mathbf{p}|\cos 0 = |\mathbf{p}||\mathbf{p}| \times 1 = |\mathbf{p}|^2 = r^2$ because the length of $\mathbf{p}$ is the radius r of the circle.
  The angle between a vector and itself is $0°$ because that's how much you have to rotate a vector by so that it's pointing in the same direction as itself.
  Also $\mathbf{q.q} = |\mathbf{q}||\mathbf{q}|\cos 0 = |\mathbf{q}||\mathbf{q}| \times 1 = |\mathbf{q}|^2 = r^2$
  Then $(\vec{AC}).(\vec{CB}) = \mathbf{p.p} - \mathbf{q.q} = r^2 - r^2 = 0$
  So AC is perpendicular to CB, i.e. angle ACB = 90°.

Exercise 4.4 —
Finding the angle between two lines

Q1 a) The direction vectors of the lines are:

  $2\mathbf{i} - 4\mathbf{j} - 6\mathbf{k} = \begin{pmatrix} 2 \\ -4 \\ -6 \end{pmatrix}$ and $-\mathbf{i} + 2\mathbf{j} + 3\mathbf{k} = \begin{pmatrix} -1 \\ 2 \\ 3 \end{pmatrix}$.

  Because $\begin{pmatrix} 2 \\ -4 \\ -6 \end{pmatrix} = -2\begin{pmatrix} -1 \\ 2 \\ 3 \end{pmatrix}$ the vectors are parallel,

  so the lines are parallel.

b) The direction vectors of the lines are:

  $\begin{pmatrix} 4 \\ -1 \\ 1 \end{pmatrix}$ and $\begin{pmatrix} 1 \\ -4 \\ 0 \end{pmatrix}$

  The lines are not parallel as one direction vector has zero $\mathbf{k}$ component and the other doesn't.
  Scalar product = 4 + 4 + 0 = 8, so they're not perpendicular.
  The lines are neither parallel nor perpendicular.

c) The direction vectors of the lines are:

  $2\mathbf{j} - 7\mathbf{k} = \begin{pmatrix} 0 \\ 2 \\ -7 \end{pmatrix}$ and $2\mathbf{i} - 7\mathbf{k} \begin{pmatrix} 2 \\ 0 \\ -7 \end{pmatrix}$

  The lines are not parallel as one direction vector has zero $\mathbf{i}$ component and the other doesn't.
  Scalar product = 0 + 0 + 49 = 49, so they're not perpendicular.
  The lines are neither parallel nor perpendicular.

d) The direction vectors of the lines are:

  $\mathbf{i} + \mathbf{j} = \begin{pmatrix} 1 \\ 1 \\ 0 \end{pmatrix}$ and $\mathbf{i} - \mathbf{j} + 2\mathbf{k} = \begin{pmatrix} 1 \\ -1 \\ 2 \end{pmatrix}$

Scalar product = $1 - 1 + 0 = 0$
The vectors are perpendicular, so the lines are perpendicular.

e) The direction vectors of the lines are: $\begin{pmatrix} 0 \\ 0 \\ 4 \end{pmatrix}$ and $\begin{pmatrix} -4 \\ 8 \\ 0 \end{pmatrix}$
Scalar product = $0 + 0 + 0 = 0$.
The lines are perpendicular.

Q2 a) $\mathbf{b}_1 = \begin{pmatrix} 2 \\ 2 \\ 1 \end{pmatrix}$, $\mathbf{b}_2 = \begin{pmatrix} 2 \\ 3 \\ 6 \end{pmatrix}$

$|\mathbf{b}_1| = 3$, $|\mathbf{b}_2| = 7$, $(\mathbf{b}_1).(\mathbf{b}_2) = 16$

$\cos \theta = \dfrac{16}{3 \times 7} \Rightarrow \theta = 40.4°$ to 1 d.p.

b) $\mathbf{b}_1 = 4\mathbf{i} + 4\mathbf{j} - 7\mathbf{k} = \begin{pmatrix} 4 \\ 4 \\ -7 \end{pmatrix}$, $\mathbf{b}_2 = 8\mathbf{i} + \mathbf{j} - 4\mathbf{k} = \begin{pmatrix} 8 \\ 1 \\ -4 \end{pmatrix}$

$\cos \theta = \dfrac{64}{9 \times 9} \Rightarrow \theta = 37.8°$ to 1 d.p.

c) $\mathbf{b}_1 = \begin{pmatrix} 6 \\ -7 \\ 5 \end{pmatrix}$, $\mathbf{b}_2 = \begin{pmatrix} 2 \\ 1 \\ -1 \end{pmatrix}$

$(\mathbf{b}_1).(\mathbf{b}_2) = 12 - 7 - 5 = 0 \Rightarrow \theta = 90°$

d) $\mathbf{b}_1 = 7\mathbf{i} - 6\mathbf{j} + 6\mathbf{k} = \begin{pmatrix} 7 \\ -6 \\ 6 \end{pmatrix}$, $\mathbf{b}_2 = -4\mathbf{i} + 2\mathbf{j} - 2\mathbf{k} = \begin{pmatrix} -4 \\ 2 \\ -2 \end{pmatrix}$

$\cos \theta = \dfrac{-52}{11 \times 2\sqrt{6}} \Rightarrow \theta = 164.8°$ to 1 d.p.
Acute angle: $180 - \theta = 15.2°$

e) $\mathbf{b}_1 = -3\mathbf{i} - 5\mathbf{j} + 2\mathbf{k} = \begin{pmatrix} -3 \\ -5 \\ 2 \end{pmatrix}$, $\mathbf{b}_2 = 2\mathbf{i} + \mathbf{k} = \begin{pmatrix} 2 \\ 0 \\ 1 \end{pmatrix}$

$\cos \theta = \dfrac{-4}{\sqrt{38}\sqrt{5}} \Rightarrow \theta = 106.9°$ to 1 d.p.
Acute angle: $180 - \theta = 73.1°$

Q3 The lines are perpendicular so:

$0 = \begin{pmatrix} 4 \\ 6 \\ -1 \end{pmatrix}.\begin{pmatrix} 5 \\ -2 \\ z \end{pmatrix} = 20 - 12 - z \Rightarrow z = 8$

Q4 a) Line containing AB:
E.g. $\mathbf{r} = \overrightarrow{OA} + \lambda\overrightarrow{AB}$

$= \begin{pmatrix} -1 \\ -2 \\ 6 \end{pmatrix} + \lambda\left(\begin{pmatrix} p \\ -1 \\ 3 \end{pmatrix} - \begin{pmatrix} -1 \\ -2 \\ 6 \end{pmatrix}\right)$

$\mathbf{r} = \begin{pmatrix} -1 \\ -2 \\ 6 \end{pmatrix} + \lambda\begin{pmatrix} p+1 \\ 1 \\ -3 \end{pmatrix}$

Line containing BC: E.g. $\mathbf{r} = \begin{pmatrix} -1 \\ 0 \\ 2 \end{pmatrix} + \mu\begin{pmatrix} p+1 \\ -1 \\ 1 \end{pmatrix}$

b) The angle ABC is $90°$ so the lines are perpendicular.
Taking the scalar product of the direction vectors:

$0 = \begin{pmatrix} p+1 \\ 1 \\ -3 \end{pmatrix}.\begin{pmatrix} p+1 \\ -1 \\ 1 \end{pmatrix} = (p+1)^2 - 1 - 3 = p^2 + 2p - 3$

$p^2 + 2p - 3 = 0 \Rightarrow (p+3)(p-1) = 0$
So $p = -3$ or $p = 1$

Q5 a) $\overrightarrow{OC} = \dfrac{3}{2}\overrightarrow{OA} = \dfrac{3}{2}\begin{pmatrix} 4 \\ 2 \\ -2 \end{pmatrix} = \begin{pmatrix} 6 \\ 3 \\ -3 \end{pmatrix}$

$\overrightarrow{OD} = 2\overrightarrow{OB} = 2\begin{pmatrix} -1 \\ 3 \\ 1 \end{pmatrix} = \begin{pmatrix} -2 \\ 6 \\ 2 \end{pmatrix}$

b) L_1: E.g.

$\mathbf{r} = \begin{pmatrix} 4 \\ 2 \\ -2 \end{pmatrix} + \lambda\left(\begin{pmatrix} -2 \\ 6 \\ 2 \end{pmatrix} - \begin{pmatrix} 4 \\ 2 \\ -2 \end{pmatrix}\right) = \begin{pmatrix} 4 \\ 2 \\ -2 \end{pmatrix} + \lambda\begin{pmatrix} -6 \\ 4 \\ 4 \end{pmatrix}$

L_2: E.g.

$\mathbf{r} = \begin{pmatrix} -1 \\ 3 \\ 1 \end{pmatrix} + \mu\left(\begin{pmatrix} 6 \\ 3 \\ -3 \end{pmatrix} - \begin{pmatrix} -1 \\ 3 \\ 1 \end{pmatrix}\right) = \begin{pmatrix} -1 \\ 3 \\ 1 \end{pmatrix} + \mu\begin{pmatrix} 7 \\ 0 \\ -4 \end{pmatrix}$

c) If the lines are intersecting they intersect when

$\begin{pmatrix} 4 \\ 2 \\ -2 \end{pmatrix} + \lambda\begin{pmatrix} -6 \\ 4 \\ 4 \end{pmatrix} = \begin{pmatrix} -1 \\ 3 \\ 1 \end{pmatrix} + \mu\begin{pmatrix} 7 \\ 0 \\ -4 \end{pmatrix}$

This gives the equations: $\quad 4 - 6\lambda = -1 + 7\mu$
$2 + 4\lambda = 3$
$-2 + 4\lambda = 1 - 4\mu$

The second equation gives $\lambda = \dfrac{1}{4}$,
putting this into the first equation gives $\mu = \dfrac{1}{2}$.
Subbing these values into the third equation
gives: $-2 + 4\left(\dfrac{1}{4}\right) = 1 - 4\left(\dfrac{1}{2}\right) \Rightarrow -1 = -1$
This is true so all of the equations are solved by the same values and the lines intersect.

d) $\cos \theta = \dfrac{-58}{\sqrt{68}\sqrt{65}} \Rightarrow \theta = 150.7°$ to 1 d.p.
Acute angle: $180 - 150.7 = 29.3°$

Q6 a) A has position vector $\begin{pmatrix} 3 \\ 8 \\ -5 \end{pmatrix}$ and B has

position vector $\begin{pmatrix} 8 \\ -2 \\ 0 \end{pmatrix}$.

L: E.g.

$\mathbf{r} = \begin{pmatrix} 3 \\ 8 \\ -5 \end{pmatrix} + \lambda\left(\begin{pmatrix} 8 \\ -2 \\ 0 \end{pmatrix} - \begin{pmatrix} 3 \\ 8 \\ -5 \end{pmatrix}\right) = \begin{pmatrix} 3 \\ 8 \\ -5 \end{pmatrix} + \lambda\begin{pmatrix} 5 \\ -10 \\ 5 \end{pmatrix}$

b) P lies on L so P has position vector:

$\begin{pmatrix} 3 \\ 8 \\ -5 \end{pmatrix} + \lambda\begin{pmatrix} 5 \\ -10 \\ 5 \end{pmatrix} = \begin{pmatrix} 3+5\lambda \\ 8-10\lambda \\ -5+5\lambda \end{pmatrix}$ for some λ.

OP is perpendicular to L so the scalar product of $\overrightarrow{OP}$ and the direction vector of L must be zero:

$0 = \begin{pmatrix} 5 \\ -10 \\ 5 \end{pmatrix}.\begin{pmatrix} 3+5\lambda \\ 8-10\lambda \\ -5+5\lambda \end{pmatrix}$

$= 5(3 + 5\lambda) - 10(8 - 10\lambda) + 5(-5 + 5\lambda)$
$\Rightarrow 150\lambda = 90 \Rightarrow \lambda = \dfrac{3}{5}$

So $\overrightarrow{OP} = \begin{pmatrix} 3+5\lambda \\ 8-10\lambda \\ -5+5\lambda \end{pmatrix} = \begin{pmatrix} 3+3 \\ 8-6 \\ -5+3 \end{pmatrix} = \begin{pmatrix} 6 \\ 2 \\ -2 \end{pmatrix}$,

and the coordinates of P are $(6, 2, -2)$.

c) The distance of P from O is:
$|\overrightarrow{OP}| = \sqrt{6^2 + 2^2 + (-2)^2} = \sqrt{44} = \sqrt{4}\sqrt{11} = 2\sqrt{11}$

Q7 a) Vector equation of l is:
$\mathbf{r} = (-3\mathbf{i} + 2\mathbf{j} + 4\mathbf{k}) + t((5\mathbf{i} - \mathbf{j} - \mathbf{k}) - (-3\mathbf{i} + 2\mathbf{j} + 4\mathbf{k}))$
$\Rightarrow \mathbf{r} = (-3\mathbf{i} + 2\mathbf{j} + 4\mathbf{k}) + t(8\mathbf{i} - 3\mathbf{j} - 5\mathbf{k})$

b) $\overrightarrow{BA} = 7\mathbf{i} - 8\mathbf{j} - 2\mathbf{k}$, $|\overrightarrow{BA}| = \sqrt{117}$, $|\overrightarrow{BC}| = \sqrt{98}$
$(\overrightarrow{BA}).(\overrightarrow{BC}) = 90$, $\cos\theta = \dfrac{90}{\sqrt{117}\sqrt{98}}$
$\theta = 32.8°$ to 1 d.p.

c)

The shortest distance from A to l is the length of the line segment AP where P lies on l and AP is perpendicular to l.
Find the length of AP using trig:
First, $|\overrightarrow{AB}| = \sqrt{117}$ from part b).
Now AP is the opposite side to angle ABP so:
Opposite = $\sin\theta \times$ Hypotenuse
$AP = \sin(32.8) \times \sqrt{117} = 5.86$ to 2 d.p.

Review Exercise — Chapter 7

Q1 *Any multiples of the vectors will do:*
  a) e.g. $\mathbf{a}$ and $4\mathbf{a}$
  b) e.g. $6\mathbf{i} + 8\mathbf{j} - 4\mathbf{k}$ and $9\mathbf{i} + 12\mathbf{j} - 6\mathbf{k}$
  c) e.g. $\begin{pmatrix} 2 \\ 4 \\ -2 \end{pmatrix}$ and $\begin{pmatrix} 4 \\ 8 \\ -4 \end{pmatrix}$

Q2 a) $\overrightarrow{AB} = \overrightarrow{AO} + \overrightarrow{OB} = -\overrightarrow{OA} + \overrightarrow{OB} = \mathbf{b} - \mathbf{a}$
Parts b) − d) are answered using the same method as a)
  b) $\overrightarrow{BA} = -\overrightarrow{OB} + \overrightarrow{OA} = \mathbf{a} - \mathbf{b}$
    or $\overrightarrow{BA} = -\overrightarrow{AB} = -(\mathbf{b} - \mathbf{a}) = \mathbf{a} - \mathbf{b}$
  c) $\overrightarrow{CB} = -\overrightarrow{OC} + \overrightarrow{OB} = \mathbf{b} - \mathbf{c}$
  d) $\overrightarrow{AC} = -\overrightarrow{OA} + \overrightarrow{OC} = \mathbf{c} - \mathbf{a}$

Q3 a) $\overrightarrow{HO}$ is parallel to $\overrightarrow{OE}$ and has the same length (as the hexagon is regular), so $\overrightarrow{HO} = \overrightarrow{OE} = \mathbf{e}$ and
$\overrightarrow{HE} = \overrightarrow{HO} + \overrightarrow{OE} = \mathbf{e} + \mathbf{e} = 2\mathbf{e}$

  b) $\overrightarrow{OG}$ is parallel to $\overrightarrow{DO}$ and has the same length so
$\overrightarrow{DG} = \overrightarrow{DO} + \overrightarrow{OG} = -\mathbf{d} + (-\mathbf{d}) = -2\mathbf{d}$

  c) $\overrightarrow{ED} = \overrightarrow{EO} + \overrightarrow{OD} = -\mathbf{e} + \mathbf{d} = \mathbf{d} - \mathbf{e}$

  d) $\overrightarrow{CO}$ is parallel to $\overrightarrow{DE}$ and has the same length so
$\overrightarrow{CE} = \overrightarrow{CO} + \overrightarrow{OE} = \overrightarrow{DE} + \overrightarrow{OE}$
$= -\overrightarrow{ED} + \overrightarrow{OE} = -(\mathbf{d} - \mathbf{e}) + \mathbf{e} = 2\mathbf{e} - \mathbf{d}$

  e) $\overrightarrow{EF}$ is parallel to $\overrightarrow{DO}$ and has the same length so
$\overrightarrow{DF} = \overrightarrow{DE} + \overrightarrow{EF} = \overrightarrow{DE} + \overrightarrow{DO}$
$= -\overrightarrow{ED} - \overrightarrow{OD} = -(\mathbf{d} - \mathbf{e}) - \mathbf{d} = \mathbf{e} - 2\mathbf{d}$

Q4 $2\mathbf{i} - 4\mathbf{j} + 5\mathbf{k}$

Q5 $\overrightarrow{XO} = -\overrightarrow{OX} = -(6\mathbf{i} - \mathbf{j}) = -6\mathbf{i} + \mathbf{j} = \begin{pmatrix} -6 \\ 1 \\ 0 \end{pmatrix}$
$\overrightarrow{YO} = -\overrightarrow{OY} = -(4\mathbf{i} - 4\mathbf{j} + 7\mathbf{k}) = -4\mathbf{i} + 4\mathbf{j} - 7\mathbf{k} = \begin{pmatrix} -4 \\ 4 \\ -7 \end{pmatrix}$

Q6 $\overrightarrow{RS} = \overrightarrow{OS} - \overrightarrow{OR} = \begin{pmatrix} -5 \\ -7 \end{pmatrix} - \begin{pmatrix} 3 \\ -1 \end{pmatrix} = \begin{pmatrix} -8 \\ -6 \end{pmatrix}$
$|\overrightarrow{RS}| = \sqrt{(-8)^2 + (-6)^2} = \sqrt{64 + 36} = \sqrt{100} = 10$

Another way to answer this question is to put the coordinates of R and S straight into the formula for the distance between two points: $\sqrt{(x_2 - x_1)^2 + (y_2 - y_1)^2}$.

Q7 a) $\sqrt{3^2 + 4^2 + (-2)^2} = \sqrt{29}$
  b) $\sqrt{1^2 + 2^2 + (-1)^2} = \sqrt{6}$

Q8 a) $\sqrt{1^2 + 2^2 + 3^2} = \sqrt{14}$
  b) $\sqrt{3^2 + (-1)^2 + (-2)^2} = \sqrt{14}$
  c) $|\overrightarrow{AB}|$ is the distance between A and B, which is given by the formula:
$\sqrt{(3 - 1)^2 + (-1 - 2)^2 + (-2 - 3)^2} = \sqrt{38}$

Q9 $\begin{pmatrix} \frac{2}{3} \\ \frac{2}{3} \\ -\frac{1}{3} \end{pmatrix}$ is the unit vector in the direction of $\overrightarrow{XY}$,
so you know that $\overrightarrow{XY} = |\overrightarrow{XY}| \begin{pmatrix} \frac{2}{3} \\ \frac{2}{3} \\ -\frac{1}{3} \end{pmatrix} = 6 \begin{pmatrix} \frac{2}{3} \\ \frac{2}{3} \\ -\frac{1}{3} \end{pmatrix} = \begin{pmatrix} 4 \\ 4 \\ -2 \end{pmatrix}$
Then $\overrightarrow{OY} = \overrightarrow{OX} + \overrightarrow{XY} = \begin{pmatrix} -2 \\ 1 \\ 0 \end{pmatrix} + \begin{pmatrix} 4 \\ 4 \\ -2 \end{pmatrix} = \begin{pmatrix} 2 \\ 5 \\ -2 \end{pmatrix}$,
and the coordinates of Y are (2, 5, −2).

Q10 a) $\mathbf{r} = (4\mathbf{i} + \mathbf{j} + 2\mathbf{k}) + t(3\mathbf{i} + \mathbf{j} - \mathbf{k})$ or $\mathbf{r} = \begin{pmatrix} 4 \\ 1 \\ 2 \end{pmatrix} + t \begin{pmatrix} 3 \\ 1 \\ -1 \end{pmatrix}$

  b) $\mathbf{r} = (2\mathbf{i} - \mathbf{j} + \mathbf{k}) + t((2\mathbf{j} + 3\mathbf{k}) - (2\mathbf{i} - \mathbf{j} + \mathbf{k}))$
$\Rightarrow \mathbf{r} = (2\mathbf{i} - \mathbf{j} + \mathbf{k}) + t(-2\mathbf{i} + 3\mathbf{j} + 2\mathbf{k})$
or $\mathbf{r} = \begin{pmatrix} 2 \\ -1 \\ 1 \end{pmatrix} + t \begin{pmatrix} -2 \\ 3 \\ 2 \end{pmatrix}$

In Q10 you're just plugging the vectors you're given into the formula for a vector line equation: $\mathbf{r} = \mathbf{a} + t\mathbf{b}$.

Q11 *All of the points are found by choosing a value for t, any points found in this way will do.*
The coordinates of the points given by $\mathbf{r}$ are:
$(3 + t(-1), 2 + t(3), 4 + t(0))$
E.g. If $t = 1$ the coordinates of the point given by $\mathbf{r}$ are: $(3 + 1(-1), 2 + 1(3), 4 + 1(0)) = (2, 5, 4)$
If $t = 2$ the coordinates of the point given by $\mathbf{r}$ are: $(3 + 2(-1), 2 + 2(3), 4 + 2(0)) = (1, 8, 4)$
If $t = -1$ the coordinates of the point given by $\mathbf{r}$ are: $(3 + -1(-1), 2 + -1(3), 4 + -1(0)) = (4, -1, 4)$

Q12 a)

  b) $\overrightarrow{OB} = \frac{1}{2}\overrightarrow{OA} = \frac{1}{2}(2\mathbf{i} + 8\mathbf{j} - 4\mathbf{k}) = \mathbf{i} + 4\mathbf{j} - 2\mathbf{k}$
$\overrightarrow{OC} = 2\overrightarrow{OA} = 2(2\mathbf{i} + 8\mathbf{j} - 4\mathbf{k}) = 4\mathbf{i} + 16\mathbf{j} - 8\mathbf{k}$
$\overrightarrow{OD} = -\overrightarrow{OA} = -(2\mathbf{i} + 8\mathbf{j} - 4\mathbf{k}) = -2\mathbf{i} - 8\mathbf{j} + 4\mathbf{k}$

  c) Line L passes through the origin so an equation is:
$\mathbf{r} = t(2\mathbf{i} + 8\mathbf{j} - 4\mathbf{k})$.

Q13 a) $\overrightarrow{PQ} = \begin{pmatrix} 5 \\ -2 \\ -1 \end{pmatrix} - \begin{pmatrix} 3 \\ -5 \\ 2 \end{pmatrix} = \begin{pmatrix} 2 \\ 3 \\ -3 \end{pmatrix}$

b) The line passes through P and is parallel to $\overrightarrow{PQ}$ so an equation is,

e.g: $\mathbf{r} = \overrightarrow{OP} + t\overrightarrow{PQ} = \begin{pmatrix} 3 \\ -5 \\ 2 \end{pmatrix} + t\begin{pmatrix} 2 \\ 3 \\ -3 \end{pmatrix}$

Q14 a) E.g. an equation for line m is $\mathbf{r} = \begin{pmatrix} 1 \\ 1 \\ 3 \end{pmatrix} + \lambda\begin{pmatrix} 3 \\ -1 \\ 4 \end{pmatrix}$,

an equation for line n is $\mathbf{r} = \begin{pmatrix} 9 \\ -3 \\ 9 \end{pmatrix} + \mu\begin{pmatrix} -1 \\ 1 \\ 1 \end{pmatrix}$

The lines aren't parallel as their direction vectors aren't scalar multiples of one another.

The lines intersect when $\begin{pmatrix} 1+3\lambda \\ 1-\lambda \\ 3+4\lambda \end{pmatrix} = \begin{pmatrix} 9-\mu \\ -3+\mu \\ 9+\mu \end{pmatrix}$

So solving these equations:

$1 - \lambda = -3 + \mu \Rightarrow \mu = 4 - \lambda$

$1 + 3\lambda = 9 - \mu \Rightarrow 1 + 3\lambda = 9 - (4 - \lambda) = 5 + \lambda$

$\Rightarrow 2\lambda = 4 \Rightarrow \lambda = 2$

Plugging this value back into the first equation gives:

$1 + (3 \times 2) = 9 - \mu \Rightarrow \mu = 2$

Plugging the λ and μ values into the third equation gives:

$3 + (4 \times 2) = 9 + 2 \Rightarrow 11 = 11$

This is true so $\lambda = 2$, $\mu = 2$ solve all the equations. So the point of intersection has position vector:

$\begin{pmatrix} 1+(3\times2) \\ 1-2 \\ 3+(4\times2) \end{pmatrix} = \begin{pmatrix} 9-2 \\ -3+2 \\ 9+2 \end{pmatrix} = \begin{pmatrix} 7 \\ -1 \\ 11 \end{pmatrix}$,

and coordinates (7, −1, 11).

b) Using the formula for the distance between two points:

$AC^2 = (7 - 1)^2 + (-1 - 1)^2 + (11 - 3)^2$
$= 36 + 4 + 64 = 104$

$CB^2 = (9 - 7)^2 + (-3 - (-1))^2 + (9 - 11)^2$
$= 4 + 4 + 4 = 12$

$BA^2 = (1 - 9)^2 + (1 - (-3))^2 + (3 - 9)^2$
$= 64 + 16 + 36 = 116$

So $BA^2 = 116 = 104 + 12 = AC^2 + CB^2$

Therefore triangle ABC is right-angled.

Q15 a) $(3\mathbf{i} + 4\mathbf{j}) \cdot (\mathbf{i} - 2\mathbf{j} + 3\mathbf{k}) = (3 \times 1) + (4 \times (-2)) + (0 \times 3)$
$= 3 - 8 + 0 = -5$

b) $\begin{pmatrix} 4 \\ 2 \\ 1 \end{pmatrix} \cdot \begin{pmatrix} 3 \\ -4 \\ -3 \end{pmatrix} = (4 \times 3) + (2 \times -4) + (1 \times -3) = 1$

Q16 a) $\overrightarrow{PQ} = -\mathbf{a} + \mathbf{b} = \mathbf{b} - \mathbf{a}$

b) Using the commutative and distributive laws and the definition of scalar product:

$(\mathbf{b} - \mathbf{a}) \cdot (\mathbf{b} - \mathbf{a}) = \mathbf{b}.\mathbf{b} + \mathbf{b}.(-\mathbf{a}) + (-\mathbf{a}).\mathbf{b} + (-\mathbf{a}).(-\mathbf{a})$
$= \mathbf{b}.\mathbf{b} - \mathbf{a}.\mathbf{b} - \mathbf{a}.\mathbf{b} + \mathbf{a}.\mathbf{a}$
$= |\mathbf{b}|^2(\cos 0) - 2|\mathbf{a}||\mathbf{b}|\cos\theta + |\mathbf{a}|^2(\cos 0)$
$= |\mathbf{b}|^2 - 2|\mathbf{a}||\mathbf{b}|\cos\theta + |\mathbf{a}|^2$
$= b^2 - 2ab\cos\theta + a^2$

c) $c^2 = |\overrightarrow{PQ}|^2$, and

$(\mathbf{b} - \mathbf{a}) \cdot (\mathbf{b} - \mathbf{a}) = \overrightarrow{PQ}.\overrightarrow{PQ} = |\overrightarrow{PQ}|^2 (\cos 0) = |\overrightarrow{PQ}|^2$,

so $c^2 = (\mathbf{b} - \mathbf{a}) \cdot (\mathbf{b} - \mathbf{a}) = b^2 - 2ab\cos\theta + a^2$
$= a^2 + b^2 - 2ab\cos\theta$

Q17 a) $\begin{pmatrix} 2 \\ -1 \\ 2 \end{pmatrix} + t\begin{pmatrix} -4 \\ 6 \\ -2 \end{pmatrix} = \begin{pmatrix} 3 \\ 2 \\ 4 \end{pmatrix} + u\begin{pmatrix} -1 \\ 3 \\ 0 \end{pmatrix}$

Where the lines intersect, these 3 equations are true:

$2 - 4t = 3 - u$
$-1 + 6t = 2 + 3u$
$2 - 2t = 4$

Solve the third equation to give $t = -1$.

Substituting $t = -1$ into the top equation gives
$2 - 4(-1) = 3 - u \Rightarrow 6 = 3 - u \Rightarrow u = -3$.

Now check $t = -1$ and $u = -3$ in the 2nd equation.
$-1 + 6t = -1 + 6(-1) = -7$ and
$2 + 3u = 2 + 3(-3) = -7$ so these values also work in the 2nd equation, so the lines intersect.

Substituting $t = -1$ in the first vector line equation (or $u = -3$ into the second vector line equation) gives the position vector of the intersection point:

$\begin{pmatrix} 6 \\ -7 \\ 4 \end{pmatrix}$

b) To find the angle between the lines, consider the direction components of the vector equations. Find their scalar product:

$\begin{pmatrix} -4 \\ 6 \\ -2 \end{pmatrix} \cdot \begin{pmatrix} -1 \\ 3 \\ 0 \end{pmatrix} = 4 + 18 + 0 = 22$

Find the magnitude of the 1st vector:
$\sqrt{(-4)^2 + 6^2 + (-2)^2} = \sqrt{56}$

and the magnitude of the 2nd vector:
$\sqrt{(-1)^2 + 3^2 + (0)^2} = \sqrt{10}$

Plugging these into the formula $\cos\theta = \dfrac{\mathbf{b}_1.\mathbf{b}_2}{|\mathbf{b}_1||\mathbf{b}_2|}$ gives:

$\cos\theta = \dfrac{22}{\sqrt{56}\sqrt{10}} \Rightarrow \theta = 21.6°$ to 1 d.p.

Q18 Find values for a, b and c that give a scalar product of 0 when the two vectors are multiplied together.

So a, b and c that solve:
$(3\mathbf{i} + 4\mathbf{j} - 2\mathbf{k}) \cdot (a\mathbf{i} + b\mathbf{j} + c\mathbf{k}) = 3a + 4b - 2c = 0$

E.g. $a = 2$, $b = 1$ and $c = 5$ give the perpendicular vector $2\mathbf{i} + \mathbf{j} + 5\mathbf{k}$

There are lots of possible answers here — to find one just pick values for a and b, then see what value of c is needed to make the scalar product zero.

Q19 a) The lines intersect when $\begin{pmatrix} x + 2\lambda \\ 1 + 2\lambda \\ 5 + 3\lambda \end{pmatrix} = \begin{pmatrix} -1 + 3\mu \\ -2 - \mu \\ 3 - 2\mu \end{pmatrix}$

Solving the bottom two equations simultaneously by taking two lots of the second equation from the third equation gives: $\lambda = -4$ and $\mu = 5$. Now plug these values into the top equation to find x:

$x + 2\lambda = -1 + 3\mu \Rightarrow x + (2 \times (-4)) = -1 + (3 \times 5)$
$\Rightarrow x = 22$

b) Plugging the value for μ into the second vector line equation gives the position vector $\begin{pmatrix} 14 \\ -7 \\ -7 \end{pmatrix}$, so the coordinates of the point of intersection are (14, −7, −7).

c) To find the angle between the lines, consider the direction components of the vector equations.

Find their scalar product:
$$\begin{pmatrix} 2 \\ 2 \\ 3 \end{pmatrix} \cdot \begin{pmatrix} 3 \\ -1 \\ -2 \end{pmatrix} = 6 - 2 - 6 = -2$$

Find the magnitude of the 1st vector:
$$\sqrt{2^2 + 2^2 + 3^2} = \sqrt{17}$$
and the magnitude of the 2nd vector:
$$\sqrt{3^2 + (-1)^2 + (-2)^2} = \sqrt{14}$$
Plugging these into the formula $\cos\theta = \dfrac{\mathbf{b_1}.\mathbf{b_2}}{|\mathbf{b_1}\|\mathbf{b_2}|}$ gives:
$$\cos\theta = \frac{-2}{\sqrt{17}\sqrt{14}} \Rightarrow \theta = 97.4° \text{ to 1 d.p.}$$
Acute angle is $180 - 97.4° = 82.6°$

Exam-Style Questions — Chapter 7

Q1 **a)** $\overrightarrow{AB} = \mathbf{b} - \mathbf{a} = \begin{pmatrix} 3 \\ 2 \\ 1 \end{pmatrix} - \begin{pmatrix} 1 \\ 5 \\ 9 \end{pmatrix} = \begin{pmatrix} 2 \\ -3 \\ -8 \end{pmatrix}$

[2 marks available — 1 mark for attempting to subtract position vector a from position vector b, 1 mark for correct answer.]

b) l_1:
$$\mathbf{r} = \mathbf{c} + \mu(\mathbf{d} - \mathbf{c}) = \begin{pmatrix} -2 \\ 4 \\ 3 \end{pmatrix} + \mu\left(\begin{pmatrix} 5 \\ -1 \\ -7 \end{pmatrix} - \begin{pmatrix} -2 \\ 4 \\ 3 \end{pmatrix}\right)$$
[1 mark]
$$\mathbf{r} = \begin{pmatrix} -2 \\ 4 \\ 3 \end{pmatrix} + \mu\begin{pmatrix} 7 \\ -5 \\ -10 \end{pmatrix} \text{ [1 mark]}$$

c) Equation of line through AB:
$$\overrightarrow{AB}: \mathbf{r} = \mathbf{a} + t(\mathbf{b} - \mathbf{a}) = \begin{pmatrix} 1 \\ 5 \\ 9 \end{pmatrix} + t\begin{pmatrix} 2 \\ -3 \\ -8 \end{pmatrix} \text{ [1 mark]}$$
At intersection of lines:
$$\begin{pmatrix} 1 \\ 5 \\ 9 \end{pmatrix} + t\begin{pmatrix} 2 \\ -3 \\ -8 \end{pmatrix} = \begin{pmatrix} -2 \\ 4 \\ 3 \end{pmatrix} + \mu\begin{pmatrix} 7 \\ -5 \\ -10 \end{pmatrix} \text{ [1 mark]}$$
Any two of: $1 + 2t = -2 + 7\mu$
$$5 - 3t = 4 - 5\mu$$
$$9 - 8t = 3 - 10\mu \qquad \text{[1 mark]}$$
Solving any two equations simultaneously gives $t = 2$ or $\mu = 1$ *[1 mark]*
Substituting $t = 2$ in the equation of the line through AB (or $\mu = 1$ in the equation for l_1) gives:
$(5, -1, -7)$ *[1 mark]*

d) (i) The vectors needed are $\begin{pmatrix} 2 \\ -3 \\ -8 \end{pmatrix}$ and $\begin{pmatrix} 7 \\ -5 \\ -10 \end{pmatrix}$ (direction vector of l_1).
$$\begin{pmatrix} 2 \\ -3 \\ -8 \end{pmatrix} \cdot \begin{pmatrix} 7 \\ -5 \\ -10 \end{pmatrix} = 14 + 15 + 80 = 109$$
[1 mark]
magnitude of 1st vector:
$$\sqrt{2^2 + (-3)^2 + (-8)^2} = \sqrt{77}$$
magnitude of 2nd vector:
$$\sqrt{7^2 + (-5)^2 + (-10)^2} = \sqrt{174}$$
[1 mark]
$$\cos\theta = \frac{109}{\sqrt{77}\sqrt{174}} \text{ [1 mark]}$$
$$\Rightarrow \theta = 19.7° \text{ [1 mark]}$$

(ii) Draw a diagram:

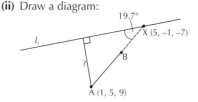

[1 mark for showing that the shortest distance is perpendicular to l_1]
X is the intersection point found in part **c)**, with coordinates $(5, -1, -7)$
Distance from A to X =
$$\sqrt{(5-1)^2 + (-1-5)^2 + (-7-9)^2} = \sqrt{308}$$
[1 mark]
Now you've got a right-angled triangle, so just use trig to find the side you want:
Shortest distance from A to l_1
$$= \sqrt{308} \times \sin 19.7° \text{ [1 mark]}$$
$$= 5.9 \text{ units [1 mark]}$$
The tricky thing here is figuring out how to go about it. Drawing a diagram definitely helps you see what you know and what you need to work out. Often, you'll be meant to use something you worked out in a previous question part.

Q2 **a)** $-3(\mathbf{i} - 4\mathbf{j} + 2\mathbf{k}) = -3\mathbf{i} + 12\mathbf{j} - 6\mathbf{k}$ *[1 mark]*

b) **i** component: $3 + (\mu \times 1) = 2$ gives $\mu = -1$
[1 mark]
So $\mathbf{r} = (3\mathbf{i} - 3\mathbf{j} - 2\mathbf{k}) - 1(\mathbf{i} - 4\mathbf{j} + 2\mathbf{k}) = 2\mathbf{i} + \mathbf{j} - 4\mathbf{k}$
[1 mark]
This is the position vector of the point A(2, 1, −4)

c) B lies on l_2 so it has position vector
$\mathbf{b} = (10\mathbf{i} - 21\mathbf{j} + 11\mathbf{k}) + \lambda(-3\mathbf{i} + 12\mathbf{j} - 6\mathbf{k})$ *[1 mark]*
So $\overrightarrow{AB} = \mathbf{b} - \mathbf{a}$
$= ((10\mathbf{i} - 21\mathbf{j} + 11\mathbf{k}) + \lambda(-3\mathbf{i} + 12\mathbf{j} - 6\mathbf{k})) - (2\mathbf{i} + \mathbf{j} - 4\mathbf{k})$
$= (8 - 3\lambda)\mathbf{i} + (-22 + 12\lambda)\mathbf{j} + (15 - 6\lambda)\mathbf{k}$ *[1 mark]*
The scalar product of the direction vector of l_1 and $\overrightarrow{AB}$ must be zero as they're perpendicular:
$(\mathbf{i} - 4\mathbf{j} + 2\mathbf{k}).((8 - 3\lambda)\mathbf{i} + (-22 + 12\lambda)\mathbf{j} + (15 - 6\lambda)\mathbf{k})$
$= (8 - 3\lambda) + (88 - 48\lambda) + (30 - 12\lambda)$
[1 mark]
$= 126 - 63\lambda = 0$
$\Rightarrow \lambda = 2$ *[1 mark]*
Substitute in $\lambda = 2$ to find the position vector **b**:
$\mathbf{b} = (10\mathbf{i} - 21\mathbf{j} + 11\mathbf{k}) + 2(-3\mathbf{i} + 12\mathbf{j} - 6\mathbf{k})$ *[1 mark]*
$= 4\mathbf{i} + 3\mathbf{j} - \mathbf{k}$
Position vector of B = $4\mathbf{i} + 3\mathbf{j} - \mathbf{k}$ *[1 mark]*
You could have found the product of $\overrightarrow{AB}$ and the direction bit of the l_2 vector equation, as $\overrightarrow{AB}$ is perpendicular to both l_1 and l_2. But the numbers for the l_1 vector are smaller, which makes your calculations easier.

d) $\overrightarrow{AB} = \mathbf{b} - \mathbf{a} = (4\mathbf{i} + 3\mathbf{j} - \mathbf{k}) - (2\mathbf{i} + \mathbf{j} - 4\mathbf{k})$
$= 2\mathbf{i} + 2\mathbf{j} + 3\mathbf{k}$ *[1 mark]*
$|\overrightarrow{AB}| = \sqrt{2^2 + 2^2 + 3^2} = \sqrt{17} = 4.1$ *[1 mark]*

Q3 **a)** $(\overrightarrow{OA}).(\overrightarrow{OB})$ *[1 mark]*
$= (3\mathbf{i} + 2\mathbf{j} + \mathbf{k}).(3\mathbf{i} - 4\mathbf{j} - \mathbf{k}) = 9 - 8 - 1 = 0$ *[1 mark]*
Therefore, side OA is perpendicular to side OB, and the triangle has a right angle. *[1 mark]*
You could also have found the lengths $|OA|$, $|OB|$ and $|AB|$ and shown by Pythagoras that AOB is a right-angled triangle $(|AB|^2 = |OA|^2 + |OB|^2)$.

b) $\overrightarrow{BA} = \mathbf{a} - \mathbf{b} = (3\mathbf{i} + 2\mathbf{j} + \mathbf{k}) - (3\mathbf{i} - 4\mathbf{j} - \mathbf{k}) = (6\mathbf{j} + 2\mathbf{k})$
[1 mark]

$\overrightarrow{BO} = -3\mathbf{i} + 4\mathbf{j} + \mathbf{k}$
$\overrightarrow{BA} \cdot \overrightarrow{BO} = 24 + 2 = 26$ *[1 mark]*
$|\overrightarrow{BA}| = \sqrt{6^2 + 2^2} = \sqrt{40}$ and
$|\overrightarrow{BO}| = \sqrt{(-3)^2 + 4^2 + 1^2} = \sqrt{26}$ *[1 mark]*
$\cos \angle ABO = \dfrac{\overrightarrow{BA} \cdot \overrightarrow{BO}}{|\overrightarrow{BA}| \cdot |\overrightarrow{BO}|} = \dfrac{26}{\sqrt{40}\sqrt{26}}$ *[1 mark]*
$\angle ABO = 36.3°$ *[1 mark]*

c) (i) $\overrightarrow{AC} = \mathbf{c} - \mathbf{a} = (3\mathbf{i} - \mathbf{j}) - (3\mathbf{i} + 2\mathbf{j} + \mathbf{k}) = (-3\mathbf{j} - \mathbf{k})$
[1 mark]
$|\overrightarrow{AC}| = \sqrt{(-3)^2 + (-1)^2} = \sqrt{10}$ and
$|\overrightarrow{OC}| = \sqrt{3^2 + (-1)^2} = \sqrt{10}$ *[1 mark]*
Sides AC and OC are the same length, so the triangle is isosceles. *[1 mark]*

(ii) You know the side lengths AC and OC from part **c) (i)**. Calculate length of OA:
$|\overrightarrow{OA}| = \sqrt{3^2 + 2^2 + 1^2} = \sqrt{14}$ *[1 mark]*

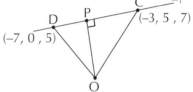

Now find the height of the triangle, x, using Pythagoras:
$x = \sqrt{(\sqrt{10})^2 - \left(\dfrac{\sqrt{14}}{2}\right)^2} = \sqrt{6.5}$ *[1 mark]*
Area $= \dfrac{1}{2}(\text{base} \times \text{height})$
$= \dfrac{1}{2}(\sqrt{14} \times \sqrt{6.5})$ *[1 mark]*
$= 4.77$ square units *[1 mark]*

d) (i) $\mathbf{r} = \mathbf{a} + t(\mathbf{b} - \mathbf{a})$
$\mathbf{r} = (3\mathbf{i} + 2\mathbf{j} + \mathbf{k}) + t((3\mathbf{i} - 4\mathbf{j} - \mathbf{k}) - (3\mathbf{i} + 2\mathbf{j} + \mathbf{k}))$
[1 mark]
$\mathbf{r} = (3\mathbf{i} + 2\mathbf{j} + \mathbf{k}) + t(-6\mathbf{j} - 2\mathbf{k})$ *[1 mark]*

(ii) $\mathbf{k}$ component: $1 - 2t = 0$, $t = \dfrac{1}{2}$ *[1 mark]*
$\mathbf{r} = (3\mathbf{i} + 2\mathbf{j} + \mathbf{k}) + \dfrac{1}{2}(-6\mathbf{j} - 2\mathbf{k}) = 3\mathbf{i} - \mathbf{j}$
$a = 3$ *[1 mark]*, $b = -1$ *[1 mark]*

Q4 a) $\overrightarrow{OC} = \overrightarrow{OD} + \overrightarrow{DC}$ *[1 mark]*
As ABCD is a parallelogram $\overrightarrow{DC} = \overrightarrow{AB}$:

so $\overrightarrow{DC} = \overrightarrow{AB} = \overrightarrow{OB} - \overrightarrow{OA} = \begin{pmatrix} -1 \\ 1 \\ 8 \end{pmatrix} - \begin{pmatrix} -5 \\ -4 \\ 6 \end{pmatrix} = \begin{pmatrix} 4 \\ 5 \\ 2 \end{pmatrix}$,
[1 mark for correctly finding $\overrightarrow{DC}$]
and $\overrightarrow{OD} = \begin{pmatrix} -7 \\ 0 \\ 5 \end{pmatrix}$,
so $\overrightarrow{OC} = \overrightarrow{OD} + \overrightarrow{DC} = \begin{pmatrix} -7 \\ 0 \\ 5 \end{pmatrix} + \begin{pmatrix} 4 \\ 5 \\ 2 \end{pmatrix} = \begin{pmatrix} -3 \\ 5 \\ 7 \end{pmatrix}$.
[1 mark for the correct answer]

b) $\overrightarrow{DC}$ is in the direction of L_1, and D lies on L_1, so an equation for L_1 is: $\mathbf{r} = \overrightarrow{OD} + t\overrightarrow{DC}$ *[1 mark]*

$= \begin{pmatrix} -7 \\ 0 \\ 5 \end{pmatrix} + t\begin{pmatrix} 4 \\ 5 \\ 2 \end{pmatrix}$ *[1 mark]*

You could have used point C instead and put the vector $\overrightarrow{OC}$ you found in part a) into the equation. The fact that the question describes L_1 as containing DC suggests that you should use $\overrightarrow{DC}$ as your direction vector.

c) A and C lie on L_2, so by plugging their position vectors into the formula for a vector line equation from two points: $\mathbf{r} = \mathbf{c} + s(\mathbf{d} - \mathbf{c})$, you get an equation for L_2: $\mathbf{r} = \overrightarrow{OA} + s(\overrightarrow{OC} - \overrightarrow{OA})$ *[1 mark]*

$= \begin{pmatrix} -5 \\ -4 \\ 6 \end{pmatrix} + s\left(\begin{pmatrix} -3 \\ 5 \\ 7 \end{pmatrix} - \begin{pmatrix} -5 \\ -4 \\ 6 \end{pmatrix}\right)$ *[1 mark]*

$= \begin{pmatrix} -5 \\ -4 \\ 6 \end{pmatrix} + s\begin{pmatrix} 2 \\ 9 \\ 1 \end{pmatrix}$ *[1 mark]*

Plugging in $\mathbf{c} = \overrightarrow{OC}$ and $\mathbf{d} = \overrightarrow{OA}$ is also fine.

d) Draw a diagram:

The shortest distance from L_1 to the origin is OP, where P lies on L_1 and OP is perpendicular to L_1.
[1 mark for showing that the shortest distance is perpendicular to L_1]
It doesn't matter if your diagram doesn't look exactly like this, as long as it shows that OP is perpendicular to L_1.

P lies on L_1, so $\overrightarrow{OP} = \begin{pmatrix} -7 + 4t \\ 5t \\ 5 + 2t \end{pmatrix}$ for some t.

The direction vector of L_1 is $\begin{pmatrix} 4 \\ 5 \\ 2 \end{pmatrix}$.

$\overrightarrow{OP}$ is perpendicular to L_1, so the scalar product of $\overrightarrow{OP}$ and the direction vector of L_1 is zero.
[1 mark for giving the two vectors and stating that their scalar product is zero]
i.e. $\begin{pmatrix} -7 + 4t \\ 5t \\ 5 + 2t \end{pmatrix} \cdot \begin{pmatrix} 4 \\ 5 \\ 2 \end{pmatrix} = 0$
$\Rightarrow -28 + 16t + 25t + 10 + 4t = 0$ *[1 mark]*
$\Rightarrow 45t = 18 \Rightarrow t = \dfrac{2}{5}$ *[1 mark]*
Plugging this back into $\overrightarrow{OP}$ gives: $\overrightarrow{OP} = \begin{pmatrix} -\frac{27}{5} \\ 2 \\ \frac{29}{5} \end{pmatrix}$,
[1 mark] so the distance from O to P
is $|\overrightarrow{OP}| = \sqrt{\left(-\frac{27}{5}\right)^2 + 2^2 + \left(\frac{29}{5}\right)^2} = 8.17$ to 3 s.f.
[1 mark]
You could also have found the angle OCP using the scalar product formula and then used trigonometry to work out $|OP| = |OC|\sin\theta$.

Q5 a) *l* passes through J and K so by plugging $\vec{OJ}$ and $\vec{OK}$ into the equation $\mathbf{r} = \mathbf{c} + t(\mathbf{d} - \mathbf{c})$ you get an equation for *l*:

$\mathbf{r} = \vec{OJ} + t(\vec{OK} - \vec{OJ})$

$= \begin{pmatrix} 2 \\ -2 \\ 1 \end{pmatrix} + t\left(\begin{pmatrix} 3 \\ 1 \\ -1 \end{pmatrix} - \begin{pmatrix} 2 \\ -2 \\ 1 \end{pmatrix} \right)$ *[1 mark]*

$= \begin{pmatrix} 2 \\ -2 \\ 1 \end{pmatrix} + t \begin{pmatrix} 1 \\ 3 \\ -2 \end{pmatrix}$ *[1 mark]*

Letting $\mathbf{c} = \vec{OK}$ *and* $\mathbf{d} = \vec{OJ}$ *is also fine.*

b) To find the acute angle between *l* and OJ use

the formula $\cos\theta = \dfrac{\mathbf{a} \cdot \mathbf{b}}{|\mathbf{a}\|\mathbf{b}|}$, where $\mathbf{a}$ is $\begin{pmatrix} 1 \\ 3 \\ -2 \end{pmatrix}$, the

direction vector of *l*, $\mathbf{b} = \vec{OJ} = \begin{pmatrix} 2 \\ -2 \\ 1 \end{pmatrix}$, and θ is the

angle between *l* and OJ that $\mathbf{a}$ and $\mathbf{b}$ both point away from.

Then: $\mathbf{a.b} = \begin{pmatrix} 1 \\ 3 \\ -2 \end{pmatrix} \cdot \begin{pmatrix} 2 \\ -2 \\ 1 \end{pmatrix} = 2 - 6 - 2 = -6$ *[1 mark]*

$|\mathbf{a}| = \sqrt{1^2 + 3^2 + (-2)^2} = \sqrt{14}$

$|\mathbf{b}| = \sqrt{2^2 + (-2)^2 + 1^2} = \sqrt{9} = 3$

[1 mark for correctly finding both magnitudes]

So $\cos\theta = \dfrac{-6}{3\sqrt{14}} \Rightarrow \theta = 122°$, to the

nearest degree. *[1 mark]* So the acute angle is $180 - \theta = 58°$ to the nearest degree. *[1 mark]*

c) J and K lie on *l*, so if J, K and G are collinear then G must lie on *l* too (as *l* is the only line that both J and K lie on and collinear points all lie on the same straight line).

If G lies on *l* then: $\begin{pmatrix} 1 \\ -5 \\ 3 \end{pmatrix} = \begin{pmatrix} 2 + t \\ -2 + 3t \\ 1 - 2t \end{pmatrix}$ for some *t*. *[1 mark]*

Solving each line gives:

$1 = 2 + t \Rightarrow t = -1$
$-5 = -2 + 3t \Rightarrow -3 = 3t \Rightarrow t = -1$
$3 = 1 - 2t \Rightarrow t = -1$

There's a consistent solution ($t = -1$) so G lies on *l* (as do J and K) so J, K and G are collinear.
[1 mark for showing and stating that there is a consistent solution]

You could answer part c) by showing that the line segments JK and KG are parallel, but the method given is easier as you already know that J and K lie on l.

d) As with **c)** H must lie on *l* if J, K and H are collinear.

If H lies on *l* then: $\begin{pmatrix} 5 \\ 11 \\ -2 \end{pmatrix} = \begin{pmatrix} 2 + t \\ -2 + 3t \\ 1 - 2t \end{pmatrix}$ for some *t*. *[1 mark]*

Solving each line gives:

$5 = 2 + t \Rightarrow t = 3$
$11 = -2 + 3t \Rightarrow 13 = 3t \Rightarrow t = \dfrac{13}{3}$
$-2 = 1 - 2t \Rightarrow t = \dfrac{3}{2}$

There's no consistent solution so G doesn't lie on *l* and J and K do — so J, K and G are not collinear.
[1 mark for showing and stating that there is no consistent solution]

Again, you could show that JK and KH aren't parallel, but the method given is easier.

Q6 a) At an intersection point:

$\begin{pmatrix} 3 \\ 0 \\ -2 \end{pmatrix} + \lambda \begin{pmatrix} 1 \\ 3 \\ -2 \end{pmatrix} = \begin{pmatrix} 0 \\ 2 \\ 1 \end{pmatrix} + \mu \begin{pmatrix} 2 \\ -5 \\ -3 \end{pmatrix}$ *[1 mark]*

This gives equations:
$3 + \lambda = 2\mu$
$3\lambda = 2 - 5\mu$
$-2 - 2\lambda = 1 - 3\mu$ *[1 mark]*

Solving the first two simultaneously gives:
$\lambda = -1, \mu = 1$ *[1 mark]*
Substituting these values in the third gives:
$-2 - 2(-1) = 1 - 3(1) \Rightarrow 0 \neq -2$ *[1 mark]*
So the lines don't intersect.
You could have solved any two of the equations simultaneously, then substituted the results in the remaining equation to show that they don't work and there's no intersection point.

b) (i) At the intersection point of PQ and l_1:

$\begin{pmatrix} 3 \\ 0 \\ -2 \end{pmatrix} + \lambda \begin{pmatrix} 1 \\ 3 \\ -2 \end{pmatrix} = \begin{pmatrix} 5 \\ 4 \\ -9 \end{pmatrix} + t \begin{pmatrix} 0 \\ 2 \\ 3 \end{pmatrix}$ *[1 mark]*

This gives equations: $3 + \lambda = 5$
$3\lambda = 4 + 2t$
$-2 - 2\lambda = -9 + 3t$
[1 mark for any two equations]
Solving two of these gives: $\lambda = 2, t = 1$
[1 mark]

Intersection point has position vector

$\begin{pmatrix} 5 \\ 4 \\ -9 \end{pmatrix} + 1 \begin{pmatrix} 0 \\ 2 \\ 3 \end{pmatrix} = \begin{pmatrix} 5 \\ 6 \\ -6 \end{pmatrix}$,

so coordinates (5, 6, –6) *[1 mark]*

(ii) If perpendicular, the scalar product of direction vectors of lines will equal 0:

$\begin{pmatrix} 0 \\ 2 \\ 3 \end{pmatrix} \cdot \begin{pmatrix} 1 \\ 3 \\ -2 \end{pmatrix}$ *[1 mark]*

$= (0 \times 1) + (2 \times 3) + (3 \times -2) = 0$ *[1 mark]*

(iii) Call intersection point X.

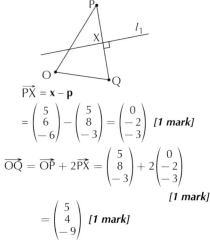

$\vec{PX} = \mathbf{x} - \mathbf{p}$

$= \begin{pmatrix} 5 \\ 6 \\ -6 \end{pmatrix} - \begin{pmatrix} 5 \\ 8 \\ -3 \end{pmatrix} = \begin{pmatrix} 0 \\ -2 \\ -3 \end{pmatrix}$ *[1 mark]*

$\vec{OQ} = \vec{OP} + 2\vec{PX} = \begin{pmatrix} 5 \\ 8 \\ -3 \end{pmatrix} + 2 \begin{pmatrix} 0 \\ -2 \\ -3 \end{pmatrix}$ *[1 mark]*

$= \begin{pmatrix} 5 \\ 4 \\ -9 \end{pmatrix}$ *[1 mark]*

The trick with this one is to realise that point Q lies the same distance from the intersection point as P does — drawing a quick sketch will definitely help.

Glossary

A

Algebraic fraction
A fraction made up of algebraic expressions.

B

Binomial expansion
A method of expanding functions of the form $(a + bx)^n$. Can be used to give a finite expansion or to find an approximation of a value.

C

Cartesian equation
An equation relating the perpendicular axes x and y in 2D, (or x, y and z in 3D).
Cartesian coordinates are given in the form (x, y) in 2D (or (x, y, z) in 3D).

Chain rule
A method for **differentiating** a function of a function.

Coefficient
The constant multiplying the variable(s) in an algebraic term.

Collinear points
Three or more points are collinear if they all lie on the same straight line.

Column vector
A **vector** written in the form of a column of numbers inside brackets.

Constant of integration
A constant term coming from an **integration**, representing any number.

Cosec
The **reciprocal** of the sine function, sometimes written as cosecant.

Cot
The **reciprocal** of the tangent function, sometimes written as cotangent.

D

Definite integral
An **integral** which is evaluated over an interval given by two **limits**.

Degree
The highest power of x in a polynomial.

Derivative
The result you get when you **differentiate** something.

Differential equation
An equation connecting variables with their rates of change.

Differentiation
A method for finding the rate of change of a function with respect to a variable — the opposite of **integration**.

Divisor
The number or expression you're dividing by in a division.

E

Equating coefficients
Forming equations from the **coefficients** of equivalent terms on each side of an **identity** in order to calculate the value of unknowns in the identity.

G

General solution
A solution to a **differential equation** that includes an unknown constant term.

I

i unit vector
The standard horizontal **unit vector** (i.e. along the x-axis).

Identity

An equation that is true for all values of a variable, usually denoted by the '≡' sign.

Implicit differentiation
A method of differentiating an **implicit relation**.

Implicit relation
An equation in x and y written in the form $f(x, y) = g(x, y)$, instead of $y = f(x)$.

Improper algebraic fraction
An **algebraic fraction** in which the **degree** of the numerator is greater than or equal to the degree of the denominator.

Indefinite integral
An **integral** which contains a constant of integration that comes from integrating without limits.

Integral
The result you get when you **integrate** something.

Integration
Process for finding the equation of a function, given its **derivative** — the opposite of **differentiation**.

Integration by parts
A method for **integrating** a product of two functions. The reverse process of the **product rule**.

Integration by substitution
A method for **integrating** a function of a function. The reverse process of the **chain rule**.

J

j unit vector
The standard vertical **unit vector** (i.e. along the y-axis).

k unit vector
The standard **unit vector** used in 3D to represent movement along the z-axis.

Limits
The numbers between which you integrate to find a **definite integral**.

Magnitude
The size of a **vector**.

Modulus
The modulus of a number is its positive numerical value.
The modulus of a function, $f(x)$, makes every value of $f(x)$ positive by removing any minus signs.
The modulus of a **vector** is the same as its **magnitude**.

N

Normal
A straight line that crosses a curve at a given point and is perpendicular to the curve at that point.

P

Parameter
The variable linking a set of **parametric equations** (usually t or θ).

Parametric equations
A set of equations defining x and y in terms of another variable, called the **parameter**.

Partial fractions
A way of writing an **algebraic fraction** with several linear factors in its denominator as a sum of fractions with linear denominators.

Particular solution
A solution to a **differential equation** where known values have been used to find the constant term.

Percentage error
The difference between a value and its approximation, as a percentage of the real value.

Position vector
A **vector** that describes the position of a point in relation to the origin.

Product rule
A method for **differentiating** a product of two functions.

Quotient
In algebraic division, the quotient is the expression you get when you divide by the **divisor**, not including the **remainder**.

Quotient rule
A method of **differentiating** one function divided by another.

Rational expression
A function that can be written as a fraction where the numerator and denominator are both polynomials.

Reciprocal
The reciprocal of a number or function is 1 divided by the number or function.

Remainder (algebraic division)
The expression left over following an algebraic division that has a **degree** lower than the **divisor**.

Resultant vector
The **vector** you get by adding two or more vectors together.

Scalar product
An operation on two **vectors** that produces a scalar result. Used for finding the angle between **vectors**.

Sec
The **reciprocal** of the cosine function, sometimes written as secant.

Separating variables
A method for solving **differential equations** by first rewriting in the form $\frac{1}{g(y)}\,dy = f(x)\,dx$ in order to integrate.

Skew lines
Lines in three dimensions that are neither parallel nor intersecting.

Stationary point
A point on a curve where the gradient is 0.

Substitution (identities)
Substituting in values of x to eliminate unknowns in order to calculate the value of other unknowns in an **identity**.

T

Tangent
A straight line which just touches a curve at a point, without going through it and that has the same gradient as the curve at that point.

Trapezium rule
A way of estimating the area under a curve by dividing it up into trapezium-shaped strips.

Turning point
A **stationary point** that is a (local) maximum or minimum point on a curve.

U

Unit vector
A **vector** with a length or magnitude of 1 unit.

V

Vector
A quantity that has both size and direction.

Volume of revolution
The volume of the 3D solid shape formed by rotating an area underneath a curve 2π radians about the x-axis.

Index

C4 Formula Sheet

These are the formulas you'll be given in the exam, but make sure you know exactly **when you need them** and **how to use them**. You might also need any formulas from the C1, C2 and C3 formula sheets in C4.

Integration

$$\int u \frac{dv}{dx} \, dx = uv - \int v \frac{du}{dx} \, dx$$

$f(x)$	$\int f(x) \, dx$
$\sec^2 kx$	$\frac{1}{k} \tan kx + C$
$\tan x$	$\ln|\sec x| + C$
$\cot x$	$\ln|\sin x| + C$
$\operatorname{cosec} x$	$\begin{cases} -\ln|\operatorname{cosec} x + \cot x| + C \\ \ln|\tan (\frac{1}{2}x)| + C \end{cases}$
$\sec x$	$\begin{cases} \ln|\sec x + \tan x| + C \\ \ln|\tan (\frac{1}{2}x + \frac{1}{4}\pi)| + C \end{cases}$

MEC4T61